TWELFTH EDITION

# THE BRADFORD BOOK OF COLLECTOR'S PLATES

*The Bradford Exchange Trading Floor in Niles, Illinois: hub of the worldwide collector's plate market.*

## CHARLES WINTHROPE & SONS

New York    Chicago    London    Frankfurt

# Foreword

Cycles of growth are fascinating to watch. Recent growth cycles in the collector's plate market have shown us how the world's largest market—the North American market of the United States and Canada—has had major influence upon its companion markets in Europe. In some ways this influence has been like a parent-child relationship, with the North American market serving as an instructive, guiding force to the newer markets.

But as in all such relationships, there comes a time for independence, and that time has come.

In the past few years, plate collectors in the European nations and Australia have grown tremendously in number. At the same time, they've established with clear voices their own preferences for favorite themes and artists. Some of these preferences are shared with their collecting cousins in North America—but some are not.

At the Bradford Exchange we have heard these new voices clearly. That is why there are now *three* editions of *The Bradford Book of Collector's Plates:* one for the North American market, one for the market in Great Britain, and one for the market in Germany, Austria and Switzerland.

Three separate *Bradford Books.* Three different viewpoints on the pleasures of collecting. In short, *three strong voices,* where before there was one.

Those of us who have watched the concept of plate collecting and trading spread around the globe in the last 15 years couldn't be more pleased. The rapid growth in new markets indicates that the future of collecting is secure.

But we who are in the parent markets still have a distinct advantage over the newer markets. That advantage is our long-term *knowledge* and *experience.* North American collectors have so many ways to share the fun of collecting: experienced dealers, active clubs, exciting collector shows, informative collector publications and access to a sophisticated system of trading. You'll find them all here in this book, presented to help you take full advantage of them.

We expect that our fellow collectors abroad will eventually be able to share these pleasures with us. If collector enthusiasm has anything to do with it, they are well on their way. As with any cycle of growth, it's nice to know the collector's plate market is renewing itself . . . again and again. But it's also nice to know that experience, after all, is on our side.

*John R. MacArthur*
John R. MacArthur
Director of the Board of Governors
The Bradford Exchange

Chicago, Illinois
September, 1987

---

*The editors acknowledge with gratitude the invaluable supplementary information supplied by:*

**Anna-Perenna, Inc.,** Klaus D. Vogt; **Arabia of Finland,** Riita Weiss; **Armstrong's,** Dave Armstrong; **Artists of the World,** James LaFond; **Belleek Pottery Ltd.,** Charles Thompson; **Bing & Grøndahl Copenhagen Porcelain, Inc.,** Paul Steffensen; **Canadian Collector Plates Limited,** Robert Henderson; **Christian Bell Porcelain Ltd.,** Horst Müller; **Creative World, Ltd.,** Richard Gabbe; **Crown Parian, Ltd.,** Jim Carter; **D'Arceau-Limoges,** André Azum; **Ernst Enterprises,** Ray Ernst; **Fairmont China,** Thomas W. Hogan; **Goebel United States,** John Eppler; **Gorham Division of Textron, Inc.,** David Wrenn; **Hackett American Collectors Co.,** James Hackett; **The Hamilton Mint,** Melanie Hart; **Haviland & Co., Inc.,** Frederick Haviland; **Hibel Studio,** William Hibel; **Hutschenreuther,** Stephen S. Barnet; **Incolay Studios Inc.,** Elvin M. Bright, Sr.; **Kaiser Porcelain Co.,** Hubert E. W. Kaiser; **Kern Collectibles,** Matthew P. Brummer; **Kosta Boda U.S.A. Ltd.,** Raymond W. Zrike; **Lenox China Co.,** Karen Cohen; **Pemberton & Oakes,** John Hugunin; **Pickard China Co.,** Henry A. Pickard; **Porcelaine Georges Boyer,** Gerard Boyer; **Rasmussen Import Co.,** R. D. Rasmussen; **Reco International Corp.,** Heio Reich; **Reed & Barton Silversmiths,** Patrice Johnson; **River Shore, Ltd.,** Arch Patterson; **Roman, Inc.,** Ronald T. Jedlinski; **Rosenthal U.S.A. Limited,** Ellen S. Miller; **Royal Copenhagen Porcelain Corp.,** Ivar Ipsen; **Royal Doulton,** Paul Warner; **Royal Worcester Spode Inc.,** R. Layne Weggeland; **Schmid,** Dennis Hurst; **Svend Jensen,** Per Jensen; **Vague Shadows,** Richard Habeeb; **Viking Import House, Inc.,** Pat Owen; **Villeroy & Boch,** Ingrid Vetterl; **Wara Intercontinental Co.,** Walter A. Rautenberg; **Wedgwood, Inc.,** Raymond W. Smyth

Plate photography by Gerald Hoos
Selected photography courtesy of *Plate World* magazine
Additional photography by Ken Oakes (pgs. 25, 26, 28, 29, 30, 33); Sebastian Studios (13, 15, 17, 27, 32, 33); Barry Stiver (36).

---

Twelfth Edition

# THE BRADFORD BOOK OF

# COLLECTOR'S PLATES

## THE OFFICIAL GUIDE TO ALL EDITIONS
## TRADED ON THE WORLD'S LARGEST EXCHANGE

THE BRADFORD EXCHANGE, LTD.
Niles/Chicago, Illinois 60648

**PUBLISHER**
Brian J. Taylor

**EXECUTIVE EDITOR**
Barbara B. White

**EDITORIAL MANAGER**
Alyson S. Wyckoff

**ART DIRECTOR**
Albert Scharpou

**EDITOR**
Lynn W. McKinven

**CONTRIBUTING EDITORS**

Kurt Brühwiler
Rainer Dembach
Annick Story Flaxman
Robert Harmer
Donna Lieberman
Shirley McCallan
Werner Peter

Anthony Polydorou
Gijsbert Rijkeboer
Mary Rowitz
Raquel M. Ryan
Jorgen Sannung
Amy Schaefer
Fred Woodley

**PRODUCTION MANAGER**
Sue Uelmen

## CHARLES WINTHROPE & SONS

New York    Chicago    London    Frankfurt

# CONTENTS

## Appendixes & Indexes

# THE COLLECTOR'S PLATE MARKET

## *Introduction*

Of all objects prized for their beauty and market value, collector's plates hold a unique position in the art world. They are the only limited-edition issues to be traded in a uniform market, which tracks collector demand around the world.

The porcelain plate that was born in the kilns of China will find its way to the living room wall of a collector in Miami, Florida. And the fine china object that brings so much pleasure to a collector in California may have the same appeal to a collector in Copenhagen or Cologne.

In fact, someday one of those two collectors, thousands of miles apart, may actually buy a plate from the other. This is possible because, while a collector's plate is an object created for its artistic value, it has another important aspect. Each limited-edition plate has the potential to be actively traded among collectors in the fast-paced secondary market.

This potential arises from the basic concept of all limited editions: once the edition limit is fulfilled, *production ends*. The edition is then *closed*, and the subse-

quent market value of plates from that edition is determined by the laws of supply and demand.

Edition sizes can be large or small. Announced edition sizes in this book range from 500 plates for the 1971 Veneto Flair *Bellini Madonna* to 30,000 for the Haviland *Christmas*. But the undisclosed edition sizes are by far the most frequent, ranging from less than 1,000 for the earliest plates into the hundreds of thousands for later ones. Regardless of the edition size, a market winner is made when demand outstrips supply. A very small edition does not automatically guarantee demand; in fact, it often discourages it through the restriction of active trading.

### Recognition as the World's Most Traded Art

Today, no other art form—regardless of style, medium or popularity—is traded in a reasonably uniform market with the same frequency and volume as collector's plates. In fact, there are more than 14,000 primary and secondary market transactions every business day in the worldwide market. This activity has led to the

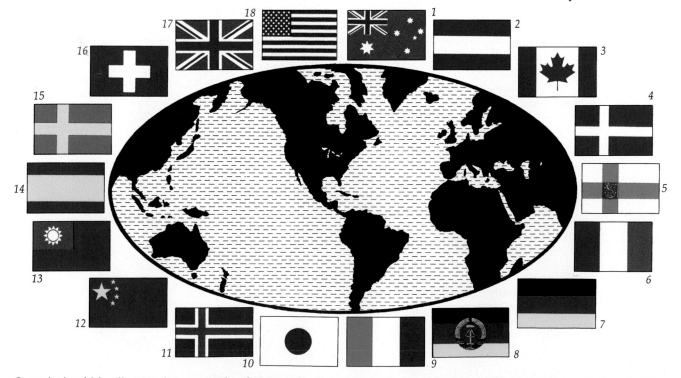

*Countries in which collector's plates are produced: 1) Australia; 2) Austria; 3) Canada; 4) Denmark; 5) Finland; 6) France; 7) Germany, West (Federal Republic of Germany); 8) Germany, East (German Democratic Republic); 9) Italy; 10) Japan; 11) Norway; 12) People's Republic of China; 13) Republic of China (Taiwan); 14) Spain; 15) Sweden; 16) Switzerland; 17) United Kingdom; 18) United States.*

recognition of collector's plates in recent years as "the world's most-traded art."

## From Humble Beginnings, the Modern Market Grows

Because the market as we know it today is but 15 years old, sometimes it is surprising to see how far today's plate collectors have come in so short a time. In the early 1970s, collector's plates were just coming into their own as a recognized art form, and information was not easy to come by. Even though the concept of the limited-edition plate had actually developed at the end of the 19th century in Scandinavia and Europe, it took 50 years for the appeal—and the trading potential—of this idea to be recognized in the United States, and shortly thereafter, worldwide.

It also took several forward-thinking American antique and collectibles dealers to create the "spark" that would ignite the idea of back-issue trading.

First this spark set fire to the prices of the blue and white porcelain plates from Europe that were the first true limited editions available here. Later, it ignited the market for plates with increasingly diverse themes and artists. Eventually the steadily burning flame of collector enthusiasm took over what a few insightful dealers had begun . . . and the modern market was born.

## The Bradford Exchange Responds to the Need for Market Organization

As active trading in back-issue collector's plates became widespread, the need for an organized market became apparent. This led to the creation of The Bradford Exchange, the world's first organized marketplace for the trading of limited editions. It also contributed directly to the evolution of the plate market as we know it today.

What follows is a concise history of that growth and a look at the current market in all parts of the world in which plates are created, bought and sold.

## A Brief History of Collector's Plates

On a cold December morning in 1895, we are told, Mr. Harald Bing, director of the Danish porcelain house of Bing & Grøndahl, ordered his astonished workers to destroy the mold for the small blue-and-white plate produced to commemorate the Christmas holiday.

The plate was entitled "Behind the Frozen Window." With Bing's unprecedented command, it became the first known limited-edition collector's plate, and the cornerstone of what is now a worldwide market. By thus limiting the plate's supply, Mr. Bing established the essential condition where demand for a plate, if it exceeds the edition size, can create an appreciation in price.

Although the idea that the laws of supply and demand can directly affect the prices of sold-out limited editions is a relatively new one, it actually harkens back to the extreme value placed on porcelain objects when the mystery of porcelain manufacture was first revealed.

## Birthplace of Porcelain in Ancient China

Although there is still some contention among experts, the birth of porcelain—or technically speaking, the "hard paste" variety of porcelain that requires special ingredients, kiln techniques and glazing processes to produce its enviable whiteness and translucency—occurred in ancient China, in approximately 600 A.D.

Here, near the town of Ching-te Chen, a deposit of remarkably pure kaolin clay—still the one essential ingredient for the production of fine porcelain—was first discovered. For nearly 700 years thereafter, Chinese artisans perfected their techniques of porcelain production, creating objects of breathtaking beauty that were entirely unknown to the Western world.

## Trade Routes to Europe Spark Demand

But in the 14th century, as the Orient was opened to European tradesmen for the first time, these magnificent Chinese wares found increasingly greater markets among well-to-do Europeans, who were awed and charmed by the delicacy of their manufacture.

*The first limited-edition collector's plate: "Behind the Frozen Window," 1895 issue in the Bing & Grøndahl Christmas series. The series has continued uninterrupted to this day.*

7

So popular was this so-called "Chinese export" porcelain that kings and emperors offered great rewards to any local potter who could learn to duplicate the Chinese process. Yet, for over three centuries, the only form of porcelain the Europeans could master was the "soft paste" variety, inferior in color, translucency and strength to the "hard paste" products of the East. And the more impossible it seemed that Europeans could create their own porcelain, the more obsessive their collecting of the Chinese porcelain became.

## German Unlocks the Ancient Secret

Then in 1708, an enterprising German potter named Johann Friedrich Bottger—in an attempt to placate royalty after his attempts at alchemy (turning lead to gold) had understandably failed—took on the task of duplicating the Chinese process in earnest. The key to the process became not only the discovery of kaolin clay in Saxony, near the town of Meissen, but also a way to fire the kiln to the extreme high temperatures necessary to achieve hard-paste quality. Through an ingenious use of solar energy, Bottger's kiln was finally pushed to the required 1350 degrees Celsius, and the first true European hard-paste porcelain was created.

The factory to produce this revolutionary ware was opened in 1710, under the name of the Royal Saxon Porcelain Manufactory in Meissen, and remains active to this day. Within a decade this factory was creating porcelain ware of equal or greater beauty than that of China. Soon, master potters trained at Meissen left to establish other factories throughout Europe, most often in areas with extensive kaolin deposits nearby.

## Commemorative Plates Become Popular

By the mid-18th century, the Konigliche Porzellan-Manufaktur Berlin (KPM) and the French Royal Factory at Sèvres were also producing fine porcelain. At roughly this period in the modern history of collecting, the idea of creating a fine porcelain plate as a decorative object, rather than just for food service, first arose.

Meissen, KPM, Sèvres and other potteries issued earthenware, china and porcelain plates honoring coronations, great battles and notable personalities of the age. The idea that fine porcelain objects are worthy of collection—which had taken hold among the wealthy years earlier—was now catching on throughout the populace.

# Firsts in Plate Collecting*

(Adapted from *Plate World* magazine)

**First Limited-Edition Collector's Plate:**
  1895 Bing & Grøndahl *Christmas*
  "Behind the Frozen Window"

**First Crystal Plate:**
  1965 Lalique *Annual* "Deux Oiseaux (Two Birds)"

**First Square Plate:**
  1969 Rörstrand *Christmas*
  "Bringing Home the Tree"

**First Bas-Relief Plate:**
  1969 Wedgwood *Christmas* "Windsor Castle"

**First Plate in Full Color:**
  1970 Pickard *Lockhart Wildlife*
  "Woodcock/Ruffled Grouse" (pair)

**First Christmas Plate in Color**
(other than blue-and-white):
  1970 Spode *Christmas* "Partridge in a Pear Tree"

**First Christmas Plates in Silver:**
  1970 Franklin Mint *Christmas*
  "Bringing Home the Tree"
  1970 Reed and Barton *Christmas*
  "A Partridge in a Pear Tree"

**First Norman Rockwell Series:**
  Franklin Mint *Christmas*

**First Norman Rockwell Series in Full Color:**
  1971 Gorham *Rockwell*
  *Four Seasons:* "A Boy and His Dog" (4-plate set)

**First Plates Showing Children:**
  1971 Gorham *Rockwell*
  *Four Seasons:* "A Boy and His Dog" (4-plate set)
  1971 Goebel *Hummel Annual*
  1971 Schmid *Hummel Christmas*

**First Plate in Wood:**
  1971 Anri *Christmas* "St. Jakob in Groden"

**First Plate in Ivory Alabaster:**
  1976 Studio Dante di Volteradici *Grand Opera*
  "Rigoletto"

**First Movie Plate:**
  1977 Knowles *The Wizard of Oz* "Over the Rainbow"

**First Plate Sponsored by
The Rockwell Society of America:**
  1974 *Christmas* "Scotty Gets His Tree"

**First Plate in Cameo Stone:**
  1977 Incolay *Romantic Poets*
  "She Walks in Beauty"

**First Plate Endorsed by
the Family of Norman Rockwell:**
  1985 Rockwell Society *Rockwell's American Dream*
  "Young Girl's Dream"

**First Plate from the Birthplace of Porcelain,
The People's Republic of China:**
  1986 Imperial Ching-te Chen
  *Beauties of the Red Mansion* "Pao-chai"

*Among plates listed on The Bradford Exchange

## Rise of the Great Ceramic Houses of Europe

In the early part of the 18th century, monarchs and princes lined entire salons from floor to ceiling with exquisite porcelain wares. By the middle of that century, there were enough production facilities in Europe to make porcelain affordable for many levels of society other than royalty. In fact, many of the manufacturers of porcelain or bone china who are still active in today's collector's plate market established their factories in this "golden age" of European porcelain.

The oldest among Bradex-listed producers is Rörstrand, founded in Sweden in 1726 (see page 254), followed by Wedgwood of Great Britain in 1759 (page 208), Royal Copenhagen of Denmark, founded in 1775 (page 68) and Spode, founded in 1776 (page 204) in England. Royal Tettau, established in Bavaria in 1794, is the parent company of another Bradex-listed plate maker featured in this book, Royal Bayreuth (page 172).

## Today's Producers Have 19th Century Origins

Because production techniques improved greatly in the 19th century, porcelain had soon evolved from the "collectible of kings" to something the common man could afford and was proud to display. Between the years 1815 and 1898, no less than 17 producers of porcelain or fine china—whose plate issues are Bradex-listed today—opened their doors, both in Europe and the United States. Among them were: Arabia, Bing & Grøndahl, Haviland, Bareuther, Berlin Design, Goebel, Heinrich, Hutschenreuther, Kaiser, Rosenthal, Belleek, Royal Doulton, Fukagawa, Orrefors, Gorham, Edwin M. Knowles and Lenox.

## Collecting Plates Stems from Danish Holiday Tradition

Among wealthy Danish landowners, it had long been the custom to distribute Christmas gifts of food to the families living on and working their lands. Eventually these gifts developed even greater value because they arrived on a decorative painted plate, most often of wood, that could be kept and displayed in the home long after Christmas. Families kept these plates for generations, and they were displayed not unlike the way modern collector's plates, issued in series, are today.

It was not surprising, then, that Danish porcelain houses would create decorative plates meant to be offered at Christmas, topped with the traditional gift of food. These, too, were kept and displayed in Scandinavian homes, but none were ever issued in limited editions of any kind.

That is, until Mr. Harald Bing broke tradition by breaking the mold of his 1895 Christmas plate—and started a collecting phenomenon that swept around the world.

---

## How to Judge the Merits of a Plate Issue:
# The Bradford Exchange Eight-Point Checklist

In 1974, The Bradford Exchange created this eight-point checklist to establish standards for collector's plates that can be used by both beginning and experienced collectors. But in using it, it's wise to keep in mind that not *all* points apply to all plate issues. A general "rule of thumb" in choosing issues is: if the plate matches on *five points or more*, it is a *good acquisition;* if it matches on *less than five points, reconsider.*

**1. MAKER:**
Is the plate maker known for its insistence on fine workmanship? Is the continuity of its past and present series reliable in regard to adherence to edition limit, delivery schedules and price?

**2. ARTISTRY:**
Is the plate artwork original, created especially for this plate by a noteworthy artist? Or is the artwork a quality adaptation of a work by a famous artistic personality? Is the subject matter one of broad, but not trite, appeal?

**3. EDITION LIMIT:**
Is the edition clearly limited, but not too limited to create a true market? If the edition is sold out, is there sufficient evidence to suggest present or future secondary market activity?

**4. COLLECTIBILITY:**
Is the plate one of a collectible periodic series, or merely a single issue? Does the theme of the series have widespread appeal?

**5. TIME OF ACQUISITION:**
Is the plate available at issue price (always preferable with new issues), or at a time when the price is still likely to rise on the secondary market?

**6. SPONSORSHIP:**
Is the plate, or the series, issued in association with a prestigious institution—preferably one which is not, in and of itself, a producer of plates?

**7. COMMEMORATIVE IMPORTANCE:**
Does the plate or the series commemorate a seasonal or historic event? If so, does it offer new insight into the event?

**8. MATERIALS:**
If ceramic, is the plate true hard-paste porcelain, bone china or fine china? If of other materials such as metal or crystal, are they of appropriate quality? Is the plate unique in its workmanship? Does it have a special feature that sets it apart from other issues?

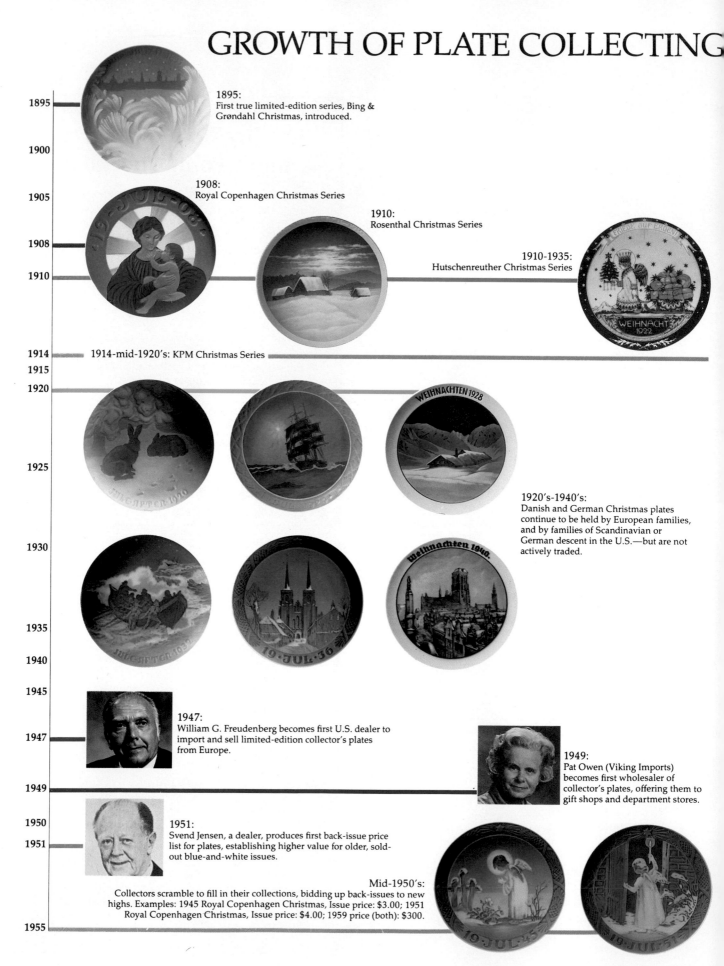

# GROWTH OF PLATE COLLECTING

**1895**

**1900**

**1895:**
First true limited-edition series, Bing & Grøndahl Christmas, introduced.

**1905**

**1908:**
Royal Copenhagen Christmas Series

**1908**

**1910**

**1910:**
Rosenthal Christmas Series

**1910-1935:**
Hutschenreuther Christmas Series

**1914**

1914-mid-1920's: KPM Christmas Series

**1915**

**1920**

**1925**

**1920's-1940's:**
Danish and German Christmas plates continue to be held by European families, and by families of Scandinavian or German descent in the U.S.—but are not actively traded.

**1930**

**1935**

**1940**

**1945**

**1947:**
William G. Freudenberg becomes first U.S. dealer to import and sell limited-edition collector's plates from Europe.

**1947**

**1949:**
Pat Owen (Viking Imports) becomes first wholesaler of collector's plates, offering them to gift shops and department stores.

**1949**

**1950**

**1951**

**1951:**
Svend Jensen, a dealer, produces first back-issue price list for plates, establishing higher value for older, sold-out blue-and-white issues.

**Mid-1950's:**
Collectors scramble to fill in their collections, bidding up back-issues to new highs. Examples: 1945 Royal Copenhagen Christmas, Issue price: $3.00; 1951 Royal Copenhagen Christmas, Issue price: $4.00; 1959 price (both): $300.

**1955**

**10**

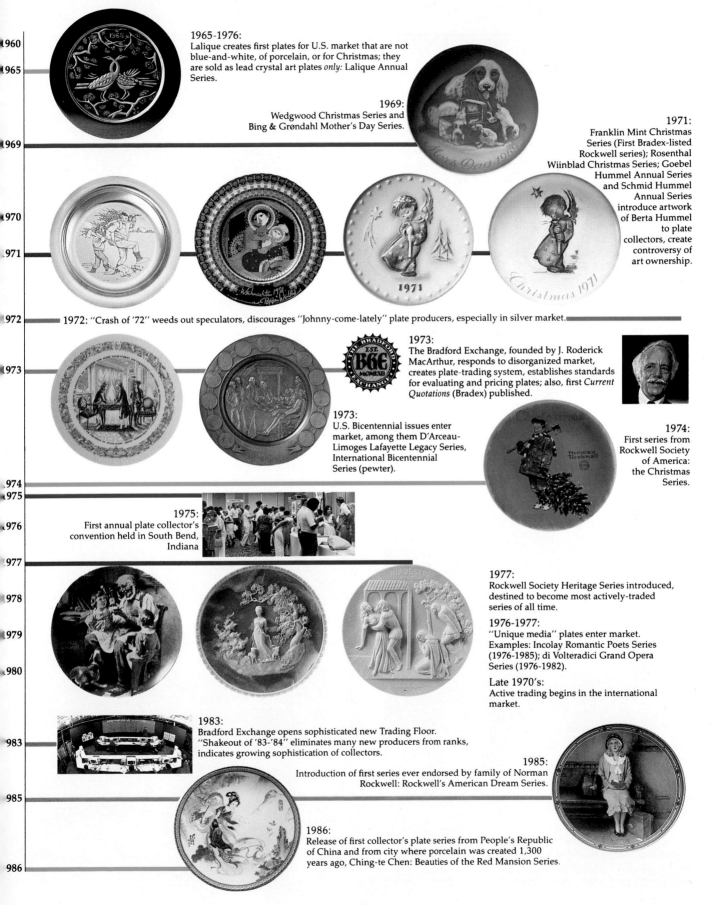

1960

1965

**1965-1976:**
Lalique creates first plates for U.S. market that are not blue-and-white, of porcelain, or for Christmas; they are sold as lead crystal art plates *only*: Lalique Annual Series.

**1969:**
Wedgwood Christmas Series and Bing & Grøndahl Mother's Day Series.

1969

**1971:**
Franklin Mint Christmas Series (First Bradex-listed Rockwell series); Rosenthal Wiinblad Christmas Series; Goebel Hummel Annual Series and Schmid Hummel Annual Series introduce artwork of Berta Hummel to plate collectors, create controversy of art ownership.

1970

1971

1972

1972: "Crash of '72" weeds out speculators, discourages "Johnny-come-lately" plate producers, especially in silver market.

1973

**1973:**
The Bradford Exchange, founded by J. Roderick MacArthur, responds to disorganized market, creates plate-trading system, establishes standards for evaluating and pricing plates; also, first *Current Quotations* (Bradex) published.

**1973:**
U.S. Bicentennial issues enter market, among them D'Arceau-Limoges Lafayette Legacy Series, International Bicentennial Series (pewter).

**1974:**
First series from Rockwell Society of America: the Christmas Series.

1974

1975

**1975:**
First annual plate collector's convention held in South Bend, Indiana

1976

1977

**1977:**
Rockwell Society Heritage Series introduced, destined to become most actively-traded series of all time.

**1976-1977:**
"Unique media" plates enter market. Examples: Incolay Romantic Poets Series (1976-1985); di Volteradici Grand Opera Series (1976-1982).

**Late 1970's:**
Active trading begins in the international market.

1978

1979

1980

**1983:**
Bradford Exchange opens sophisticated new Trading Floor. "Shakeout of '83-'84" eliminates many new producers from ranks, indicates growing sophistication of collectors.

1983

**1985:**
Introduction of first series ever endorsed by family of Norman Rockwell: Rockwell's American Dream Series.

1985

**1986:**
Release of first collector's plate series from People's Republic of China and from city where porcelain was created 1,300 years ago, Ching-te Chen: Beauties of the Red Mansion Series.

1986

# PLATE COLLECTING IN THE UNITED STATES

In the early years of what is called the "modern market" for plate collecting, collectors in the United States had most of their collecting needs fulfilled by domestic plate producers. In the recent past, all that has changed. Coinciding with rapid growth in collectors' markets outside the United States, dozens of new issues from foreign producers have entered the U.S. market and are now more accessible to collectors than ever before. The first plates from the People's Republic of China and several first plates from prestigious makers in Europe have already won wide acclaim among collectors here. And every day, more news of first releases from exotic countries or renowned makers reaches these shores.

## Evidence of Rapid Sellouts and Appreciation

These foreign issues have taken the U.S. market by storm. Several were immediate and resounding successes—they sold out quickly and moved onto the secondary market, appreciating more rapidly than expected.

The best example of this was the 1986 New Edition of the year in the U.S. market: Dominion China's first issue in the *Wings Upon the Wind* series, "The Landing." Issued at $21.80 early in 1986, this plate traded at $74 by the end of the year, posting a net gain of 239 per cent.

Market performance of this kind is especially noteworthy because this was the first series from a new *Canadian* producer. "The Landing" earned its wings— and a place in collecting history—as one of only two non-U.S. issues ever to be named New Edition of the Yer in the U.S. market. And the other ("The Annunciation," third issue in the Studio Dante di Volteradici *Ghiberti Doors* series) had been named just the year before.

The 1986 Plate of the Year, on the other hand, was a more traditional choice: one of the best-known secondary market issues of artist Donald Zolan. "Erik and Dandelion," 1978 issue in the Viletta *Zolan's Children* series, posted a net gain of 150 per cent for the year and closed at $249 in December, 1986.

## Chance to Identify a New Trend

Why the increased popularity of foreign issues should occur in the last few years has become an important

*The Rockwell Society of America introduced a new series in 1987 titled* Rockwell's Golden Moments, *which is also endorsed by the Rockwell Family Trust. Plate One is "Grandpa's Gift."*

*Big news for fans of Gone With the Wind: a new series commemorating the 50th anniversary of the film made its debut in 1987. First plate, shown here: "Scarlett and Her Suitors."*

topic of discussion among exchange experts. Of course, all through modern collecting history, plates from prestigious European makers have always been available to collectors in the United States and other leading markets. But what is the big difference between those times past and today's market? The answer, it seems, is in the method and the timing of the release of these new foreign issues.

In the past, most prestigious non-U.S. plates were first released to collectors in the countries in which they were made. Then—weeks, months or sometimes even years later—these series, if not already sold out, were released cautiously into other markets.

Lately, though, improved avenues of introduction have allowed non-U.S. issues to enter the market with the accessibility usually reserved for "home-grown" plates. In the last few years, more than three dozen new series from Canada and Europe have earned Bradex listing on the U.S. market—the largest number of foreign issues ever to enter the market in so short a time.

Foreign producers who earned Bradex listing for the first time in the U.S. market in recent years included Fürstenberg of Germany, with its series titled *Muninger's Romantic Winter Impressions* (first issue: "Ice Skaters in the Evening Sun") and Royal Grafton of England, with its *Braithwaite Game Birds Collection* (first issue: "Pheasants in Flight.").

Without local collector enthusiasm to support these and other examples of new art from abroad, the market might have waivered when they were first introduced. But it did not, apparently because the many new collectors who entered the marketplace were looking for something different and found it in the foreign issues.

## U.S. Collectors Now Number Seven Million

The estimated number of plate collectors in the United States increased by more than 300,000 in 1986-87, topping 7 million for the first time in history. Many of these collectors entered the market by acquiring the non-U.S. issues mentioned earlier. But to set the record straight, it's important to note that the majority of collectors here still support domestic plate issues— with plates featuring children, wildlife art, movie images and Rockwell themes as the acknowledged winners.

## Collector Preferences Hold Steady

When it comes to domestic plate issues, collectors' preferences for particular artists and themes actually have changed very little in recent years. According to Bradford Exchange experts, some of the most popular new issues were "Pao-Chai," first plate in the *Beauties of the Red Mansion* series from Imperial Ching-te Chen

*Temptations on the secondary market: a selection of plates for sale at the California Plate and Collectible Show.*

*Leading the trend in secondary-market sales: "Scarlett," first plate in Knowles' Gone With the Wind series. Movie plates continue to outrank others in back-issue sales.*

Porcelain, "The Sound of Music," first issue in the series of the same name from Edwin M. Knowles, and "Young Girl's Dream," first issue in the *Rockwell's American Dream* series from the Rockwell Society of America.

In *Plate World* magazine's 1987 reader survey, the most-favored primary market plates were "Brave and Free," first issue in the *Pride of America's Indians* series from Vague Shadows (not Bradex listed), "Pao-chai" and "The Landing," first issue in the *Wings Upon the Wind* series from Dominion China (mentioned earlier as The Bradford Exchange's 1986 New Edition of the Year).

Among living artists, *Plate World* respondents named Donald Zolan and Sandra Kuck as favorites, with Edna Hibel, Gregory Perillo, John McClelland and Pat Buckley Moss also highly rated.

Also according to the *Plate World* survey, most collectors continue to acquire their plates for the pleasure they bring into the home, although more than a third of the market collects for both pleasure *and* investment. Although there's some loyalty to favorite artists, almost half those collectors surveyed said that it's the *artwork itself* that determines whether they'll buy a plate—not just who painted it. Significantly, nearly half the collectors also said that they buy "individual

# A Profile of the U.S. Plate Collector, 1987:
(adapted from the *Plate World* magazine Reader Survey)
# Do You See Yourself and Your Favorites Here?

**Favorite Plates Bought in 1986:**
1. "Brave and Free," first issue in *Pride of America's Indians* series from Vague Shadows (not Bradex-listed)
2. "Pao-chai," first issue in *Beauties of the Red Mansions* series from Imperial Ching-te Chen Porcelain
3. "The Landing," first issue in *Wings Upon the Wind* series from Dominion China
4. "Times Remembered," first issue in the *Sandra Kuck Annual Mother's Day* series from Reco International (not Bradex-listed)
5. "Jack and Jill," eighth issue in the *McClelland's Mother Goose* series from Reco International

**Favorite Living Artists:**
Sandra Kuck, Donald Zolan, Edna Hibel, John McClelland, Gregory Perillo, Pat Buckley Moss (not Bradex-listed), Mario Fernandez (not Bradex-listed)

**Favorite Deceased Artists:**
Norman Rockwell, Ted DeGrazia, Frances Hook

**How Long Have You Been a Plate Collector?**
(ranked in order of response):
1. 3 to 5 years
2. 6 to 10 years
3. More than 10 years
4. 1 to 2 years

**How Do You Collect?**
1. I buy individual plates I like
2. By complete series
3. By artist

**How Many Plates Do You Own?**
1. 76–150          4. More than 150
2. 31–50           5. 21–30
3. 51–75

**How Many Series Do You Have in Your Collection?**
1. 6 to 10
2. 2 to 5
3. 11 to 15
4. More than 20

**Why Do You Collect Plates?**
1. Mostly for pleasure
2. For pleasure and investment
3. For investment only

**Where Do You Get Most of Your Plates?**
1. Mail order
2. Both mail order and collectibles dealers
3. Collectibles dealers only

**What Type of Subject Matter Do You Like Most?**
1. Children
2. Scenes of human situations
3. Birds
4. Animals
5. Movie/show scenes

**What Are the Most Important Factors in Your Decision to Buy?**
1. The artwork itself
2. The theme of the series
3. The artist
4. Whether I can afford it at the time
5. Whether it's the first in the series
6. Investment potential
7. Number of plates in the series
8. The producer

**What Else Do You Collect Besides Plates?**
1. Figurines          5. Dolls
2. Ornaments          6. Bells
3. Miniature plates
4. Lithographs and prints

plates that I like," while only about 25 per cent feel compelled to complete full series.

## Movie Plates and Foreign Issues Emerge as Big Secondary-Market Winners

Although Donald Zolan's "Erik and Dandelion" led all secondary market plates in 1986, it had a real "run for the money" among other issues. Market-leading editions in 1986 and early 1987 included the first three plates in Knowles' *Gone With the Wind* series—"Scarlett," "Ashley" and "Melanie," with heavy trading across the entire series. Also moving up steadily in the market were the *Annie* and *The King and I* series. These three series were among the top five most actively-traded series on the U.S. secondary market in 1986. The other two market leaders were the Rockwell Society *Heritage* and Reco *McClelland's Mother Goose* series.

In single-issue appreciation, it was foreign issues that set the trends in 1986. Besides "The Landing," leading issues included "The Baked Potato Man," first issue in Wedgwood's *Street Sellers of London*, and "Bodenseehaus," sixth issue in Königszelt Bayern's *German Half-Timbered Houses*. There was also a renewal of interest in many well-known Christmas series, icluding the oldest series of all, the Bing & Grøndahl *Christmas*.

Most surprising was the demand for the 1895 Bing and Grøndahl *Christmas* issue, "Behind the Frozen Window"—at a recently-traded price of $3,400, it's the most costly plate currently listed on the U.S. *Current Quotations*. At mid-year in 1986, exchange analysts contacted market sources all over the world to locate at least two of these landmark issues for clients of the Trading Floor. And even after those trades were made, the demand continued for this historic plate issue.

## New Makers and Issues Enter the Market

In the U.S. market, two new producers earned Bradex listing in 1986 and 1987: the W. S. George Pottery Company and Rhodes Studios. The first series from W. S. George is particularly worth watching. It's the *Gone With the Wind: Golden Anniversary* series, issued to celebrate the upcoming 50th anniversary of the 1939 release of the film.

Because the first *Gone With the Wind* series from Knowles is such a huge market success, exchange experts predict considerable collector interest in this second *GWTW* series, especially from new collectors who were unable to buy into the first series before its market appreciation.

## Local Shows and Dealer Activities Bring Artists, Collectors Together

At the 5th Annual California Plate and Collectibles Show held in Pasadena in April, 1987, nearly 17,000

*Popular artist Gregory Perillo, who paints the American West, greets some of his young fans at a recent collectibles show. Meeting favorite artists is a big "plus" at such shows.*

*"Brave and Free," first issue in the* Pride of America's Indians *series by Gregory Perillo (not Bradex-listed), was a hit with collectors in 1987. It was named "Plate of the Year (under $50)" at the Pasadena Silver Chalice Awards and was the top-rated new acquisition among readers of* Plate World *magazine.*

Ever since the first publication of *The Bradford Book of Collector's Plate* in 1976, The Bradford Exchange has designated the plate which appreciates the most among all Bradex-listed plates (in a given year) as *Plate of the Year*. In 1980 a second award category was created. The plate which appreciates the most in its year of issue is now named *New Edition of the Year*.

◀ *1986* **Plate of the Year "Erik and Dandelion"** *1979 Viletta* Zolan's Children *Bradex No. 84-V36-1.1*

## Plate of the Year

1976: **"Alba Madonna"**
1976 Pickard *Christmas*
Bradex No. 84-P29-2.1

1977: **"She Walks in Beauty"**
1977 Incolay *Romantic Poets*
Bradex No. 84-I31-1.1

1978: **"Girl With Watering Can"**
1978 Pickard *Children of Renoir*
Bradex No. 84-P29-4.1

1979: **"Sabina in the Grass"**
1979 Viletta *Zolan's Children*
Bradex No. 84-V36-1.2

*1986* **New Edition of** ▶ **the Year "The Landing"** *1986 Dominion China* Wings Upon the Wind *Bradex No. 8-D52-1.1*

1980: **"Mary, Mary"**
1979 Reco *McClelland Mother Goose*
Bradex No. 84-R60-2.1

1981: **"Little Boy Blue"**
1980 Reco *McClellend Mother Goose*
Bradex No. 84-R60-2.2

1982: **"Renee"**
1981 Fairmont/Hackett American
*Playful Memories*
Bradex No. 84-H4-10.1

## New Edition of the Year

1980: **"Miracle"**
1980 Pickard *Mother's Love*
Bradex No. 84-P29-6.1

1981: **"Hearts-a-Flutter"**
1981 Schmid *Peanuts Mother's Day*
Bradex No. 42-S12-7.5

1982: **"Merry Little Indian"**
1982 Fairmont/Artists of the World
*DeGrazia Children*
Bradex No. 84-F4-4.5

1983:          **"Annie and Sandy"** 1983 Knowles *Annie*
Bradex No. 84-K41-5.1
(Winner of both titles in 1983)

1984: **"This is the Room That Light Made"**
1983 Rockwell Society *Rockwell's Light Campaign*
Bradex No. 84-R70-6.1

1984: **"Abby and Lisa"**
1984 Knowles *Hibel Mother's Day*
Bradex No. 84-K41-9.1

1985: **"A Puzzlement"**
1984 Knowles *The King and I*
Bradex No. 84-K41-11.1

1985: **"The Annunciation"**
1985 Studio Dante di Volteradici *Ghiberti Doors*
Bradex No. 84-V90-3.3

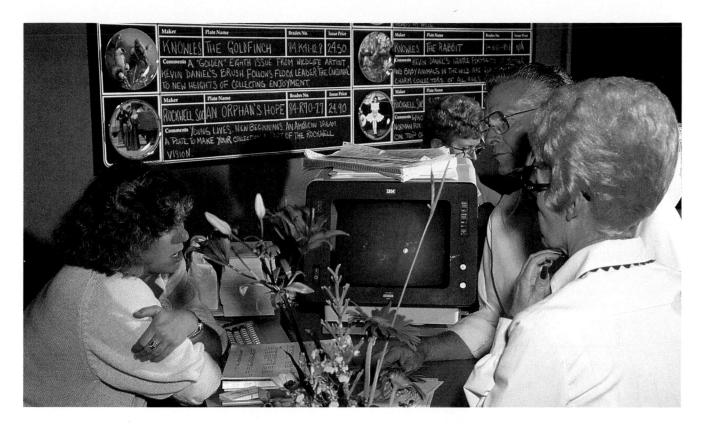

*Collectors consult brokers in the booth of The Bradford Exchange at a recent collector show. Computer terminals are tied in directly to the Exchange's Trading Floor, allowing clients to place bids for back-issue favorites right at the show.*

collectors were delighted with the new issues, favorite artists and producer-sponsored special events.

The Silver Chalice Awards that originate at this show named Sandra Kuck and Mario Fernandez as joint "Artists of the Year" for 1986. Chosen as "Plate of the Year (under $50)" was "Brave and Free" by Gregory Perillo; "Plate of the Year (over $50)" was "Wings of Freedom" by Mario Fernandez (neither issue is Bradex-listed). The Silver Chalice awards are determined by the polling of collectors' clubs throughout the United States.

Throughout the year, favorite artists and notables appeared at dealer-sponsored open houses and other events. Rosenthal artist Bjørn Wiinblad, creator of the *Christmas* series that bears his name, toured the nation in 1986 to introduce a new ceramic design. Knowles artists William Chambers (*Annie, The King and I, Portraits of Motherhood, Tom Sawyer*) and Tony Crnkovich (*The Sound of Music*) also made dealer appearances.

And Tom Rockwell, the son of Norman Rockwell and the administrator of The Norman Rockwell Family Trust, made a rare appearance in upstate New York on behalf of the Rockwell Society plates being sponsored by the Trust.

## New Dealer Program Improves Service, Boosts Trading Volume

A select group of 50 Bradford Exchange dealers also hosted open houses to introduce collectors to a new installation in their stores: The Bradford Exchange Information Center. This special center showcases leading primary and secondary market issues, displays latest prices from the Bradford Exchange Trading Floor and provides market data to help collectors make informed buying and selling decisions.

Each dealer with an Information Center has considerable knowledge of the secondary market and can provide advice and special service to customers intersted in trading. As collectors became familiar with this service in recent years, secondary market trading volume at these 50 leading dealers increased significantly.

Overall, a surge in trading at the dealer level gave dealers an unprecedented 32 per cent of the total sales volume on the secondary market in 1986. History repeats itself: just as in the early years of collecting, dealers are now a significant driving force in the U.S. secondary market, where their expertise continues to be extremely useful to collectors.

# THE WORLDWIDE MARKET FOR COLLECTOR'S PLATES

One of the great benefits of plate collecting is that it allows a collector to bring art into his home from a far-away place. Any collector in the world can experience the exotic, whether it's the *Ghiberti Doors* series from Italy in a Canadian home, the *Beauties of the Red Mansion* series, the first from the People's Republic of China, in a British home, or the *Summer at Skagen* series from Denmark in a German home. As each new country contributes to the market, collectors are exposed to the excitement of new art from a new culture.

The tremendous growth in non-U.S. markets can be traced not just to this selection of art from all over the world, but also to a greater selection of art that is "close to home." In markets outside the United States, what captures collectors' interests are series featuring local artists of renown, local landmarks, and local flora and fauna. The familiar, made beautiful, has just as much appeal as the exotic. And when these plates are also produced in each of the "home" countries, the acceptance and appreciation of collectors in those countries is even greater.

## PLATE COLLECTING IN CANADA:
### Canadian Collectors "Break Molds"

Canadian collectors continue to explore new territory in the limited-edition market, and much of that territory is their own. Canada is now firmly established as one of the most active plate-producing countries in the Western world.

Canadian artists like Donald Pentz, Gerda Neubacher and Stewart Sherwood—all Bradex-listed artists in the United States as well as Canada—are producing series that have Canadian home life, landscapes and wildlife as themes. Yet these series also attract collectors in the United States—so much so, in fact, that Donald Pentz's first issue, "The Landing," was named 1986 New Edition of the Year in the highly-competitive U.S. market. (See "Plate Collecting in the United States.") Christian Bell and Dominion China, both Canadian producers, have been tested by secondary-market success of their issues in many markets of the world besides Canada.

The market in Canada is also growth-oriented, with a current emphasis on regional activities that keep collectors in touch with what's new. The 22 active collectors' clubs in Canada, with 1,800 members, are scattered all over the nation. The greatest concentrations of collectors are in southern Ontario, British Columbia, and in the English-speaking regions in general.

## Growth Reported or Expected in All Areas of Canada

Steady market growth is reported in all the English-speaking regions of Canada; the estimated number of plate collectors in that market now stands at 840,000. The Canadian office of the The Bradford Exchange also predicts particular improvements in the French-speaking markets.

## Local "Buy and Sell" Events Offer New Potential

Although the Collectors Platemakers Association of Canada was dissolved after the 1986 collector's show took place in Toronto, the gap has been filled by innovative regional events that take collecting "out to the heartland."

For instance, The Bradford Exchange introduced a series of free-standing "Buy and Sell" events across Canada; in 1986, these were held in Calgary, Alberta and London, Ontario.

Collectors in Canada were also introduced to the concept of active trading at home-and-garden shows, where The Bradford Exchange maintained a booth. These shows have been held in Vancouver, British Columbia; Winnipeg, Manitoba; Halifax, Nova Scotia; Toronto, Ontario and London, Ontario.

Dealer-sponsored shows are also popping up everywhere, which helps to establish Canadian dealers as local authorities in their areas.

*"Swing Time," fourth issue in the Knowles* Father's Love *series, was named 1986 Plate of the Year in Canada.*

*1986 New Edition of the Year was another Knowles issue, "Annie and Miss Hannigan," sixth plate in the* Annie *series.*

# How a Plate is Made:
# The Bing & Grøndahl Christmas Plate

Bing & Grøndahl, the very first maker of limited-edition collector's plates, produces its annual *Christmas* issue as shown below. All underglaze blue-and-white plates are produced in this way. Four-color plates differ in that they may be hand painted, or in that an art transfer may be applied to the plate before the final firing. Either of those steps would replace Steps 6 and 7 below.

*1. From the artwork, a modeller sculpts the master mold from which working molds will be made.*

*2. Pouring liquid plaster into the mold, a mold-maker casts a working mold.*

*3. Quartz, feldspar and kaolin are the raw materials from which porcelain is made.*

*4. After these materials are mixed, the resulting clay is pressed over a plaster mold and fired.*

*5. These bisquit-fired plates are being carried to the decorating area.*

*6. A painter applies a spray of cobalt blue to the bisque porcelain.*

*7. A decorator selectively removes the blue to highlight the design.*

*8. The plate's backstamp, its "birth certificate," is applied.*

*9. The plate is sprayed with a glaze which will become clear in firing.*

*10. Plates are fired in the kiln 48 hours to become hard-paste porcelain.*

*11. The fired plates are removed, sorted and inspected for imperfections.*

*12. Imperfect plates are destroyed; perfect ones are issued worldwide.*

### New Development in Secondary-Market Trading

One of the major goals of The Bradford Exchange in Canada has been to introduce a secondary-market trading system that closely mirrors the one used in the United States. In 1987, this new system was "up and running," with activity of buy orders and sell orders quite similar to the U.S. market. However, the commission structure is somewhat different from the U.S. market.

### Nationals Look for the Backstamp Marked "Made in Canada," Yet Have Cosmopolitan Tastes

Canadians continue to seek out their own artists and producers, but they are also remarkably receptive to the types of plates that appeal to their U.S. cousins as well. While *Wings Upon the Wind* by Canadian producer Dominion China was the second most popular series in Canada in 1986, the top-ranked series was actually Knowles' *Birds of Your Garden* by Kevin Daniel. Imperial Ching-te Chen's *Beauties of the Red Mansion* ranked third.

Wildlife and scenic series gain the most kudos here, and Norman Rockwell continues to be Canadians' favorite artist, followed closely in popularity by Donald Zolan and the native wildlife painter Donald Pentz.

Canadians have the best of both worlds: easy acess to the most sought-after limited-editions on the U.S. and international markets, and their own respected group of plate artists and producers who capture the unique beauty and history of their own nation.

### PLATE COLLECTING IN THE UNITED KINGDOM: British Market Embraces Many New Collectors

In terms of growth and potential, the British market became the one to watch in recent years. Market analysts estimate that, as of 1987, the size of the U.K. market swelled to 750,000 collectors among 56 million inhabitants, making it the largest outside of North America.

Though children are still popular subjects for plate series in the United Kingdom, animals and bird scenes now offer stiff competition. Also high on the list of favorites are country scenes and landscapes, scenes with great human interest and movie series.

### U.K. Tastes Cross International Borders

Of the most popular recent series in Britain, the top two are Christian Seltmann's *Lückel's Idyllic Village Life* and Wedgwood's *Street Sellers of London*. Other winning series show the international diversity of British preferences: Tirschenreuth's *Songbirds of Europe*, the U.S. Rockwell Society's *Rockwell's American Dream,*

Wedgwood's *Finnie's Victorian Christmas,* the U.S. Knowles' *Birds of Your Garden,* Taiwan's *Chinese Children's Games* and Canada's *Wings Upon the Wind.*

Britons still rank the American artists Norman Rockwell, John McClelland and Donald Zolan among their favorites, but they're equally fond of native Britons Mary Vickers and John Finnie as well as German artist Ursula Band.

### Respect Continues for Time-Honored Makers

In the North American market, some newer plate-producing companies have built their reputations exclusively in limited editions. By contrast, in the United Kingdom, the most popular limited editions are from older companies, whose reputations were built on quality dinnerware, giftware and figurines. But limited-edition plates as a collectible on their own have been steadily growing in importance.

### Wedgwood

Wedgwood is one example of a time-honored firm with offshoots in the modern collector's market. In 1969, the company introduced a classic-style Jasperware *Christmas* plate, "Windsor Castle," in an annual series that is still being issued and distributed worldwide. "The limited-edition plate business plays a very important role in our company and is rapidly growing. And Wedgwood puts a lot of effort into this development," says a group product development executive at Wedgwood.

### Belleek

A company renowned for its translucent parian china is Belleek, of Northern Ireland. Belleek's designs in the field of limited-edition plates have always concentrated on Irish themes. The company's most popular series have been the *Book of Kells,* followed by the *Christmas* series (1970 to 1977).

### Royal Doulton

Royal Doulton is very selective in both the number of plate series it produces and the artists it chooses; the plates are always numbered editions and are packaged with an informative brochure. Fay Handley, product manager for collectibles, explains that the British market is still less developed than the U.S. market: "In the United Kingdom, we stress the aesthetic appeal of a particular collectible more than its investment potential," she points out.

### A New Acceptance of Diversity and Style

In the United Kingdom, plate issues that present traditionally British themes of local history, landscapes and decorative arts have always won approval. Even so, the mainstream of British collectors are now enjoy-

ing art from many sources and cultures other than their own. Their fondness for American, European, Chinese and Canadian issues shows that this market is growing not only in numbers, but also in diversity and sophistication.

## PLATE COLLECTING IN GERMANY:
**Familiar Art by Respected Makers Heralds Rapid Growth**

Today, West Germany ranks among the leading European nations both in plate production and in percentage of collectors among the population. There are now an estimated 500,000 collectors among 62 million Germans.

Although every shop that sells well-known brands of porcelain such as Rosenthal, Hutschenreuther and Heinrich also sells limited-edition plates, most German dealers that sell plates do not actively promote the concept of collecting. But this situation is being remedied: there are now several authorized Bradford Exchange dealers in Germany that can offer not only a good selection of limited editions, but also the inside market knowledge of full-service dealers.

### Long-Term Favorites Share Spotlight With New Issues

Since plate collecting was first introduced in Germany, the most popular issues have been the traditional blue-and-white plates, such as the Bing & Grøndahl and Royal Copenhagen *Christmas* series. More recently, front-runners have included editions by Berlin Design *(Christmas)*, Heinrich *(Russian Fairy Tales)* and Rosenthal *(Christmas Songs)*. German producers are now developing a greater number of plates that are geared toward the tastes and lifestyle of a new breed of German collector.

### Much Interest in Nature and Landscapes

Art that depicts the outdoors, with a great emphasis on landscapes and pleasant scenes of nature, is still the preferred type in Germany.

Although present market emphasis is on artists who are German nationals, the work of notable Danish artist Bjørn Wiinblad and Americans Norman Rockwell and Eve Licea also are valued highly. They join the ranks of favorite German artists Ursula Band, Karl Bedal, Christian Lückel, Ludwig Muninger, Gero Trauth and Sulamith Wülfing.

The leading primary-market success in Germany in recent years has been the *Band's Songbirds of Europe* series, from Tirschenreuth. Other leading primary-market series among German collectors in recent years were Band's *Bouquets of the Seasons* (from Hutschenreuther), *Lückel's Idyllic Village Life* (from Christian Seltmann), *Muninger's Romantic Winter Impressions* (from

Fürstenberg), *Wülfing Christmas* (from Königszelt Bayern), and *Magical Fairy Tales from Old Russia* (from Heinrich/Villeroy & Boch).

Brokerage trading has expanded by more than 50 percent in Germany recently. The most sought-after secondary market plates are those in the *Heritage, Russian Fairy Tales, German Farmhouses* and *Living Madonnas* series. And with full service plate dealers now on the scene, the prospects are even better for the immediate future of active trading.

## PLATE COLLECTING IN SWITZERLAND:
**Tastes for the Beauty of the Outdoors**

Surrounded with the awe-inspiring beauty of the Alpine landscape, it's no wonder that the collectors of Switzerland would want to bring some of that spectacular scenery indoors. Perhaps that explains the success of plate series that feature local scenery or the bounty of nature.

There are an estimated 50,000 collectors in Switzerland among a population of 6.5 million people. In 1986, the first true limited edition collector's plate from Langenthal, a Swiss maker, entered the worldwide market—and the Swiss market has never been the same since.

Langenthal created its first series from the work of

*Royal Grafton of Great Britain earned Bradex-listing on the U.S. market for the first time in 1987. The first plate to appear here from this well-known company is "Pheasants in Flight," first issue in the* Braithwaite Game Birds Collection *by wildlife artist Derek Braithwaite.*

Albert Anker, who is one of Switzerland's best-known artists. So it's not surprising that "Grandfather Tells a Story," first issue in Langenthal's series titled *Anker's Heritage,* was the front-runner among all plates sold in Switzerland in recent years.

Other highly-regarded series included *Bouquets of the Seasons, Lückel's Idyllic Village Life* and *Muninger's Romantic Winter Impressions.*

## PLATE COLLECTING IN AUSTRIA:
### In Its Infancy, But Developing Fast

Austria shares much of the magnificent Alpine landscape with Switzerland. As the Austrian market, now estimated at 15,000 collectors, moves out of its infancy, its tastes in collector's plates are apparently influenced by its more-experienced Swiss neighbor.

In fact, the four best-selling plate series in Switzerland in recent years (see above) were also the top four plates in the Austrian market. Austrians were particularly fond of the new German issues from Hutschenreuther, Christian Seltmann and Fürstenberg. And out of respect to their neighbor nation, the first Swiss plate from Langenthal also ranked highly there.

### Young Market is Eager for Top Notch Issues

The Austrian market is so new that it is eager to accept leading issues from many markets. While German and Swiss plates are the market leaders, there is also much enthusiasm here for French and Italian plates and even American issues. The one thing these plates have in common is that they all feature art by respected artists of long standing.

But the one element missing in this market is a plate series produced just for Austrian tastes. With enthusiasm so high, market-watchers expect to see the first limited-edition issue from an Austrian plate producer in the near future.

## PLATE COLLECTING IN AUSTRALIA:
### Immigrants Establish a Collectors' Market; Bicentennial Issues Are Created

Australia is an island almost as large as the continental United States but with only 16 million inhabitants. Collecting habits and tastes there are formed somewhat by British traditions but mostly by the influence of European immigrants. Some expansion in the Australian market can also be traced to an acceptance of series produced specifically for and about Australia.

Plate collectors in Australia are now estimated at 110,000 strong, and they are collecting in ever-growing diversity. In the past, favorite plate producers included such internationally-known companies as Wedgwood, Royal Doulton, Royal Copenhagen, Bing & Grøndahl and The Franklin Mint. Now producers such as the Heritage Collection and the Australian Collectors' Treasury are making considerable inroads in the market.

With the Australian Bicentennial celebration occurring in 1988, Wedgwood's *Australian Bicentennial Series* is a hit with collectors. Also inspired by that upcoming event is Benz Ceramics' *Ships That Made Australia* and Westminster's *Australian Songbirds* series. But these series are commemorative only, and not true limited editions.

In recent years, German producers have also won favor, particularly Tirschenreuth, Christian Seltmann and Villeroy & Boch. Knowles and the Rockwell Society of America are the leading producers from the United States. Several of the top-selling limited-editions in Australia in recent years were Rockwell issues.

### Australians "Make the Scene"

Although Australians favor scenes of wildlife and children, scenic series also caught the public fancy. The first plate of Christian Seltmann's *Idyllic Village Life,* from Germany, was the best-seller among all new issues last year. Another issue that is expected to become a front-runner is "Pao-chai," the first plate from The People's Republic of China.

### Secondary Market Comes Into Its Own

The Sydney office of The Bradford Exchange opened its Brokerage Division in May of 1986, and trading on

*Another prestigious European maker to make its first entry into the U.S. market was Fürstenberg of Germany. "Ice Skaters in the Evening Sun" won acclaim in many markets.*

the Australian exchange began in the fall of 1987, as the first Australian *Current Quotations* was published and distributed to collectors. As the choice of issues now available in the Australian market grows into the hundreds, experts look for the interest in back issues to intensify.

## PLATE COLLECTING IN DENMARK:
### Awareness of a Proud Heritage

It all began with a small blue-and-white Christmas plate sold in 1895 that became the first true limited-edition collector's plate. After all these years, Danish plate collectors are still aware of their artistic heritage.

But their awareness now extends much further. Since 1986, Bing & Grøndahl's *Summer at Skagen* series, which features the artwork of Danish artist Peter Severin Krøyer, has been the most popular plate series since the heydays of the early '70s. *Moments of Truth*, by Kurt Ard, has been another resounding success.

To the 150,000 people now collecting in Denmark, maker names are important: Bing & Grøndahl and Royal Copenhagen still claim the lion's share of the market. The emphasis here is on scenic art, rather than on romantic or sentimental themes.

What's more, the newer, full-color plates are being bought by new collectors. The expanded market created by these new issues is served by 400 plate dealers in Denmark, who support the old collecting tradition as well as they encourage the new.

## PLATE COLLECTING IN SWEDEN:
### New German Issues Capture Market

The Swedish market is also being swept up in the collecting world's recent enthusiasm for new issues from Germany. Both *Band's Songbirds of Europe* and *Lückel's Idyllic Village Life* have been recent successes here. Among Sweden's 8.3 million residents, approximately 110,000 are plate collectors. And although their favorite limited editions are still the Bing & Grøndahl and the Royal Copenhagen *Christmas* series, German series such as *Songbirds of Europe* and *Idyllic Village Life* have definitely made their mark.

Rörstrand, one of the oldest porcelain houses in Europe and a local Swedish firm, is also an important producer in this market. Although Rörstrand's only Bradex-listed series in the United States is the *Christmas* series, in Sweden the *Mother's Day*, *Father's Day* and another *Christmas* series are well-appreciated. Rörstrand produces many full-color series in Sweden for this ready market.

## PLATE COLLECTING IN THE ORIENT:
### Source of Tradition and Beauty for the World

Among the ancient nations that first developed the production of porcelain and elevated it to a fine art,

three are now important regular sources for plate collectors in the West. Today, the People's Republic of China, the Republic of China (Taiwan) and Japan produce some of the most respected and successful plate series in the market.

### People's Republic Has Created Landmark Series

Since its introduction in 1985, the first collector's plate series form the birthplace of porcelain—the city of Ching-te Chen in the People's Republic—has swept the collecting world. The *Beauties of the Red Mansion* series has achieved landmark status in the United States, Canadian and European markets.

Collectors' enthusiasm for the series was conveyed to the officials of the Imperial Ching-te Chen Porcelain Factory, and dignitaries from this factory have visited the United States to experience this enthusiasm for themselves. Consequently, there is speculation as to whether a second series from Imperial Ching-te Chen is planned for the near future.

### The Republic of China (Taiwan) Expands Its Influence

In 1986, the *Chinese Children's Games* series, with artwork by Kee Fung Ng, debuted in the United States and other Western markets. The series has generated an excellent showing.

It earned the endorsement of Bradford Exchange analysts because it is the first series sponsored by a major Chinese cultural institution, the Hwa Kang Museum of the Chinese Cultural University.

### Japanese Market: An Enigma, But Poised for Growth

The Japanese market remains enigmatic because it is difficult to track. The Japanese have produced extremely fine porcelain art objects for centuries, including some collector's plate series that have found their way into the United States and other markets. And for the past several years, it has been known that the Japanese themselves are interested in limited-edition art, particularly the issues produced by the major European porcelain makers.

Their interest also extends to the process of trading plates. The Bradford Exchange and its organized market have been the subjects of television specials and articles in the prestigious *Japan Economic Journal*. The world headquarters of the exchange also periodically hosts visiting delegations of Japanese business people.

Yet, because Japanese homes are small by Western standards and their display space is very limited, it is not customary to hang objects on the walls. Exchange experts still have mixed opinions as to whether this market can support growth similar to what has occurred recently in Europe.

# HOW TO TRADE ON THE SECONDARY MARKET

The message flashes over the Telefax lines to London, England, from the Trading Floor of The Bradford Exchange in a suburb of Chicago: "Your urgent request for 'Dreaming in the Attic' plates acknowledged. Now checking our sources in U.S. market." The broker checks her computer; there are dozens of sell-orders for the plate, and at good prices. The British office confirms: buy! Within weeks, a plate from a collector in Santa Barbara finds its way to an eager secondary-market trader in London.

This type of plate trading activity has significance for all collectors—even if they have no intention of ever buying or selling any of their plates on the secondary market. For when the laws of supply and demand come into play, there is a good chance that the value of one's collection may increase over time. In the meantime, it is rewarding and fun to watch the market prices of special issues rise and fall and rise again. This is the real lure of the secondary market!

## How Organized Trading Helps the Collector

Because each plate in a limited edition is identical to all others, the price that is established for *one* plate within a certain time span should be fairly representative of the market price for *all* such plates. On this concept of orderly and organized trading, The Bradford Exchange—the world's largest trading center for limited-edition plates—was founded.

At the Exchange, only "mint condition" plates are traded. This is a plate with no visible surface flaws—such as minute cracks, chips, tears or bubbles in the art transfer—and complete with all original documentation, including the Certificate of Authenticity, if any. The original box is also required for a plate to be traded through the Exchange.

Today, the information and services that the Exchange provides are used by individual collectors and dealers to make intelligent buying and selling decisions—even if they choose to trade by means other than through the Exchange.

## Options for Buying and Selling Back Issues

There are four options for trading plates, accessible to virtually all collectors:

### Trade Through a Collectible Dealer

Most knowledgeable dealers offer some level of service in the buying and selling of plates. Some even maintain their own "want to buy" and "want to sell" files and encourage transactions among their own customers.

Authorized Bradford Exchange Dealers have direct access to the Exchange's Trading Floor and can act on the collector's behalf to buy or sell directly through the Exchange. The customer pays no additional premium or fee for this service, other than the commissions that are normally charged by the Exchange (see "How a Trade Takes Place on the Bradford Exchange Trading Floor" in this chapter).

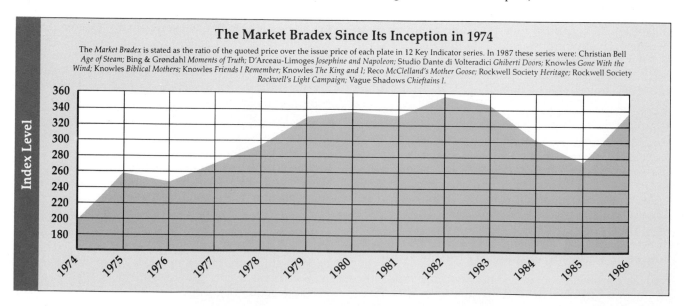

**The Market Bradex Since Its Inception in 1974**

The *Market Bradex* is stated as the ratio of the quoted price over the issue price of each plate in 12 Key Indicator series. In 1987 these series were: Christian Bell *Age of Steam*; Bing & Grøndahl *Moments of Truth*; D'Arceau-Limoges *Josephine and Napoleon*; Studio Dante di Volteradici *Ghiberti Doors*; Knowles *Gone With the Wind*; Knowles *Biblical Mothers*; Knowles *Friends I Remember*; Knowles *The King and I*; Reco McClelland's *Mother Goose*; Rockwell Society *Heritage*; Rockwell Society *Rockwell's Light Campaign*; Vague Shadows *Chieftains I*.

Index Level: 360, 340, 320, 300, 280, 260, 240, 220, 200, 180

1974, 1975, 1976, 1977, 1978, 1979, 1980, 1981, 1982, 1983, 1984, 1985, 1986

# How A Trade Takes Place
## On The Bradford Exchange Trading Floor

**Trading Floor**

### If Buy Order And Sell Order Match,
## A Trade Occurs

**Trading Floor Notifies Buyer And Seller**

**Inspection**

**● WHAT THE SELLER DOES:**
Places a sell order (called an "ask") with the Bradford Exchange Trading Floor. This can be done through an authorized Bradford Exchange dealer, or directly by phone or mail. There is no fee for this service until the sell order is successfully matched.

**SELL ORDER ("ASK")**

**● THE SELL ORDER** stays active for 90 days, or until a match occurs and a trade is made. The seller may change his price any time within that 90 days if a trade has not already occurred.

**● IF NO TRADE** at the end of 90 days, the sell order expires automatically.

**A SELL ORDER UNMATCHED 90 DAYS**

**● THE SELLER** sends his plate to the Trading Floor for inspection to verify "mint condition."

**SEND PLATE** YES

**● THE SELLER** is sent a check (or, if trading with a dealer, receives payment from that dealer). A fee that is 30 percent of the selling price is charged.

**● WHAT THE BUYER DOES:**
Places a buy order (called a "bid") with the Bradford Exchange Trading Floor. This can be done through an authorized Bradford Exchange dealer, or directly by phone or mail. There is no fee for this service until the buy order is successfully matched.

**BUY ORDER ("BID")**

**● THE BUY ORDER** stays active for 90 days, or until a match occurs and a trade is made. The buyer may change his price any time within that 90 days if a trade has not already occurred.

**● IF NO TRADE** at the end of 90 days, the buy order expires automatically.

**A BUY ORDER UNMATCHED 90 DAYS**

**● THE BUYER** sends his check to the Trading Floor for clearing and processing. A fee that is 4 percent of the purchase price ($4.00 minimum) is charged.

**SEND CHECK** YES

**● THE BUYER** is shipped his plate (or, if trading with a dealer, receives it from that dealer).

The Bradford Exchange Trading Floor (or an authorized Bradford Dealer acting as its agent) *guarantees* both sides of the transaction, so that both buyer and seller are protected.

---

And, although all Bradford Exchange dealers are qualified to advise on secondary market trading, there are 50 dealers, spread across the United States, who offer a special level of expertise and service. These dealers display The Bradford Exchange Information Center in their stores. It signifies that they are unusually well-qualified to help their customers in secondary market transactions of any kind.

## Shop the "Buy-and-Sell" Exchange at Shows

The excitement of "one-on-one" trading is often what draws collectors to the huge "Buy-and-Sell" events at major collector shows. These events give secondary-market shoppers a chance to examine and compare prices on hundreds of plates at a time. If a plate is "hot" on the market, half the fun is scanning the sales tables to find it offered at a good price, or to compare prices from table to table. And spirited bargaining is often the order of the day.

## Trade Among Fellow Club Members

One major benefit of collector club membership is the direct access to other collectors who may be ready to trade. Club members frequently exchange buy and sell information among themselves, and sometimes even swap parts of one collection for another. Through trading, members discover common likes and dislikes. And what starts out as a transaction among strangers often ends up as a real collecting friendship.

## Use Classified Advertising

Some traders prefer to use local or national classified listings to trade. Trading with another collector by mail, however, does pose some risks. For the buyer, the big-

A collector consults *The Bradford Exchange* Current Quotations *to check market prices on several back-issues by Edna Hibel. If the market looks "right," he may place a buy order with his dealer.*

gest question is: will the plate truly be in mint condition? For the seller, the question is: should I send off my plate *before* I know the check is good? If these questions can be resolved, both parties can trade in confidence.

## Choose The Bradford Exchange as Your Market Resouce

If a qualified dealer is unavailable, a collector can always trade directly through The Bradford Exchange Trading Floor, by phone or by mail. Any transaction that occurs on the Exchange (whether through a dealer or by an individual) is fully *guaranteed*, so that neither the buyer nor the seller bears any risk. For a look at how these trades occur, see "How a Trade Takes Place on The Bradford Exchange Trading Floor" in this chapter.

### *Current Quotations* is the Key to the Market

For any and all types of secondary-market transactions, most collectors usually check a current edition of The Bradford Exchange *Current Quotations* report,

issued bi-monthly, to get some idea of the latest market prices. This report tracks the market performance of more than 1,400 of the most actively-traded plates. It indicates the issue price of each plate and the price at which it sold most recently. It also offers a "quote" price, which is the Exchange's best estimate of what that plate should be trading for in the immediate future.

You will find a complete reprint of the *Current Quotations* on page 379 of this book, current as of the printing of this Twelfth Edition book (Fall, 1987). *Use it to determine the market prices of virtually every plate pictured in this book* as of that date. For later market information, you may request a free copy of the most recent *Current Quotations* report from your local authorized Bradford Exchange dealer or directly from the Exchange.

## TRENDS IN SECONDARY MARKET TRADING: Movie Theme Issues Maintain Market Lead

Collector's plates with movie themes continued to set trends on the secondary market. For the past several years, these plates have accounted for a significant portion of *trading volume* on The Bradford Exchange (see accompanying graph). Several issues—most notably those in the Knowles *Gone With the Wind* series—have also led the market in *price appreciation* (see The Bradford Exchange *Current Quotations* at the rear of this book, page 379).

From December 1985 to December 1986, for example, the average price of a single issue in the six movie series then listed on the Exchange rose about 14 per cent, from $48.93 to $56.89. These six series were *The Wizard of Oz, Gone With the Wind, The King and I, Oklahoma, Annie* (all from Knowles) and *Gigi* (from

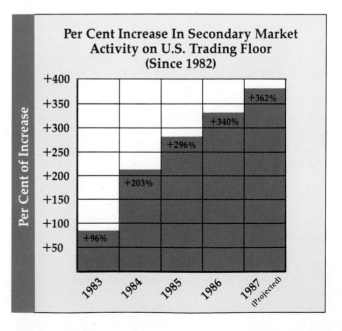

D'Arceau-Limoges). A seventh series—*The Sound of Music*—was trading only on the primary market at that time, but has already begun to register exceptional trading volume at that level.

Brokerage market analysts for the Exchange identified *Gone With the Wind* as the top-traded series of 1986, and in overall trading, one out of four plates traded on the Exchange in 1986 was a movie issue.

In trading volume on the U.S. Exchange, the top-ranked series of 1986 were:

1. Edwin M. Knowles
   *Gone With the Wind*
2. Rockwell Society of America
   *Rockwell's Rediscovered Women*
3. Rockwell Society of America
   *Heritage*
4. Reco International
   *McClelland's Mother Goose*
5. Edwin M. Knowles
   *The King and I*
6. Edwin M. Knowles
   *Annie*
7. Pemberton & Oakes
   *Wonders of Childhood*
8. Rockwell Society of America
   *Rockwell's Light Campaign*
9. Edwin M. Knowles
   *Csatari Grandparents*
10. Rockwell Society of America
    *Mother's Day*

## Pressure from Overseas Markets Drives Up Prices of European Secondary Issues

The growing European markets began to exert their influence on the secondary markets in the United States and Canada in the late 1980s. As certain single plate issues sold out quickly in Europe, Bradford Exchange offices there turned to the larger market here to satisfy collector demand. As a result, such issues as "Baked Potato Man" (Wedgwood's *Street Sellers of London*) and "Bodenseehaus," (Königszelt Bayern's *German Half-Timbered Houses*) experienced unusual market appreciation here. (See "Plate Collecting in the United States" and "The Worldwide Market for Collector's Plates.")

And in the reverse situation, Exchange brokers began to turn to the European markets to satisfy heavy demand among collectors here. Such plates as "Grandpa's Treasure Chest," "Dreaming in the Attic," "Mammy Lacing Scarlett" and even "Behind the Frozen Window," the granddaddy of them all, were sought on all European Exchanges to fill in collections in the United States.

Global influence is everywhere in plate collecting, and it's clearly here to stay—just as in the world in general in the 1980s.

*Transaction between interested parties: one collector makes a secondary-market purchase from another at a plate exchange. These events are a highlight of most major collector shows; hundreds of plates often change hands and bargaining is expected.*

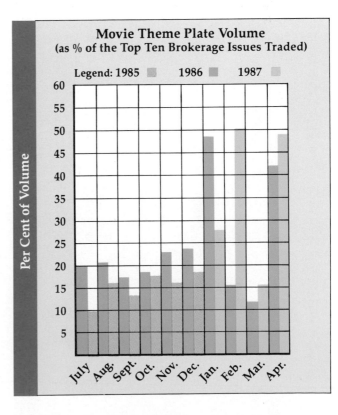

**Movie Theme Plate Volume**
(as % of the Top Ten Brokerage Issues Traded)

Legend: 1985 ▨  1986 ▨  1987 ▨

Per Cent of Volume

July, Aug., Sept., Oct., Nov., Dec., Jan., Feb., Mar., Apr.

# HOW TO ENHANCE YOUR EXPERIENCE AS A COLLECTOR

Collectors who examine their hobby from every perspective are the ones who find it the most rewarding and fascinating. In this chapter, you'll learn how to identify and use the resources that will help put you on the cutting edge of plate collecting.

In all, there are nine activities that can make collecting more fun, more rewarding and more profitable. They are: joining a collectors' club; perusing publications for collectors; visiting plate museums and factories, attending collector shows; shopping at the store of a knowledgeable dealer, decorating—and redecorating—with plates; giving plates as gifts; protecting your collection; and playing the secondary market.

## Join a Collectors' Club

It takes one to know one. Who will share your passion for plates more than *another* plate-smitten collector? Or better yet, a whole roomful? That's where collectors' clubs come in. They give plate buyers a chance to mingle, "talk plates" and share information and insights with other collectors.

That's not all. Plate clubs offer an endless supply of information on new releases, group trips to factories

and shows and perhaps even a special price break from the plate dealer who sponsors the club. Club members may even do a little plate trading among

*Collectors' club members are often easy to spot at collector shows: they're the ones having the most fun!*

*Clubs bring together collectors of varied ages and backgrounds. What's discussed at meetings? Anything from new issues by favorite artists to big winners in the secondary market to old favorites, like the Haviland Christmas plates shown here.*

themselves to trim down a collection or build up a new one.

The most active clubs know that there is strength in numbers. They ask for—and get—special attention from artists and platemaking companies when it comes to special programs. Artists and company representatives are happy to appear at club meetings. Often the stories they tell about the creation of their new issues are insightful, amusing and include information collectors couldn't get anywhere else. They also offer product previews and tips on collecting.

Clubs may also plan programs that feature an insurance expert one evening and an interior decorator the next. Between meetings, members stay informed through club newsletters.

Thousands of plate collectors now attend club meetings across North America. There are 102 clubs in the United States and 22 clubs in Canada, so there's no alibi for being absent. To locate a club in your area, check listings in collectibles publications or call a local dealer. Who knows? If that dealer doesn't sponsor a club, perhaps he'd like to start one with your help.

## Enjoy Publications for Collectors

On paper, the easiest and most in-depth method of finding the inside scoops on collecting is through magazines and newsletters devoted to collectibles.

Of these, *Plate World* magazine is the only national publication that focuses on plates and plates alone. It's published bi-monthly in full color and features dozens of photos of new plates and market winners in each issue. Articles profile artists, producers and collectors, and report on shows, decorating ideas, tours, clubs and other collector events.

Another source of market news is The Bradford Exchange *Current Quotations*, commonly known as the "Bradex." The bi-monthly report lists the current market prices of more than 1,400 plates that are actively traded on the Exchange. This report is bound into each issue of *Plate World* and is available on request from dealers and directly from The Bradford Exchange. (For more information, see the previous chapter.)

In addition, there are several other publications (see photo at right) that devote at least some space to plates. All are worthwhile.

## Explore a Factory or Museum

For collectors who really what to know "where plates come from," there are connoisseurs' tours of plate production facilities and collectors' museums, both in the United States and abroad.

You'll appreciate how complex of a work of art a plate really is when you've seen the steps involved in its creation. (For more on this, see "The Worldwide Market for Collector's Plates" in this book.) Among the producers that will demonstrate the genesis of a plate from the mixing of the clay to the firing of the edition are: Bing & Grøndahl in Denmark; Arabia in Finland; S.A. Faienceries de Quimper in France; Goebel, Rosenthal and Villeroy & Boch in Germany; Royal Doulton, Royal Worcester and Wedgwood in Great Britain; Royal Delft in Holland; Belleek in Ireland; Anri in Italy, Porsgrund in Norway; and, in the United States, Frankoma Pottery in Oklahoma and Crown Parian in California.

If you want to be overwhelmed by the beauty of the finished product, immerse yourself in the world-class plate collections on display in museums in Illinois, Florida and Arizona.

*The Bradford Museum of Collector's Plates, Niles, Illinois* This "museum in a garden" showcases the more than 1,400 plate issues that are listed on the Exchange. Visitors are guided through the history of collecting, viewing plate series from 60 makers in 16 nations of the world. Special Plexiglas cases reveal both the art and the backstamp of every issue. In the center of the museum, the Bradford Exchange Trading Floor is open to public view, displaying market activity as it occurs. Guided tours are available. 9333 Milwaukee Avenue, Niles, Illinois 60648.

*Leading publications for collectors include (clockwise from top):* Collectibles Market Guide & Price Index; Collectors Mart *and* Collector Editions *magazines;* The Bradford Exchange Current Quotations; Plate World *magazine. Also shown is an article on plate collecting that appeared in* Sky, Delta Airlines' *inflight magazine, in 1987.*

The Bradford Museum of Collector's Plates, located in the headquarters of The Bradford Exchange, displays the 1,400 plates that are listed on the Exchange. Special cases show both the fronts and backs of all plates. The Trading Floor can be seen at center, rear.

*The Plate World Magazine Hall of Fame and Trading Exhibit, Palm Beach Gardens, Florida* Nestled in the lobby of MacArthur's Holiday Inn, this small but significant exhibit highlights the ''big winners'' that made history in the worldwide market. Nearly 130 plates are featured, along with a televised readout of prices from the Bradford Exchange Trading Floor. MacArthur's Holiday Inn, 4431 PGA Boulevard at I-95, Palm Beach Gardens, Florida 33410.

*The Stanley J. Solon Collection, Brevard Community College, Cocoa, Florida* The late Stanley J. Solon, a veteran collector, bequeathed his 1,500-plate collection to Brevard shortly before his death in 1986. Students in the college's woodworking classes built many of the shelves that display the art in the campus library and Fine Arts Auditorium. Brevard Community College, 1519 Clearlake Rd., Cocoa, Florida 32922.

*The Hibel Museum of Art, Palm Beach, Florida* The works of Edna Hibel fill this museum—including the dozens of plate issues she has designed over the past 15 years. Hibel remains among the most prolific of plate artists and also works in oils, lithographs and other porcelain media. 150 Royal Poinciana Plaza, Palm Beach, Florida, 33480.

*Gallery in the Sun, Tucson, Arizona* The late Ted DeGrazia constructed this partial adobe structure, overlooking saguaro-laden landscapes and the Arizona country whose people he loved and painted. The gallery displays his collector's plates and works in many other media, and features a film on his life and work. Tours are available. 6300 N. Swan Rd., Tucson, Arizona 85718.

## Attend a Plate Show

Spend a day with dozens of plate artists, producers, dealers and thousands of other collectors at the plate show nearest you. Collectors bring home artists' autographs, new plate acquisitions from secondary-market ''buy-and-sell'' events, lots of new product information and, best of all, happy memories. It's hard to say what's most memorable from among hundreds of exhibits, seminars on collecting, panel discussions, films, videos and slide shows, plus rousing question-and-answer sessions with favorite artists.

Most collectors attend shows to see new issues before they appear in dealers' shops or to see new work by their favorite artists. For those who can't wait to acquire the very newest plates, orders can often be

# Collecting By Theme

Many collectors get great pleasure by collecting series or single issues with artwork that has the same subject, or *theme*. To help you discover subjects in this book that interest you, here are 21 major themes in which collector's plate art can be grouped.

Under each theme category are the names of all series in this book with that theme. The series are listed in the order in which they appear in this book; to locate each series, see the *Table of Contents*.

**ANIMALS** (Domestic and Pets):
Bing & Grøndahl *Mother's Day;* Royal Copenhagen *Motherhood;* Lalique *Annual;* Anna-Perenna *Uncle Tad's Cats,* Uncle Tad's *Golden Oldies;* Kaiser *Mother's Day;* Edwin M. Knowles *Friends in the Forest, Amy Brackenbury's Cat Tales* (See also: WILDLIFE)

**ARCHITECTURE:**
D'Arceau-Limoges *Twelve Parisian Places of Louis Dali;* Bareuther *Father's Day;* Königszelt-Bayern *German Half-Timbered Houses;* Wedgwood *Christmas;* Orrefors *Annual Cathedrals*

**ARTISTS:**

| | |
|---|---|
| Chambers, William: | Edwin M. Knowles *Annie, The King and I, Portraits of Motherhood, Tom Sawyer* |
| DeGrazia, Ted: | Artists of the World *Children of the Sun;* Fairmont *DeGrazia Holiday, Children, Children at Play, Western;* Gorham *DeGrazia Children* |
| Hibel, Edna: | Hibel Studio *David,* Rosenthal *Nobility of Children, Oriental Gold;* Royal Doulton *Mother and Child;* Edwin M. Knowles *Hibel Christmas; Hibel Mother's Day* |
| Hook, Frances: | Edwin M. Knowles *Frances Hook Legacy;* Roman *A Child's Play* |
| Hummel, Berta (or Sister M. I.): | Goebel Hummel *Annual, Anniversary;* Schmid *Christmas, Mother's Day* |
| Kuck, Sandra: | Reco *Days Gone By* |
| McClelland, John: | Reco *World of Children, Mother Goose, Children's Circus, Becky's Day* |
| Perillo, Gregory: | Vague Shadows *Chieftains I* |
| Rockwell, Norman: | Franklin Mint *Christmas;* Gorham *Four Seasons, Rockwell Christmas;* Rockwell Society of America *Christmas, Mother's Day, Heritage, Rediscovered Women, Rockwell on Tour, Light Campaign, American Dream, Colonials: The Rarest Rockwells, A Mind of Her Own, Golden Moments,* Royal Devon *Christmas* |
| Skelton, Red: | Crown Parian *Freddie the Freeloader, Freddie's Adventures;* Fairmont *Famous Clowns* |
| Spencer, Irene: | Pickard *Mother's Love, Symphony of Roses* |
| Zolan, Donald: | Pemberton & Oakes *Wonder of Childhood, Children at Christmas, Children and Pets;* Viletta *Zolan's Children* |

**BEAUTIFUL WOMEN:**
Imperial Ching-te Chen *Beauties of the Red Mansion;* D'Arceau-Limoges *Women of the Century, Girls of the Seasons, Women of the Belle Epoque;* Haviland Parlon *The Lady and the Unicorn;* Heinrich/Villeroy & Boch *Dreams of Katharina;* Wedgwood *Portraits of First Love;* Le Porcellane Fontana Dei Medici *Women of Puccini;* Studio Dante di Volteradici *Benvenuti's Muses;* Fairmont *Classical American Beauties;* Edwin M. Knowles *Four Ancient Elements;* Morgantown Crystal *Michael Yates' Country Ladies;* Pickard *Oleg Cassini's Most Beautiful Women of All Time, Symphony of Roses;* Rockwell Society of America *Rediscovered Women*

**BIRDS:**
Dominion China *Wings Upon the Wind;* Grande Copenhagen *Ugly Duckling;* Tirschenreuth *Songbirds of Europe;* Royal Grafton *Braithwaite Game Birds Collection;* Lenox *Boehm Bird;* Edwin M. Knowles *Birds of Your Garden, Upland Birds of North America, Living with Nature: Jerner's Ducks*

**CARTOON CHARACTERS:**
Schmid *Peanuts Christmas, Disney Christmas, Disney Mother's Day*

**CHILDREN** (contemporary):
Dominion China *Reflections of Canadian Childhood;* Pavilion of T'sang Ying Hsuan Chinese *Children's Games;* Bing & Grøndahl *Moments of Truth, Children's Day, Family Portraits;* D'Arceau-Limoges *Christmas in France;* Limoges-Turgot *Durand's Children;* Wedgwood *Blossoming of Suzanne, My Memories;* Artists of the World *Children of Aberdeen,* DeGrazia's *Children of the Sun;* Ernst *Seems Like Yesterday;* Fairmont *DeGrazia Children, Playful Memories,* DeGrazia's *Children at Play;* Gorham *Sugar & Spice;* Kern *Leaders of Tomorrow,* Edwin M. Knowles *Jeanne Down's Friends I Remember, Frances Hook Legacy, A Swan Is Born;* Pemberton & Oakes *Wonder of Childhood, Children at Christmas, Children and Pets;* Roman *A Child's Play;* Viletta *Zolan's Children*

**CHILDREN** (nostalgic):
Limoges-Turgot *Children of the Turn of the Century;* Goebel Hummel *Annual,* Hummel *Anniversary;* Kaiser *Classic Lullabies of the World;* Rosenthal *Nobility of Children;* Schmid *Christmas, Mother's Day;* Davenport Pottery *Treasury of Classic Children's Verse;* Royal Doulton *Portraits of Innocence;* Fukagawa *Haiku About Children;* Langenthal *Anker's*

*Heritage;* Edwin M. Knowles *Americana Holidays, American Innocents, J. W. Smith's Childhood Holiday Memories;* Newell Pottery *S. S. Weber Calendar;* Pickard *Children of Renoir;* Rockwell Society of America *A Mind of Her Own*

**CHRISTMAS:**
Bing & Grøndahl, Grande Copenhagen, Royal Copenhagen, D'Arceau-Limoges *Stained Glass Christmas, Christmas in France;* Haviland *Twelve Days of Christmas;* Haviland & Parlon, Bareuther, Berlin Design, Kaiser, Königszelt-Bayern *Heidi Keller Christmas;* Rosenthal *Traditional Classic Rose Christmas, Wiinblad Christmas;* Schmid *Hummel Christmas;* Belleek *Christmas, Irish Wildlife Christmas;* Royal Doulton *Beswick Christmas;* Spode; Wedgwood; Anri; Schmid *Peanuts Christmas, Disney Christmas;* Porsgrund *Christmas, Traditional Norwegian Christmas;* Rörstrand; Franklin Mint *Rockwell Christmas;* Edwin M. Knowles *Hibel Christmas, Licea Christmas;* Pemberton & Oakes *Children at Christmas;* Pickard; Rockwell Society of America; Reed & Barton; Roman *Fantanini Christmas Story;* Royal Devon; Viletta *Nutcracker Ballet*

**FANTASY:**
Grande Copenhagen *Christmas;* Haviland-Parlon *Tapestry, The Lady and the Unicorn;* Limoges-Turgot Quellier's *Morals of Perrault;* Anna-Perenna *Uncle Tad's Golden Oldies;* Heinrich/Villeroy & Boch *Russian Fairy Tales, Fairies of the Fields and Flowers, Once Upon a Rhyme;* Königszelt *Grimm's Fairy Tales;* Viletta *Nutcracker Ballet*

**FATHERS/FATHER'S DAY/GRANDFATHERS:**
Bareuther *Father's Day;* Edwin M. Knowles *Csatari Grandparents, A Father's Love,* Rockwell Society *Heritage, Golden Moments*

**FLOWERS:**
Heinrich/Villeroy & Boch *Fairies of the Fields and Flowers;* Hutschenreuther *Bouquets of the Seasons;* King's *Flowers of America;* Pickard *Symphony of Roses*

**FOLKLORE:**
Arabia *Kalevala;* Davenport Pottery *Toby;* Royal Doulton *Commedia Dell-Arte;* Wedgwood *Legend of King Arthur;* Studio Dante di Volteradici *Benvenuti's Muses;* Crown Parian *American Folk Heroes;* Incolay *Voyage of Ulysses, The Fall of Troy;* Edwin M. Knowles *Four Ancient Elements*

**HISTORY:**
Christian Bell *Age of Steam, Yesterday's Memories;* D'Arceau-Limoges *Lafayette Legacy, Women of the Century, Very Rich Hours, Josephine and Napoleon, Women of the Belle Epoque;* Hibel Studio *David;* Royal Doulton *The Log of the "Dashing Wave;"* Wedgwood *Street Sellers of London;* Incolay *Great Romances of History;* Edwin M. Knowles *Lincoln—Man of America;* Rhodes Studios *Treasures of the Doré Bible;* RiverShore *Famous Americans;* Rockwell Society *Rockwell's Colonials—The Rarest Rockwells;* Vague Shadows *The Chieftains I*

**LITERATURE:**
Imperial Ching-te Chen *Beauties of the Red Mansion;* Grande Copenhagen *Ugly Duckling;* Arabia *Kalevala;* Haviland *1001 Arabian Nights;* Porcelain Georges Boyer *Alice in Wonderland;* Heinrich/Villeroy & Boch *Russian Fairy Tales;* Davenport Pottery *Treasury of Classic Children's Verse;* Longton Crown *Canterbury Tales;* Studio Dante di Volteradici *Grand Opera;* Fukagawa *Haiku About Children;* Incolay *Romantic Poets, Voyage of Ulysses, Love Sonnets of Shakespeare, The Fall of Troy;* Edwin M. Knowles *Tom Sawyer*

**LOVERS/VALENTINE'S DAY:**
Anna-Perenna *Romantic Loves;* Hutschenreuther *Love for All Seasons;* Königszelt-Bayern *Sulamith's Love Song, A Woman's Love and Life;* Royal Doulton *Valentine's Day;* Incolay *Romantic Poets, Great Romances of History*

**MOTHERS AND CHILDREN/MOTHER'S DAY/ GRANDMOTHERS:**
Bing & Grøndahl *Mother's Day,* Royal Copenhagen *Motherhood;* D'Arceau-Limoges *Cambier Mother's Day;* Kaiser *Mother's Day;* Königszelt-Bayern *Wülfing Mother's Day;* Royal Bayreuth *Mother's Day;* Schmid *Mother's Day;* Royal Doulton *Mother and Child;* Wedgwood *Mothers;* Studio Dante di Volteradici *Living Madonnas, Renaissance Madonnas: Gifts of Maternal Love;* Schmid *Disney Mother's Day;* Porsgrund *Mother's Day;* Lladró *Mother's Day;* Edwin M. Knowles *Csatari Grandparents, Biblical Mothers, Hibel Mother's Day, Portraits of Motherhood;* Pickard *Christmas, Mother's Love;* RiverShore *Signs of Love;* Rockwell Society *Mother's Day*

**MOVIES:**
D'Arceau-Limoges *Gigi;* W. S. George Pottery *Gone With the Wind: Golden Anniversary;* Edwin M. Knowles *The Wizard of Oz, Gone With the Wind, Annie, The King and I, Oklahoma, The Sound of Music, South Pacific*

**RELIGIOUS** (Madonnas, Biblical Figures, Churches):
Haviland-Parlon *Christmas;* Anna-Perenna *Triptych,* Hibel Studio *David;* Veneto Flair *Bellini Madonna, The Last Supper, St. Mark's of Venice;* Studio Dante di Volteradici *Living Madonnas, Ghiberti Doors, Renaissance Madonnas: Gifts of Maternal Love, The Christmas Creche;* Orrefors *Annual Cathedrals;* Edwin M. Knowles *Biblical Mothers;* Pickard *Christmas;* Rhodes Studio *Treasures of the Doré Bible;* Roman *Fontanini Christmas Story*

**SCENIC:**
Bing & Grøndahl *Summer at Skagen;* D'Arceau-Limoges *Twelve Parisian Places of Louis Dali, French Country Landscapes;* Berlin Design *Holiday Week of the Family Kappelmann;* Christian Seltmann *Lückel's Idyllic Village Life;* Fürstenberg *Romantic Winter Impressions;* Royal Worcester *Happy England;* Wedgwood *Colin Newman's Country Panorama;* Edwin M. Knowles *Living with Nature: Jerner's Ducks*

**WESTERN:**
Fairmont *DeGrazia Western;* Edwin M. Knowles *Oklahoma!;* Vague Shadows *The Chieftains I*

**WILDLIFE:**
Dominion China *Wings Upon the Wind;* Belleek *Irish Wildlife Christmas;* Royal Grafton *Braithwaite Game Birds Collection;* Edwin M. Knowles *Birds of Your Garden, Upland Birds of North America, Living With Nature: Jerner's Ducks, Friends in the Forest;* Lenox *Boehm Bird;* Pickard *Lockhart Wildlife;* RiverShore *Signs of Love*

*For non-stop excitement, nothing matches a day or two spent at a collector show. Hundreds of new issues, dozens of favorite artists and special programs on every aspect of collecting are right at the collector's fingertips, all for a modest admission fee.*

placed right at the show, to be fulfilled later by a dealer.

The International Plate and Collectible Exposition, held each July in South Bend, Indiana, is the longest-running collectors' show on record. At the 12th annual event in 1986, collectors viewed hundreds of brand-new products and traded 3,000 back-issue plates valued at $85,000. Another annual show, the California Plate and Collectible Show, is held in various cities in that state; in 1986 and 1987, the show was held in Pasadena. In April of 1987, it drew 16,000 avid collectors. Other cities that host smaller, regional plate shows are Worcester, Massachusetts, and Durham, Ontario and Vancouver, British Columbia. Check with local dealers or watch for ads in collectibles publications to be sure you don't miss the next show in your area.

### Shop at Plate Stores

If you can't attend a plate show, you should be able to find a local dealer who attends them regularly and can fill you in. Plate dealers are the best everyday source

for news on new releases, display ideas and secondary market advice. And the plate you've admired in *Plate World* can be examined in person in a dealer's store and can probably be taken home immediately.

Before long, you'll develop a rewarding relationship with your dealer. You'll receive newsletters, announcements on incoming issues the dealer thinks you'll like and invitations to store events. One dealer in Iowa, for example, recently sponsored presentations by an insurance agent, a home security expert and a video-inventory representative to help her customers learn how to protect their valuable collections.

Also, while most dealers possess a certain amount of market knowledge, some are more expert than others. All authorized Bradford Exchange Dealer Members have access to the Exchange's Trading Floor and can act on your behalf. But even among these dealers, a select group of 50 now offer collectors the superior facilities of The Bradford Exchange Information Centers. (For more information on these facilities,

see "Plate Collecting in the United States" and "How to Trade on the Secondary Market" in this book.)

## Give Plates as Gifts

The only warmer feeling than receiving a plate is giving one. You can create a family tradition that endures for years by giving plates that commemorate annual events, such as Christmas, Mother's Day or Valentine's Day.

Plates make wonderful gifts because they embody emotions that sum up personal events better than words ever could. Romantic plates for weddings, protraits of babies for births and christenings and loving couples or happy families for anniversaries all say something nice about the giver and the recipient.

Ships, horses, Indian warriors, sports figures and classic cars are well-received by men. Grandparents love plates that resemble their grandchildren. Children love dogs and sports plates, fairy tales, doll plates or nursery rhymes. And young women enjoy floral themes and portraits of women in lovely gowns.

Fans of classic movies can become confirmed collectors when they open boxes bearing plates based on their favorites. Wildlife lovers make animal plates their pet hobby, and so on. There really *is* a plate for every person and every taste. It's been said that "the only thing better than being a collector is giving the gift that creates a new collector."

## Decorate—and Redecorate—with Plates

To get the most decorative mileage from your plate

*A dealer can be an asset, especially when it comes time to make a decision on a new acquisition, a special gift or a secondary-market purchase. After all, who knows the market better than a pro?*

collection, flex your imagination. Don't just line your plates up in rows on the wall; experiment with new patterns and arrangements. Put plates from different countries in different rooms. Try displaying plates by theme, regardless of artist or producer. You'll be surprised at how well they look together.

Perk up your wall, shelf and tabletop arrangements with any of the wide array of plate accessories available today. They can add new shape, texture and depth to

*Continued on page 36*

*Collectors attend seminars geared to their special tastes. Here, the Knowles company presents a program on decorating with plates.*

# Decorating With Collector's Plates:
## A Guide to the Display of the Most Common Series Lengths

Artwork you love deserves to be displayed to its best advantage. Why hang your plates in even, horizontal rows—even though it saves a bit of space—when there's so much *more* you can do to make them look their very best in each room?

This pictorial guide shows eight different plate display ideas, two each for the four most common series lengths: *four, six, eight* and *twelve* plates. You can also adapt these ideas for plates series of other lengths (three, five, seven, nine, etc.).

**Four Plates:** *Setting A* displays the *Uncle Tad's Cats* series in an arched arrangement. This idea also works well over a sofa or a wide doorway. *Setting B* offers a variation, a four-point "diamond" pattern.

**Six Plates:** *Setting C* staggers three vertical rows and repeats the shape of the wrought iron bed. *Setting D* nestles six plates in the *McClelland's Mother Goose* series into a narrow space between headboard and window. This puts them in a well-lit area right at eye level for best viewing.

**Eight Plates:** Why restrict a favorite series to just one room? The *Days Gone By* series in *Setting E* is positioned to be dramatic in both living and dining room. A variation in *Setting F* leads the eye from one room to the other.

**Twelve Plates:** Longer series also look extra-special when displayed in more than one room, as in *Setting G*. In *Setting H*, a plate rail allows the *Rockwell's Rediscovered Women* series to be displayed harmoniously in very little space.

Plate frames and rails courtesy of Van Hygan & Smythe.

*Setting A*

*Setting B*

*Setting C*

*Setting D*

*Setting H*

*Setting E*

*Setting G*

*Setting F*

*Continued from page 33*

your collection. Beautiful wooden frames make "old" plates look new and important. They soften the look of plates against painted or panelled walls. Frames in shapes other than circles, such as squares, hexagons or ovals, break up the sameness of circular images in a wall grouping.

Plate stands allow you to display plates "off the walls" in book cases, on a mantle or even at the base of a brick fireplace. Use multi-plate frames or rails to really bring a series together.

## Keep Your Plates Intact; Know Their Value

If you're serious about enjoying your plates for years to come, you'll need to learn how to protect them now. Many collectors also find a certain sense of satisfaction in holding all the records of their plates in their hands and updating them regularly.

Starting with the very first plate you collect, get in the habit of saving the certificate (if any) and the box from each purchase. They preserve the full market value, or the "mint condition" of your plates should you decide to trade or sell them later. Then keep tabs on your collection by starting and maintaining a record book. List each plate by *title, artist, series, producer, sponsor, date and place purchased* and *issue price*. Keep a

*Smart collectors keep records that show the extent of their collection and its value, useful for insurance purposes and for planning acquisitions. Certificates, other documents can be filed in a decorative album, as here.*

scrapbook of photos of your plates, whether they are home photos or pictures from brochures or magazines. You can also rent a video camera and record your collection as it's displayed in your home.

If you're really ambitious, put your collection "on line" by storing your records on a personal computer. Then update the value of your collection by consulting The Bradford Exchange *Current Quotations* every few months. You can also keep the most current copy filed with your records.

Although maintaining accurate, current records can be time-consuming, they'll help you determine the value of your collection if it becomes lost or damaged through theft, breakage, fire or earthquake. Check with your home insurance agent to see if you'll need additional coverage for your collection. Replacement-value coverage for breakable collectibles is easily obtainable and reasonably priced.

But don't overlook everyday threats to your plates, either. Replace loose or ill-fitting hangers and check mounting nails to be sure they are firmly in place. Keep plates out of high-traffic areas like narrow hallways. A boisterous child or a frisky dog might brush against the wall and dislodge your treasure.

As for cleaning, plates take well to a monthly gentle dusting, especially on the lower rim, with a non-abrasive dusting brush. About once a year, they can be handwashed with a mild solution of lotion soap, such as the kind sold for hand use.

Care of and attention to your collection will ensure the full beauty of your plates no matter how long you keep and display them.

## Play the Secondary Market

One of the unique benefits of plate collecting is the chance to follow the changing prices of your plates on the secondary market. Which will become more valuable, your "Puzzlement" plate, your "Annie and Sandy," your "Cardinal" or your "Young Girl's Dream?" Since collector's plates are the only limited-edition collectible traded in an organized market, you can easily track the value of your plates for fun and profit.

To do this, obtain a copy of Bradford's *Current Quotations* and become familiar with its terminology. (See "How to Trade on the Secondary Market" in this book.) Compare performance histories, predict trends and plan your future "buys" and "sells."

As a hedge against future plans, some collectors buy two of each new issue they like, one to trade and one to keep. If their acquisitions increase in value (and remember, some plates decrease in value as well as increase), they can trade their duplicates for capital to invest in a whole new group of winners.

# AN INTRODUCTION TO INFORMATION IN THE GALLERY SECTION

The following Gallery section of *The Bradford Book of Collector's Plates* offers complete information on all major issues regularly traded in the market. The plates are arranged in an order exactly corresponding to The Bradford Exchange *Current Quotations:* first, by *country* of the plate's origin, in alphabetical order; second, by *plate maker* within each country, also in alphabetical order; third, by *series* of each maker, in chronological order beginning with the maker's first series; and fourth, by *plate position* in each series, also in chronological order beginning with the first plate.

To speed identification, each plate is listed by its Bradex number, a codified form of the information above. *These numbers are in sequence but not necessarily consecutive.* The number on the upper left-hand corner of each page indicates the first plate listed on that page.

## HOW TO READ THE BRADEX NUMBER

(The number used as an example here is that of the 1904 Bing & Grøndahl *Christmas* plate)

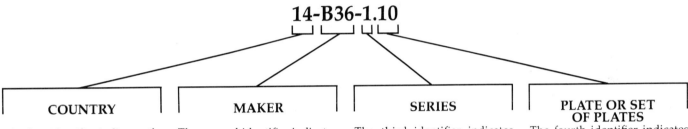

**14-B36-1.10**

| COUNTRY | MAKER | SERIES | PLATE OR SET OF PLATES |
|---|---|---|---|
| The first identifier indicates *the country of origin;* in this case the number *14* is for Denmark. | The second identifier indicates the *plate maker.* The alpha-numeric combination of *B36* represents Bing & Grøndahl. This number is assigned according to a system similar to that used in libraries for the classification of authors' works. | The third identifier indicates the maker's *series,* listed in the chronological order in which it was produced. Thus the number *1* represents Bing & Grøndahl's first series, the *Christmas* series. | The fourth identifier indicates the individual plate (or set of plates) within each series, listed in chronological order. The number *10* is for the tenth plate in the Bing & Grøndahl *Christmas* series, *View of Copenhagen from Frederiksberg Hill,* the 1904 issue. Plates issued in sets use an additional successive digit to indicate their position within a set (example: 22-A3-3.1-1). |

For your convenience in determining the location of a listing in this book, you will find individual plates indexed by *country,* by *maker* and *sponsor,* by *type* (or theme) of series, by *plate title* and by *plate artist* in the Indices and Appendices at the back of this book. Please consult the Table of Contents for the correct page number of these items.

## HOW TO LOCATE ADDITIONAL PLATE INFORMATION

*Maker's listings:* contain information on history and trademarks.
*Series listings:* contain information on artist, medium, edition limits, numbering, plate diameter and hanging provisions.
*Individual plate listings:* provide the Bradex number, plate title, artist and issue price.

## HOW TO DETERMINE EDITION LIMITS

*Edition limited to 10,000* means that the maker established 10,000 plates as the maximum to be produced in the edition.
*Edition size undisclosed; limited by period of issue* means that the edition was limited to the number of plates produced during an announced time period. This could be the period preceding a commemorative date, as with Christmas or Mother's Day issues, or it could be the period of manufacture, often expressed as "firing days," the days the kilns are in operation to produce the series.
*Edition size undisclosed, limited by year of issue* means the edition was limited to the number of plates produced during the year of issue.

## CHRISTIAN BELL
Mount Forest, Ontario

Founded in 1979, Christian Bell Porcelain Ltd. traces its name to founder Horst S. Muller's great-grandfather, Christian Bell, a prominent figure in the white-ware industry of Siebenbürgen in pre-World War I Austria-Hungary.

The firm's first collector's plate series, *Preserving a Way of Life*, (not U.S. Bradex-listed) began in 1980. Their *Age of Steam* series began in 1981 and celebrates the vital role of the railroads in Canada's national heritage. Their second Bradex-listed series is *Yesterday's Memories*.

Theodore "Ted" Xaras is the artist for both series.

## Age of Steam Series

Artist: Theodore Xaras. Artist's signature appears on front

Hard-paste porcelain

Diameter: 24.1 centimeters (9½ inches)

No hanger

Edition size limited to 15,000

Numbered, without certificate through 1982; with certificate thereafter

**8-C30-1.1**
1981 *Symphony in Steam*
Issue price: $65.00

**8-C30-1.2**
1982 *Brief Encounter*
Issue price: $65.00

**8-C30-1.3**
1983 *No Contest*
Issue price: $65.00

**8-C30-1.4**
1984 *Timber Country*
Issue price: $65.00

**8-C30-1.5**
1985 *White Pass, Gateway to the Yukon*
Issue price: $65.00

## Yesterday's Memories Series

Artist: Theodore Xaras. Artist's signature appears on front

Hard-paste porcelain banded in 22k gold

Diameter: 21 centimeters (8¼ inches)

No hanger

Edition size undisclosed, limited by announced period of issue

Not numbered, without certificate

**8-C30-8.1**
1984 *Ice*
Issue price: $45.00

## DOMINION CHINA
Toronto, Ontario

Dominion China, Ltd. produces fine china using the exact standards and time-honored techniques of porcelain-making that have been practiced for centuries. Today, it is one of the best-known of the Canadian plate-producing companies to have recently entered the market.

Dominion China, Ltd. initiated its first collector's plate series in 1986 with the *Wings Upon the Wind* series by wildlife artist Donald Pentz, a native Canadian and resident of Nova Scotia. The *Wings Upon the Wind* series depicts scenes of migratory behavior of the most graceful and majestic of wildfowl, the Canada goose.

In 1987, Dominion China introduced its second series, *Reflections of Canadian Childhood,* by Stewart Sherwood. This series features children in well-remembered activities, set amidst a variety of Canadian landscapes.

---

### *Wings Upon the Wind Series*

Artist: Donald Pentz. Artist's signature appears on front

China

Diameter: 21.6 centimeters (8½ inches)

No hanger

Edition size undisclosed, limited by announced period of issue

Numbered with certificate

**8-D52-1.1**
1986 *The Landing*
Issue price: $21.80

**8-D52-1.2**
1986 *Nesting*
Issue price: $21.80

**8-D52-1.3**
1986 *The Courtship*
Issue price: $24.80

**8-D52-1.4**
1987 *The Family*
Issue price: $24.80

## Reflections of Canadian Childhood Series

Artist: Stewart Sherwood. Artist's signature appears on front

China

Diameter: 21.6 centimeters (8½ inches)

No hanger

Edition size undisclosed, limited by announced period of issue

Numbered, with certificate

**8-D52-2.1**
1987 *Dreams of Glory*
Issue price: $24.80

**8-D52-2.2**
1987 *A Quiet Moment*
Issue price: $24.80

**8-D52-2.3**
1987 *Pick of the Crop*
Issue price: $27.80

## IMPERIAL CHING-TE CHEN
Ching-te Chen (Jingdezhen), Kiangxi Province

Imperial Ching-te Chen Porcelain is located in the area where porcelain was first created, in the People's Republic of China. Most scholars agree that the porcelain-making process was most likely invented during the Sui dynasty (sixth century A.D.). Thus, Chinese potters had been working with porcelain for twelve centuries before European porcelain makers began their craft in the 1700s.

In the T'ang dynasty (A.D. 621), the porcelain makers of the city of Ching-te Chen were officially charged with the responsibility of supplying the emperor. During the reign of the Sung Emperor, Chen Tsung (A.D. 1004), the emperor gave the city its modern name. In the Ming dynasty (A.D. 1369), the imperial factory was established just south of the city's Pearl Hill.

Imperial Ching-te Chen Porcelain works under the patronage of China National Arts and Crafts, which is responsible for disseminating Chinese cultural artifacts to other countries. China National Arts and Crafts applies rigorous standards to artistic objects before they are approved for export.

Porcelain from Ching-te Chen is known throughout the world for its translucent delicacy and beauty. The eggshell-thin, luminous quality of the pieces has been a tradition for centuries. Today, the artisans of Ching-te Chen draw upon skills of ceramic manufacture that have been handed down for generations, to create this first "modern" collector's plate series from The People's Republic of China: *Beauties of the Red Mansion.*

This series presents the work of native Chinese artisan Zhao Huimin in a skillful fusion of figurative and landscape painting. The series is based on "A Dream of Red Mansions," a classic romantic novel of the eighteenth century, and one of China's greatest literary masterpieces. Imperial Ching-te Chen Porcelain introduced the *Beauties of the Red Mansion* series in 1986.

*Beauties of the Red Mansion Series*

Artist: Zhao Huimin. Artist's signature appears on front

Porcelain

Diameter: 21.6 centimeters (8½ inches)

No hanger

Edition size undisclosed, limited by announced period of issue

Numbered with certificate

**10-I50-1.1**
1986 *Pao-chai*
Issue price: $27.92

**10-I50-1.2**
1986 *Yuan-chun*
Issue price: $27.92

**10-I50-1.3**
1987 *Hsi-feng*
Issue price: $27.92

## PAVILION OF T'SANG YING-HSÜAN
Hsin Pu

Chinese porcelain-making reached a high point during the K'ang Hsi Empire (1662-1722). Authorities on Chinese porcelain consider this to be the most remarkable period of multi-color decoration on pure white porcelain. The Pavilion of T'sang Ying-Hsüan takes its name—and its standards of excellence in porcelain manufacture—from this historic era.

In the seventeenth century, Emperor K'ang Hsi desired porcelain whose beauty would surpass that of all previous ages. To fulfill his dream, he constructed an Imperial porcelain works and appointed T'sang Ying-Hsüan as its director. T'sang recruited the best craftsmen in the country to produce magnificent dragon bowls, delicate figurines and porcelain screens for the Emperor. It has been said that "when T'sang was in charge of the factory, the god laid his finger on the designs and protected the porcelain in the kilns so that it naturally came out perfect."

The Pavilion of T'sang Ying-Hsüan uses the same strict principles to create and judge the quality of its porcelain. Colors must be exceptional, the glaze must be brilliant, the shape of the porcelain must be uniformly proportioned, and when tapped, the porcelain must ring like a bell. If these rigorous tests of artistic quality are passed, the plates are allowed to carry the mark of the Pavilion of T'sang Ying-Hsüan.

The *Chinese Children's Games* series is the first issue of artist Kee Fung Ng for this producer, but it is his second plate series (see United States, ARTISTS OF THE WORLD). Begun in 1986, the series is sponsored by the Hwa Kang Museum of the Chinese Cultural University, under the hallmark of Artists of the World. The *Chinese Children's Games* series depicts scenes of children playing ancient Chinese games and is based on memories of the artist's youth.

**10-P8-1.1**

*Chinese Children's Games Series*

Artist: Kee Fung Ng. Artist's signature appears on front

Porcelain

Diameter: 21.6 centimeters (8½ inches)

No hanger

Edition size undisclosed, limited by announced period of issue

Numbered with certificate

**10-P8-1.1**
1986 *Chinese Chess*
Issue price: $29.00

**10-P8-1.2**
1986 *Kite Flying*
Issue price: $29.00

**10-P8-1.3**
1987 *Spinning Tops*
Issue price: $32.00

**10-P8-1.4**
1987 *Rolling Hoops*
Issue price: $32.00

# DENMARK
## BING & GRØNDAHL

**14-B36-0.0**

## BING & GRØNDAHL
Copenhagen

Bing & Grøndahl, Denmark's second oldest existing porcelain maker (after Royal Copenhagen), was established in 1853 by Frederick Vilhelm Grøndahl and Meyer and Jacob Bing. Grøndahl, a young sculptor previously employed by Royal Copenhagen, supplied the artistic talent while the Bing brothers provided financial backing. Although Grøndahl died before the manufactory's third year of operation, his name was retained in honor of his contribution. Bing & Grøndahl has continued under the leadership of the Bing family for five generations.

The world's first collector's plate, "Behind the Frozen Window," was issued by Bing & Grøndahl in 1895. This began its *Christmas* series which has been produced each year without interruption despite wars and economic crises. Plates in this series are now the most widely collected of all plates in the market. In 1969 Bing & Grøndahl issued the first Mother's Day plate, "Dog and Puppies."

Their *Moments of Truth* series started in 1984.

Besides limited-edition collector's plates, Bing & Grøndahl makes a variety of porcelain articles, including figurines and tableware. Many of their porcelain works can be found in museums around the world, and they have achieved the distinction of appointment to the royal courts of Denmark, Sweden, and Great Britain. This distinction is symbolized by the crown which is part of their trademark.

The artist for the very first collector's plate was Frans August Hallin, a Swede who moved to Copenhagen in 1885. After Harald Bing named him chief designer in 1895, Hallin created a distinctive item for the maker's Christmas giftware line—"Behind the Frozen Window." Its success assured his niche in history. He also designed the Christmas plates for 1896 and 1897. From 1897 to 1929 he served as manager of Bing & Grøndahl's exhibitions abroad and in 1924 rose to the position of Assisting Director of the maker's artware line. Hallin retired in 1934 and died in Copenhagen in 1947.

Artist Henry Thelander's association with Bing & Grøndahl is unparalleled on the collector's plate market. He has been the principal designer of the *Christmas* series, creating 22 consecutive issues between 1963 and 1984 (later issues were designed by Edvard Jensen). He also has designed every Bing & Grøndahl *Mother's Day* issue—eighteen in all.

In 1986, Bing & Grøndahl produced "A Summer at Skagen" series, the first limited edition collector's plate series showing the work of the Danish Impressionist Peter Severin Krøyer. The series depicts idyllic scenes of a turn-of-the-century Scandinavian artists' colony.

For information on other Bing & Grøndahl series that are not Bradex-listed, see the OVER-THE-COUNTER SECTION of this book.

## Christmas Series

Artist: as indicated

True underglaze-decorated porcelain hand-painted in Copenhagen blue on bas-relief

Diameter: 17.8 centimeters (7 inches)

Pierced foot rim

Edition size undisclosed, limited by year of issue

Not numbered, without certificate; individually initialed on back by each painter

**14-B36-1.1**
1895 *Behind the Frozen Window*
Artist: Frans August Hallin
Issue price: $.50

**14-B36-1.2**
1896 *New Moon over Snow-covered Trees*
Artist: Frans August Hallin
Issue price: $.50

**14-B36-1.3**
1897 *Christmas Meal of the Sparrows*
Artist: Frans August Hallin
Issue price: $.75

**14-B36-1.4**
1898 *Christmas Roses and Christmas Star*
Artist: Fanny Garde
Issue price: $.75

**14-B36-1.5**
1899 *The Crows Enjoying Christmas*
Artist: Dahl Jensen
Issue price: $.75

**14-B36-1.6**
1900 *Church Bells Chiming in Christmas*
Artist: Dahl Jensen
Issue price: $.75

**14-B36-1.7**
1901 *The Three Wise Men from the East*
Artist: S. Sabra
Issue price: $1.00

**14-B36-1.8**
1902 *Interior of a Gothic Church*
Artist: Dahl Jensen
Issue price: $1.00

# DENMARK
## BING & GRØNDAHL
### 14-B36-1.9

**14-B36-1.9**
1903 *Happy Expectation of Children*
Artist: Margrethe Hyldahl
Issue price: $1.00

**14-B36-1.10**
1904 *View of Copenhagen from Frederiksberg Hill*
Artist: Cathinka Olsen
Issue price: $1.00

**14-B36-1.11**
1905 *Anxiety of the Coming Christmas Night*
Artist: Dahl Jensen
Issue price: $1.00

**14-B36-1.12**
1906 *Sleighing to Church on Christmas Eve*
Artist: Dahl Jensen
Issue price: $1.00

**14-B36-1.13**
1907 *The Little Match Girl*
Artist: E. Plockross
Issue price: $1.00

**14-B36-1.14**
1908 *St. Petri Church of Copenhagen*
Artist: Povl Jorgensen
Issue price: $1.00

**14-B36-1.15**
1909 *Happiness over the Yule Tree*
Artist: Aarestrup
Issue price: $1.50

**14-B36-1.16**
1910 *The Old Organist*
Artist: C. Ersgaard
Issue price: $1.50

**14-B36-1.17**
1911 *First It Was Sung by Angels to Shepherds in the Fields*
Artist: H. Moltke
Issue price: $1.50

**14-B36-1.18**
1912 *Going to Church on Christmas Eve*
Artist: Einar Hansen
Issue price: $1.50

**14-B36-1.19**
1913 *Bringing Home the Yule Tree*
Artist: Th. Larsen
Issue price: $1.50

**14-B36-1.20**
1914 *Royal Castle of Amalienborg,
Copenhagen*
Artist: Th. Larsen
Issue price: $1.50

**14-B36-1.21**
1915 *Chained Dog Getting Double Meal
on Christmas Eve*
Artist: Dahl Jensen
Issue price: $1.50

**14-B36-1.22**
1916 *Christmas Prayer of the Sparrows*
Artist: J. Bloch Jorgensen
Issue price: $1.50

**14-B36-1.23**
1917 *Arrival of the Christmas Boat*
Artist: Achton Friis
Issue price: $1.50

**14-B36-1.24**
1918 *Fishing Boat Returning Home
for Christmas*
Artist: Achton Friis
Issue price: $1.50

**14-B36-1.25**
1919 *Outside the Lighted Window*
Artist: Achton Friis
Issue price: $2.00

**14-B36-1.26**
1920 *Hare in the Snow*
Artist: Achton Friis
Issue price: $2.00

# DENMARK
## BING & GRØNDAHL
### 14-B36-1.27

**14-B36-1.27**
1921 *Pigeons in the Castle Court*
Artist: Achton Friis
Issue price: $2.00

**14-B36-1.28**
1922 *Star of Bethlehem*
Artist: Achton Friis
Issue price: $2.00

**14-B36-1.29**
1923 *Royal Hunting Castle, the Ermitage*
Artist: Achton Friis
Issue price: $2.00

**14-B36-1.30**
1924 *Lighthouse in Danish Waters*
Artist: Achton Friis
Issue price: $2.50

**14-B36-1.31**
1925 *The Child's Christmas*
Artist: Achton Friis
Issue price: $2.50

**14-B36-1.32**
1926 *Churchgoers on Christmas Day*
Artist: Achton Friis
Issue price: $2.50

**14-B36-1.33**
1927 *Skating Couple*
Artist: Achton Friis
Issue price: $2.50

**14-B36-1.34**
1928 *Eskimo Looking at Village Church
in Greenland*
Artist: Achton Friis
Issue price: $2.50

**14-B36-1.35**
1929 *Fox Outside Farm on Christmas Eve*
Artist: Achton Friis
Issue price: $2.50

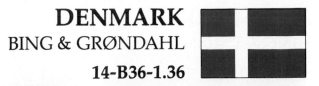

**14-B36-1.36**
1930 *Yule Tree in Town Hall Square*
*of Copenhagen*
Artist: H. Flugenring
Issue price: $2.50

**14-B36-1.37**
1931 *Arrival of the Christmas Train*
Artist: Achton Friis
Issue price: $2.50

**14-B36-1.38**
1932 *Lifeboat at Work*
Artist: H. Flugenring
Issue price: $2.50

**14-B36-1.39**
1933 *The Korsor-Nyborg Ferry*
Artist: H. Flugenring
Issue price: $3.00

**14-B36-1.40**
1934 *Church Bell in Tower*
Artist: Immanuel Tjerne
Issue price: $3.00

**14-B36-1.41**
1935 *Lillebelt Bridge Connecting Funen*
*with Jutland*
Artist: Ove Larsen
Issue price: $3.00

**14-B36-1.42**
1936 *Royal Guard Outside Amalienborg*
*Castle in Copenhagen*
Artist: Ove Larsen
Issue price: $3.00

**14-B36-1.43**
1937 *Arrival of Christmas Guests*
Artist: Ove Larsen
Issue price: $3.00

**14-B36-1.44**
1938 *Lighting the Candles*
Artist: Immanuel Tjerne
Issue price: $3.00

# DENMARK
## BING & GRØNDAHL

**14-B36-1.45**

**14-B36-1.45**
1939 *Ole Lock-Eye, the Sandman*
Artist: Immanuel Tjerne
Issue price: $3.00

**14-B36-1.46**
1940 *Delivering Christmas Letters*
Artist: Ove Larsen
Issue price: $4.00

**14-B36-1.47**
1941 *Horses Enjoying Christmas Meal in Stable*
Artist: Ove Larsen
Issue price: $4.00

**14-B36-1.48**
1942 *Danish Farm on Christmas Night*
Artist: Ove Larsen
Issue price: $4.00

**14-B36-1.49**
1943 *The Ribe Cathedral*
Artist: Ove Larsen
Issue price: $5.00

**14-B36-1.50**
1944 *Sorgenfri Castle*
Artist: Ove Larsen
Issue price: $5.00

**14-B36-1.51**
1945 *The Old Water Mill*
Artist: Ove Larsen
Issue price: $5.00

**14-B36-1.52**
1946 *Commemoration Cross in Honor of Danish Sailors Who Lost Their Lives in World War II*
Artist: Margrethe Hyldahl
Issue price: $5.00

**14-B36-1.53**
1947 *Dybbol Mill*
Artist: Margrethe Hyldahl
Issue price: $5.00

**14-B36-1.54**
1948 *Watchman, Sculpture of Town Hall,*
*Copenhagen*
Artist: Margrethe Hyldahl
Issue price: $5.50

**14-B36-1.55**
1949 *Landsoldaten, 19th Century*
*Danish Soldier*
Artist: Margrethe Hyldahl
Issue price: $5.50

**14-B36-1.56**
1950 *Kronborg Castle at Elsinore*
Artist: Margrethe Hyldahl
Issue price: $5.50

**14-B36-1.57**
1951 *Jens Bang, New Passenger Boat*
*Running Between Copenhagen*
*and Aalborg*
Artist: Margrethe Hyldahl
Issue price: $6.00

**14-B36-1.58**
1952 *Old Copenhagen Canals at*
*Wintertime with Thorvaldsen Museum*
*in Background*
Artist: Borge Pramvig
Issue price: $6.00

**14-B36-1.59**
1953 *Royal Boat in Greenland Waters*
Artist: Kjeld Bonfils
Issue price: $7.00

**14-B36-1.60**
1954 *Birthplace of Hans Christian*
*Andersen, with Snowman*
Artist: Borge Pramvig
Issue price: $7.50

**14-B36-1.61**
1955 *Kalundborg Church*
Artist: Kjeld Bonfils
Issue price: $8.00

**14-B36-1.62**
1956 *Christmas in Copenhagen*
Artist: Kjeld Bonfils
Issue price: $8.50

# DENMARK
## BING & GRØNDAHL

**14-B36-1.63**

**14-B36-1.63**
1957 *Christmas Candles*
Artist: Kjeld Bonfils
Issue price: $9.00

**14-B36-1.64**
1958 *Santa Claus*
Artist: Kjeld Bonfils
Issue price: $9.50

**14-B36-1.65**
1959 *Christmas Eve*
Artist: Kjeld Bonfils
Issue price: $10.00

**14-B36-1.66**
1960 *Danish Village Church*
Artist: Kjeld Bonfils
Issue price: $10.00

**14-B36-1.67**
1961 *Winter Harmony*
Artist: Kjeld Bonfils
Issue price: $10.50

**14-B36-1.68**
1962 *Winter Night*
Artist: Kjeld Bonfils
Issue price: $11.00

**14-B36-1.69**
1963 *The Christmas Elf*
Artist: Henry Thelander
Issue price: $11.00

**14-B36-1.70**
1964 *The Fir Tree and Hare*
Artist: Henry Thelander
Issue price: $11.50

**14-B36-1.71**
1965 *Bringing Home the Christmas Tree*
Artist: Henry Thelander
Issue price: $12.00

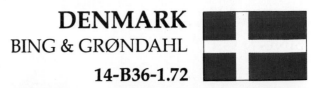

**14-B36-1.72**
*1966 Home for Christmas*
Artist: Henry Thelander
Issue price: $12.00

**14-B36-1.73**
*1967 Sharing the Joy of Christmas*
Artist: Henry Thelander
Issue price: $13.00

**14-B36-1.74**
*1968 Christmas in Church*
Artist: Henry Thelander
Issue price: $14.00

**14-B36-1.75**
*1969 Arrival of Christmas Guests*
Artist: Henry Thelander
Issue price: $14.00

**14-B36-1.76**
*1970 Pheasants in the Snow at Christmas*
Artist: Henry Thelander
Issue price: $14.50

**14-B36-1.77**
*1971 Christmas at Home*
Artist: Henry Thelander
Issue price: $15.00

**14-B36-1.78**
*1972 Christmas in Greenland*
Artist: Henry Thelander
Issue price: $16.50

**14-B36-1.79**
*1973 Country Christmas*
Artist: Henry Thelander
Issue price: $19.50

**14-B36-1.80**
*1974 Christmas in the Village*
Artist: Henry Thelander
Issue price: $22.00

# DENMARK
## BING & GRØNDAHL
### 14-B36-1.81

**14-B36-1.81**
1975 *The Old Water Mill*
Artist: Henry Thelander
Issue price: $27.50

**14-B36-1.82**
1976 *Christmas Welcome*
Artist: Henry Thelander
Issue price: $27.50

**14-B36-1.83**
1977 *Copenhagen Christmas*
Artist: Henry Thelander
Issue price: $29.50

**14-B36-1.84**
1978 *A Christmas Tale*
Artist: Henry Thelander
Issue price: $32.00

**14-B36-1.85**
1979 *White Christmas*
Artist: Henry Thelander
Issue price: $36.50

**14-B36-1.86**
1980 *Christmas in the Woods*
Artist: Henry Thelander
Issue price: $42.50

**14-B36-1.87**
1981 *Christmas Peace*
Artist: Henry Thelander
Issue price: $49.50

**14-B36-1.88**
1982 *The Christmas Tree*
Artist: Henry Thelander
Issue price: $54.50

**14-B36-1.89**
1983 *Christmas in the Old Town*
Artist: Henry Thelander
Issue price: $54.50

**14-B36-1.90**
1984 *The Christmas Letter*
Artist: Henry Thelander
Issue price: $54.50

**14-B36-1.91**
1985 *Christmas Eve at the Farmhouse*
Artist: Edvard Jensen
Issue price: $54.50

**14-B36-1.92**
1986 *Silent Night, Holy Night*
Artist: Edvard Jensen
Issue price: $54.50

**14-B36-1.93**
1987 *Snowman's Christmas Eve*
Artist: Edvard Jensen
Issue price: $59.50

## Mother's Day Series

Artist: Henry Thelander

True underglaze-decorated porcelain hand-painted in Copenhagen blue on bas-relief

Diameter: 15.2 centimeters (6 inches)

Pierced foot rim

Edition size undisclosed, limited by year of issue

Not numbered, without certificate; individually initialed on back by each painter

**14-B36-3.1**
1969 *Dog and Puppies*
Issue price: $9.75

**14-B36-3.2**
1970 *Bird and Chicks*
Issue price: $10.00

# DENMARK
## BING & GRØNDAHL

### 14-B36-3.3

**14-B36-3.3**
1971 *Cat and Kitten*
Issue price: $11.00

**14-B36-3.4**
1972 *Mare and Foal*
Issue price: $12.00

**14-B36-3.5**
1973 *Duck and Ducklings*
Issue price: $13.00

**14-B36-3.6**
1974 *Bear and Cubs*
Issue price: $16.50

**14-B36-3.7**
1975 *Doe and Fawns*
Issue price: $19.50

**14-B36-3.8**
1976 *Swan Family*
Issue price: $22.50

**14-B36-3.9**
1977 *Squirrel and Young*
Issue price: $23.50

**14-B36-3.10**
1978 *Heron*
Issue price: $24.50

**14-B36-3.11**
1979 *Fox and Cubs*
Issue price: $27.50

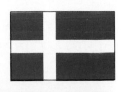

**14-B36-3.12**
1980 *Woodpecker and Young*
Issue price: $29.50

**14-B36-3.13**
1981 *Hare and Young*
Issue price: $36.50

**14-B36-3.14**
1982 *Lioness and Cubs*
Issue price: $39.50

**14-B36-3.15**
1983 *Raccoon and Young*
Issue price: $39.50

**14-B36-3.16**
1984 *Stork and Nestlings*
Issue price: $39.50

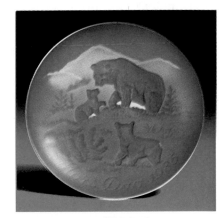

**14-B36-3.17**
1985 *Bear with Cubs*
Issue price: $39.50

**14-B36-3.18**
1986 *Elephant with Calf*
Issue price: $39.50

**14-B36-3.19**
1987 *Sheep with Lambs*
Issue price: $42.50

# DENMARK
## BING & GRØNDAHL

### 14-B36-7.1

*Moments of Truth Series*

Artist: Kurt Ard. Artist's signature
appears on front

Porcelain

Diameter: 21.1 centimeters
(8⁵⁄₁₆ inches)

Pierced foot rim

Edition size undisclosed, limited
by announced period of issue

Numbered with certificate

**14-B36-7.1**
1984 *Home Is Best*
Issue price: $29.50

**14-B36-7.2**
1984 *The Road to Virtuosity*
Issue price: $29.50

**14-B36-7.3**
1985 *First Things First*
Issue price: $29.50

**14-B36-7.4**
1985 *Unfair Competition*
Issue price: $29.50

**14-B36-7.5**
1986 *Bored Sick*
Issue price: $29.50

**14-B36-7.6**
1986 *First Crush*
Issue price: $29.50
*Series Closed*

## Children's Day Series

Artist: Carole Roller

True underglaze-decorated porcelain hand-painted in Copenhagen blue on bas-relief

Diameter: 13 centimeters (5⅛ inches)

Pierced foot rim

Edition size undisclosed, limited by year of issue

Not numbered, without certificate; individually initialed on back by each painter

**14-B36-13.1**
1985 *The Magical Tea Party*
Issue price: $24.50

**14-B36-13.2**
1986 *A Joyful Flight*
Issue price: $26.50

**14-B36-13.3**
1987 *The Little Gardener*
Issue price: $29.50

# DENMARK
## BING & GRØNDAHL

### 14-B36-20.1

*Family Portraits Series*

Artist: Kurt Ard. Artist's signature appears on front

Porcelain

Diameter: 21.1 centimeters (8⁵/₁₆ inches)

Pierced foot rim

Edition size undisclosed, limited by announced period of issue

Numbered, with certificate

**14-B36-20.1**
1987 *The Card Sharks*
Issue price: $35.50

**14-B36-20.2**
1987 *The Intruder*
Issue price: $35.50

**14-B36-20.3**
1987 *Midnight Serenade*
Issue price: $35.50

## A Summer at Skagen Series

Artist: Peter Severin Krøyer.
Artist's signature appears on front

Porcelain

Diameter: 21.3 centimeters
(8⅜ inches)

Pierced foot rim

Edition size undisclosed, limited
by announced period of issue

Numbered with certificate

**14-B36-22.1**
*1986 Summer Evening at Skagen, the
Artist's Wife with a Dog on the Beach*
Issue price: $34.50

**14-B36-22.2**
*1987 Luncheon at the Krøyers'*
Issue price: $34.50

**14-B36-22.3**
*1987 Hip-Hip-Hurrah!*
Issue price: $34.50

**14-B36-22.4**
*1987 The Artist's Wife Resting in the
Garden*
Issue price: $34.50

## GRANDE COPENHAGEN
Copenhagen

Grande Copenhagen plates are produced at the Eslau porcelain factory near Copenhagen. Grande Copenhagen began its *Christmas* series of plates depicting Danish winter scenes in 1975. The series ended in 1984.

Artists for Grande Copenhagen *Christmas* plates prior to 1980 were undisclosed. The artist for the 1980 and subsequent issues was Frode Bahnsen of Aarhus, Jutland, Denmark.

The *Ugly Duckling* series began in 1985; it represents the first Grande Copenhagen series to be created in full color. The *Ugly Duckling* series is also the first by artist Karen J. Bornholt. The series depicts one of Hans Christian Andersen's most beloved stories.

---

## *Christmas Series*

Artist: as indicated

True underglaze-decorated porcelain hand-painted in Copenhagen blue on bas-relief

Diameter: 18.4 centimeters (7¼ inches)

Pierced foot rim

Edition size undisclosed, limited by year of issue

Not numbered, without certificate through 1979; numbered with certificate thereafter

**14-G65-1.1**
1975 *Alone Together*
Artist: undisclosed
Issue price: $24.50

**14-G65-1.2**
1976 *Christmas Wreath*
Artist: undisclosed
Issue price: $24.50

**14-G65-1.3**
1977 *Fishwives at Gammelstrand*
Artist: undisclosed
Issue price: $26.50

**14-G65-1.4**
1978 *Hans Christian Andersen*
Artist: undisclosed
Issue price: $32.50

**14-G65-1.5**
1979 *Pheasants in the Snow*
Artist: undisclosed
Issue price: $34.50

**14-G65-1.6**
1980 *The Snow Queen in the Tivoli*
Artist: Frode Bahnsen
Issue price: $39.50

**14-G65-1.7**
1981 *Little Match Girl in Nyhavn*
Artist: Frode Bahnsen
Issue price: $42.50

**14-G65-1.8**
1982 *The Shepherdess and the
Chimney Sweep*
Artist: Frode Bahnsen
Issue price: $45.00

**14-G65-1.9**
1983 *The Little Mermaid Near Kronborg*
Artist: Frode Bahnsen
Issue price: $45.00

**14-G65-1.10**
1984 *The Sandman at Amalienborg*
Artist: Frode Bahnsen
Issue price: $45.00
*Series Closed*

# DENMARK
## GRANDE COPENHAGEN

### 14-G65-2.1

*Ugly Duckling Series*

Artist: Karen J. Bornholt. Artist's initials appear on front

Porcelain

Diameter: 19 centimeters (7½ inches)

Pierced foot rim

Edition sized undisclosed, limited by announced period of issue

Numbered with certificate

**14-G65-2.1**
1985 *Not Like the Others*
Issue price: $29.00

**14-G65-2.2**
1986 *He Will Grow Up Strong*
Issue price: $29.00

**14-G65-2.3**
1986 *Come with Us*
Issue price: $32.00

**14-G65-2.4**
1986 *You Don't Understand Me*
Issue price: $32.00

**14-G65-2.5**
1986 *What Beautiful Birds*
Issue price: $32.00

**14-G65-2.6**
1986 *Most Beautiful of All*
Issue price: $32.00
*Series Closed*

**14-R59-1.1** "Madonna and Child"
1908 Royal Copenhagen *Christmas*
The first limited-edition plate to be produced by Denmark's oldest porcelain house, "Madonna and Child" began an annual series that continues uninterrupted to this day. The blue underglaze artwork depicts an unusual figure of the Madonna in that she is not wearing a head mantle. Only one other image of the Madonna, this time hooded, appears in the entire series; it occurs on the 1920 issue.

# DENMARK
## ROYAL COPENHAGEN

**14-R59-0.0**

## ROYAL COPENHAGEN
Copenhagen

The Royal Copenhagen Porcelain Manufactory, Denmark's oldest existing porcelain maker, was established by Franz Henrich Muller with the support of Denmark's queen dowager, Juliane Marie, in January 1775. Since the 1760s, members of the Danish royal family had been interested in the white hard-paste porcelain made in China, but it was not until 1772 that Muller, a Danish pharmacist and chemist, was able to duplicate the fine porcelain. In 1779 "The Danish Porcelain Factory," as Royal Copenhagen was then called, came under royal control.

The Danish Court controlled the firm from 1779 to 1867, a period in its history that is still symbolized by the crown in its trademark. The three wavy lines under the crown, part of the factory trademark since 1775, pay tribute to Denmark's tradition as a seafaring nation and represent Denmark's three ancient waterways: the Sound, the Great Belt and the Little

Belt. In 1867 the factory was sold and has since been under private ownership. It is still a supplier to the royal court in Denmark.

The first Royal Copenhagen *Christmas* plate was issued in 1908, and the series has continued every year since then. From the beginning, the motif for each year's *Christmas* plate has been selected from suggestions submitted by employees of the Royal Copenhagen factory. Until 1941, small quantities of plates in the *Christmas* series were created with the word "Christmas" translated into other languages to meet the demand from non-Danish collectors.

In 1982, the Royal Copenhagen *Motherhood* series started with artwork by Sven Vestergaard.

Christian Thomsen, designer of the first Royal Copenhagen collector's plate, served an apprenticeship as a woodcarver before joining the firm in 1898. His porcelain creations won a silver medal in a Milan exhibit in 1908 and a

gold medal in a Brussels exhibit in 1910. His work now hangs in the Museum of Decorative Arts in Copenhagen. Arnold Krog innovated the famed cobalt-blue underglaze design technique which has become a tradition in Danish plate making. He worked for Royal Copenhagen from 1884 to 1916, rising to art director and taking the Grand Prix for decorative art in Paris in 1900. Krog's most famous creation is his fountain located in The Hague, The Netherlands. Artist Kai Lange has been with Royal Copenhagen since the age of 17 and, after more than half a century with the firm, is regarded as one of the most knowledgeable artists working in the porcelain medium today. The first Kai Lange design selected for the annual *Christmas* plate was for the 1940 issue, and since 1963 every plate, except the 1976 issue, has been a Kai Lange creation.

## Christmas Series

Artist: as indicated. Artist's name appears on back since 1955

True underglaze-decorated porcelain hand-painted in Copenhagen blue on bas-relief

Diameter: 15.2 centimeters (6 inches) for 1908 through 1910; 17.8 centimeters (7 inches) thereafter

Pierced foot rim

Edition size undisclosed, limited by year of issue

Not numbered, without certificate; individually initialed on back by each painter

**14-R59-1.1**
*1908 Madonna and Child*
Artist: Christian Thomsen
Issue price: $1.00

**14-R59-1.2**
*1909 Danish Landscape*
Artist: St. Ussing
Issue price: $1.00

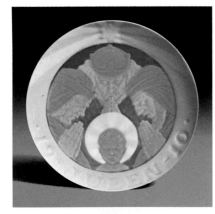

**14-R59-1.3**
*1910 The Magi*
Artist: Christian Thomsen
Issue price: $1.00

**14-R59-1.4**
*1911 Danish Landscape*
Artist: Oluf Jensen
Issue price: $1.00

**14-R59-1.5**
*1912 Elderly Couple by Christmas Tree*
Artist: Christian Thomsen
Issue price: $1.00

**14-R59-1.6**
*1913 Spire of Frederik's Church, Copenhagen*
Artist: A. Boesen
Issue price: $1.50

**14-R59-1.7**
*1914 Sparrows in Tree at Church of the Holy Spirit, Copenhagen*
Artist: A. Boesen
Issue price: $1.50

**14-R59-1.8**
*1915 Danish Landscape*
Artist: Arnold Krog
Issue price: $1.50

# DENMARK
## ROYAL COPENHAGEN
### 14-R59-1.9

**14-R59-1.9**
1916 *Shepherd in the Field on Christmas Night*
Artist: Ricard Böcher
Issue price: $1.50

**14-R59-1.10**
1917 *Tower of Our Savior's Church, Copenhagen*
Artist: Oluf Jensen
Issue price: $2.00

**14-R59-1.11**
1918 *Sheep and Shepherds*
Artist: Oluf Jensen
Issue price: $2.00

**14-R59-1.12**
1919 *In the Park*
Artist: Oluf Jensen
Issue price: $2.00

**14-R59-1.13**
1920 *Mary with the Child Jesus*
Artist: G. Rode
Issue price: $2.00

**14-R59-1.14**
1921 *Aabenraa Marketplace*
Artist: Oluf Jensen
Issue price: $2.00

**14-R59-1.15**
1922 *Three Singing Angels*
Artist: Ellinor Selschau
Issue price: $2.00

**14-R59-1.16**
1923 *Danish Landscape*
Artist: Oluf Jensen
Issue price: $2.00

**14-R59-1.17**
1924 *Christmas Star over the Sea and Sailing Ship*
Artist: Benjamin Olsen
Issue price: $2.00

**14-R59-1.18**
1925 *Street Scene from Christianshavn,*
*Copenhagen*
Artist: Oluf Jensen
Issue price: $2.00

**14-R59-1.19**
1926 *View of Christianshavn Canal,*
*Copenhagen*
Artist: Ricard Böcher
Issue price: $2.00

**14-R59-1.20**
1927 *Ship's Boy at the Tiller on*
*Christmas Night*
Artist: Benjamin Olsen
Issue price: $2.00

**14-R59-1.21**
1928 *Vicar's Family on Way to Church*
Artist: G. Rode
Issue price: $2.00

**14-R59-1.22**
1929 *Grundtvig Church, Copenhagen*
Artist: Oluf Jensen
Issue price: $2.00

**14-R59-1.23**
1930 *Fishing Boats on the Way*
*to the Harbor*
Artist: Benjamin Olsen
Issue price: $2.50

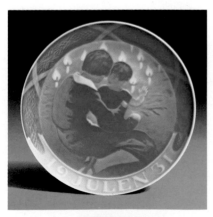

**14-R59-1.24**
1931 *Mother and Child*
Artist: G. Rode
Issue price: $2.50

**14-R59-1.25**
1932 *Frederiksberg Gardens with Statue*
*of Frederik VI*
Artist: Oluf Jensen
Issue price: $2.50

**14-R59-1.26**
1933 *The Great Belt Ferry*
Artist: Benjamin Olsen
Issue price: $2.50

**14-R59-1.27**
1934 *The Hermitage Castle*
Artist: Oluf Jensen
Issue price: $2.50

**14-R59-1.28**
1935 *Fishing Boat off Kronborg Castle*
Artist: Benjamin Olsen
Issue price: $2.50

**14-R59-1.29**
1936 *Roskilde Cathedral*
Artist: Ricard Böcher
Issue price: $2.50

**14-R59-1.30**
1937 *Christmas Scene in Main Street, Copenhagen*
Artist: Nils Thorsson
Issue price: $2.50

**14-R59-1.31**
1938 *Round Church in Osterlars on Bornholm*
Artist: Herne Nielsen
Issue price: $3.00

**14-R59-1.32**
1939 *Expeditionary Ship in the Pack-Ice of Greenland*
Artist: Sv. Nic. Nielsen
Issue price: $3.00

**14-R59-1.33**
1940 *The Good Shepherd*
Artist: Kai Lange
Issue price: $3.00

**14-R59-1.34**
1941 *Danish Village Church*
Artist: Th. Kjolner
Issue price: $3.00

**14-R59-1.35**
1942 *Bell Tower of Old Church in Jutland*
Artist: Nils Thorsson
Issue price: $4.00

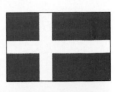

**14-R59-1.36**
1943 *Flight of Holy Family into Egypt*
Artist: Nils Thorsson
Issue price: $4.00

**14-R59-1.37**
1944 *Typical Danish Winter Scene*
Artist: Viggo Olsen
Issue price: $4.00

**14-R59-1.38**
1945 *A Peaceful Motif*
Artist: Ricard Böcher
Issue price: $4.00

**14-R59-1.39**
1946 *Zealand Village Church*
Artist: Nils Thorsson
Issue price: $4.00

**14-R59-1.40**
1947 *The Good Shepherd*
Artist: Kai Lange
Issue price: $4.50

**14-R59-1.41**
1948 *Nodebo Church at Christmastime*
Artist: Th. Kjolner
Issue price: $4.50

**14-R59-1.42**
1949 *Our Lady's Cathedral, Copenhagen*
Artist: Hans H. Hansen
Issue price: $5.00

**14-R59-1.43**
1950 *Boeslunde Church, Zealand*
Artist: Viggo Olsen
Issue price: $5.00

**14-R59-1.44**
1951 *Christmas Angel*
Artist: Ricard Böcher
Issue price: $5.00

# DENMARK
## ROYAL COPENHAGEN

**14-R59-1.45**

**14-R59-1.45**
1952 *Christmas in the Forest*
Artist: Kai Lange
Issue price: $5.00

**14-R59-1.46**
1953 *Frederiksberg Castle*
Artist: Th. Kjolner
Issue price: $6.00

**14-R59-1.47**
1954 *Amalienborg Palace, Copenhagen*
Artist: Kai Lange
Issue price: $6.00

**14-R59-1.48**
1955 *Fano Girl*
Artist: Kai Lange
Issue price: $7.00

**14-R59-1.49**
1956 *Rosenborg Castle, Copenhagen*
Artist: Kai Lange
Issue price: $7.00

**14-R59-1.50**
1957 *The Good Shepherd*
Artist: Hans H. Hansen
Issue price: $8.00

**14-R59-1.51**
1958 *Sunshine over Greenland*
Artist: Hans H. Hansen
Issue price: $9.00

**14-R59-1.52**
1959 *Christmas Night*
Artist: Hans H. Hansen
Issue price: $9.00

**14-R59-1.53**
1960 *The Stag*
Artist: Hans H. Hansen
Issue price: $10.00

**14-R59-1.54**
1961 *Training Ship Danmark*
Artist: Kai Lange
Issue price: $10.00

**14-R59-1.55**
1962 *The Little Mermaid at Wintertime*
Artist: Undisclosed
Issue price: $11.00

**14-R59-1.56**
1963 *Hojsager Mill*
Artist: Kai Lange
Issue price: $11.00

**14-R59-1.57**
1964 *Fetching the Christmas Tree*
Artist: Kai Lange
Issue price: $11.00

**14-R59-1.58**
1965 *Little Skaters*
Artist: Kai Lange
Issue price: $12.00

**14-R59-1.59**
1966 *Blackbird at Christmastime*
Artist: Kai Lange
Issue price: $12.00

**14-R59-1.60**
1967 *The Royal Oak*
Artist: Kai Lange
Issue price: $13.00

**14-R59-1.61**
1968 *The Last Umiak*
Artist: Kai Lange
Issue price: $13.00

**14-R59-1.62**
1969 *The Old Farmyard*
Artist: Kai Lange
Issue price: $14.00

# DENMARK
## ROYAL COPENHAGEN
### 14-R59-1.63

**14-R59-1.63**
1970 *Christmas Rose and Cat*
Artist: Kai Lange
Issue price: $14.00

**14-R59-1.64**
1971 *Hare in Winter*
Artist: Kai Lange
Issue price: $15.00

**14-R59-1.65**
1972 *In the Desert*
Artist: Kai Lange
Issue price: $16.00

**14-R59-1.66**
1973 *Train Homeward Bound for Christmas*
Artist: Kai Lange
Issue price: $22.00

**14-R59-1.67**
1974 *Winter Twilight*
Artist: Kai Lange
Issue price: $22.00

**14-R59-1.68**
1975 *Queen's Palace*
Artist: Kai Lange
Issue price: $27.50

**14-R59-1.69**
1976 *Danish Watermill*
Artist: Sven Vestergaard
Issue price: $27.50

**14-R59-1.70**
1977 *Immervad Bridge*
Artist: Kai Lange
Issue price: $32.00

**14-R59-1.71**
1978 *Greenland Scenery*
Artist: Kai Lange
Issue price: $35.00

**14-R59-1.72**
1979 *Choosing the Christmas Tree*
Artist: Kai Lange
Issue price: $42.50

**14-R59-1.73**
1980 *Bringing Home the Christmas Tree*
Artist: Kai Lange
Issue price: $49.50

**14-R59-1.74**
1981 *Admiring the Christmas Tree*
Artist: Kai Lange
Issue price: $52.50

**14-R59-1.75**
1982 *Waiting for Christmas*
Artist: Kai Lange
Issue price: $54.50

**14-R59-1.76**
1983 *Merry Christmas*
Artist: Kai Lange
Issue price: $54.50

**14-R59-1.77**
1984 *Jingle Bells*
Artist: Kai Lange
Issue price: $54.50

**14-R59-1.78**
1985 *The Snowman*
Artist: Sven Vestergaard
Issue price: $54.50

**14-R59-1.79**
1986 *Christmas Vacation*
Artist: Sven Vestergaard
Issue price: $54.50

**14-R59-1.80**
1987 *Winter Birds*
Artist: Sven Vestergaard
Issue price: $59.50

# DENMARK
## ROYAL COPENHAGEN

### 14-R59-4.1

## *Motherhood Series*

Artist: Sven Vestergaard

True underglaze-decorated porcelain hand-painted in Copenhagen blue on bas-relief

Diameter: 15.2 centimeters (6 inches)

Pierced foot rim

Edition size undisclosed, limited by year of issue

Not numbered, without certificate

**14-R59-4.1**
1982 *Mother Robin and Her Young Ones*
Issue price: $29.50

**14-R59-4.2**
1983 *Mother Cat and Kitten*
Issue price: $29.50

**14-R59-4.3**
1984 *Mare with Foal*
Issue price: $29.50

**14-R59-4.4**
1985 *Mother Rabbit with Bunny*
Issue price: $32.50

**14-R59-4.5**
1986 *Dog and Puppies*
Issue price: $34.50

**14-R59-4.6**
1987 *Goat and Kid*
Issue price: $37.50

**16-A69-1.1** "Vainamoinen's Sowing"
1976 Arabia *Kalevala*
This series bears the name of the Finnish
national epic, the *Kalevala,* whose heroes it
depicts. The series, much like the saga, has
run continuously since 1976. Arabia is famous for the density and durability of its
stoneware, which is fired three times like
fine china; ordinary stoneware is fired
only twice.

# FINLAND
## ARABIA
### 16-A69-1.1

**ARABIA FINLAND**

## ARABIA
Helsinki

In 1873, Arabia was founded as a subsidiary of the Swedish firm Rörstrand (see Sweden, RÖRSTRAND). The factory was located on the outskirts of Helsinki, a site chosen in hopes of supplying the growing markets for ceramics in Finland and the Russian Empire. Early products included dinner services, pitchers and mugs, almost all based on Rörstrand designs.

In 1884 Arabia was reorganized as a Finnish company, Arabia Aktiefabrik, and developed its own designs from that time on. The company won a gold medal at the Paris World Exhibition in 1900 and is the only company producing both household and art ceramics in Finland today.

To celebrate the 100th anniversary of the firm in 1973, Arabia produced a limited-edition anniversary plate. Its success, in turn, led to the introduction in 1976 of an annual limited-edition series based on the Finnish national epic, the *Kalevala*, by artist Raija Uosikkinen.

## *Kalevala Series*

Artist: Raija Uosikkinen

Stoneware

Diameter: 19 centimeters square (7½ inches square)

Pierced foot rim

Edition size undisclosed

Not numbered, without certificate

**16-A69-1.1**
1976 *Vainamoinen's Sowing*
Issue price: $30.00

**16-A69-1.2**
1977 *Aino's Fate*
Issue price: $30.00

**16-A69-1.3**
1978 *Lemminkainen's Chase*
Issue price: $39.00

**16-A69-1.4**
1979 *Kullervo's Revenge*
Issue price: $39.50

**16-A69-1.5**
1980 *Vainamoinen's Rescue*
Issue price: $45.00

**16-A69-1.6**
1981 *Vainamoinen's Magic*
Issue price: $49.50

**16-A69-1.7**
1982 *Joukahainen Shoots the Horse*
Issue price: $55.50

**16-A69-1.8**
1983 *Lemminkainen's Escape*
Issue price: $60.00

**16-A69-1.9**
1984 *Lemminkainen's Magic Feathers*
Issue price: $60.00

**16-A69-1.10**
1985 *Lemminkainen's Grief*
Issue price: $60.00

**16-A69-1.11**
1986 *Osmatar Creating Ale*
Issue price: $60.00

# FRANCE
## PORCELAINE GEORGES BOYER

**18-B61-0.0**

PORCELAINE

LIMOGES

## PORCELAINE GEORGES BOYER
Limoges

Porcelaine Georges Boyer of Limoges, France, was founded in 1933 by Georges Boyer; his is the second generation of Boyers to work in porcelain. His father, Jean Boyer, originally worked for the house of Haviland before forming his own company in which Georges worked as technical director. Today, the firm is managed by Gerard Boyer, son of Georges, thus continuing the family tradition.

Porcelaine Georges Boyer is the third-ranking company in the renowned porcelain center of Limoges, producing porcelain dinnerware as well as limited-edition collector's plates. The firm numbers among its efforts the production of extremely small limited-edition plate series based upon the works of Pierre Auguste Renoir and Maurice Utrillo. In 1982, Porcelaine Georges Boyer introduced its first collector's series for the United States market under its own name—the *Alice in Wonderland* series by British artist Sandy Nightingale.

*Alice in Wonderland Series*

Artist: Sandy Nightingale

Overglaze-decorated porcelain banded in 24k gold

Diameter: 21.6 centimeters (8½ inches)

Attached back hanger

Edition size undisclosed, limited by announced period of issue

Numbered with certificate

**18-B61-1.1**
1982 *Alice and the White Rabbit*
Issue price: $36.96

**18-B61-1.2**
1983 *Alice and the Caterpillar*
Issue price: $36.96

**18-B61-1.3**
1983 *Alice and the Cheshire Cat*
Issue price: $36.96

**18-B61-1.4**
1983 *Alice and the Mad Hatter*
Issue price: $36.96

**18-B61-1.5**
1984 *Painting the Roses*
Issue price: $36.96

**18-B61-1.6**
1984 *Alice and the Croquet Game*
Issue price: $36.96

**18-B61-1.7**
1984 *The Gryphon and Mock Turtle*
Issue price: $36.96

**18-B61-1.8**
1984 *The Knave of Hearts*
Issue price: $36.96
*Series Closed*

## D'ARCEAU-LIMOGES
Limoges

The hallmark of Henri d'Arceau L. & Fils is one of the most prestigious in the famous porcelain center of Limoges. The firm, which claims to adhere to the original "Grellet Standard" of 1768 for handcraftsmanship, is today directed by Gerard Boyer, a descendant of the founder.

The firm was commissioned by L'Association l'Esprit de Lafayette to produce the six-plate bicentennial series *Collection Le Patrimoine de Lafayette (Lafayette Legacy Collection)*, 1973-1975, which chronicles the role of the Marquis de Lafayette in America's War of Independence. The D'Arceau-Limoges *Christmas* series, *Noël Vitrail*, begun in 1975, was inspired by the stained-glass windows of the cathedral at Chartres. It ended in 1982. *Les Femmes du Siècle (Women of the Century)*, a twelve-plate series commissioned by the Chambre Syndicale de la Couture Parisienne, began in 1976 and ended in 1979. This series, recognized by the United Nations, depicts Western women's fashions from 1865 to 1965. Introduced in 1978 was *Les Jeunes Filles des Saisons (Girls of the Seasons)*, which ended in 1981, and in 1979 *Les Très Riches Heures (The Very Rich Hours)*, which adapts its artwork from an early fifteenth-century illuminated manuscript. This series ended in 1984. In 1980, the firm, in collaboration with La Société de Paris et Son Histoire, issued Louis Dali's *Les Douze Sites Parisiens de Louis Dali (The Twelve Parisian Places of Louis Dali)* series, a collection of the artist's unique impressions of the famous city. The series closed in 1983. In 1984 *Joséphine et Napoléon* was introduced with artwork by Claude Boulmé. The series ended in 1986. The *Cambier Mother's Day* series began in 1983 with artwork by French classicist Guy Cambier. In early 1985, D'Arceau-Limoges introduced its first series relating to a classic motion picture, *Gigi*, by Jean-Claude Guidou. In 1986, Guidou began his second series for the firm, a contemporary Christmas series titled *Les Noëls de France*.

In 1986, D'Arceau-Limoges introduced *Les Femmes de la Belle Epoque (The Women of the Beautiful Era)* series, an historic tribute to the women of the grand couture of Paris at the turn of the century. The artist for the series is Pierre-Laurent Brenot. The year 1987 saw the introduction of the series *Paysages de France (French Country Landscapes)*, painted in the difficult *lavis* technique by Michel Julien.

Among the artists who have designed works for D'Arceau-Limoges are the late André Restieau, world authority on the techniques of re-creating medieval stained glass coloration in porcelain; neo-Classicist Guy Cambier, and the late François Ganeau, resident consultant to the Theatre Comédie Française, as well as Louis Dali.

## Collection *Le Patrimoine de Lafayette*

*(The Lafayette Legacy Collection)*

Artist: André Restieau. Artist's signature appears on front, initials on back

Overglaze-decorated porcelain

Diameter: 21.6 centimeters (8½ inches)

Attached back hanger

Edition size undisclosed, limited by announced period of issue

Numbered with certificate

**18-D15-1.1**
1973 *The Secret Contract*
Issue price: $14.82

**18-D15-1.2**
1973 *The Landing at North Island*
Issue price: $19.82

**18-D15-1.3**
1974 *The Meeting at City Tavern*
Issue price: $19.82

**18-D15-1.4**
1974 *The Battle of Brandywine*
Issue price: $19.82

**18-D15-1.5**
1975 *The Messages to Franklin*
Issue price: $19.82

**18-D15-1.6**
1975 *The Siege at Yorktown*
Issue price: $19.82
*Series Closed*

# FRANCE
## D'ARCEAU-LIMOGES

### 18-D15-2.1

*Noël Vitrail*

*(Stained-glass Christmas)*

Artist: André Restieau. Artist's signature appears on front, initials on back

Overglaze-decorated porcelain

Diameter: 21.6 centimeters (8½ inches)

Attached back hanger

Edition size undisclosed, limited by announced period of issue

Numbered with certificate

**18-D15-2.1**
1975 *La Fuite en Egypte*
*(Flight into Egypt)*
Issue price: $24.32

**18-D15-2.2**
1976 *Dans la Crêche*
*(In the Manger)*
Issue price: $24.32

**18-D15-2.3**
1977 *Le Refus d'Hébergement*
*(No Room at the Inn)*
Issue price: $24.32

**18-D15-2.4**
1978 *La Purification*
*(The Purification)*
Issue price: $26.81

**18-D15-2.5**
1979 *L'Adoration des Rois*
*(The Adoration of Kings)*
Issue price: $26.81

**18-D15-2.6**
1980 *Joyeuse Nouvelle*
*(Tidings of Great Joy)*
Issue price: $28.74

**18-D15-2.7**
1981 *Guidés par l'Etoile*
*(Guided by the Star)*
Issue price: $28.74

**18-D15-2.8**
1982 *L'Annonciation*
*(The Annunciation)*
Issue price: $30.74
*Series Closed*

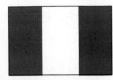

## Les Femmes du Siècle
*(The Women of the Century)*

Artist: François Ganeau. Artist's signature appears on front, initials on back

Overglaze-decorated porcelain

Diameter: 21.6 centimeters (8½ inches)

Attached back hanger

Edition size undisclosed, limited by announced period of issue

Numbered with certificate

**18-D15-3.1**
1976 *Scarlet en Crinoline*
Issue price: $17.67

**18-D15-3.2**
1976 *Sarah en Tournure*
Issue price: $22.74

**18-D15-3.3**
1976 *Colette, la Femme Sportive*
Issue price: $22.74

**18-D15-3.4**
1976 *Léa, la Femme Fleur*
Issue price: $22.74

**18-D15-3.5**
1977 *Albertine, la Femme Liane*
Issue price: $22.74

**18-D15-3.6**
1977 *Edith, la Femme Pratique*
Issue price: $22.74

**18-D15-3.7**
1977 *Daisy, la Garçonne*
Issue price: $22.74

**18-D15-3.8**
1977 *Marlène, la Vamp*
Issue price: $22.74

# FRANCE
## D'ARCEAU-LIMOGES
### 18-D15-3.9

**18-D15-3.9**
1978 *Hélène, l'Intrépide*
Issue price: $22.74

**18-D15-3.10**
1978 *Sophie, la Féminité Retrouvée*
Issue price: $22.74

**18-D15-3.11**
1979 *Françoise en Pantalon*
Issue price: $22.74

**18-D15-3.12**
1979 *Brigitte en Mini-jupe*
Issue price: $22.74
*Series Closed*

## *Les Jeunes Filles des Saisons*

*(The Girls of the Seasons)*

Artist: Guy Cambier. Artist's signature appears on front

Overglaze-decorated porcelain banded in gold

Diameter: 24.8 centimeters (9¾ inches)

Attached back hanger

Edition size limited to 15,000

Numbered with certificate

**18-D15-4.1**
1978 *La Jeune Fille d'Eté*
*(Summer Girl)*
Issue price: $105.00

**18-D15-4.2**
1979 *La Jeune Fille d'Hiver*
*(Winter Girl)*
Issue price: $105.00

**18-D15-4.3**
1980 *La Jeune Fille du Printemps*
*(Spring Girl)*
Issue price: $105.00

**18-D15-4.4**
1981 *La Jeune Fille d'Automne*
*(Autumn Girl)*
Issue price: $105.00
*Series Closed*

## Les Très Riches Heures

*(The Very Rich Hours)*

Artist: Jean Dutheil through 1984;
Albert Delage thereafter.

Overglaze-decorated porcelain

Diameter: 24.8 centimeters
(9¾ inches)

Attached back hanger

Edition size unannounced

Numbered with certificate

**18-D15-5.1**
1979 *Janvier (January)*
Issue price: $75.48

**18-D15-5.2**
1980 *Avril (April)*
Issue price: $75.48

**18-D15-5.3**
1981 *Août (August)*
Issue price: $75.48

**18-D15-5.4**
1982 *Juin (June)*
Issue price: $75.48

**18-D15-5.5**
1983 *Mai (May)*
Issue price: $75.48

# FRANCE
## D'ARCEAU-LIMOGES

### 18-D15-5.6

**18-D15-5.6**
1984 *Octobre (October)*
Issue price: $75.48

**18-D15-5.7**
1985 *Février (February)*
Issue price: $75.48

*Les Douze Sites Parisiens de Louis Dali* (The Twelve Parisian Places of Louis Dali)

Artist: Louis Dali. Artist's signature appears on front

Overglaze-decorated porcelain

Diameter: 21.6 centimeters (8½ inches)

Attached back hanger

Edition size undisclosed, limited by announced period of issue

Numbered with certificate

**18-D15-6.1**
1980 *L'Arc de Triomphe (The Arch of Triumph)*
Issue price: $22.94

**18-D15-6.2**
1981 *La Cathédrale Notre-Dame (Notre Dame Cathedral)*
Issue price: $24.94

**18-D15-6.3**
1981 *La Place de la Concorde (Concord Place)*
Issue price: $24.94

**18-D15-6.4**
1981 *L'Église Saint-Pierre et le Sacré-Coeur de Montmartre (St. Peter's Church and Sacred Heart Basilica)*
Issue price: $26.83

**18-D15-6.5**
1982 *Le Marché aux Fleurs et la Conciergerie (The Flower Market and the Conciergerie)*
Issue price: $26.83

**18-D15-6.6**
1982 *La Pointe du Vert Galant et le Pont Neuf (Vert Galant Point and the New Bridge)*
Issue price: $26.83

**18-D15-6.7**
1983 *Le Jardin des Tuileries (The Garden of the Tuileries)*
Issue price: $26.83

**18-D15-6.8**
1983 *Le Moulin Rouge (The Moulin Rouge)*
Issue price: $26.83

**18-D15-6.9**
1983 *Le Pont Alexandre III (The Alexander III Bridge)*
Issue price: $26.83

**18-D15-6.10**
1983 *L'Opéra (The Opera)*
Issue price: $26.83

**18-D15-6.11**
1983 *La Tour Eiffel (The Eiffel Tower)*
Issue price: $26.83

**18-D15-6.12**
1983 *L'Hôtel de Ville de Paris (The Hotel de Ville de Paris)*
Issue price: $26.83
*Series Closed*

# FRANCE
## D'ARCEAU-LIMOGES

### 18-D15-7.1

*Joséphine et Napoléon*
(Josephine and Napoleon)

Artist: Claude Boulmé. Artist's signature appears on front

Overglaze-decorated porcelain

Diameter: 21.6 centimeters (8½ inches)

Attached back hanger

Edition size undisclosed, limited by announced period of issue

Numbered with certificate

**18-D15-7.1**
1984 *L'Impératrice Joséphine*
*(The Empress Josephine)*
Issue price: $29.32

**18-D15-7.2**
1984 *Bonaparte traversant les Alpes*
*(Bonaparte Crossing the Alps)*
Issue price: $29.32

**18-D15-7.3**
1984 *La Rencontre*
*(The Meeting)*
Issue price: $29.32

**18-D15-7.4**
1985 *Sacre de Napoléon*
*(The Coronation)*
Issue price: $29.32

**18-D15-7.5**
1985 *Le Divorce*
*(The Divorce)*
Issue price: $34.32

**18-D15-7.6**
1986 *Le Souvenir*
*(The Memory)*
Issue price: $34.32
*Series Closed*

## Cambier Mother's Day Series

Artist: Guy Cambier. Artist's signature appears on front

Overglaze-decorated porcelain

Diameter: 21.6 centimeters (8½ inches)

Attached back hanger

Edition size undisclosed, limited by year of issue

Numbered with certificate

**18-D15-8.1**
*1983 Michèle et Sylvie*
Issue price: $32.84

**18-D15-8.2**
*1984 Marie et Jacqueline*
Issue price: $32.84

**18-D15-8.3**
*1985 Monique et François*
Issue price: $32.84

**18-D15-8.4**
*1986 Marianne et Thérèse*
Issue price: $35.84
*Series Closed*

## Gigi Series

Artist: Jean-Claude Guidou. Artist's signature appears on front

Overglaze-decorated porcelain

Diameter: 21.6 centimeters (8½ inches)

Attached back hanger

Edition size undisclosed, limited by announced period of issue

Numbered with certificate

**18-D15-9.1**
*1985 Gigi*
Issue price: $24.73

**18-D15-9.2**
*1985 The Night They Invented Champagne*
Issue price: $24.73

93

# FRANCE
## D'ARCEAU-LIMOGES
### 18-D15-9.3

**18-D15-9.3**
1986 *I Remember It Well*
Issue price: $24.73

**18-D15-9.4**
1986 *Gigi Is in Love*
Issue price: $24.73
*Series Closed*

## *Les Femmes de la Belle Epoque Series*

*(The Women of the Beautiful Era)*

Artist: Pierre-Laurent Brenot. Artist's signature appears on front

Overglaze-decorated porcelain

Diameter: 21.6 centimeters (8½ inches)

Attached back hanger

Edition size undisclosed, limited by announced period of issue

Numbered with certificate

**18-D15-10.1**
1986 *Sarah Bernhardt as Marguerite in "The Lady of the Camellias"*
Issue price: $24.96

**18-D15-10.2**
1986 *Liane de Pougy Makes Her Entrance at Maxim's*
Issue price: $24.96

**18-D15-10.3**
1987 *Caroline Otéro Pauses in Front of the Opera at Monte Carlo*
Issue price: $24.96

**18-D15-10.4**
1987 *Anna Pavlova Greets an Admirer at the Ballet Russes*
Issue price: $24.96
*Series Closed*

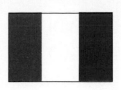

## Les Noëls de France Series

*(Christmas in France)*

Artist: Jean-Claude Guidou.
Artist's signature appears on front

Overglaze-decorated porcelain

Diameter: 21.6 centimeters
(8½ inches)

Attached back hanger

Edition size undisclosed, limited
by announced period of issue

Numbered with certificate

**18-D15-11.1**
1986 *The Magical Window*
Issue price: $28.47

## Paysages de France Series

*(French Country Landscapes)*

Artist: Michel Julien. Artist's
signature appears on front

Overglaze-decorated porcelain

Diameter: 21.6 centimeters
(8½ inches)

Edition size undisclosed, limited
by announced period of issue

Numbered, with certificate

**18-D15-12.1**
1987 *Along the Riverside*
Issue price unavailable
at press time

## HAVILAND
Limoges

In 1839 David Haviland of New York City became the first American importer of Limoges porcelain made from white kaolin clay. When, in 1842, he realized that French factories would not adjust methods to meet the tastes of his American market, Haviland established his own pottery in Limoges.

In 1892 his son, Theodore, left the firm but remained in Limoges to set up Theodore Haviland & Company for production of porcelain dinnerware and decorative pieces. In the 1930s, Theodore Haviland & Company opened an American Haviland factory to produce tableware; the firm also bought the original Haviland &

Company established by David Haviland.

All Haviland collector's plates are produced in Limoges, France. *The Twelve Days of Christmas* series, begun in 1970, is based on the carol of the same title. 1979 marked the beginning of the *Mille et Une Nuits* series based on the literary classic *One Thousand and One Arabian Nights*.

Adept in a variety of styles, French painter Remy Hétreau is the principal artist for Haviland collector's plates, with two distinctively different series to his credit. Noted watercolorist Liliane Tellier is the creator of the *Mille et Une Nuits* series.

## The Twelve Days of Christmas Series

Artist: Remy Hétreau. Artist's signature appears on back

Overglaze-decorated porcelain

Diameter: 21.3 centimeters (8³⁄₈ inches)

No hanger

Edition size limited to announced quantity of 30,000

Not numbered, without certificate

**18-H6-1.1**
1970 *A Partridge in a Pear Tree*
Issue price: $25.00

**18-H6-1.2**
1971 *Two Turtle Doves*
Issue price: $25.00

**18-H6-1.3**
1972 *Three French Hens*
Issue price: $27.50

**18-H6-1.4**
1973 *Four Colly Birds*
Issue price: $28.50

**18-H6-1.5**
1974 *Five Golden Rings*
Issue price: $30.00

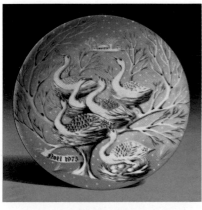

**18-H6-1.6**
1975 *Six Geese A'Laying*
Issue price: $32.50

**18-H6-1.7**
1976 *Seven Swans A'Swimming*
Issue price: $38.00

**18-H6-1.8**
1977 *Eight Maids A'Milking*
Issue price: $40.00

**18-H6-1.9**

**18-H6-1.9**
1978 *Nine Ladies Dancing*
Issue price: $45.00

**18-H6-1.10**
1979 *Ten Lords A'Leaping*
Issue price: $50.00

**18-H6-1.11**
1980 *Eleven Pipers Piping*
Issue price: $55.00

**18-H6-1.12**
1981 *Twelve Drummers Drumming*
Issue price: $60.00
*Series Closed*

## Mille et Une Nuits

*(1001 Arabian Nights)*

Artist: Liliane Tellier. Artist's signature appears on front

Porcelain banded in gold

Diameter: 24.1 centimeters (9½ inches)

No hanger

Edition size undisclosed, limited by period of issue

Numbered with certificate

**18-H6-4.1**
1979 *Le Cheval Magique*
*(The Magic Horse)*
Issue price: $54.50

**18-H6-4.2**
1980 *Aladin et la Lampe Merveilleuse*
*(Aladin and the Wonderful Lamp)*
Issue price: $54.50

**18-H6-4.3**
1981 *Scheherazade*
Issue price: $54.50

**18-H6-4.4**
1982 *Sinbad the Sailor*
Issue price: $54.50
*Series Closed*

**18-H8-1.1** *"Unicorn in Captivity"*
1971 Haviland & Parlon *Tapestry*
This series captures the delightful mythical quality and great detail of "The Hunt of the Unicorn," a series of French medieval tapestries now hanging in The Cloisters of New York's Metropolitan Museum of Art.

## HAVILAND & PARLON
Limoges

Haviland & Parlon is a chapter in the intricate Haviland porcelain story. In 1853 Robert Haviland left New York City to work for his brother David Haviland in Limoges (see France, HAVILAND). In 1870 Robert's son Charles Field Haviland also established a porcelain factory in Limoges and used "Ch. Field Haviland" as his trade name. After he retired in 1881, the firm was known by several different names until 1942, when Robert Haviland (Robert's great-grandson) purchased it. The firm is now known as Robert Haviland & C. Parlon but retains the "Ch. Field Haviland" trademark.

The *Tapestry* series, begun in 1971, reproduced six scenes from the French medieval tapestries, "The Hunt of the Unicorn," now hanging in the Cloisters of New York's Metropolitan Museum of Art. The *Christmas* series of famous Renaissance Madonnas began in 1972 and ended in 1979; a second *Tapestry* series of six plates began in 1977, reproducing scenes from "The Lady and the Unicorn" tapestries hanging in the Cluny Museum in Paris.

Designs for the *Christmas* series are taken from works by the great masters as indicated.

## Tapestry Series

Artist: unknown. Reproduced from French medieval tapestries

Overglaze-decorated porcelain banded in gold

Diameter: 25.4 centimeters (10 inches)

No hanger

Edition size limited to announced quantity of 10,000

Not numbered, without certificate

**18-H8-1.1**
1971 *The Unicorn in Captivity*
Issue price: $35.00

**18-H8-1.2**
1972 *Start of the Hunt*
Issue price: $35.00

**18-H8-1.3**
1973 *Chase of the Unicorn*
Issue price: $35.00

**18-H8-1.4**
1974 *End of the Hunt*
Issue price: $37.50

**18-H8-1.5**
1975 *The Unicorn Surrounded*
Issue price: $40.00

**18-H8-1.6**
1976 *The Unicorn Is Brought
to the Castle*
Issue price: $42.50
*Series Closed*

# FRANCE
## HAVILAND & PARLON

### 18-H8-2.1

### *Christmas Series*

Artist: as indicated

Overglaze-decorated porcelain banded in gold

Diameter: 25.4 centimeters (10 inches)

No hanger

Edition size: as indicated

Numbered without certificate

**18-H8-2.1**
1972 *Madonna and Child*
Artist: Raphael/Edition: 5,000
Issue price: $35.00

**18-H8-2.2**
1973 *Madonnina*
Artist: Feruzzi/Edition: 5,000
Issue price: $40.00

**18-H8-2.3**
1974 *Cowper Madonna and Child*
Artist: Raphael/Edition: 5,000
Issue price: $42.50

**18-H8-2.4**
1975 *Madonna and Child*
Artist: Murillo/Edition: 7,500
Issue price: $42.50

**18-H8-2.5**
1976 *Madonna and Child*
Artist: Botticelli/Edition: 7,000
Issue price: $45.00

**18-H8-2.6**
1977 *Madonna and Child*
Artist: Bellini/Edition: 7,500
Issue price: $48.00

**18-H8-2.7**
1978 *Madonna and Child*
Artist: Fra Filippo Lippi/
Edition: 7,500
Issue price: $48.00

**18-H8-2.8**
1979 *Madonna of the Eucharist*
Artist: Botticelli/Edition: 7,500
Issue price: $49.50
*Series Closed*

## The Lady and the Unicorn Series

Artist: unknown. Reproduced from French medieval tapestries

Overglaze-decorated porcelain banded in gold

Diameter: 25.4 centimeters (10 inches)

No hanger

Edition size: as indicated

Not numbered, without certificate

**18-H8-4.1**
1977 *To My Only Desire*
Edition: 20,000
Issue price: $45.00

**18-H8-4.2**
1978 *Sight*
Edition: 20,000
Issue price: $45.00

**18-H8-4.3**
1979 *Sound*
Edition: 20,000
Issue price: $47.50

**18-H8-4.4**
1980 *Touch*
Edition: 15,000
Issue price: $52.50

**18-H8-4.5**
1981 *Scent*
Edition: 10,000
Issue price: $59.00

**18-H8-4.6**
1982 *Taste*
Edition: 10,000
Issue price: $59.00
*Series Closed*

# FRANCE
## LALIQUE
### 18-L3-0.0

## LALIQUE
Alsace

René Lalique, founder of the firm that bears his name, began his career as a goldsmith and jeweler in the late nineteenth century. His clients included such notables as Sarah Bernhardt and the dealers Cartier and Boucheron.

In 1902 his interests turned to glassmaking and he acquired a small glassworks at Clairfontaine, France. In 1909 he opened a glass factory near Paris where he produced bottles for the leading Parisian *parfumeurs*, and in 1918 he opened the present Lalique factory in Alsace. Here he began to produce glass items in the Art Deco style. His designs, usually created in pressed glass, are noted for the frosted and satin effects of the glass. Until his death in 1945, Lalique produced numerous commercial glass objects such as perfume bottles, vases and figurines.

Upon René's death in 1945, his son Marc—himself a noted artist—inherited the firm and served as its president until his death in 1977. The firm is currently headed by Marc's daughter, Marie-Claude. As Lalique's chief designer she created the *Annual* series of Lalique crystal collector's plates which began in 1965 and ended in 1976.

## Annual Series

Artist: Marie-Claude Lalique

Full lead crystal with incised designs

Diameter: 21.6 centimeters (8½ inches)

No hanger

Edition size: as indicated. Announced between 5,000 and 8,000 from 1967 through 1976

Not numbered, without certificate; engraved "Lalique-France" on back

**18-L3-1.1**
1965 *Deux Oiseaux (Two Birds)*
Edition: 2,000
Issue price: $25.00

**18-L3-1.2**
1966 *Rose de Songerie (Dream Rose)*
Edition: 5,000
Issue price: $25.00

**18-L3-1.3**
1967 *Ballet de Poisson (Fish Ballet)*
Issue price: $25.00

**18-L3-1.4**
1968 *Gazelle Fantaisie (Gazelle Fantasy)*
Issue price: $25.00

**18-L3-1.5**
1969 *Papillon (Butterfly)*
Issue price: $30.00

**18-L3-1.6**
1970 *Paon (Peacock)*
Issue price: $30.00

**18-L3-1.7**
1971 *Hibou (Owl)*
Issue price: $35.00

**18-L3-1.8**
1972 *Coquillage (Shell)*
Issue price: $40.00

# FRANCE
## LALIQUE

**18-L3-1.9**

**18-L3-1.9**
1973 *Petit Geai (Jayling)*
Issue price: $42.50

**18-L3-1.10**
1974 *Sous d'Argent (Silver Pennies)*
Issue price: $47.50

**18-L3-1.11**
1975 *Duo de Poisson (Fish Duet)*
Issue price: $50.00

**18-L3-1.12**
1976 *Aigle (Eagle)*
Issue price: $60.00
*Series Closed*

**18-L52-2.1** ''Cinderella''
1983 Limoges-Turgot *Quellier's Morals of Perrault*
Many of today's most beloved children's tales began as serious examples of morality for adults. Such was true of ''Cinderella,'' a tale with origins in 17th century France, here interpreted in the graceful style of that period by André Quellier.

## LIMOGES-TURGOT
Limoges

The porcelain house of Limoges-Turgot draws upon a tradition of porcelain making which began with A.-R.-J. Turgot, Baron de l'Aulne, Louis XVI's administrator for the Limousin province of which Limoges was the capital. When kaolin clay, the key ingredient in true hard-fire porcelain, was discovered in 1768 at the nearby town of Saint-Yrieix, it was largely due to Turgot's efforts that the Limoges porcelain industry was established and achieved world renown.

*Les Enfants de Durand, (Durand's Children Collection)*, by Paul Durand, began in 1978 and is the first proprietary series by Limoges-Turgot. The series ended in 1980. *Quellier's Morals of Perrault* series, by André Quellier, began in 1983. Their third series, entitled *Children of the Turn of the Century*, was created by Bernard Peltriaux.

## Les Enfants de Durand
*(Durand's Children)*

Artist: Paul Durand. Artist's signature appears on front

Overglaze-decorated porcelain

Diameter: 20.3 centimeters (8 inches)

Attached back hanger

Edition size undisclosed, limited by year of issue

Numbered with certificate

**18-L52-1.1**
1978 *Marie-Ange*
Issue price: $36.40

**18-L52-1.2**
1979 *Emilie et Philippe*
Issue price: $36.40

**18-L52-1.3**
1980 *Christiane et Fifi*
Issue price: $36.40

**18-L52-1.4**
1980 *Cécile et Raoul*
Issue price: $36.40
*Series Closed*

## Quellier's Morals of Perrault Series

Artist: André Quellier. Artist's signature appears on front

Overglaze-decorated porcelain

Diameter: 21.6 centimeters (8½ inches)

Attached back hanger

Edition size undisclosed, limited by announced period of issue

Numbered with certificate

**18-L52-2.1**
1983 *Cinderella*
Issue price: $28.67

**18-L52-2.2**
1984 *Little Tom Thumb*
Issue price: $28.67

# FRANCE
## LIMOGES-TURGOT

### 18-L52-2.3

**18-L52-2.3**
1984 *Little Red Riding Hood*
Issue price: $28.67

**18-L52-2.4**
1985 *Sleeping Beauty*
Issue price: $28.67
*Series Closed*

## Les Enfants de la Fin du Siècle de Peltriaux

*(Peltriaux's Children of the Turn of the Century)*

Artist: Bernard Peltriaux. Artist's signature appears on front

Overglaze-decorated porcelain

Diameter: 21.6 centimeters (8½ inches)

Attached back hanger

Edition size undisclosed, limited by announced period of issue

Numbered with certificate

**18-L52-3.1**
1985 *Patinage au Trocadéro*
*(Skating at the Trocadéro)*
Issue price: $24.82

**18-L52-3.2**
1985 *Petits Voiliers au Bassin des Tuileries (Setting Sail at the Tuileries)*
Issue price: $29.82

**18-L52-3.3**
1985 *Guignol au Luxembourg*
*(At the Puppet Show in Luxemburg)*
Issue price: $29.82

**18-L52-3.4**
1986 *Manège aux Champs-Elysées*
*(Merry Go Round on the Champ-Elysées)*
Issue price: $29.82

**22-A3-3.1-1** ''Gabriel''
1979 Anna-Perenna *Triptych*
This issue is one of a three-plate set entitled ''The Byzantine Triptych.'' A modern interpretation of the three-paneled altarpieces of the 14th century, called triptychs, it is the work of husband-and-wife artist team Frank Russell and Gertrude Barrer.

## ANNA-PERENNA
Stuttgart

Named for Anna Perenna, the Roman goddess associated with health, abundance and the rebirth of spring, Anna-Perenna, Inc. was founded in 1977 by its president, Klaus D. Vogt, exclusively to produce high-quality limited-edition plates in hard-paste porcelain.

Two *Triptych* sets, inspired by the portable altar-pieces of the Middle Ages, were issued in 1979 and 1980. Each three-plate set reinterprets ancient Byzantine religious motifs. In 1979, Anna-Perenna introduced *Romantic Loves*, a four-plate series celebrating great romantic loves of history. Their four-plate series, *Uncle Tad's Cats*, began in 1979 and ended in 1981.

Frank Russell and Gertrude Barrer, the creators of the *Triptych* and the *Romantic Loves* series, are husband-and-wife co-workers who have blended their talents to become a successful art-producing team. Thaddeus Krumeich ("Uncle Tad") is the artist for the *Uncle Tad's Cats* series.

In 1986, Anna-Perenna introduced *Uncle Tad's Golden Oldies* series, again with artwork by Thaddeus Krumeich.

## The Triptych Series

Artist: Frank Russell and Gertrude Barrer. Artists' signatures appear on front

Hard-paste porcelain with hinged frame

Diameter: plates one and three, 21.6 cm. (8½ in.); plate two, 24.8 cm (9¾ in.); overall triptych, 88.9 cm. x 45.7 cm. (35 in. x 18 in.) for 1979 set; 83.8 cm. x 38.1 cm. (33 in. x 15 in.) for 1980 set

Attached back hanger

Edition size limited to 5,000 sets

Individually hand-numbered with certificate

**22-A3-3.1-1**
1979 *Gabriel*

**22-A3-3.1-2**
1979 *Madonna and Child*

*The Byzantine Triptych*
Issue price: $325.00

**22-A3-3.1-3**
1979 *Michael*

**22-A3-3.2-1**
1980 *Saul*

**22-A3-3.2-2**
1980 *David*

*The Jerusalem Triptych*
Issue price: $350.00
*Series Closed*

**22-A3-3.2-3**
1980 *Solomon*

# GERMANY
## ANNA-PERENNA

### 22-A3-4.1

### Romantic Loves Series

Artist: Frank Russell and Gertrude Barrer. Artists' signatures appear on front

Hard-paste porcelain banded in gold

Diameter: 25 centimeters (9⅞ inches)

Attached back hanger

Edition size limited to 7,500

Individually hand-numbered with certificate

**22-A3-4.1**
1979 *Romeo and Juliet*
Issue price: $95.00

**22-A3-4.2**
1980 *Lancelot and Guinevere*
Issue price: $95.00

**22-A3-4.3**
1981 *Helen and Paris*
Issue price: $95.00

**22-A3-4.4**
1982 *Lovers of the Taj Mahal*
Issue price: $95.00
*Series Closed*

### Uncle Tad's Cats Series

Artist: Thaddeus Krumeich. Artist's signature appears on front

Hard-paste porcelain

Diameter: 24.8 centimeters (9¾ inches)

Attached back hanger

Edition size limited to 5,000

Individually hand-numbered with certificate

**22-A3-5.1**
1979 *Oliver's Birthday*
Issue price: $75.00

**22-A3-5.2**
1980 *Peaches and Cream*
Issue price: $75.00

**22-A3-5.3**
1981 *Princess Aurora, Queen of the Night*
Issue price: $80.00

**22-A3-5.4**
1981 *Walter's Window*
Issue price: $85.00
*Series Closed*

## Uncle Tad's Golden Oldies Series

Artist: Thaddeus Krumeich.
Artist's signature appears on front

Hard-paste porcelain

Diameter: 20.3 centimeters
(8 inches)

Pierced foot rim

Edition size undisclosed, limited
by announced period of issue

Individually hand-numbered with
certificate

**22-A3-26.1**
1986 *My Merry Oldsmobile*
Issue price: $39.50

**22-A3-26.2**
1986 *Down by the Old Mill Stream*
Issue price: $39.50

**22-A3-26.3**
1986 *Ramona*
Issue price: $39.50

**22-A3-26.4**
1987 *Paddlin' Madeline Home*
Issue price: $39.50
*Series Closed*

## BAREUTHER
Waldsassen

The Bareuther & Company porcelain factory began to produce dinnerware, vases and giftware in 1867. The small shop was established with a porcelain kiln and an annular brick kiln by sculptor Johann Matthaeus Ries. In 1884 Ries's son sold the shop to Oskar Bareuther who continued to produce fine tableware.

To observe the 100th anniversary of the factory in 1967, Bareuther began a series of limited-edition *Christmas* plates. A *Father's Day* series depicting the great castles of Germany was started in 1969.

Hans Mueller is the principal artist for all Bareuther series.

## Christmas Series

Artist: Hans Mueller, except 1971

Porcelain decorated in cobalt blue underglaze

Diameter: 20.3 centimeters (8 inches)

Pierced foot rim

Edition size limited to announced quantity of 10,000

Not numbered, without certificate

**22-B7-1.1**
1967 *Stiftskirche*
Issue price: $12.00

**22-B7-1.2**
1968 *Kappl*
Issue price: $12.00

**22-B7-1.3**
1969 *Christkindlesmarkt*
Issue price: $12.00

**22-B7-1.4**
1970 *Chapel in Oberndorf*
Issue price: $12.50

**22-B7-1.5**
1971 *Toys for Sale*
From drawing by Ludwig Richter
Issue price: $12.75

**22-B7-1.6**
1972 *Christmas in Munich*
Issue price: $14.50

**22-B7-1.7**
1973 *Christmas Sleigh Ride*
Issue price: $15.00

**22-B7-1.8**
1974 *Church in the Black Forest*
Issue price: $19.00

**• 22-B7-1.9**
1975 *Snowman*
Issue price: $21.50

**22-B7-1.10**
1976 *Chapel in the Hills*
Issue price: $23.50

**22-B7-1.11**
1977 *Story Time*
Issue price: $24.50

**22-B7-1.12**
1978 *Mittenwald*
Issue price: $27.50

**22-B7-1.13**
1979 *Winter Day*
Issue price: $35.00

**22-B7-1.14**
1980 *Miltenberg*
Issue price: $37.50

**22-B7-1.15**
1981 *Walk in the Forest*
Issue price: $39.50

**22-B7-1.16**
1982 *Bad Wimpfen*
Issue price: $39.50

**22-B7-1.17**
1983 *The Night Before Christmas*
Issue price: $39.50

**22-B7-1.18**
1984 *Zeil on the River Main*
Issue price: $42.50

**22-B7-1.19**
1985 *Winter Wonderland*
Issue price: $42.50

**22-B7-1.20**
1986 *Market Place in Forchheim*
Issue price: $42.50

## Father's Day Series

Artist: Hans Mueller

Porcelain decorated in cobalt blue underglaze

Diameter: 20.3 centimeters (8 inches)

Pierced foot rim

Edition size limited to announced quantity of 2,500

Not numbered, without certificate

**22-B7-2.1**
1969 *Castle Neuschwanstein*
Issue price: $10.50

**22-B7-2.2**
1970 *Castle Pfalz*
Issue price: $12.50

**22-B7-2.3**
1971 *Castle Heidelberg*
Issue price: $12.75

**22-B7-2.4**
1972 *Castle Hohenschwangau*
Issue price: $14.50

**22-B7-2.5**
1973 *Castle Katz*
Issue price: $15.00

**22-B7-2.6**
1974 *Wurzburg Castle*
Issue price: $19.00

**22-B7-2.7**
1975 *Castle Lichtenstein*
Issue price: $21.50

**22-B7-2.8**
1976 *Castle Hohenzollern*
Issue price: $23.50

**22-B7-2.9**
1977 *Castle Eltz*
Issue price: $24.50

**22-B7-2.10**
1978 *Castle Falkenstein*
Issue price: $27.50

**22-B7-2.11**
1979 *Castle Rheinstein*
Issue price: $35.00

**22-B7-2.12**
1980 *Castle Cochem*
Issue price: $37.50

**22-B7-2.13**
1981 *Castle Gutenfels*
Issue price: $39.50

**22-B7-2.14**
1982 *Castle Zwingenberg*
Issue price: $39.50

**22-B7-2.15**
1983 *Castle Lauenstein*
Issue price: $39.50

**22-B7-2.16**
1984 *Castle Neuenstein*
Issue price: $42.50

**22-B7-2.17**
1985 *Castle Wartburg Near Eisenach*
Issue price: $42.50

**22-B7-2.18**
1986 *Castle Hardegg*
Issue price: $42.50

**22-B7-2.19**
1987 *Castle Buerresheim*
Issue price: $46.50

## BERLIN DESIGN
### Staffelstein

Berlin Design's limited-edition plates, mugs and other collectibles are manufactured by the Kaiser Porcelain Company (see Germany, KAISER), and are identified by the distinctive bear-and-crown symbol of the city of Berlin.

The *Christmas* series, intro-duced in 1970, depicts Yule festiv-ities in German towns. Artists for Berlin Design *Christmas* plates are not disclosed.

The *Holiday Week of the Family Kappelmann* series began in 1984. It is by artist Detlev Nitschke.

---

## *Christmas Series*

Artist: undisclosed

Porcelain decorated in cobalt blue underglaze

Diameter: 19.7 centimeters (7¾ inches)

Pierced foot rim

Edition size limited to 4,000 in 1970; 20,000 thereafter

Not numbered, without certificate

**22-B20-1.1**
1970 *Christmas in Bernkastel*
Issue price: $14.50

**22-B20-1.2**
1971 *Christmas in Rothenburg on Tauber*
Issue price: $14.50

**22-B20-1.3**
1972 *Christmas in Michelstadt*
Issue price: $15.00

**22-B20-1.4**
1973 *Christmas in Wendelstein*
Issue price: $20.00

**22-B20-1.5**
1974 *Christmas in Bremen*
Issue price: $25.00

**22-B20-1.6**
1975 *Christmas in Dortland*
Issue price: $30.00

**22-B20-1.7**
1976 *Christmas Eve in Augsburg*
Issue price: $32.00

**22-B20-1.8**
1977 *Christmas Eve in Hamburg*
Issue price: $32.00

**22-B20-1.9**
1978 *Christmas Market at the Dome of Berlin*
Issue price: $36.00

**22-B20-1.10**
1979 *Christmas Eve in Greetsiel*
Issue price: $47.50

**22-B20-1.11**
1980 *Christmas Eve in Miltenberg*
Issue price: $55.00

# GERMANY
## BERLIN DESIGN

**22-B20-1.12**

**22-B20-1.12**
1981 *Christmas Eve in Hahnenklee*
Issue price: $55.00

**22-B20-1.13**
1982 *Christmas Eve in Wasserburg*
Issue price: $55.00

**22-B20-1.14**
1983 *The Chapel in Oberndorf*
Issue price: $55.00

**22-B20-1.15**
1984 *Christmas Eve in Ramsau*
Issue price: $55.00

**22-B20-1.16**
1985 *Christmas Eve in Bad Wimpfen*
Issue price: $55.00

**22-B20-1.17**
1986 *Christmas Eve in Gelnhausen*
Issue price: $65.00

## Holiday Week of the Family Kappelmann Series

Artist: Detlev Nitschke. Artist's signature appears on front

Overglaze-decorated porcelain

Diameter: 19 centimeters (7½ inches)

Pierced foot rim

Edition size undisclosed, limited by announced period of issue

Numbered with certificate

**22-B20-4.1**
1984 *Monday*
Issue price: $33.00

**22-B20-4.2**
1984 *Tuesday*
Issue price: $33.00

**22-B20-4.3**
1985 *Wednesday*
Issue price: $33.00

**22-B20-4.4**
1985 *Thursday*
Issue price: $35.00

**22-B20-4.5**
1986 *Friday*
Issue price: $35.00

**22-B20-4.6**
1986 *Saturday*
Issue price: $35.00

**22-B20-4.7**
1986 *Sunday*
Issue price: $35.00
*Series Closed*

*Seltmann Weiden*

## CHRISTIAN SELTMANN
Weiden/Oberpfalz

The Christian Seltmann porcelain factory was established in 1901 by a talented, 30-year-old porcelain maker of the same name. Seltmann started his porcelain-making career as a young apprentice in a porcelain-making factory near Schlottenhof, Germany. In 1894 he made a special mold that helped his company win an important American contract. To show its gratitude, the company sent him to Teplitz-Schonau, the most prestigious porcelain-making school of the time.

Soon afterwards, Mr. Seltmann was promoted to factory manager, and eventually, the enterprising young man went into business on his own.

Since 1901, Christian Seltmann Porcelain has achieved considerable prestige and esteem by maintaining the high standards of its founder. Throughout its history, the firm has consistently produced exquisitely-wrought porcelain objects, well-known in Europe.

The *Lückel's Idyllic Village Life* series by artist Christian Lückel is produced on true hard-fire German porcelain. This series, which began in 1986, depicts scenes from a typical Bavarian village of the early 19th century.

## Lückel's Idyllic Village Life Series

Artist: Christian Lückel. Artist's signature appears on front

Porcelain

Diameter: 19 centimeters (7½ inches)

Pierced foot rim

Edition size undisclosed, limited by announced period of issue

Numbered with certificate

**22-C32-1.1**
1986 *The Blacksmith*
Issue price: $24.50

**22-C32-1.2**
1986 *Arrival of the Stagecoach*
Issue price: $24.50

**22-C32-1.3**
1987 *Stop at the Village Inn*
Issue price: $27.50

**22-C32-1.4**
1987 *In the Fields at Harvest Time*
Issue price: $27.50

**22-C32-1.5**
1987 *On the Way to the Market*
Issue price: $27.50

**22-C32-1.6**
1987 *At the Village Fountain*
Issue price: $27.50

**22-C32-1.7**
1987 *The Fishermen*
Issue price: $27.50

PORZELLANMANUFAKTUR
FÜRSTENBERG
SEIT 1747

## FÜRSTENBERG PORZELLAN
Fürstenberg

Fürstenberg, West Germany's oldest existing porcelain works, was founded by order of Charles I, Duke of Brunswick, in 1747. The porcelain manufactory took up residence in the 14th-century castle of Fürstenberg, high on the banks of the river Weser. To produce the quality of porcelain that in the 18th century was called "white gold," the Duke assembled a blue-ribbon group of artists and craftsmen. Six years later, in 1753, he decreed that each piece of porcelain from the Fürstenberg works be marked with a blue "F," which was later enhanced by the addition of a crown.

Through the centuries the Fürstenberg logo has changed little, while the porcelain produced there continues to represent the high achievements of the ceramicist's art. However, it was not until 1986 that the firm earned Bradex listing in the United States with the series titled *Muninger's Romantic Winter Impressions*. The artist for this series, Ludwig Muninger, is German-born and European-trained. Although his work is contemporary, it emulates the outstanding work of the Dutch landscape artists of the 17th century.

## Muninger's Romantic Winter Impressions Series

Artist: Ludwig Muninger. Artist's signature appears on front

Overglaze-decorated porcelain

Diameter: 19 centimeters (7½ inches)

Edition size undisclosed, limited by announced period of issue

Numbered, with certificate

**22-F82-6.1**
1987 *Ice Skaters in the Evening Sun*
Issue price: $34.50

**22-F82-6.2**
1987 *Ice Fishers on the Village Pond*
Issue price: $34.50

# Goebel

## GOEBEL
Rödenthal

W. Goebel Porzellanfabrik was established in 1871 in Oeslau by Franz-Detleff Goebel and his son William. Now headed by Wilhelm Goebel, who represents the fifth generation of the founding family, Goebel produces handcrafted figurines, plates, dinnerware, and gift items.

In 1935 Goebel introduced the famous M. I. Hummel figurines based on sketches by the Franciscan nun. In 1971, to celebrate the 100th anniversary of the firm, Goebel inaugurated an *Annual* series of limited-edition plates featuring M. I. Hummel motifs.

The three-issue M. I. Hummel *Anniversary* series began in 1975, with the second and third plates issued in 1980 and 1985.

## Hummel Annual Series

Artist: Sister M. I. Hummel.
Artist's signature incised on front

Porcelain with hand-painted bas-relief

Diameter: 19 centimeters
(7½ inches)

Pierced foot rim

Edition size undisclosed, limited by year of issue

Not numbered, without certificate

**22-G54-1.1**
1971 *Heavenly Angel*
Issue price: $25.00

**22-G54-1.2**
1972 *Hear Ye, Hear Ye*
Issue price: $30.00

**22-G54-1.3**
1973 *Globe Trotter*
Issue price: $32.50

**22-G54-1.4**
1974 *Goose Girl*
Issue price: $40.00

**22-G54-1.5**
1975 *Ride into Christmas*
Issue price: $50.00

**22-G54-1.6**
1976 *Apple Tree Girl*
Issue price: $50.00

**22-G54-1.7**
1977 *Apple Tree Boy*
Issue price: $50.00

**22-G54-1.8**
1978 *Happy Pastime*
Issue price: $65.00

# GERMANY
## GOEBEL
### 22-G54-1.9

**22-G54-1.9**
1979 *Singing Lesson*
Issue price: $90.00

**22-G54-1.10**
1980 *School Girl*
Issue price: $100.00

**22-G54-1.11**
1981 *Umbrella Boy*
Issue price: $100.00

**22-G54-1.12**
1982 *Umbrella Girl*
Issue price: $100.00

**22-G54-1.13**
1983 *The Postman*
Issue price: $108.00

**22-G54-1.14**
1984 *Little Helper*
Issue price: $108.00

**22-G54-1.15**
1985 *Chick Girl*
Issue price: $110.00

**22-G54-1.16**
1986 *Playmates*
Issue price: $125.00

**22-G54-1.17**
1987 *Feeding Time*
Issue price: $135.00

## Hummel Anniversary Series

Artist: Sister M. I. Hummel. Artist's signature incised on front

Porcelain with hand-painted bas-relief

Diameter: 25.4 centimeters (10 inches)

Pierced foot rim

Edition size undisclosed, limited by year of issue

Not numbered, without certificate

**22-G54-3.1**
1975 *Stormy Weather*
Issue price: $100.00

**22-G54-3.2**
1980 *Spring Dance*
Issue price: $225.00

**22-G54-3.3**
1985 *Auf Wiedersehen*
Issue price: $225.00
*Series Closed*

## HEINRICH/VILLEROY & BOCH
Selb

The history of Heinrich Porzellan dates from the opening by Franz Heinrich of a porcelain-painting studio in 1896 in Selb, Bavaria, near the Czechoslovakian border. In 1901, Heinrich established his own porcelain factory, Heinrich & Co., which produced fine table- and giftware. The firm remained under the control of the Heinrich family until 1976, when it was purchased by Villeroy & Boch. Heinrich creations are now distributed worldwide through Villeroy & Boch's marketing channels.

From 1980 thru 1983, Heinrich issued a 12-plate series of porcelain plates entitled *Russian Fairy Tales*, adapted from the artwork of famous Russian illustrator Boris Zvorykin. The *Fairies of the Fields and Flowers* series began in 1982, with artwork by Cicely Mary Barker. The *Once Upon a Rhyme* series began in 1984, featuring for the first time the work of an American artist, Renée Faure.

The unusual symbolist art of Gero Trauth was introduced in *The Dreams of Katharina* series in 1986.

## *Russian Fairy Tales Series*

Artist: Boris Zvorykin

Hard-paste porcelain banded in gold

Diameter: 21 centimeters (8¼ inches)

No hanger

Edition size limited to 27,500

Not numbered, with certificate

**22-H18-1.1**
1980 *The Snow Maiden*
Issue price: $70.00

**22-H18-1.2**
1980 *The Snow Maiden at the Court of Tsar Berendei*
Issue price: $70.00

**22-H18-1.3**
1980 *The Snow Maiden and Lel the Shepherd Boy*
Issue price: $70.00

**22-H18-1.4**
1981 *The Red Knight*
Issue price: $70.00

**22-H18-1.5**
1981 *Vassilissa and Her Stepsisters*
Issue price: $70.00

**22-H18-1.6**
1981 *Vassilissa Is Presented to the Tsar*
Issue price: $70.00

**22-H18-1.7**
1982 *In Search of the Firebird*
Issue price: $70.00

**22-H18-1.8**
1982 *Ivan and Tsarevna on the Grey Wolf*
Issue price: $70.00

# GERMANY
## HEINRICH/VILLEROY & BOCH
### 22-H18-1.9

**22-H18-1.9**
1982 *The Wedding of Tsarevna Elena the Fair*
Issue price: $70.00

**22-H18-1.10**
1983 *Maria Morevna and Tsarevich Ivan*
Issue price: $70.00

**22-H18-1.11**
1983 *Koshchey Carries off Maria Morevna*
Issue price: $70.00

**22-H18-1.12**
1983 *Tsarevich Ivan and the Beautiful Castle*
Issue price: $70.00
*Series Closed*

## Fairies of the Fields and Flowers Series

Artist: Cicely Mary Barker

Bone china banded in 24k gold

Diameter: 21.6 centimeters (8½ inches)

Attached back hanger

Edition size undisclosed, limited by announced period of issue

Numbered with certificate

**22-H18-3.1**
1982 *Ragged Robin*
Issue price: $49.00

**22-H18-3.2**
1983 *Willow*
Issue price: $49.00

**22-H18-3.3**
1984 *Elderberry*
Issue price: $49.00

**22-H18-3.4**
1984 *Vetch*
Issue price: $49.00

**22-H18-3.5**
1984 *Narcissus*
Issue price: $49.00

**22-H18-3.6**
1985 *Nasturtium*
Issue price: $49.00

**22-H18-3.7**
1985 *Phlox*
Issue price: $49.00

**22-H18-3.8**
1985 *Gorse*
Issue price: $49.00
*Series Closed*

# GERMANY
## HEINRICH/VILLEROY & BOCH

### 22-H18-8.1

*Once Upon a Rhyme Series*

Artist: Renée Faure. Artist's signature appears on front

Overglaze-decorated porcelain

Diameter: 19.7 centimeters (7¾ inches)

Attached back hanger

Edition size undisclosed, limited by announced period of issue

Numbered with certificate

**22-H18-8.1**
1984 *Roses Are Red*
Issue price: $35.00

**22-H18-8.2**
1984 *A Tisket, a Tasket*
Issue price: $35.00

**22-H18-8.3**
1985 *Mary Had a Little Lamb*
Issue price: $35.00

**22-H18-8.4**
1985 *Star Light, Star Bright*
Issue price: $35.00

**22-H18-8.5**
1986 *Tom, Tom, the Piper's Son*
Issue price: $35.00

**22-H18-8.6**
1986 *Over the River and through the Woods*
Issue price: $35.00
*Series Closed*

## Dreams of Katharina Series

Artist: Gero Trauth. Artist's signature appears on front

Overglaze-decorated porcelain

Diameter: 21.6 centimeters (8½ inches)

Edition size limited to 19,900

Numbered, with certificate

**22-H18-12.1**
1986 *Katharina Receives a Promise of Love*
Issue price: $75.00

**22-H18-12.2**
1986 *Katharina's Aura and Her Earthly Laments*
Issue price: $75.00

**22-H18-12.3**
1986 *Katharina's Dream Castle*
Issue price: $75.00

**22-H18-12.4**
1986 *Katharina's Blossoming Love*
Issue price: $75.00

## HIBEL STUDIO
Staffelstein

Hibel Studio was founded in 1976. Headquartered in Riviera Beach, Florida, the studio specializes in original stone lithographs, lithographs on porcelain and limited-edition collector's plates. All artwork is approved by Edna Hibel, and plates are made by Kaiser Porcelain and Rosenthal China (see Germany, KAISER, ROSENTHAL).

Hibel Studio began its first series of collector's plates, the *David* series, in 1979. The four-plate series, with artwork by Edna Hibel, is based on the biblical story of King David.

## David Series

Artist: Edna Hibel. Artist's signature appears on front

Porcelain highlighted and banded in gold

Diameter: 25.7 centimeters (10⅛ inches)

Pierced foot rim

Edition size limited to 5,000

Numbered with certificate

**22-H31-1.1**
1979 *The Wedding of David and Bathsheba*
Issue price: $250.00

**22-H31-1.2**
1980 *David, Bathsheba and Solomon*
Issue price: $275.00

**22-H31-1.3**
1982 *David the King*
Issue price: $275.00

**22-H31-1.4**
1983 *Bathsheba*
Issue price: $275.00
*Series Closed*

# GERMANY
## HUTSCHENREUTHER

**22-H82-6.1**

**HUTSCHENREUTHER**
GERMANY

## HUTSCHENREUTHER
Selb

Hutschenreuther has produced limited-edition collector's plates since 1973, when they introduced their *Canada Christmas* series (not U.S. Bradex-listed). The *Love for All Seasons* series was issued in 1982 and 1983 and depicts six scenes of medieval romance as portrayed by the artist team of Charlotte and William Hallett.

In 1986, Hutschenreuter introduced the *Bouquets of the Seasons* series by noted naturalist painter Ursula Band, who has also produced plates for Tirschenreuth (see Germany, TIRSCHENREUTH).

---

### *Love for All Seasons Series*

Artist: Charlotte and William Hallett. Artists' signatures appear on back

Hard-paste porcelain with gold design on border

Diameter: 20.3 centimeters (8 inches)

Attached back hanger

Edition size limited to 10,000

Not numbered, without certificate

**22-H82-6.1**
1982 *The Minstrel Song*
Issue price: $125.00

**22-H82-6.2**
1982 *Affection*
Issue price: $125.00

**22-H82-6.3**
1982 *The Tournament*
Issue price: $125.00

**22-H82-6.4**
1983 *The Falcon Hunt*
Issue price: $125.00

**22-H82-6.5**
1983 *Winter Romance*
Issue price: $125.00

**22-H82-6.6**
1983 *The Ride Out*
Issue price: $125.00
*Series Closed*

## Bouquets of the Seasons Series

Artist: Ursula Band. Artist's signature appears on front

Overglaze-decorated porcelain banded in gold

Diameter: 19.7 centimeters (7¾ inches)

Edition size undisclosed, limited by announced period of issue

Numbered, with certificate

**22-H82-26.1**
1987 *Spring Morning*
Issue price: $24.50

**22-H82-26.2**
1987 *Easter Bouquet*
Issue price: $24.50

## KAISER
Staffelstein

Kaiser porcelain dates to 1872 when porcelain painter August Al-both set up his own workshop in Coburg. When he retired in 1899, his son Ernst moved the pottery to Bavaria. Marriage united the Al-both and Kaiser families in 1922, resulting in the ALKA trade-mark—a combination of the first two letters of both names.

In 1938 the firm purchased the old Bavarian pottery of Silbermann Brothers, which had been awarded a royal diploma in 1882 for its "magnificent" cobalt blue under-glaze. The company opened its modern factory in Staffelstein in 1953 and in 1970 the trademark was changed to Kaiser Porcelain.

Long a producer of porcelain coffee sets, dinnerware, and figu-rines, Kaiser introduced its first se-ries of limited-edition plates, the *Christmas* series, in 1970. The se-ries ended in 1982. The *Mother's Day* series began in 1971 and end-ed in 1983. These series feature the artwork of Toni Schoener and Nori Peter. The *Classic Fairy Tales Collec-tion* began in 1982, with artwork by Gerda Neubacher. The series ended in 1984.

In 1985, Kaiser introduced the *Classic Lullabies of the World* series, also designed by Gerda Neubach-er. *Classic Lullabies of the World* is a tribute to the beloved melodies shared by parents and children all over the world.

---

## *Christmas Series*

Artist: as indicated

Porcelain decorated in cobalt blue underglaze

Diameter: 19 centimeters (7½ inches)

Pierced foot rim

Edition size undisclosed, limited by year of issue except 1974

Not numbered, without certificate

**22-K4-1.1**
1970 *Waiting for Santa Claus*
Artist: Toni Schoener
Issue price: $12.50

**22-K4-1.2**
1971 *Silent Night*
Artist: Kurt Bauer
Issue price: $13.50

**22-K4-1.3**
1972 *Welcome Home*
Artist: Kurt Bauer
Issue price: $16.50

**22-K4-1.4**
1973 *Holy Night*
Artist: Toni Schoener
Issue price: $18.00

**22-K4-1.5**
1974 *Christmas Carolers*
Artist: Kurt Bauer/Edition: 8,000
Issue price: $25.00

**22-K4-1.6**
1975 *Bringing Home the Christmas Tree*
Artist: Joann Northcott
Issue price: $25.00

**22-K4-1.7**
1976 *Christ the Saviour Is Born*
Artist: Carlo Maratti
Issue price: $25.00

**22-K4-1.8**
1977 *The Three Kings*
Artist: Toni Schoener
Issue price: $25.00

**22-K4-1.9**
1978 *Shepherds in the Field*
Artist: Toni Schoener
Issue price: $30.00

**22-K4-1.10**
1979 *Christmas Eve*
Artist: Hannelore Blum
Issue price: $32.00

**22-K4-1.11**
1980 *Joys of Winter*
Artist: Hannelore Blum
Issue price: $40.00

**22-K4-1.12**

**22-K4-1.12**
1981 *Most Holy Night*
Artist: Kurt Bauer
Issue price: $40.00

**22-K4-1.13**
1982 *Bringing Home the Christmas Tree*
Artist: Kurt Bauer
Issue price: $40.00
*Series Closed*

## Mother's Day Series

Artist: as indicated

Porcelain decorated in cobalt blue underglaze

Diameter: 19 centimeters
(7½ inches)

Pierced foot rim

Edition size undisclosed, limited by year of issue except 1974

Not numbered, without certificate

**22-K4-2.1**
1971 *Mare and Foal*
Artist: Toni Schoener
Issue price: $13.00

**22-K4-2.2**
1972 *Flowers for Mother*
Artist: Toni Schoener
Issue price: $16.50

**22-K4-2.3**
1973 *Cats*
Artist: Toni Schoener
Issue price: $17.00

**22-K4-2.4**
1974 *Fox*
Artist: Toni Schoener/Edition: 7,000
Issue price: $22.00

**22-K4-2.5**
1975 *German Shepherd*
Artist: Toni Schoener
Issue price: $25.00

**22-K4-2.6**
1976 *Swan and Cygnets*
Artist: Toni Schoener
Issue price: $25.00

**22-K4-2.7**
1977 *Mother Rabbit and Young*
Artist: Toni Schoener
Issue price: $25.00

**22-K4-2.8**
1978 *Hen and Chicks*
Artist: Toni Schoener
Issue price: $30.00

**22-K4-2.9**
1979 *A Mother's Devotion*
Artist: Nori Peter
Issue price: $32.00

**22-K4-2.10**
1980 *Raccoon Family*
Artist: Joann Northcott
Issue price: $40.00

**22-K4-2.11**
1981 *Safe Near Mother*
Artist: Hannelore Blum
Issue price: $40.00

**22-K4-2.12**
1982 *Pheasant Family*
Artist: Kurt Bauer
Issue price: $40.00

**22-K4-2.13**
1983 *Tender Care*
Artist: Kurt Bauer
Issue price: $40.00
*Series Closed*

# GERMANY
## KAISER

### 22-K4-5.1

*Classic Fairy Tales Collection*

Artist: Gerda Neubacher. Artist's signature appears on front

Porcelain banded in 24k gold

Diameter: 19.7 centimeters (7¾ inches)

Pierced foot rim

Edition size undisclosed, limited by announced period of issue

Numbered with certificated booklet

**22-K4-5.1**
1982 *The Frog King*
Issue price: $39.50

**22-K4-5.2**
1983 *Puss in Boots*
Issue price: $39.50

**22-K4-5.3**
1983 *Little Red Riding Hood*
Issue price: $39.50

**22-K4-5.4**
1983 *Hansel and Gretel*
Issue price: $39.50

**22-K4-5.5**
1984 *Cinderella*
Issue price: $39.50

**22-K4-5.6**
1984 *Sleeping Beauty*
Issue price: $39.50
*Series Closed*

## Classic Lullabies of the World Series

Artist: Gerda Neubacher. Artist's signature appears on front

Porcelain banded in gold

Diameter: 19.7 centimeters (7¾ inches)

Pierced foot rim

Edition size undisclosed, limited by announced period of issue

Numbered with certificated booklet

**22-K4-22.1**
1985 *Sleep, Baby, Sleep*
Issue price: $39.50

**22-K4-22.2**
1986 *Rock-a-bye-Baby*
Issue price: $39.50

**22-K4-22.3**
1986 *The Mocking-Bird*
Issue price: $39.50

**22-K4-22.4**
1986 *Au Clair de la Lune*
Issue price: $39.50

**22-K4-22.5**
1987 *All Through the Night*
Issue price: $39.50

**22-K4-22.6**
1987 *Brahms Lullaby*
Issue price: $39.50

# GERMANY
## KÖNIGSZELT BAYERN

**22-K46-0.0**

## KÖNIGSZELT BAYERN
Waldsassen

Königszelt Bayern entered the collector's plate market in 1979 with the first issue in its *Hedi Keller Christmas* series, more than a century after the creation of the first porcelain bearing the hallmark of Königszelt of Silesia. The likeness of Wilhelm I (1797-1888), king of Prussia and first sovereign of a united Germany, is incorporated in the hallmark of Königszelt Bayern—a tribute to his early patronage under which Bavarian porcelain began its rise to prominence among the porcelain creations of the world. In 1981 the *Grimm's Fairy Tales* series began in commemoration of the two-hundredth anniversary of the Grimm brothers' birth, with art by Charles Gehm. *Sulamith's Love Song* series, created by Sulamith Wülfing, began in 1982. Her *Christmas* series made its debut in 1985. In 1986, *A Woman's Love and Life* series was introduced, with artwork by this same artist. The *German Half-Timbered Houses* series, by Karl Bedal, was introduced in 1984.

## Hedi Keller Christmas Series

Artist: Hedi Keller. Artist's signature appears on front

Overglaze-decorated porcelain

Diameter: 24 centimeters (9½ inches)

Pierced foot rim

Edition size undisclosed, limited by year of issue

Numbered with certificate

**22-K46-1.1**
1979 *The Adoration*
Issue price: $29.50

**22-K46-1.2**
1980 *Flight into Egypt*
Issue price: $29.50

**22-K46-1.3**
1981 *Return into Galilee*
Issue price: $29.50

**22-K46-1.4**
1982 *Following the Star*
Issue price: $29.50

**22-K46-1.5**
1983 *Rest on the Flight*
Issue price: $29.50

**22-K46-1.6**
1984 *The Nativity*
Issue price: $29.50

**22-K46-1.7**
1985 *Gift of the Magi*
Issue price: $34.50

**22-K46-1.8**
1986 *The Annunciation*
Issue price: $34.50
*Series Closed*

# GERMANY
## KÖNIGSZELT BAYERN

### 22-K46-2.1

*Grimm's Fairy Tales Series*

Artist: Charles Gehm. Artist's signature appears on front

Overglaze-decorated porcelain

Diameter: 19 centimeters (7½ inches)

Pierced foot rim

Edition size undisclosed, limited by announced period of issue

Numbered with certificate

**22-K46-2.1**
1981 *Rumpelstilzchen*
Issue price: $23.00

**22-K46-2.2**
1982 *Rapunzel*
Issue price: $25.00

**22-K46-2.3**
1982 *Hänsel and Gretel*
Issue price: $25.00

**22-K46-2.4**
1983 *The Shoemaker and the Elves*
Issue price: $25.00

**22-K46-2.5**
1984 *The Golden Goose*
Issue price: $29.00

**22-K46-2.6**
1985 *The Shoes That Were Danced to Pieces*
Issue price: $29.00

**22-K46-2.7**
1986 *Sleeping Beauty*
Issue price: $29.00

**22-K46-2.8**
1987 *Snow White and the Seven Dwarves*
Issue price: $29.00
*Series Closed*

## Sulamith's Love Song Series

Artist: Sulamith Wülfing. Artist's signature appears on front

Overglaze-decorated porcelain

Diameter: 19 centimeters (7½ inches)

Pierced foot rim

Edition size undisclosed, limited by announced period of issue

Numbered with certificate

**22-K46-3.1**
1982 *The Music*
Issue price: $29.00

**22-K46-3.2**
1983 *The Pledge*
Issue price: $29.00

**22-K46-3.3**
1983 *The Vision*
Issue price: $29.00

**22-K46-3.4**
1983 *The Gift*
Issue price: $29.00

**22-K46-3.5**
1984 *The Circle*
Issue price: $29.00

**22-K46-3.6**
1984 *The Centre*
Issue price: $29.00

**22-K46-3.7**
1984 *The Journey*
Issue price: $29.00

**22-K46-3.8**
1984 *The Completion*
Issue price: $29.00
*Series Closed*

# GERMANY
## KÖNIGSZELT BAYERN

### 22-K46-4.1

*Deutsches Fachwerk*
(German Half-Timbered Houses)

Artist: Karl Bedal. Artist's signature appears on front

Overglaze-decorated porcelain

Diameter: 19 centimeters (7½ inches)

Pierced foot rim

Edition size undisclosed, limited by announced period of issue

Numbered with certificate

**22-K46-4.1**
1984 *Bauernhaus in Fronhausen*
Issue price: $24.00

**22-K46-4.2**
1984 *Niedersachsenhaus bei Thedinghausen*
Issue price: $24.00

**22-K46-4.3**
1985 *Moselhaus in Rißbach*
Issue price: $27.00

**22-K46-4.4**
1985 *Westfalenhaus aus Delbrück*
Issue price: $27.00

**22-K46-4.5**
1985 *Mittelfrankenhaus in Ernhofen*
Issue price: $27.00 Low $27.00;

**22-K46-4.6**
1986 *Bodenseehaus in Immenstaad*
Issue price: $27.00
*Series Closed*

## Sulamith's Christmas Series

Artist: Sulamith Wülfing. Artist's signature appears on front

Overglaze-decorated porcelain double-banded in 24k gold

Diameter: 24.1 centimeters (9½ inches)

No hanger

Edition size undisclosed, limited by year of issue

Numbered with certificate

**22-K46-5.1**
1985 *The Angels' Vigil*
Issue price: $35.00

**22-K46-5.2**
1986 *The Christmas Child*
Issue price: $35.00

**22-K46-5.3**
1987 *Christmas Angels*
Issue price: $35.00

# GERMANY
## KÖNIGSZELT BAYERN

### 22-K46-6.1

## A Woman's Love and Life Series

Artist: Sulamith Wülfing. Artist's signature appears on front

Overglaze-decorated porcelain

Diameter: 19 centimeters (7½ inches)

Pierced foot rim

Edition size undisclosed, limited by announced period of issue

Numbered with certificate

**22-K46-6.1**
1986 *Since I First Saw Him*
Issue price: $29.85

**22-K46-6.2**
1986 *He, the Noblest of All*
Issue price: $29.85

**22-K46-6.3**
1986 *I Can't Understand It*
Issue price: $29.85

**22-K46-6.4**
1987 *You, Ring on my Finger*
Issue price: $29.85

## *Wülfing Mother's Day Series*

Artist: Sulamith Wülfing

Overglaze-decorated porcelain

Diameter: 19 centimeters (7½ inches)

Pierced foot rim

Edition size undisclosed, limited by announced period of issue

Numbered, with certificate

**22-K46-8.1**
1987 *Spring's New Life*
Price unavailable
at press time

# GERMANY
## ROSENTHAL

### 22-R55-0.0

## ROSENTHAL

Selb, Rothbühl, Kronach, Amberg, Bad Soden, Landstuhl, Thomas Kulm, Waldershofen

Philipp Rosenthal, Sr. began his business in 1879 in the town of Selb in Bavaria. He initially purchased ''white ware'' from various porcelain manufacturers in Selb (including Hutschenreuther) and painted it with his own designs.

In 1895 he established his own factory in Kronach where he produced fine porcelain signed *Rosenthal* on the back, making him one of the first porcelain makers to use his name rather than a symbol. Philipp died in 1937 and the business was taken over by his son, Philipp, Jr., who still heads the firm.

Rosenthal's *Traditional Classic Rose Christmas* series began in 1910 and continues through 1984. In 1974, Rosenthal changed its backstamp to reflect their Classic Rose Collection. From 1969 to 1971 some of the earlier plates were reissued in small quantities (no more than 500 per reissue). Reissued plates, regardless of the year depicted, have a post-1957 backstamp and their foot rims are not pierced. After 1971, the firm discontinued the practice of reissuing plates from previous years, and each Rosenthal collector's plate is now produced only during its current year. The *Traditional Classic Rose Christmas* plates now qualify as limited editions.

In 1971 Rosenthal began the first of its Studio-Linie collections with the *Wiinblad Christmas* series, by noted designer Bjorn Wiinblad. These plates carry intricate modern designs partially hand-painted in as many as eighteen colors and are embellished with platinum and 18k gold. The *Nobility of Children* series and the *Oriental Gold* series also began in 1976 and carried Rosenthal's Classic Rose Collection backstamp. Both series ended in 1979. They featured the artwork of Edna Hibel.

## Traditional Classic Rose Christmas Series

Artist: as indicated. Artist's name appears on back

Overglaze-decorated porcelain, many in series have gold inner rim and lettering

Diameter: 21.6 centimeters (8½ inches)

Pierced foot rim until 1971; attached back hanger thereafter

Edition size undisclosed

Not numbered, without certificate

**22-R55-1.1**
1910 *Winter Peace*
Artist: Jul V. Guldbrandson
Issue price: $1.34

**22-R55-1.2**
1911 *The Three Wise Men*
Artist: Heinrich Vogoler
Issue price: $1.95

**22-R55-1.3**
1912 *Shooting Stars*
Artist: Paul Rieth
Issue price: $1.03

**22-R55-1.4**
1913 *Christmas Lights*
Artist: Julius Dietz
Issue price: $1.47

**22-R55-1.5**
1914 *Christmas Song*
Artist: Prof. Ludwig von Zumbusch
Issue price: $1.47

**22-R55-1.6**
1915 *Walking to Church*
Artist: Jul V. Guldbrandson
Issue price: $1.47

**22-R55-1.7**
1916 *Christmas During War*
Artist: Jul V. Guldbrandson
Issue price: $1.47

**22-R55-1.8**
1917 *Angel of Peace*
Artist: Prof. Mermagen
Issue price: $1.47

**22-R55-1.9**
1918 *Peace on Earth*
Artist: K. Pfeiffer
Issue price: $1.47

**22-R55-1.10**
1919 *St. Christopher with the Christ Child*
Artist: Dr. W. Schertel
Issue price: $5.96

**22-R55-1.11**
1920 *The Manger in Bethlehem*
Artist: Dr. W. Schertel
Issue price: $5.96

**22-R55-1.12**
1921 *Christmas in the Mountains*
Artist: Jupp Wiertz
Issue price: $5.96

**22-R55-1.13**
1922 *Advent Branch*
Artist: Friedrich Nicolai
Issue price: $5.96

**22-R55-1.14**
1923 *Children in the Winter Wood*
Artist: Ernst Hofer
Issue price: $5.96

**22-R55-1.15**
1924 *Deer in the Woods*
Artist: Theo Karner
Issue price: $2.98

**22-R55-1.16**
1925 *The Three Wise Men*
Artist: Otto Tauscheck
Issue price: $2.98

**22-R55-1.17**
1926 *Christmas in the Mountains*
Artist: Theo Schmutz-Baudiss
Issue price: $2.98

**22-R55-1.18**
*1927 Station on the Way*
Artist: Theo Schmutz-Baudiss
Issue price: $2.98

**22-R55-1.19**
*1928 Chalet Christmas*
Artist: Heinrich Fink
Issue price: $2.98

**22-R55-1.20**
*1929 Christmas in the Alps*
Artist: Heinrich Fink
Issue price: $2.98

**22-R55-1.21**
*1930 Group of Deer under the Pines*
Artist: Theo Karner
Issue price: $2.98

**22-R55-1.22**
*1931 Path of the Magi*
Artist: Heinrich Fink
Issue price: $3.09

**22-R55-1.23**
*1932 Christ Child*
Artist: Otto Koch
Issue price: $3.09

**22-R55-1.24**
*1933 Through the Night to Light*
Artist: Hans Schiffner
Issue price: $3.09

**22-R55-1.25**
*1934 Christmas Peace*
Artist: Heinrich Fink
Issue price: $3.09

**22-R55-1.26**
*1935 Christmas by the Sea*
Artist: Heinrich Fink
Issue price: $3.09

# GERMANY
## ROSENTHAL
### 22-R55-1.27

**22-R55-1.27**
1936 *Nurnberg Angel*
Artist: Heinrich Fink
Issue price: $3.09

**22-R55-1.28**
1937 *Berchtesgaden*
Artist: Heinrich Fink
Issue price: $3.09

**22-R55-1.29**
1938 *Christmas in the Alps*
Artist: Heinrich Fink
Issue price: $3.09

**22-R55-1.30**
1939 *Schneekoppe Mountain*
Artist: Heinrich Fink
Issue price: $3.09

**22-R55-1.31**
1940 *Marien Church in Danzig*
Artist: Walter Mutze
Issue price: $3.09

**22-R55-1.32**
1941 *Strassburg Cathedral*
Artist: Walter Mutze
Issue price: $3.09

**22-R55-1.33**
1942 *Marianburg Castle*
Artist: Walter Mutze
Issue price: $3.09

**22-R55-1.34**
1943 *Winter Idyll*
Artist: Amadeus Dier
Issue price: $3.09

**22-R55-1.35**
1944 *Wood Scape*
Artist: Willi Hein
Issue price: $3.09

**22-R55-1.36**
1945 *Christmas Peace*
Artist: Alfred Mundel
Issue price: $3.09

**22-R55-1.37**
1946 *Christmas in an Alpine Valley*
Artist: Willi Hein
Issue price: $3.09

**22-R55-1.38**
1947 *The Dillingen Madonna*
Artist: Louis Hagen
Issue price: $6.00

**22-R55-1.39**
1948 *Message to the Shepherds*
Artist: Richard Hoffman
Issue price: $6.00

**22-R55-1.40**
1949 *The Holy Family*
Artist: Prof. Karl
Issue price: $6.00

**22-R55-1.41**
1950 *Christmas in the Forest*
Artist: Willi Hein
Issue price: $5.25

**22-R55-1.42**
1951 *Star of Bethlehem*
Artist: Anne V. Groote
Issue price: $5.75

**22-R55-1.43**
1952 *Christmas in the Alps*
Artist: Willi Hein
Issue price: $5.75

**22-R55-1.44**
1953 *The Holy Light*
Artist: Willi Hein
Issue price: $5.75

# GERMANY
## ROSENTHAL

**22-R55-1.45**

**22-R55-1.45**
1954 *Christmas Eve*
Artist: Willi Hein
Issue price: $6.25

**22-R55-1.46**
1955 *Christmas in a Village*
Artist: Willi Hein
Issue price: $6.25

**22-R55-1.47**
1956 *Christmas in the Alps*
Artist: Willi Hein
Issue price: $6.25

**22-R55-1.48**
1957 *Christmas by the Sea*
Artist: Willi Hein
Issue price: $6.25

**22-R55-1.49**
1958 *Christmas Eve*
Artist: Willi Hein
Issue price: $6.50

**22-R55-1.50**
1959 *Midnight Mass*
Artist: Willi Hein
Issue price: $6.75

**22-R55-1.51**
1960 *Christmas in Small Village*
Artist: Willi Hein
Issue price: $7.25

**22-R55-1.52**
1961 *Solitary Christmas*
Artist: Willi Hein
Issue price: $7.75

**22-R55-1.53**
1962 *Christmas Eve*
Artist: Willi Hein
Issue price: $8.75

**22-R55-1.54**
*1963 Silent Night*
Artist: Willi Hein
Issue price: $8.75

**22-R55-1.55**
*1964 Christmas Market in Nurnberg*
Artist: Georg Küspert
Issue price: $8.75

**22-R55-1.56**
*1965 Christmas in Munich*
Artist: Georg Küspert
Issue price: $11.00

**22-R55-1.57**
*1966 Christmas in Ulm*
Artist: Georg Küspert
Issue price: $11.00

**22-R55-1.58**
*1967 Christmas in Regensburg*
Artist: Georg Küspert
Issue price: $11.00

**22-R55-1.59**
*1968 Christmas in Bremen*
Artist: Georg Küspert
Issue price: $11.00

**22-R55-1.60**
*1969 Christmas in Rothenburg*
Artist: Georg Küspert
Issue price: $15.75

**22-R55-1.61**
*1970 Christmas in Cologne*
Artist: Georg Küspert
Issue price: $16.00

**22-R55-1.62**
*1971 Christmas in Garmisch*
Artist: Georg Küspert
Issue price: $66.00

# GERMANY
## ROSENTHAL
### 22-R55-1.63

**22-R55-1.63**
1972 *Christmas Celebration in Franconia*
Artist: Georg Küspert
Issue price: $66.00

**22-R55-1.64**
1973 *Christmas in Lübeck-Holstein*
Artist: Georg Küspert
Issue price: $84.00

**22-R55-1.65**
1974 *Christmas in Wurzburg*
Artist: Georg Küspert
Issue price: $85.00

**22-R55-1.66**
1974 *Memorial Church in Berlin*
Artist: Helmut Drexler
Issue price: $84.00

**22-R55-1.67**
1975 *Freiburg Cathedral*
Artist: Helmut Drexler
Issue price: $75.00

**22-R55-1.68**
1976 *The Castle Cochem*
Artist: Helmut Drexler
Issue price: $95.00

**22-R55-1.69**
1977 *Hannover Town Hall*
Artist: Helmut Drexler
Issue price: $125.00

**22-R55-1.70**
1978 *Cathedral at Aachen*
Artist: Helmut Drexler
Issue price: $150.00

**22-R55-1.71**
1979 *Cathedral in Luxemburg*
Artist: Helmut Drexler
Issue price: $165.00

**22-R55-1.72**
1980 *Christmas in Brussels*
Artist: Helmut Drexler
Issue price: $190.00

**22-R55-1.73**
1981 *Christmas in Trier*
Artist: Helmut Drexler
Issue price: $190.00

**22-R55-1.74**
1982 *Milan Cathedral*
Artist: Helmut Drexler
Issue price: $190.00

**22-R55-1.75**
1983 *Church at Castle Wittenberg*
Artist: Helmut Drexler
Issue price: $195.00

**22-R55-1.76**
1984 *City Hall of Stockholm*
Artist: Helmut Drexler
Issue price: $195.00

**22-R55-1.77**
1985 *Christmas in Augsburg*
Artist: Helmut Drexler
Issue price: $195.00

**22-R55-1.78**
1986 *Christmas in Amsterdam*
Artist: Helmut Drexler
Issue price: $210.00

**22-R55-1.79**
1987 *National Theatre of Munich in the
19th Century*
Artist: Helmut Drexler
Issue price: $210.00

# GERMANY
## ROSENTHAL

### 22-R55-2.1

*Wiinblad Christmas Series*

Artist: Bjørn Wiinblad. Artist's signature appears on front

Overglaze-decorated porcelain partially hand-painted in 18 colors with 18k gold design on border

Diameter: 29.2 centimeters (11½ inches)

Attached back hanger

Edition size undisclosed

Not numbered, without certificate

**22-R55-2.1**
1971 *Maria and Child*
Issue price: $100.00

**22-R55-2.2**
1972 *Caspar*
Issue price: $100.00

**22-R55-2.3**
1973 *Melchior*
Issue price: $125.00

**22-R55-2.4**
1974 *Balthazar*
Issue price: $125.00

**22-R55-2.5**
1975 *The Annunciation*
Issue price: $195.00

**22-R55-2.6**
1976 *Angel with Trumpet*
Issue price: $195.00

**22-R55-2.7**
1977 *Adoration of the Shepherds*
Issue price: $225.00

**22-R55-2.8**
1978 *Angel with Harp*
Issue price: $275.00

**22-R55-2.9**
1979 *Exodus from Egypt*
Issue price: $310.00

**22-R55-2.10**
1980 *Angel with a Glockenspiel*
Issue price: $360.00

**22-R55-2.11**
1981 *Christ Child Visits Temple*
Issue price: $375.00

**22-R55-2.12**
1982 *Christening of Christ*
Issue price: $375.00
*Series Closed*

## The Nobility of Children Series

Artist: Edna Hibel. Artist's signature appears on front

Overglaze-decorated porcelain banded in gold

Diameter: 25.4 centimeters (10 inches)

Attached back hanger

Edition size limited to 12,750

Numbered with certificate

**22-R55-6.1**
1976 *La Contessa Isabella*
Issue price: $120.00

**22-R55-6.2**
1977 *Le Marquis Maurice-Pierre*
Issue price: $120.00

# GERMANY
## ROSENTHAL

**22-R55-6.3**

**22-R55-6.3**
1978 *Baronesse Johanna-Maryke Van Vollendam Tot Marken*
Issue price: $130.00

**22-R55-6.4**
1979 *Chief Red Feather*
Issue price: $140.00
*Series Closed*

## Oriental Gold Series

Artist: Edna Hibel. Artist's signature appears on front

Overglaze-decorated porcelain highlighted in gold

Diameter: 25.4 centimeters (10 inches)

Attached back hanger

Edition size limited to 2,000

Numbered with certificate

**22-R55-8.1**
1976 *Yasuko*
Issue price: $275.00

**22-R55-8.2**
1977 *Mr. Obata*
Issue price: $275.00

**22-R55-8.3**
1978 *Sakura*
Issue price: $295.00

**22-R55-8.4**
1979 *Michio*
Issue price: $325.00
*Series Closed*

**22-R58-2.7** *"Young Americans VI"*
1979 Royal Bayreuth *Mother's Day*
Luminous eyes and realistic flesh tones
characterized the artwork of the late Leo
Jansen.

# GERMANY
## ROYAL BAYREUTH

**22-R58-2.1**

## ROYAL BAYREUTH
Tettau

The pottery now known as Royal Bayreuth began in 1794 in the mountain village of Tettau as the Koniglich Privilegierter Porzellanfabrik Tettau, the first porcelain manufacturer in Bavaria. Now a subsidiary of Royal Tettau, Royal Bayreuth began its *Mother's Day* series in 1973 with art by contemporary artists. The series ended in 1982.

Brazilian Ozz Franca, a specialist in the art of children's portraiture, began the *Mother's Day* series in 1973. In 1974 Leo Jansen succeeded him as the series artist.

---

## *Mother's Day Series*

Artist: as indicated. Artist's signature appears on back until 1975; on front thereafter

Overglaze-decorated porcelain

Diameter: 19.7 centimeters (7¾ inches)

Attached back hanger

Edition size: as indicated

Numbered without certificate

**22-R58-2.1**
1973 *Consolation*
Artist: Ozz Franca/Edition: 4,000
Issue price: $16.50

**22-R58-2.2**
1974 *Young Americans*
Artist: Leo Jansen/Edition: 4,000
Issue price: $25.00

**22-R58-2.3**
1975 *Young Americans II*
Artist: Leo Jansen/Edition: 5,000
Issue price: $25.00

**22-R58-2.4**
1976 *Young Americans III*
Artist: Leo Jansen/Edition: 5,000
Issue price: $30.00

**22-R58-2.5**
1977 *Young Americans IV*
Artist: Leo Jansen/Edition: 5,000
Issue price: $40.00

**22-R58-2.6**
1978 *Young Americans V*
Artist: Leo Jansen/Edition: 5,000
Issue price: $45.00

**22-R58-2.7**
1979 *Young Americans VI*
Artist: Leo Jansen/Edition: 5,000
Issue price: $60.00

**22-R58-2.8**
1980 *Young Americans VII*
Artist: Leo Jansen/Edition: 5,000
Issue price: $65.00

**22-R58-2.9**
1981 *Young Americans VIII*
Artist: Leo Jansen/Edition: 5,000
Issue price: $65.00

**22-R58-2.10**
1982 *Young Americans IX*
Artist: Leo Jansen/Edition: 5,000
Issue price: $65.00
*Series Closed*

# Schmid

## SCHMID
Selb

Schmid was established in Boston in the 1930s. Since then the firm has been a specialized importer of fine quality gifts, including collector's plates. Schmid limited-edition plates are produced by the Porzellanfabrik Johann Seltmann Vohenstrauss GmbH factory in Germany.

Both the *Christmas* series, which began in 1971, and the *Mother's Day* series, which started the following year, feature art created by the late Berta Hummel. The Hummel plates bear her signature depending on whether Berta Hummel had signed the original artwork.

Both Hummel series feature art created by Berta Hummel before she entered the Franciscan order at Siessen in 1934 and took the name Sister Maria Innocentia Hummel (see Germany, GOEBEL). Prior to taking her vows, she had received extensive training at art academies in Simbach and Munich, where she evolved the distinctive style that instantly identifies her work to collectors worldwide.

## Christmas Series

Artist: Berta Hummel. Artist's signature or initials appear on front from 1971 through 1974, 1976 and 1978 through 1980

Overglaze-decorated porcelain

Diameter: 19.7 centimeters (7¾ inches)

Attached back hanger

Edition size undisclosed, limited by year of issue

Not numbered, without certificate

**22-S12-1.1**
1971 *Angel in a Christmas Setting*
Issue price: $15.00

**22-S12-1.2**
1972 *Angel with Flute*
Issue price: $15.00

**22-S12-1.3**
1973 *The Nativity*
Issue price: $15.00

**22-S12-1.4**
1974 *The Guardian Angel*
Issue price: $18.50

**22-S12-1.5**
1975 *Christmas Child*
Issue price: $25.00

**22-S12-1.6**
1976 *Sacred Journey*
Issue price: $27.50

**22-S12-1.7**
1977 *Herald Angel*
Issue price: $27.50

**22-S12-1.8**
1978 *Heavenly Trio*
Issue price: $32.50

# GERMANY
## SCHMID

**22-S12-1.9**

**22-S12-1.9**
1979 *Starlight Angel*
Issue price: $38.00

**22-S12-1.10**
1980 *Parade into Toyland*
Issue price: $45.00

**22-S12-1.11**
1981 *A Time to Remember*
Issue price: $45.00

**22-S12-1.12**
1982 *Angelic Procession*
Issue price: $45.00

**22-S12-1.13**
1983 *Angelic Messenger*
Issue price: $45.00

**22-S12-1.14**
1984 *A Gift from Heaven*
Issue price: $45.00

**22-S12-1.15**
1985 *Heavenly Light*
Issue price: $45.00

**22-S12-1.16**
1986 *Tell the Heavens*
Issue price: $45.00

**22-S12-1.17**
1987 *Angelic Gift*
Issue price: $47.50

## Mother's Day Series

Artist: Berta Hummel. Artist's signature or initials appear on front from 1972 thru 1975, and 1977

Overglaze-decorated porcelain

Diameter: 19.7 centimeters (7¾ inches)

Attached back hanger

Edition size undisclosed, limited by year of issue

Not numbered, without certificate

**22-S12-2.1**
1972 *Playing Hooky*
Issue price: $15.00

**22-S12-2.2**
1973 *The Little Fisherman*
Issue price: $15.00

**22-S12-2.3**
1974 *The Bumblebee*
Issue price: $18.50

**22-S12-2.4**
1975 *Message of Love*
Issue price: $25.00

**22-S12-2.5**
1976 *Devotion for Mother*
Issue price: $27.50

**22-S12-2.6**
1977 *Moonlight Return*
Issue price: $27.50

**22-S12-2.7**
1978 *Afternoon Stroll*
Issue price: $32.50

**22-S12-2.8**
1979 *Cherub's Gift*
Issue price: $38.00

# GERMANY
## SCHMID
**22-S12-2.9**

**22-S12-2.9**
1980 *Mother's Little Helpers*
Issue price: $45.00

**22-S12-2.10**
1981 *Playtime*
Issue price: $45.00

**22-S12-2.11**
1982 *The Flower Basket*
Issue price: $45.00

**22-S12-2.12**
1983 *Spring Bouquet*
Issue price: $45.00

**22-S12-2.13**
1984 *A Joy to Share*
Issue price: $45.00

**22-S12-2.14**
1985 *A Mother's Journey*
Issue price: $45.00

**22-S12-2.15**
1986 *Home from School*
Issue price: $45.00

**22-S12-2.16**
1987 *Mother's Little Learner*
Issue price: $47.50

**22-T40-1.1** ''Blue Titmouse''
1985 Tirschenreuth *Band's Songbirds of Europe*
Evolving from her many years as a porcelain artist of some renown, German artist Ursula Band's approach to nature painting is scrupulously accurate, yet highly personal. This is her first work in the medium of collector's plates.

## TIRSCHENREUTH
Tirschenreuth

Since production of Tirschenreuth china began in 1838, Porzellanfabrik Tirschenreuth has continued to create magnificent porcelain objects for discerning collectors on five continents, including royalty and heads of state.

Their first entry into the limited-edition plate field is the series entitled *Band's Songbirds of Europe.*

It was created by artist Ursula Band, a native of Meissen, Germany, who received her professional training at the prestigious Painting and Drawing School of the Meissen State Porcelain Factory. In her first series, Frau Band has chosen to portray the songbirds which surround her home in Germany.

The series is the first depicting birds in their natural habitats to be produced under the auspices of the World Wildlife Fund, whose international president is H.R.H. The Duke of Edinburgh, Prince Philip, of Great Britain.

## Band's Songbirds of Europe Series

Artist: Ursula Band. Artist's signature appears on front

Overglaze-decorated porcelain banded in 22k gold

Diameter: 19 centimeters (7½ inches)

No hanger

Edition size undisclosed, limited by announced period of issue

Numbered with certificate

**22-T40-1.1**
1985 *Blue Titmouse*
Issue price: $19.50

**22-T40-1.2**
1986 *Firecrest*
Issue price: $19.50

**22-T40-1.3**
1986 *Corsican Nuthatch*
Issue price: $22.50

**22-T40-1.4**
1986 *Golden Oriole*
Issue price: $22.50

**22-T40-1.5**
1987 *Great Titmouse*
Issue price: $22.50

**22-T40-1.6**
1987 *Red Robin*
Issue price: $22.50

**22-T40-1.7**
1987 *Chaffinch*
Issue price: $22.50

**22-T40-1.8**
1987 *Redstart*
Issue price: $22.50

## BELLEEK
Belleek, County Fermanagh

Belleek Pottery Ltd., maker of thin, translucent parian china, was established in 1857 by David Mc-Birney and Robert W. Armstrong on the banks of the River Erne near the small village of Belleek in County Fermanagh, Northern Ireland. The site is near deposits of clay discovered when the owner of Castle Caldwell in Fermanagh became interested in the brilliant whitewash used on local cottages and found that his entire estate lay on a bed of feldspar clay.

When combined with metallic washes, this clay produces the unique iridescent effect for which Belleek is known—a mother-of-pearl luster that is used on tea sets, figurines, and tableware. Queen Victoria and her son, the Prince of Wales, are among those who commissioned elaborate table services from the firm. Belleek ware is still made today much as it was a century ago.

Belleek's *Christmas* series, based on Irish subjects, began in 1970 and ended in 1977. The *Irish Wildlife Christmas* series began in 1978.

Artists for Belleek plates are not disclosed.

## Christmas Series

Artist: undisclosed

Parian china

Diameter: 21.6 centimeters
(8½ inches)

No hanger

Edition size limited to announced quantity of 7,500

Not numbered, without certificate

**26-B18-1.1**
1970 *Castle Caldwell*
Issue price: $25.00

**26-B18-1.2**
1971 *Celtic Cross*
Issue price: $25.00

**26-B18-1.3**
1972 *Flight of the Earls*
Issue price: $30.00

**26-B18-1.4**
1973 *Tribute to W. B. Yeats*
Issue price: $38.50

**26-B18-1.5**
1974 *Devenish Island*
Issue price: $45.00

**26-B18-1.6**
1975 *The Celtic Cross*
Issue price: $48.00

**26-B18-1.7**
1976 *Dove of Peace*
Issue price: $55.00

**26-B18-1.8**
1977 *Wren*
Issue price: $55.00
*Series Closed*

# GREAT BRITAIN

## BELLEEK

### 26-B18-2.1

*Irish Wildlife Christmas Series*

Artist: undisclosed

Parian china

Diameter: 22.9 centimeters
(9 inches)

No hanger

Edition size undisclosed

Not numbered, without certificate

**26-B18-2.1**
1978 *A Leaping Salmon*
Issue price: $55.00

**26-B18-2.2**
1979 *Hare at Rest*
Issue price: $58.50

**26-B18-2.3**
1980 *Hedgehog*
Issue price: $66.50

**26-B18-2.4**
1981 *Red Squirrel*
Issue price: $78.00

**26-B18-2.5**
1982 *Irish Seal*
Issue price: $78.00

**26-B18-2.6**
1983 *Red Fox*
Issue price: $85.00
*Series Closed*

**26-D8-1.1** ''Toby Fillpot''
*1984 Davenport Pottery* Toby
Created in the animated style of the famous character mugs of England, this portly, jovial fellow displays the careful modeling and hand painting that have contributed to the widespread popularity of these items. It was this selfsame Toby Fillpot who gave his name to the genre of character mugs, now called ''tobies.''

## DAVENPORT POTTERY
Staffordshire

The Davenport Pottery was founded by Arthur Wood and Son, descendants of esteemed potters who made their name and fortune by crafting Toby jugs at the close of the eighteenth century. Davenport is committed to preserving the tradition of fine British pottery, still relying on techniques that have been carefully handed down through generations of craftsmen.

With its move into the medium of limited-edition plates, The Davenport Pottery introduced, in 1983, the first collector's plate series based on the 200-year-old Toby tradition with "Toby Fillpot," the first issue in the Toby Plate Collection. Each plate in this edition is hand-cast and hand-painted by artisans using techniques that date back to the eighteenth century.

W. A. Blandford was commissioned as master modeller to design the "Toby Fillpot" plate. Subsequent plates have been modelled by Douglas Tootle.

In 1986, Davenport Pottery introduced the *Treasury of Classic Children's Verse* series, with artwork by Linda Worrall. Sponsored by the Poetry Society of London, the series depicts scenes from classic children's poems.

## Toby Plate Collection

Artist: as indicated. Artist's signature appears on front

Earthenware

Diameter: 21.6 centimeters (8½ inches)

No hanger

Edition size undisclosed, limited by announced period of issue

Numbered with certificate

**26-D8-1.1**
1984 *Toby Fillpot*
Artist: Wilfred Blandford
Issue price: $35.00

**26-D8-1.2**
1984 *Falstaff*
Artist: Douglas Tootle
Issue price: $35.00

**26-D8-1.3**
1985 *Jack Tar*
Artist: Douglas Tootle
Issue price: $40.00

**26-D8-1.4**
1986 *Mr. Pickwick*
Artist: Douglas Tootle
Issue price: $40.00

**26-D8-1.5**
1986 *Friar Tuck*
Artist: Douglas Tootle
Issue price: $40.00

**26-D8-1.6**
1986 *Long John Silver*
Artist: Douglas Tootle
Issue price: $40.00

# GREAT BRITAIN
## DAVENPORT POTTERY

### 26-D8-2.1

*Treasury of Classic Children's Verse Series*

Artist: Linda Worrall. Artist's signature appears on front

Earthenware

Diameter: 21.6 centimeters (8½ inches)

No hanger

Edition size undisclosed, limited by announced period of issue

Numbered with certificate

**26-D8-2.1**
1986 *All Things Bright and Beautiful*
Issue price: $29.00

**22-D8-2.2**
1986 *Pirate's Story*
Issue price: $29.00

**26-D8-2.3**
1986 *The Star*
Issue price: $29.00

**26-D8-2.4**
1987 *Animal Crackers*
Issue price: $29.00

**26-L46-1.4** "The Wife of Bath's Tale"
1982 Longton Crown *Canterbury Tales*
The Canterbury Tales, written by poet
Geoffrey Chaucer in the late 14th century,
helped earn him the reputation as the
most important figure in English literature
before Shakespeare. The tales—some rich
with morals, some full of ribaldry, but all
entertaining—are told by pilgrims travel-
ling together from London to the shrine of
St. Thomas at Canterbury. The vivid nar-
rative style of Chaucer's masterpiece is
well-captured visually by contemporary
artist G. A. Hoover in this Longton Crown
series.

## LONGTON CROWN POTTERY
Longton, Stoke-on-Trent, Staffordshire

Longton Crown Pottery maintains a long tradition of quality English bone china manufacture. Josiah Spode perfected the process by which animal bone ash is added to china clay to produce bone china, which is creamy white and translucent. His formula came to be known as English bone china and remains the standard today.

Longton Crown Pottery began its first Baronet bone china collector's plate series in 1981 with *The Canterbury Tales* collection, interpreting Geoffrey Chaucer's literary classic of the same name, and with the sponsorship of the Centre for Medieval & Renaissance Studies of Oxford, England. The series ended in 1982.

The artist for the series was G. A. Hoover.

## The Canterbury Tales Collection

Artist: G. A. Hoover. Artist's signature appears on front

Baronet bone china

Diameter: 21.6 centimeters (8½ inches)

No hanger

Edition size undisclosed, limited by announced period of issue

Numbered with certificate

**26-L46-1.1**
1981 *The Man of Law's Tale*
Issue price: $29.80

**26-L46-1.2**
1982 *The Franklin's Tale*
Issue price: $29.80

**26-L46-1.3**
1982 *The Knight's Tale*
Issue price: $31.80

**26-L46-1.4**
1982 *The Wife of Bath's Tale*
Issue price: $31.80
*Series Closed*

# GREAT BRITAIN
## ROYAL DOULTON

**26-R62-0.0**

## ROYAL DOULTON
Burslem, Stoke-on-Trent, Staffordshire

Royal Doulton dates from 1815, when a potter named John Doulton invested his life savings of £100 in a one-kiln pottery in the Lambeth section of London.

At the International Exhibition of 1871, John's son Henry Doulton exhibited many of his experimental art pieces. Their favorable reception led to the development of decorative ceramics whose extensive range of colors and decorative techniques ultimately established Doulton Lambethware as an art form.

In 1877, Henry Doulton turned his attention to the development of tableware. At a small earthenware factory in Burslem, Staffordshire, table services for everyday use were produced along with more costly services with raised gold and acid-etched decorations, often combined with the finest of hand painting. Queen Victoria conferred knighthood upon Henry Doulton in 1887 for his accomplishments in the area of ceramic techniques, thus making him the first potter in England to receive such an honor. In 1901 the company received its first Royal warrant, and was henceforth known, by Royal Command, as *Royal Doulton.*

The *Beswick Christmas* series, sponsored by Royal Doulton's Beswick Potteries from 1972 to 1978, depicted Christmas traditions from around the world. The Collector's International Gallery of "Fine Art on Fine China" began with the *Mother and Child* series in 1973. These plates show mothers and children of various countries. Other series in the Collector's International group are by contemporary artists and include the *Commedia Dell' Arte* series begun in 1974 and ended in 1978, and *The Log of the "Dashing Wave"* series which began in 1976 and ended in 1982. The *Valentine's Day* series also began in 1976 with artwork from Victorian prints. The series ended in 1985. In 1980 Royal Doulton began the *Portraits of Innocence* series. The series ended in 1983.

Royal Doulton has recruited several important artists to design its collector's plates. Among them are John Stobart, Edna Hibel, LeRoy Neiman and Francisco J. J. C. Masseria.

## Beswick Christmas Series

Artist: as indicated

Earthenware in hand-cast bas-relief, hand-painted in 15 colors

Diameter: 20.5 centimeters square (8 inches square)

Pierced foot rim

Edition size limited to 15,000

Not numbered, without certificate

**26-R62-1.1**
1972 *Christmas in England*
Artist: Harry Sales
Issue price: $35.00

**26-R62-1.2**
1973 *Christmas in Mexico*
Artist: Chavela Castrejon
Issue price: $37.50

**26-R62-1.3**
1974 *Christmas in Bulgaria*
Artist: Dimitri Yordanov
Issue price: $37.50

**26-R62-1.4**
1975 *Christmas in Norway*
Artist: Alton Toby
Issue price: $45.00

**26-R62-1.5**
1976 *Christmas in Holland*
Artist: Alton Toby
Issue price: $50.00

**26-R62-1.6**
1977 *Christmas in Poland*
Artist: Alton Toby
Issue price: $50.00

**26-R62-1.7**
1978 *Christmas in America*
Artist: Alton Toby
Issue price: $55.00
*Series Closed*

# GREAT BRITAIN
## ROYAL DOULTON

### 26-R62-2.1

#### *Mother and Child Series*

Artist: Edna Hibel. Artist's signature appears on front

Bone china banded in gold

Diameter: 21 centimeters (8¼ inches)

No hanger

Edition size limited to 15,000

Numbered since 1974, without certificate

**26-R62-2.1**
1973 *Colette and Child*
Issue price: $40.00

**26-R62-2.2**
1974 *Sayuri and Child*
Issue price: $40.00

**26-R62-2.3**
1975 *Kristina and Child*
Issue price: $50.00

**26-R62-2.4**
1976 *Marilyn and Child*
Issue price: $55.00

**26-R62-2.5**
1977 *Lucia and Child*
Issue price: $60.00

**26-R62-2.6**
1978 *Kathleen and Child*
Issue price: $85.00
*Series Closed*

## Commedia Dell' Arte Series

Artist: LeRoy Neiman. Artist's signature appears on front

Bone china banded in gold

Diameter: 25.4 centimeters (10 inches)

No hanger

Edition size limited to 15,000

Numbered without certificate

**26-R62-3.1**
1974 *Harlequin*
Issue price: $50.00

**26-R62-3.2**
1975 *Pierrot*
Issue price: $60.00

**26-R62-3.3**
1977 *Columbine*
Issue price: $70.00

**26-R62-3.4**
1978 *Punchinello*
Issue price: $70.00
*Series Closed*

## The Log of the "Dashing Wave" Series

Artist: John Stobart. Artist's signature appears on front

Bone china banded in gold

Diameter: 26.7 centimeters (10½ inches)

No hanger

Edition size limited to 15,000

Numbered without certificate

**26-R62-6.1**
1976 *Sailing with the Tide*
Issue price: $65.00

**26-R62-6.2**
1977 *Running Free*
Issue price: $70.00

## ROYAL DOULTON

### 26-R62-6.3

**26-R62-6.3**
1978 *Rounding the Horn*
Issue price: $70.00

**26-R62-6.4**
1979 *Hong Kong*
Issue price: $75.00

**26-R62-6.5**
1981 *Bora Bora*
Issue price: $95.00

**26-R62-6.6**
1982 *Journey's End*
Issue price: $95.00
*Series Closed*

## Valentine's Day Series

Artist: unknown. Reproduced from nineteenth-century Victorian prints

Bone china banded in gold

Diameter: 21 centimeters (8¼ inches)

No hanger

Edition size undisclosed, limited by period of issue

Not numbered, without certificate

**26-R62-7.1**
1976 *Victorian Boy and Girl*
Issue price: $25.00

**26-R62-7.2**
1977 *My Sweetest Friend*
Issue price: $25.00

**26-R62-7.3**
1978 *If I Loved You*
Issue price: $25.00

**26-R62-7.4**
1979 *My Valentine*
Issue price: $29.95

**26-R62-7.5**
1980 *On a Swing*
Issue price: $32.95

**26-R62-7.6**
1981 *Sweet Music*
Issue price: $35.00

**26-R62-7.7**
1982 *From My Heart*
Issue price: $40.00

**26-R62-7.8**
1983 *Cherub's Song*
Issue price: $40.00

**26-R62-7.9**
1984 *Love in Bloom*
Issue price: $40.00

**26-R62-7.10**
1985 *With Loving Care*
Issue price: $40.00
*Series Closed*

# GREAT BRITAIN
## ROYAL DOULTON

### 26-R62-11.1

*Portraits of Innocence Series*

Artist: Francisco Masseria. Artist's signature appears on front

Bone china banded in gold

Diameter: 20.3 centimeters (8 inches)

No hanger

Edition size limited to 15,000

Numbered without certificate

**26-R62-11.1**
1980 *Panchito*
Issue price: $75.00

**26-R62-11.2**
1981 *Adrien*
Issue price: $85.00

**26-R62-11.3**
1982 *Angelica*
Issue price: $95.00

**26-R62-11.4**
1983 *Juliana*
Issue price: $95.00
*Series Closed*

**26-R65-2.1** "Pheasants in Flight"
1987 Royal Grafton *Braithwaite Game Birds Collection*
With the introduction of this series in 1987, Royal Grafton earned its first Bradex listing on the international market. This vivid and realistic depiction of game birds by British artist Derek Braithwaite is enhanced by a final glaze firing, which is somewhat unusual among overglaze-decorated issues.

## ROYAL GRAFTON CHINA
Longton, Stoke-on-Trent

It was in 1876 that Albert B. Jones started his first factory, Grafton China Works. Demand for his products was so strong that on January 1, 1900, Jones took into partnership his two sons and, at the same time, moved to a new factory on the present site in Longton, Stoke-on-Trent.

The firm, which had changed its name to A. B. Jones & Sons, then announced that it "still makes tea and breakfast sets for the Home, Colonial and American market." By 1906, A. B. Jones & Sons had diversified, making a special line of miniature coat-of-arms china. The demand for these hand-painted commemorative items lasted well into the 1920s; today, they are still highly sought-after as collector's pieces.

During the next thirty years, the firm specialized in quality tea sets and distinctive hand-painted decorated items. In 1956, a line of dinnerware was reintroduced, Today, the firm is recognized as an established maker of fine English bone china dinnerware and giftware. Royal Grafton offered its first limited-edition collector's plate series to the worldwide market with the 1987 introduction of the *Braithwaite Game Birds Collection* by the accomplished British wildlife illustrator Derek Braithwaite.

## *Braithwaite Game Birds Collection*

Artist: Derek Braithwaite. Artist's signature appears on front

Overglaze-decorated bone china

Diameter: 21.6 centimeters (8½ inches)

No hanger

Edition size undisclosed, limited by announced period of issue

Numbered, with certificate

**26-R65-2.1**
1987 *Pheasants in Flight*
Issue price unavailable
at press time

**26-R76-0.0**

ROYAL
WORCESTER
CROWN WARE
ENGLAND

MADE IN ENGLAND

## ROYAL WORCESTER
Worcester

The Worcester Porcelain Company, the oldest porcelain manufactory in England today, was established in Worcester, England, in 1751. Two of its original stockholders—Dr. John Wall, a physician and an amateur artist, and William Davis, an apothecary—are credited with perfecting a formula for making soft-paste porcelain from soapstone (steatite). Their formula was used until the introduction of bone china in the 19th century.

In 1788, King George III gave the company permission to call itself "Manufacturers to Their Majesties." After undergoing a number of changes in ownership, the firm was reorganized in 1862 as the Royal Worcester Porcelain Company in recognition of its long history of royal patronage. More recently, in 1976, Royal Worcester merged with Spode; however, each company has retained its own trademark.

In the early days of limited-edition plate collecting, Royal Worcester produced a few series for the U.S. market, which can now be found in the OVER-THE-COUNTER SECTION at the back of this book. The firm's newest plate series, begun in 1987, is titled *Happy England* and features scenes of 19th-century country life, created with a light touch by artist Helen Allingham.

## Happy England Series

Artist: Helen Allingham. Artist's signature appears on front

Overglaze-decorated bone china

Diameter: 21 centimeters (8¼ inches)

No hanger

Edition size undisclosed, limited by period of issue

Numbered, with certificate

**26-R76-4.1**
1987 *Pausing at the Stile*
Issue price unavailable
at press time

## SPODE
Stoke-on-Trent, Staffordshire

Josiah Spode I established the Spode Works at Stoke-on-Trent, England, in 1776 after spending nearly 30 years learning every facet of the pottery business. From the beginning, the Spode name was highly respected, and the firm has been awarded the Royal warrant by each English monarch since George III.

Josiah Spode perfected the process by which animal bone ash is added to china clay to produce bone china, which is creamy white and translucent. His formula came to be known as English bone china and remains the standard to this day.

Upon Spode's death in 1797, his son, Josiah Spode II, continued the trade with William Copeland in charge of sales. Josiah Spode III in turn headed the business, but upon his death, Copeland became sole owner. From 1827 his descen-

dants operated the firm. Under their direction it was called W. T. Copeland & Sons, Ltd., but retained the Spode trademark. Between 1967 and 1976, the firm was owned by Carborundum Company, but in 1976 Spode merged with Royal Worcester of England. The Spode trademark has been retained and the present factory is located on the site of the original pottery.

Spode's bone china *Christmas* series, which began in 1970 and ended in 1981, is based on old English carols. The plate body itself reproduces an original 18th-century Spode model; the designs are based on work by Gillian West, a prominent 19th-century British ceramics artist. The 1970 and 1971 plates are decorated in gold; thereafter, decorations are in gold plus a second color which is changed every two years.

## Christmas Series

Artist: Gillian West

Bone china decorated in gold

Diameter: 20.3 centimeters
(8 inches)

No hanger

Edition size undisclosed, limited
by year of issue

Not numbered, without certificate

**26-S63-1.1**
1970 *Partridge in a Pear Tree*
Issue price: $35.00

**26-S63-1.2**
1971 *In Heaven the Angels Singing*
Issue price: $35.00

**26-S63-1.3**
1972 *We Saw Three Ships A'Sailing*
Issue price: $35.00

**26-S63-1.4**
1973 *We Three Kings of Orient Are*
Issue price: $35.00

**26-S63-1.5**
1974 *Deck the Halls*
Issue price: $35.00

**26-S63-1.6**
1975 *Christbaum*
Issue price: $45.00

**26-S63-1.7**
1976 *Good King Wenceslas*
Issue price: $45.00

**26-S63-1.8**
1977 *The Holly and the Ivy*
Issue price: $45.00

# GREAT BRITAIN
## SPODE
### 26-S63-1.9

**26-S63-1.9**
1978 *While Shepherds Watched*
Issue price: $45.00

**26-S63-1.10**
1979 *Away in a Manger*
Issue price: $50.00

**26-S63-1.11**
1980 *Bringing in the Boar's Head*
Issue price: $60.00

**26-S63-1.12**
1981 *Make We Merry*
Issue price: $65.00
*Series Closed*

**26-W90-1.1** "Windsor Castle"
1969 Wedgwood *Christmas*
**26-W90-2.1** "Sportive Love" and
**26-W90-2.11** "Mare and Foal"
1971 and 1981 Wedgwood *Mothers*
Three examples of the varied colors of
Wedgwood's vitreous, unglazed stoneware, known as Jasper ware. The white or
colored bas-relief decorations are applied
by hand.

## WEDGWOOD
Barlaston, Stoke-on-Trent, Staffordshire

Josiah Wedgwood I, Fellow of the Royal Society, is known as the "father of English potters." He founded the firm that bears his name in 1759 and built a new factory, which he called "Etruria," 10 years later.

Wedgwood himself developed many of the processes and materials used by the firm today. He is perhaps best known for his "Jasper ware," which he perfected in 1774. A vitreous, unglazed stoneware, Jasper is pure white in its original form but can be stained to produce a wide variety of colored backgrounds—green, lilac, yellow, primrose, black, and most popular of all, classic "Wedgwood blue"—onto which white or colored bas-relief decorations of the same material are applied by hand while in the "cheese hard" state. The object is then fired only once, fusing the decoration to the base object.

Although potters in England and abroad tried to duplicate Jasper ware, none was successful. To this day, the Wedgwood name is so firmly linked with Jasper that many people mistakenly think it is the only ware Wedgwood produces and that it is made only in blue.

In 1940, having outgrown the pottery at Etruria, the firm moved to what has been described as the most up-to-date pottery in the world, near the village of Barlaston, Stoke-on-Trent, Staffordshire, England. There, in 1969, the firm celebrated the 200th anniversary of the Etruria pottery by introducing a *Christmas* series of classic Wedgwood blue-and-white Jasper collector's plates commemorating famous English monuments. In 1971, Wedgwood began an annual series of *Mothers* plates made in Black Basalt ware and Jasper wares and bearing designs created in the late 18th century. *The Blossoming of Suzanne* series on Wedgwood bone china, with designs by Mary Vickers, started in 1977. The series ended in 1980. The *Mary Vickers My Memories* series began in 1981 and ended in 1986.

In 1986, the *Street Sellers of London* series was introduced with artwork by John Finnie, a tribute to 19th-century street life in Victorian London. *The Legend of King Arthur* series on Wedgwood bone china, with artwork by Richard Hook, and Mary Vickers' *Portraits of First Love* series on Queen's ware, were also introduced in 1986.

1987 was the year of introduction for *Colin Newman's Country Panorama* series, a unique collection that shows a 360-degree view of an English landscape.

Artists for Wedgwood over the past two centuries have included some of the most distinguished names in the world. William Hackwood was a modeler for Wedgwood from 1769 to 1832, and his 18th-century designs have been used on Wedgwood Jasper ware for generations. Lady Elizabeth Templetown was a designer for Wedgwood from 1783 to 1787. Most of her designs were modeled by William Hackwood. Among the renowned artists who have worked with Wedgwood over the past 40 years are Rex Whistler, Eric Ravilious, Edward Bawden, Arnold Machin, Richard Guyatt and Eduardo Paolozzi.

## Christmas Series

Artist: Tom Harper until 1978; undisclosed thereafter

Jasper stoneware

Diameter: 20.3 centimeters (8 inches)

No hanger

Edition size undisclosed, limited by year of issue

Not numbered, with certificate

**26-W90-1.1**
*1969 Windsor Castle*
Issue price: $25.00

**26-W90-1.2**
*1970 Christmas in Trafalgar Square*
Issue price: $30.00

**26-W90-1.3**
*1971 Piccadilly Circus, London*
Issue price: $30.00

**26-W90-1.4**
*1972 St. Paul's Cathedral*
Issue price: $35.00

**26-W90-1.5**
*1973 The Tower of London*
Issue price: $40.00

**26-W90-1.6**
*1974 The Houses of Parliament*
Issue price: $40.00

**26-W90-1.7**
*1975 Tower Bridge*
Issue price: $45.00

**26-W90-1.8**
*1976 Hampton Court*
Issue price: $55.00

**26-W90-1.9**
1977 *Westminster Abbey*
Issue price: $55.00

**26-W90-1.10**
1978 *The Horse Guards*
Issue price: $60.00

**26-W90-1.11**
1979 *Buckingham Palace*
Issue price: $65.00

**26-W90-1.12**
1980 *St. James Palace*
Issue price: $70.00

**26-W90-1.13**
1981 *Marble Arch*
Issue price: $75.00

**26-W90-1.14**
1982 *Lambeth Palace*
Issue price: $80.00

**26-W90-1.15**
1983 *All Souls, Langham Palace*
Issue price: $80.00

**26-W90-1.16**
1984 *Constitutional Hill*
Issue price: $80.00

**26-W90-1.17**
1985 *Tate Gallery*
Issue price: $80.00

**26-W90-1.18**
1986 *Albert Memorial*
Issue price: $80.00

## Mothers Series

Artist: as indicated

Jasper stoneware in varying colors

Diameter: 16.5 centimeters
(6½ inches)

No hanger

Edition size undisclosed, limited
by year of issue

Not numbered, without certificate

**26-W90-2.1**
1971 *Sportive Love*
Artist: Lady Elizabeth Templetown
Issue price: $20.00

**26-W90-2.2**
1972 *The Sewing Lesson*
Artist: Emma Crewe
Issue price: $20.00

**26-W90-2.3**
1973 *The Baptism of Achilles*
Artist: Lady Elizabeth Templetown
Issue price: $25.00

**26-W90-2.4**
1974 *Domestic Employment*
Artist: Lady Elizabeth Templetown
Issue price: $30.00

**26-W90-2.5**
1975 *Mother and Child*
Artist: Lady Elizabeth Templetown
Issue price: $35.00

**26-W90-2.6**
1976 *The Spinner*
Artist: William Hackwood
Issue price: $35.00

**26-W90-2.7**
1977 *Leisure Time*
Artist: William Hackwood
Issue price: $35.00

**26-W90-2.8**
1978 *Swan and Cygnets*
Artist: undisclosed
Issue price: $40.00

**26-W90-2.9**
1979 *Deer and Fawn*
Artist: undisclosed
Issue price: $45.00

**26-W90-2.10**
1980 *Birds*
Artist: undisclosed
Issue price: $47.50

**26-W90-2.11**
1981 *Mare and Foal*
Artist: undisclosed
Issue price: $50.00

**26-W90-2.12**
1982 *Cherubs with Swing*
Artist: undisclosed
Issue price: $55.00

**26-W90-2.13**
1983 *Cupid and Butterfly*
Artist: undisclosed
Issue price: $55.00

**26-W90-2.14**
1984 *Cupid and Music*
Artist: undisclosed
Issue price: $55.00

**26-W90-2.15**
1985 *Cupid and Doves*
Artist: undisclosed
Issue price: $55.00

**26-W90-2.16**
1986 *Cupids at Play*
Artist: undisclosed
Issue price: $55.00

**26-W90-2.17**
1987 *Anemones*
Artist: undisclosed
Issue price: $55.00

## Blossoming of Suzanne Series

Artist: Mary Vickers. Artist's signature appears on front

Bone china banded in gold

Diameter: 23.5 centimeters (9¼ inches)

No hanger

Edition size limited to 17,000 in 1977; 24,000 thereafter

Numbered with certificate

**26-W90-4.1**
1977 *Innocence*
Issue price: $60.00

**26-W90-4.2**
1978 *Cherish*
Issue price: $60.00

**26-W90-4.3**
1979 *Daydream*
Issue price: $65.00

**26-W90-4.4**
1980 *Wistful*
Issue price: $70.00
*Series Closed*

# GREAT BRITAIN
## WEDGWOOD

### 26-W90-5.1

*Mary Vickers My Memories Series*

Artist: Mary Vickers. Artist's signature appears on front

Queensware banded in gold

Diameter: 20.3 centimeters (8 inches)

No hanger

Edition size undisclosed, limited by announced period of issue

Numbered with certificate

**26-W90-5.1**
1981 *Be My Friend*
Issue price: $27.00

**26-W90-5.2**
1982 *Playtime*
Issue price: $27.00

**26-W90-5.3**
1983 *Our Garden*
Issue price: $27.00

**26-W90-5.4**
1984 *The Recital*
Issue price: $27.00

**26-W90-5.5**
1985 *Mother's Treasures*
Issue price: $29.00

**26-W90-5.6**
1986 *Riding High*
Issue price: $29.00
*Series Closed*

## Street Sellers of London Series

Artist: John Finnie. Artist's signature appears on front

Bone china

Diameter: 21.3 centimeters (8⅜ inches)

No hanger

Edition size undisclosed, limited by announced period of issue

Numbered with certificate

**26-W90-10.1**
1986 *The Baked Potato Man*
Issue price: $25.00

**26-W90-10.2**
1986 *Street Seller of Hot Elder Wine*
Issue price: $25.00

**26-W90-10.3**
1986 *Ginger Beer Fountain*
Issue price: $25.00

**26-W90-10.4**
1986 *Street Seller of Green Peas*
Issue price: $25.00

**26-W90-10.5**
1986 *Water Carrier*
Issue price: $25.00

**26-W90-10.6**
1986 *Street Seller of Fried Fish*
Issue price: $25.00

**26-W90-10.7**
1986 *The Milk Man*
Issue price: $25.00

**26-W90-10.8**
1986 *The Bread Roundsman*
Issue price: $25.00

# GREAT BRITAIN
## WEDGWOOD

### 26-W90-17.1

*The Legend of King Arthur Series*

Artist: Richard Hook. Artist's signature appears on front

Bone china

Diameter: 23 centimeters (9 inches)

No hanger

Edition size undisclosed, limited by announced period of issue

Numbered with certificate

**26-W90-17.1**
1986 *Arthur Draws the Sword*
Issue price: $39.00

**26-W90-17.2**
1986 *Arthur Is Crowned King*
Issue price: $39.00

**26-W90-17.3**
1987 *Excalibur*
Issue price: $39.00

## Portraits of First Love Series

Artist: Mary Vickers. Artist's signature appears on front

Queensware

Diameter: 21.6 centimeters (8½ inches)

No hanger

Edition size undisclosed, limited by announced period of issue

Numbered with certificate

**26-W90-18.1**
1986 *The Love Letter*
Issue price: $27.00

**26-W90-18.2**
1986 *The Ring*
Issue price: $27.00

**26-W90-18.3**
1986 *The Gift*
Issue price: $27.00

**26-W90-18.4**
1986 *The Pearls*
Issue price: $27.00

## Colin Newman's Country Panorama Series

Artist: Colin Newman. Artist's signature appears on front

Overglaze-decorated bone china

Diameter: 21 centimeters (8¼ inches)

No hanger

Edition size undisclosed, limited by announced period of issue

Numbered, with certificate

**26-W90-27.1**
1986 *Meadows and Wheatfields*
Issue price unavailable
at press time

**26-W90-27.2**
1987 *The Meandering Stream*
Issue price unavailable
at press time

# ITALY
## ANRI

**38-A54-0.0**

Exclusively through Schmid

## ANRI
Santa Christina

The House of Anri, which claims to be the world's largest woodcarving manufactory, is a family firm that was established in 1916 by Anton Riffeser, Sr. It is now headed by his grandson, Ernst Riffeser. The factory is located in the Tyrolean Alps, an area with a long tradition of wood carving.

Anri's *Christmas* series began in 1971. Using a material known as "toriart," the plates are handcrafted in wood material and hand-painted to produce a three-dimensional effect. Each plate is mounted in a circular European maple frame.

A master woodcarver from Saint Ulrich, Italy, Josef Malfertheiner is the predominant artist who produces this series.

## Christmas Series

Artist: Josef Malfertheiner until 1978; undisclosed thereafter

Hand-painted molded wood material

Diameter: 30.5 centimeters (12 inches)

Attached back hanger

Edition size limited to 10,000 until 1976; 6,000 thereafter

Numbered since 1972, without certificate

**38-A54-1.1**
1971 *St. Jakob in Gröden*
Issue price: $37.50

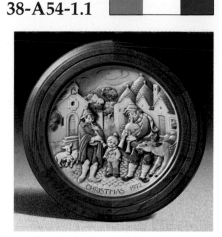

**38-A54-1.2**
1972 *Pipers at Alberobello*
Issue price: $45.00

**38-A54-1.3**
1973 *Alpine Horn*
Issue price: $45.00

**38-A54-1.4**
1974 *Young Man and Girl*
Issue price: $50.00

**38-A54-1.5**
1975 *Christmas in Ireland*
Issue price: $60.00

**38-A54-1.6**
1976 *Alpine Christmas*
Issue price: $65.00

**38-A54-1.7**
1977 *Legend of Heiligenblut*
Issue price: $65.00

**38-A54-1.8**
1978 *The Klöckler Singers*
Issue price: $80.00

**38-A54-1.9**
1979 *The Moss Gatherers of Villnoess*
Issue price: $135.00

**38-A54-1.10**
1980 *Wintry Church-going in Santa Christina*
Issue price: $165.00

**38-A54-1.11**
1981 *Santa Claus in Tyrol*
Issue price: $165.00

**38-A54-1.12**
1982 *Star Singers*
Issue price: $165.00

**38-A54-1.13**
1983 *Unto Us a Child Is Born*
Issue price: $165.00

**38-A54-1.14**
1984 *Yuletide in the Valley*
Issue $165.00

**38-A54-1.15**
1985 *Good Morning, Good Cheer*
Issue price: $165.00

**38-A54-1.16**
1986 *A Gröden Christmas*
Issue price $165.00

**38-A54-1.17**
1987 *Down From the Alps*
Issue price: $195.00

**38-K32-2.5** ''Anemones''
*1977 King's* Flowers of America
These plates are among the few in the
market to have such high-relief decoration,
carefully hand-applied. They are also
hand-painted. The level of handwork
made them difficult to produce; they were
issued in an extremely limited edition of
1,000.

## KING'S
Usmate, Milan

King's Porcelain was established in the original Giuseppe Cappe factory in the 1960s. The factory had been known for its Cappe figurines of which King's has retained the original molds.

King's *Flowers of America* series began in 1973 and ended in 1977.

Chief sculptor for King's Porcelain is the Italian artist Aldo Falchi, who studied sculpture in Milan and later collaborated with Bjørn Wiinblad on works for Rosenthal of Germany. Some of his pieces in terra cotta can be found in Verona, Mantova and Bozzolo, Italy.

## Flowers of America Series

Artist: Aldo Falchi. Artist's signature appears on back since 1975

High-relief, hand-painted porcelain banded in gold

Diameter: 22.3 centimeters (8¾ inches)

Attached back hanger

Edition size limited to 1,000

Numbered without certificate

**38-K32-2.1**
*1973 Pink Carnation*
Issue price: $85.00

**38-K32-2.2**
*1974 Red Roses*
Issue price: $100.00

**38-K32-2.3**
*1975 Yellow Dahlia*
Issue price: $110.00

**38-K32-2.4**
*1976 Bluebells*
Issue price: $130.00

**38-K32-2.5**
*1977 Anemones*
Issue price: $130.00
*Series Closed*

# ITALY
## LE PORCELLANE FONTANA DEI MEDICI

**38-P63-0.0**

## LE PORCELLANE FONTANA DEI MEDICI
Verona

The artistic heritage of Le Porcellane Fontana dei Medici dates back four centuries, to 1575. In that year, the Florentines, Orazio Fontana and Bernardo Buontalenti, with the patronage of the powerful Francesco de Medici, succeeded in creating the first soft-paste porcelain ever made in Europe. The very few examples of this early porcelain known to exist today are in private collections or museums.

*The Women of Puccini* series by master painter Riccardo Benvenuti is the first offering of Le Porcellane Fontana dei Medici in the collector's plate medium. *The Women of Puccini* series was initiated in 1986. This historic series presents a full-color gallery of six heroines from Puccini's immortal grand operas.

## The Women of Puccini Series

Artist: Riccardo Benvenuti. Artist's signature appears on front

Porcelain banded in 24k gold

Diameter: 21 centimeters (8¼ inches)

No hanger

Edition size undisclosed, limited by announced period of issue

Numbered with certificate

**38-P63-1.1**
1986 *Musetta*
Issue price: $39.00

**38-P63-1.2**
1986 *Mimi*
Issue price: $39.00

**38-P63-1.3**
1986 *Manon*
Issue price: $39.00

**38-P63-1.4**
1986 *Madama Butterfly*
Issue price: $39.00

**38-P63-1.5**
1987 *Tosca*
Issue price: $39.00

**38-P63-1.6**
1987 *Turandot*
Issue price: $39.00
*Series Closed*

# ITALY
## VENETO FLAIR

**38-A54-0.0**

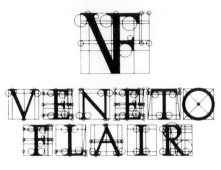

## VENETO FLAIR
Treviso

Veneto Flair was established in 1946 by a consortium of potters and painters. Creative World of White Plains, New York, acts as importer and distributor of Veneto Flair collector's plates.

A centuries-old technique is used to create Veneto Flair plates. The resulting decorated and glazed earthenware is known as majolica, or faience pottery. In this ancient process, terra cotta is hand-thrown on a potter's wheel and the design is incised with a scalpel on the baked clay. Colors are then hand-applied and the plates undergo a series of paintings and firings before a final firing with a secret-formula glaze, which produces Veneto Flair's unique mosaic-effect finish.

In 1971, Veneto Flair entered the limited-edition plate market with a single issue, the Bellini "Madonna" plate. The *Last Supper* series, based on Leonardo da Vinci's painting, started in 1973. Their *St. Mark's of Venice* series began in 1984.

Born in Torgiano, Italy, Vincente Tiziano is credited with reviving ancient Etruscan techniques of ceramic production. His classical style was greatly influenced by the ceramic traditions of the 16th century. He is a recipient of the Amerigo Longhi Award from the International Ceramic Show of Deruta in the Italian province of Perugia. Many of his works are on display at the Deruta Ceramic Museum.

## Bellini Plate

Artist: Vincente Tiziano (after Bellini's *Madonna)*

Terra cotta banded in gold

Diameter: 21.6 centimeters (8½ inches)

Pierced foot rim

Edition size limited to 500

Numbered with certificate

**38-V22-1.1**
1971 *Madonna*
Issue price: $45.00
*Series Closed*

## Last Supper Series

Artist: Vincente Tiziano (after Leonardo da Vinci's *Last Supper*). Artist's signature appears on front

Terra cotta banded in gold

Diameter: 21.6 centimeters (8½ inches)

Pierced foot rim

Edition size limited to 2,000

Numbered with certificate

**38-V22-6.1**
1973 *Last Supper—Scene I*
Issue price: $100.00

**38-V22-6.2**
1973 *Last Supper—Scene II*
Issue price: $70.00

**38-V22-6.3**
1974 *Last Supper—Scene III*
Issue price: $70.00

**38-V22-6.4**
1975 *Last Supper—Scene IV*
Issue price: $70.00

**38-V22-6.5**
1976 *Last Supper—Scene V*
Issue price: $70.00
*Series Closed*

# ITALY
## VENETO FLAIR

### 38-V22-15.1

*St. Mark's of Venice Series*

Artist: Franco Lamincia.
Artist's signature appears on front

Majolica-style earthenware, hand-painted and banded in gold

Diameter: 20.3 centimeters
(8 inches)

Pierced foot rim

Edition size undisclosed, limited by year of issue

Numbered with certificate

**38-V22-15.1**
1984 *Noah and the Dove*
Issue price: $60.00

**38-V22-15.2**
1985 *Moses and the Burning Bush*
Issue price: $60.00

**38-V22-15.3**
1986 *Abraham and the Journey*
Issue price: $60.00

**38-V22-15.4**
1986 *Joseph and the Coat*
Issue price: $63.00
*Series Closed*

**38-V90-1.3** "Carmen"
**1978 di Volteradici** *Grand Opera*
The dramatic, sculptural undercarving of
this first series from Studio Dante di Volteradici shows the remarkable skill of the
Tuscan stonecarvers who created it. All di
Volteradici plates are made of ivory alabaster, which is mined from the hills that surround the studio in Italy.

# ITALY
## STUDIO DANTE DI VOLTERADICI

**38-V90-0.0**

## STUDIO DANTE DI VOLTERADICI
Toscana

Located in Tuscany, world center for the mining and carving of alabaster, the Studio Dante di Volteradici continues the Italian tradition of.alabaster sculpturing.

Di Volteradici's *Grand Opera* series, commissioned by the Museo Teatrale alla Scala to commemorate the 200th anniversary of La Scala Opera House, began in 1976 and ended in 1982. *Madonne Viventi (Living Madonnas)*, its first proprietary series, began in 1978 and ended in 1984. Their *Ghiberti Doors* series began in 1983. In 1985, they introduced a series by contemporary sculptor Sergio Benvenuti, entitled *Benvenuti's Muses.*

Gino Ruggeri, a sculptor in the neo-classic tradition, is best known for his work "The Crucifix," sculpted from the Casa Serena Institute of Cecina Mare, and his two sculptures, "Memorials to the Fall-en," which pay tribute to World War I victims. Now in his late 70s, Ruggeri's last completed work was the "Aida" plate. His successor as designer of the *Grand Opera* series was Franco Ingargiola, whom Ruggeri personally tutored and who worked in onyx and ceramics as well as alabaster. Alberto Santangela, current sculptor of the *Madonne Viventi* and *Ghiberti Doors* series, sculpts in the style of the Italian High Renaissance.

In 1986, Alberto Santangela created the *Renaissance Madonnas: Gifts of Maternal Love* series, the first ivory alabaster collector's plate series ever to be hand-painted. Also in 1986, *The Christmas Crèche* series was started, with designs by Ennio Furiesi in the tradition of 18th- and 19th-century Neapolitan Christmas crèche figures.

## Grand Opera Series

Artist: Gino Ruggeri through 1979; Franco Ingargiola thereafter. Artist's signature appears on front

Ivory alabaster

Diameter: 21.6 centimeters (8½ inches)

Attached back hanger

Edition size undisclosed, limited by announced period of issue

Numbered with certificate

**38-V90-1.1**
1976 *Rigoletto*
Issue price: $35.00

**38-V90-1.2**
1977 *Madama Butterfly*
Issue price: $35.00

**38-V90-1.3**
1978 *Carmen*
Issue price: $40.00

**38-V90-1.4**
1979 *Aida*
Issue price: $40.00

**38-V90-1.5**
1980 *The Barber of Seville*
Issue price: $40.00

**38-V90-1.6**
1981 *Tosca*
Issue price: $40.00

**38-V90-1.7**
1982 *I Pagliacci*
Issue price: $40.00
*Series Closed*

# ITALY
## STUDIO DANTE DI VOLTERADICI

### 38-V90-2.1

*Madonne Viventi*
(Living Madonnas)

Artist: Ado Santini in 1978;
Alberto Santangela thereafter.
Artist's signature appears on front

Ivory alabaster

Diameter: 21.6 centimeters
(8½ inches)

Attached back hanger

Edition size undisclosed, limited
by announced period of issue

Numbered with certificate

**38-V90-2.1**
1978 *Madonna Pensosa*
*(The Pensive Madonna)*
Issue price: $45.00

**38-V90-2.2**
1979 *Madonna Serena*
*(The Serene Madonna)*
Issue price: $45.00

**38-V90-2.3**
1980 *Madonna Beata*
*(The Beatific Madonna)*
Issue price: $45.00

**38-V90-2.4**
1981 *Madonna Profetica*
*(The Prophetic Madonna)*
Issue price: $45.00

**38-V90-2.5**
1982 *Madonna Modesta*
*(The Demure Madonna)*
Issue price: $45.00

**38-V90-2.6**
1983 *Madonna Saggio*
*(The Wise Madonna)*
Issue price: $45.00

**38-V90-2.7**
1984 *Madonna Tenera*
*(The Tender Madonna)*
Issue price: $45.00
*Series Closed*

## *Ghiberti Doors Series*

Artist: Alberto Santangela.
Artist's signature appears on front

Ivory alabaster

Diameter: 21.6 centimeters
(8½ inches)

Attached back hanger

Edition size undisclosed, limited
by announced period of issue

Numbered with certificate

**38-V90-3.1**
1983 *Adoration of the Magi*
Issue price: $50.00

**38-V90-3.2**
1984 *The Nativity*
Issue price: $50.00

**38-V90-3.3**
1985 *The Annunciation*
Issue price: $50.00

**38-V90-3.4**
1986 *Christ Among the Doctors*
Issue price: $55.00

**38-V90-3.5**
1986 *Christ Walks on the Water*
Issue price $55.00

**38-V90-3.6**
1986 *Christ and the Expulsion of the
Moneychangers*
Issue price: $55.00

**38-V90-3.7**
1987 *Entry Into Jerusalem*
Issue price: $55.00

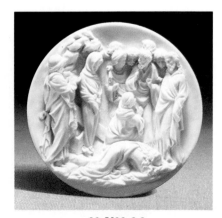

**38-V90-3.8**
1987 *The Raising of Lazarus*
Issue price: $55.00
*Series Closed*

# ITALY
## STUDIO DANTE DI VOLTERADICI

### 38-V90-4.1

*Benvenuti's Muses Series*

Artist: Sergio Benvenuti. Artist's signature appears on front

Ivory alabaster

Diameter: 21.6 centimeters (8½ inches)

Attached black hanger

Edition size undisclosed, limited by announced period of issue

Numbered with certificate

**38-V90-4.1**
1985 *Erato*
Issue price: $50.00

**38-V90-4.2**
1985 *Clio*
Issue price: $50.00

**38-V90-4.3**
1986 *Terpsichore*
Issue price: $55.00

**38-V90-4.4**
1986 *Euterpe*
Issue price: $55.00
*Series Closed*

*Renaissance Madonnas: Gifts of Maternal Love Series*

Artist: Alberto Santangela. Artist's signature appears on front

Hand-painted ivory alabaster

Diameter: 21.6 centimeters (8½ inches)

Edition size undisclosed, limited by announced period of issue

Numbered with certificate

**38-V90-5.1**
1986 *The Gift of Wisdom*
Issue price: $65.00

**38-V90-5.2**
1987 *The Gift of Faith*
Issue price: $65.00

## The Christmas Crèche Series

Artist: Ennio Furiesi. Artist's signature appears on front

Ivory alabaster

Diameter: 20.3 centimeters (8 inches)

Attached back hanger

Edition size undisclosed, limited by year of issue

Numbered with certificate

**38-V90-7.1**
1986 *Joy to the World*
Issue price: $55.00

**38-V90-7.2**
1987 *Hark, the Herald Angels Sing*
Issue price: $55.00

## FUKAGAWA
Arita

Although the present Fukagawa Porcelain factory was organized in Arita in the 1880s by the Fukagawa family, the heritage of its Izumi-stone porcelain goes back some four centuries to the discovery of kaolin deposits on the island of Kyushu, Japan. It was there, on the slopes of Mount Izumi, that the Korean master potter Yi Samp'yŏng ended his 20-year search for a pure white clay base to be used in the manufacture of fine porcelain. As the direct result of his discovery, a number of small porcelain workshops—the first in all Japan—sprang up in the nearby town of Arita. Delicate plates and saucers were being shipped to the West from the harbor city of Imari decades before porcelain manufacture began in Europe.

The establishment of Fukagawa Porcelain was actually a merger of a number of small workshops whose standards and techniques dated back to the time of Yi Samp'yŏng. In 1913, Fukagawa was granted the title "Purveyor to the Imperial Household," which indicates patronage from the royal family of Japan. In recognition of this honor, all Fukagawa ceramics bear the imprint "Imperial." The factory, which is still in the hands of the Fukagawa family, continues to employ the original Izumiyama clay from Mount Izumi to give its porcelain a uniquely white body.

In 1977, Fukagawa began its first series of collector's plates—the *Warabe No Haiku (Haiku about Children)* series. The series ended in 1980.

Master of the traditional "Sea of Whiteness" style, Suetomi is the principal artist for Fukagawa and is the recipient of the Gold Prize from Japan's Ministry of International Trade and Industry.

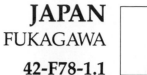

## Warabe No Haiku
*(Haiku about Children)*

Artist: Suetomi. Artist's signature and seal appear on front

Overglaze-decorated porcelain

Diameter: 26 centimeters (10¼ inches)

No hanger

Edition size undisclosed, limited by year of issue

Numbered with certificate

Original Haiku poem appears on front

**42-F78-1.1**
1977 *Beneath the Plum Branch*
Issue price: $38.00

**42-F78-1.2**
1978 *Child of Straw*
Issue price: $42.00

**42-F78-1.3**
1979 *Dragon Dance*
Issue price: $42.00

**42-F78-1.4**
1980 *Mask Dancing*
Issue price: $42.00
*Series Closed*

# Schmid

## SCHMID
Seto City

A Japanese subsidiary of Schmid (see Germany, SCHMID) produces several series of plates based on contemporary cartoon characters.

The *Peanuts Christmas* series began in 1972 and ended in 1982. The *Disney Christmas* series was introduced in 1973 and the *Disney Mother's Day* series began in 1974.

Both ended in 1982.

Cartoonist Charles Schulz, creator of the widely-syndicated cartoon strip "Peanuts," designed or approved all plates in the *Peanuts* series. Walt Disney Productions staff artists designed both *Disney* series.

## Peanuts Christmas Series

Artist: Charles Schulz. Artist's signature appears on front

Overglaze-decorated porcelain

Diameter: 19 centimeters (7½ inches)

Attached back hanger

Edition size undisclosed, limited by year of issue through 1978; 15,000 thereafter

Not numbered through 1978; numbered thereafter, without certificate

**42-S12-1.1**
1972 *Snoopy Guides the Sleigh*
Issue price: $10.00

**42-S12-1.2**
1973 *Christmas Eve at the Doghouse*
Issue price: $10.00

**42-S12-1.3**
1974 *Christmas Eve at the Fireplace*
Issue price: $10.00

**42-S12-1.4**
1975 *Woodstock, Santa Claus*
Issue price: $12.50

**42-S12-1.5**
1976 *Woodstock's Christmas*
Issue price: $13.00

**42-S12-1.6**
1977 *Deck the Doghouse*
Issue price: $13.00

**42-S12-1.7**
1978 *Filling the Stocking*
Issue price: $15.00

**42-S12-1.8**
1979 *Christmas at Hand*
Issue price: $17.50

# JAPAN
## SCHMID

**42-S12-1.9**

**42-S12-1.9**
1980 *Waiting for Santa*
Issue price: $17.50

**42-S12-1.10**
1981 *A Christmas Wish*
Issue price: $17.50

**42-S12-1.11**
1982 *Perfect Performance*
Issue price: $18.50
*Series Closed*

## Disney Christmas Series

Artist: undisclosed

Overglaze-decorated porcelain

Diameter: 19 centimeters
(7½ inches)

Attached back hanger

Edition size undisclosed, limited by year of issue through 1978; 15,000 thereafter

Not numbered through 1978; numbered thereafter, without certificate

**42-S12-3.1**
1973 *Sleigh Ride*
Issue price: $10.00

**42-S12-3.2**
1974 *Decorating the Tree*
Issue price: $10.00

**42-S12-3.3**
1975 *Caroling*
Issue price: $12.50

**42-S12-3.4**
1976 *Building a Snowman*
Issue price: $13.00

**42-S12-3.5**
1977 *Down the Chimney*
Issue price: $13.00

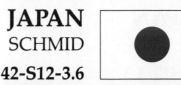

**42-S12-3.6**
1978 *Night Before Christmas*
Issue price: $15.00

**42-S12-3.7**
1979 *Santa's Surprise*
Issue price: $17.50

**42-S12-3.8**
1980 *Sleigh Ride*
Issue price: $17.50

**42-S12-3.9**
1981 *Happy Holidays*
Issue price: $17.50

**42-S12-3.10**
1982 *Winter Games*
Issue price: $18.50
*Series Closed*

## Disney Mother's Day Series

Artist: undisclosed

Overglaze-decorated porcelain

Diameter: 19 centimeters
(7½ inches)

Attached back hanger

Edition size undisclosed, limited by year of issue through 1978; 10,000 thereafter

Not numbered through 1978; numbered thereafter, without certificate

**42-S12-4.1**
1974 *Flowers for Mother*
Issue price: $10.00

**42-S12-4.2**
1975 *Snow White and the Seven Dwarfs*
Issue price: $12.50

# JAPAN
## SCHMID

**42-S12-4.3**

**42-S12-4.3**
1976 *Minnie Mouse and Friends*
Issue price: $13.00

**42-S12-4.4**
1977 *Pluto's Pals*
Issue price: $13.00

**42-S12-4.5**
1978 *Flowers for Bambi*
Issue price: $15.00

**42-S12-4.6**
1979 *Happy Feet*
Issue price: $17.50

**42-S12-4.7**
1980 *Minnie's Surprise*
Issue price: $17.50

**42-S12-4.8**
1981 *Playmates*
Issue price: $17.50

**42-S12-4.9**
1982 *A Dream Come True*
Issue price: $18.50
*Series Closed*

**54-P62-5.1** "Guests Are Coming for Christmas Eve"
1978 Porsgrund *Traditional Norwegian Christmas*
From Norway's only porcelain factory, this is the first issue in one of two Christmas series produced between 1968 and 1982. The first series shows religious scenes; this second series, called *Traditional Norwegian Christmas*, depicts landscapes and scenes of country life.

## PORSGRUND
Porsgrunn, Telemark County

Johan Jeremiason established Porsgrund, Norway's only porcelain factory, in 1885. Jeremiason began his business by importing English clay which was modeled by ceramist Carl Bauer. Porcelain tableware and decorative wares have been produced since then. Porsgrund's first collector's plate was a 1909 Christmas issue entitled "Christmas Flowers" (OTC). The series was abandoned after a single issue.

A *Christmas* series based on religious themes was introduced in 1968 and ended with the 1977 issue. The *Mother's Day* series began in 1970. In 1978 Porsgrund began a nostalgic Christmas series entitled the *Traditional Norwegian Christmas* series. The series closed in 1982.

Born in Fredrikstad, Norway, Gunnar Bratlie is a master of the traditional Norwegian folk art known as "rosemaling." He is the principal artist for Porsgrund.

## Christmas Series

Artist: Gunnar Bratlie

Porcelain decorated in cobalt blue underglaze

Diameter: 17.8 centimeters (7 inches)

Pierced foot rim

Edition size undisclosed, limited by year of issue

Not numbered, without certificate

**54-P62-1.1**
1968 *Church Scene*
Issue price: $12.00

**54-P62-1.2**
1969 *Three Kings*
Issue price: $12.00

**54-P62-1.3**
1970 *Road to Bethlehem*
Issue price: $12.00

**54-P62-1.4**
1971 *A Child Is Born in Bethlehem*
Issue price: $12.00

**54-P62-1.5**
1972 *Hark, the Herald Angels Sing*
Issue price: $12.00

**54-P62-1.6**
1973 *Promise of the Savior*
Issue price: $15.00

**54-P62-1.7**
1974 *The Shepherds*
Issue price: $15.00

**54-P62-1.8**
1975 *Jesus on the Road to the Temple*
Issue price: $19.50

# NORWAY
## PORSGRUND
### 54-P62-1.9

**54-P62-1.9**
1976 *Jesus and the Elders*
Issue price: $22.00

**54-P62-1.10**
1977 *The Draught of Fish*
Issue price: $24.00
*Series Closed*

## Mother's Day Series

Artist: Gunnar Bratlie through 1982; Thorstein Rittun thereafter

Porcelain decorated in cobalt blue underglaze

Diameter: 12.7 centimeters (5 inches)

Pierced foot rim

Edition size undisclosed, limited by year of issue

Not numbered, without certificate

**54-P62-2.1**
1970 *Mare and Foal*
Issue price: $7.50

**54-P62-2.2**
1971 *Boy and Geese*
Issue price: $7.50

**54-P62-2.3**
1972 *Doe and Fawn*
Issue price: $10.00

**54-P62-2.4**
1973 *Cat and Kittens*
Issue price: $10.00

**54-P62-2.5**
1974 *Boy and Goats*
Issue price: $10.00

**54-P62-2.6**
1975 *Dog and Puppies*
Issue price: $12.50

**54-P62-2.7**
1976 *Girl and Calf*
Issue price: $15.00

**54-P62-2.8**
1977 *Boy and Chickens*
Issue price: $16.50

**54-P62-2.9**
1978 *Girl and Pigs*
Issue price: $17.50

**54-P62-2.10**
1979 *Boy and Reindeer*
Issue price: $19.50

**54-P62-2.11**
1980 *Girl and Lambs*
Issue price: $21.50

**54-P62-2.12**
1981 *Boy and Birds*
Issue price: $24.00

**54-P62-2.13**
1982 *Girl and Rabbits*
Issue price: $26.00

**54-P62-2.14**
1983 *Mother and Kittens*
Issue price: $26.00

# NORWAY
## PORSGRUND
### 54-P62-2.15

**54-P62-2.15**
1984 *By the Pond*
Issue price: $25.00

## Traditional Norwegian Christmas Series

Artist: Gunnar Bratlie. Artist's initials appear on back

Porcelain decorated in cobalt blue underglaze

Diameter: 17.8 centimeters (7 inches)

Pierced foot rim

Edition size undisclosed, limited by year of issue

Not numbered, without certificate

**54-P62-5.1**
1978 *Guests Are Coming for Christmas Eve*
Issue price: $27.00

**54-P62-5.2**
1979 *Home for Christmas*
Issue price: $30.00

**54-P62-5.3**
1980 *Preparing for Christmas*
Issue price: $34.00

**54-P62-5.4**
1981 *Christmas Skating*
Issue price: $38.00

**54-P62-5.5**
1982 *White Christmas*
Issue price: $42.00
*Series Closed*

**72-L41-2.2** "Bird and Chicks"
1972 Lladró *Mother's Day*
Lladró's unique bas-relief plates feature
bisque-fired centers and highly-glazed
porcelain borders with a gold banded rim.

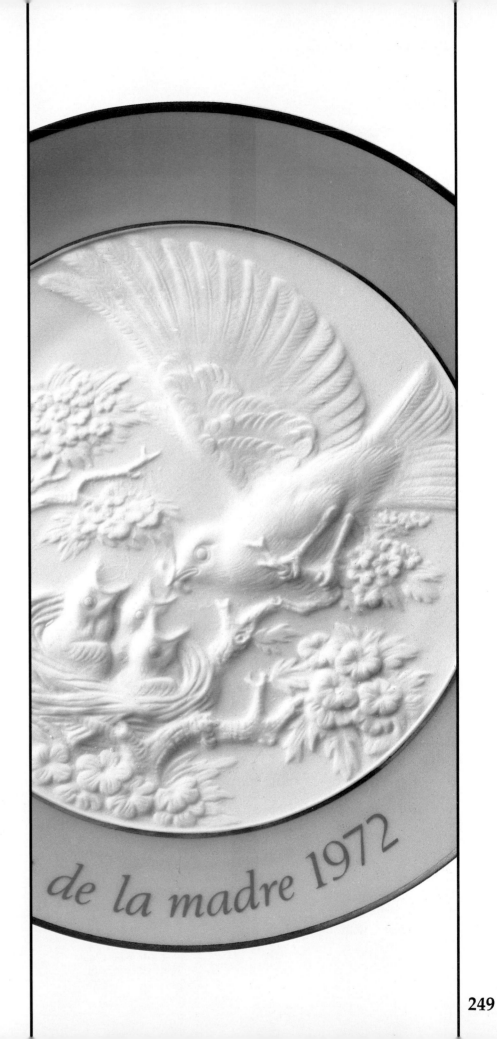

# SPAIN
## LLADRÓ

### 72-L41-2.1

**LLADRÓ**

## LLADRÓ

Tabernes Blanques, Valencia

The Lladró porcelain factory was established in the 1950s by three Lladró brothers—Juan, Jose and Vicente, sons of a peasant. At night, they studied porcelain designing, modeling and firing and built their first kiln while in their teens. By 1970, their factory was one of the best-equipped in Europe and had become known for its vases and figurines.

Lladró initiated its limited-edition *Mother's Day* series in 1971. The series closed in 1979.

Artists for Lladró plates were not disclosed.

## Mother's Day Series

Artist: undisclosed

White bisque center in bas-relief with underglaze-decorated porcelain border and banded in gold

Diameter: 20.3 centimeters (8 inches)

No hanger

Edition size undisclosed, limited by year of issue

Not numbered, without certificate

**72-L41-2.1**
1971 *Kiss of the Child*
Issue price: $27.50

**72-L41-2.2**
1972 *Bird and Chicks*
Issue price: $27.50

**72-L41-2.3**
*1973 Mother and Children*
Issue price: $35.00

**72-L41-2.4**
*1974 Mother Nursing*
Issue price: $45.00

**72-L41-2.5**
*1975 Mother and Child*
Issue price: $60.00

**72-L41-2.6**
*1976 Tender Vigil*
Issue price: $60.00

**72-L41-2.7**
*1977 Mother and Daughter*
Issue price: $67.50

**72-L41-2.8**
*1978 The New Arrival*
Issue price: $80.00

**72-L41-2.9**
*1979 Off to School*
Issue price: $90.00
*Series Closed*

## ORREFORS
Orrefors, Smaland

Orrefors was originally established in 1726 as an ironworks. In 1898 they began manufacturing glass ink bottles and window glass. Although the ironworks was no longer profitable, Johan Ekman purchased the property in 1913. He was interested in improving the facilities for glassmaking and recognized the importance of the valuable forest land of the area as fuel for glass furnaces. He eventually built an entire community around the glassworks.

Orrefors crystal is made from a mixture of seashore sand and potash, plus a heavy lead content. The ornamentation is created by master blowers who apply liquid molten glass in desired shapes.

In 1970, Orrefors began its *Annual Cathedral* series made in untinted crystal and depicting famous places of worship. This series ended in 1978. These plates are handmade with the designs engraved in the crystal and filled with 24-karat gold.

John Selbing is regarded as one of the world's leading photographers of glass. He is credited with developing the technique which enabled production of inlaid-gold crystal plates. At the age of 19 he joined Orrefors and for 46 years handled their design, photography and advertising projects. During the last several years, he has been working independently in fine art.

## *Annual Cathedral Series*

Artist: John Selbing

Leaded crystal with engraved designs inlaid in 24k gold

Diameter: 25.4 centimeters (10 inches)

No hanger

Edition size limited to 5,000 through 1975; 3,000 thereafter

Numbered since 1975, without certificate

**76-O74-1.1**
1970 *Notre Dame Cathedral*
Issue price: $50.00

**76-O74-1.2**
1971 *Westminster Abbey*
Issue price: $50.00

**76-O74-1.3**
*1972 Basilica di San Marco*
Issue price: $50.00

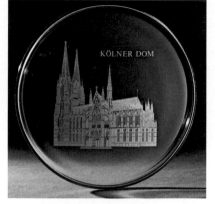

**76-O74-1.4**
*1973 Cologne Cathedral*
Issue price: $50.00

**76-O74-1.5**
*1974 Temple Rue de la Victoire, Paris*
Issue price: $60.00

**76-O74-1.6**
*1975 Basilica di San Pietro, Rome*
Issue price: $85.00

**76-O74-1.7**
*1976 Christ Church, Philadelphia*
Issue price: $85.00

**76-O74-1.8**
*1977 Masjid-E-Shah*
Issue price: $90.00

**76-O74-1.9**
*1978 Santiago de Compostela*
Issue price: $95.00
*Series Closed*

Röcstrand
SWEDEN

## RÖRSTRAND
Lidkoping

The Rörstrand porcelain factory is Sweden's oldest pottery and the second oldest in Europe. Originally founded in Stockholm in 1726 under government patronage, the plant was later moved inland to Lidkoping for safety reasons during World War II.

Rörstrand is one of the few factories in the world that produces all three ceramic bodies—porcelain, stoneware and high-fired earthenware. The output of the factory includes both dinnerware and dec-

orative art, including collector's plates. Rörstrand's first collector's plate series was a *Christmas* series (OTC), started in 1904 and ended in 1926. In 1968 Rörstrand began its series of square *Christmas* plates with designs derived from Swedish folk tales and traditions.

Rörstrand artist Gunnar Nylund has exhibited his work at the Swedish National Museum and is widely known for his monumental ceramic reliefs.

## Christmas Series

Artist: Gunnar Nylund

Porcelain decorated in Scandia blue underglaze

Diameter: 19 centimeters (7½ inches square)

Pierced foot rim

Edition size undisclosed, limited by year of issue

Not numbered, without certificate

**76-R54-1.1**
1968 *Bringing Home the Tree*
Issue price: $12.00

**76-R54-1.2**
1969 *Fisherman Sailing Home*
Issue price: $13.50

**76-R54-1.3**
*1970 Nils with His Geese*
Issue price: $13.50

**76-R54-1.4**
*1971 Nils in Lapland*
Issue price: $15.00

**76-R54-1.5**
*1972 Dalecarlian Fiddler*
Issue price: $15.00

**76-R54-1.6**
*1973 Farm in Smaland*
Issue price: $16.00

**76-R54-1.7**
*1974 Vadstena*
Issue price: $19.00

**76-R54-1.8**
*1975 Nils in Vastmanland*
Issue price: $20.00

**76-R54-1.9**
*1976 Nils in Uppland*
Issue price: $20.00

**76-R54-1.10**
*1977 Nils in Värmland*
Issue price: $29.50

**76-R54-1.11**
*1978 Nils in Fjallbacka*
Issue price: $32.50

# SWEDEN
## RÖRSTRAND

**76-R54-1.12**

**76-R54-1.12**
*1979 Nils in Vaestergoetland*
Issue price: $38.50

**76-R54-1.13**
*1980 Nils in Halland*
Issue price: $55.00

**76-R54-1.14**
*1981 Nils in Gotland*
Issue price: $55.00

**76-R54-1.15**
*1982 Nils at Skansen in Stockholm*
Issue price: $47.50

**76-R54-1.16**
*1983 Nils in Oland*
Issue price: $42.50

**76-R54-1.17**
*1984 Nils in Angermanland*
Issue price: $42.50

**76-R54-1.18**
*1985 Nils in Jämtland*
Issue price: $42.50

**76-R54-1.19**
*1986 Nils in Karlskrona*
Issue price: $46.50

**78-L5-1.1** "Grandfather Tells a Story"
1986 Langenthal *Anker's Heritage Series*
This plate was introduced in 1986 as the
first from Switzerland, which has a small
but highly-regarded porcelain industry.
The series features the 19th-century artwork of Albert Anker, Switzerland's best-
known native artist, who also had a reputation as a civic activist and an advocate of
government support of the arts.

# SWITZERLAND
## LANGENTHAL

**78-L5-0.0**

## LANGENTHAL
Langenthal

The Langenthal Swiss China Works was founded 80 years ago when a group of Swiss investors decided to apply their business skills to the manufacture of hard-paste porcelain. The decision was not an easy one because everything, from raw materials to skilled craftsmen, had to be imported.

Today, Langenthal is respected all over the world as a superior manufacturer of fine porcelain. Although materials must still be imported, Langenthal craftsmen are locally trained through the company's rigorous aprenticeship program. Known as a pioneer in applying modern technology to the ancient traditions of porcelain-making, the company is an excellent example of Swiss efficiency. Scientists and craftsmen work together to insure that every piece of porcelain is unsurpassed in delicacy, translucency and strength.

The *Anker's Heritage* series introduces the first collector's plate series based on artwork by the beloved Swiss painter Albert Anker. Initiated in 1986, the series is endorsed by the Neuchatel Museum of Fine Arts, home of one of the largest and finest Anker collections in the world.

Albert Anker, one of the best-known of Swiss artists, is also perhaps the most accomplished of native Swiss painters. The *Anker's Heritage* series, depicting scenes of everyday Swiss village life from the 19th century, reflects the strong values of hardy self-reliance, industry, order and respect for the individual that define the Swiss character.

## Anker's Heritage Series

Artist: Albert Anker. Artist's
signature appears on front

Porcelain banded in 14k gold

Diameter: 22.9 centimeters
(9 inches)

Pierced foot rim

Edition size undisclosed, limited
by announced period of issue

Numbered with certificate

**78-L5-1.1**
1986 *Grandfather Tells a Story*
Issue price: $34.86

**78-L5-1.2**
1987 *The First Smile*
Issue price: $34.86

**78-L5-1.3**
1987 *Girl Feeding Chickens*
Issue price: $34.86

## ARTISTS OF THE WORLD
Scottsdale, Arizona

Initially organized as DeGrazia of Scottsdale, the company was founded by James LaFond to represent Arizona artist Ted De-Grazia. The present name, Artists of the World, was adopted in 1977 when the company's scope was enlarged to include additional artists.

Most DeGrazia plate issues produced by the company are to-day listed under the dual heading Fairmont/Artists of the World; they are found in this book under the Fairmont name, which was the company that originally manufac-tured them.

*Children of Aberdeen,* a proprietary series with artwork by Kee Fung Ng, began in 1979 and de-picts the children who live on boats anchored at the fishing village of Aberdeen near Hong Kong. The series closed in 1984. (For another Ng series, see China, Republic of, PAVILION OF T'SANG YING HSÜAN.)

In 1987, Artist's of the World introduced the *Children of the Sun* series by Ted DeGrazia; it was made on Knowles china.

## Children of Aberdeen Series

Artist: Kee Fung Ng. Artist's signature appears on front

China banded in gold

Diameter: 25.4 centimeters (10 inches)

No hanger

Edition size undisclosed, limited by year of issue

Numbered with certificate

**84-A72-1.1**
1979 *Girl with Little Brother*
Issue price: $50.00

**84-A72-1.2**
1980 *Sampan Girl*
Issue price: $50.00

**84-A72-1.3**
1981 *Girl with Little Sister*
Issue price: $55.00

**84-A72-1.4**
1982 *Girl with Seashells*
Issue price: $60.00

**84-A72-1.5**
1983 *Girl with Seabirds*
Issue price: $60.00

**84-A72-1.6**
1984 *Brother and Sister*
Issue price: $60.00
*Series Closed*

# UNITED STATES
## ARTISTS OF THE WORLD

### 84-A72-13.1

*DeGrazia's Children of the Sun Series*

Artist: Ted DeGrazia. Artist's signature appears on front

Overglaze-decorated china

Diameter: 21.6 centimeters (8½ inches)

No hanger

Edition size undisclosed, limited to announced period of issue

Numbered, with certificate

**84-A72-13.1**
1987 *Spring Blossoms*
Issue price: $34.50

**84-A72-13.2**
1987 *My Little Pink Bird*
Issue price: $34.50

**84-C72-1.1** ''Freddie in the Bathtub''
1979 Crown Parian
*Freddie the Freeloader*
This issue marked comedian Red Skelton's entry as an artist into the world of collector's plates. Now, says Skelton, a whole new generation of admirers knows him not for the beloved comic characters he played on television—such as Freddie the Freeloader, depicted here—but for his limited-edition art featuring Freddie as the hero.

# UNITED STATES
## CROWN PARIAN

**84-C72-1.1**

## CROWN PARIAN
South El Monte, California

Crown Parian, Ltd. was incorporated in South El Monte, California in 1978 for the purpose of producing fine porcelain limited-edition plates and related products.

Crown Parian has introduced two series by well-known comedian Red Skelton: the *Freddie the Freeloader* series, which ran from 1979 through 1982, and *Freddie's Adventures* series, which began in 1981 and closed in 1984. The *American Folk Heroes* series began in 1983 with artwork by Gene Boyer.

## Freddie the Freeloader Series

Artist: Red Skelton. Artist's signature appears on front

Overglaze-decorated porcelain banded in gold

Diameter: 21.6 centimeters (8½ inches)

No hanger

Edition size limited to 10,000

Numbered without certificate

**84-C72-1.1**
1979 *Freddie in the Bathtub*
Issue price: $55.00

**84-C72-1.2**
1980 *Freddie's Shack*
Issue price: $55.00

**84-C72-1.3**
1981 *Freddie on the Green*
Issue price: $60.00

**84-C72-1.4**
1982 *Love That Freddie*
Issue price: $60.00
*Series Closed*

## American Folk Heroes Series

Artist: Gene Boyer. Artist's signature appears on front

Overglaze-decorated porcelain banded in gold

Diameter: 21.6 centimeters (8½ inches)

No hanger

Edition size undisclosed, limited by announced period of issue

Numbered with certificate

**84-C72-2.1**
1983 *Johnny Appleseed*
Issue price: $35.00

**84-C72-2.2**
1984 *Davy Crockett*
Issue price: $35.00

**84-C72-2.3**
1985 *Betsy Ross*
Issue price: $35.00

**84-C72-2.4**
1985 *Buffalo Bill*
Issue price: $35.00

**84-C72-2.5**
1986 *Casey Jones*
Issue price: $40.00

# UNITED STATES
## CROWN PARIAN

### 84-C72-2.6

**84-C72-2.6**
1987 *Sacajewea*
Issue price: $40.00
*Series Closed*

## Freddie's Adventures Series

Artist: Red Skelton. Artist's signature appears on front

Overglaze-decorated porcelain banded in gold

Diameter: 21.6 centimeters (8½ inches)

No hanger

Edition size limited to 15,000

Numbered without certificate

**84-C72-3.1**
1981 *Captain Freddie*
Issue price: $60.00

**84-C72-3.2**
1982 *Bronco Freddie*
Issue price: $60.00

**84-C72-3.3**
1983 *Sir Freddie*
Issue price: $62.50

**84-C72-3.4**
1984 *Gertrude and Heathcliffe*
Issue price: $62.50
*Series Closed*

**84-E74-1.1** "Stop and Smell the Roses"
1981 Ernst, Inc. *Seems Like Yesterday*
This popular plate introduced artist Rusty Money to the collector's plate market. It highlights her soft palette and unique painting style, giving a watercolor effect.

## ERNST
San Marcos, California

Ernst, Inc. was founded in 1976 by Ray and Marilyn Ernst. Originally operating from a collectibles gallery in Escondido, California, the company now has expanded offices in San Marcos. Ernst, Inc. produces a variety of limited-edition collectibles as well as collector's plates.

In 1982, the Ernst plate series *Seems Like Yesterday* introduced artist Rusty Money to the collector's market. The series ended in 1984.

## Seems Like Yesterday Series

Artist: Rusty Money. Artist's signature appears on front

Porcelain

Diameter: 21.6 centimeters (8½ inches)

No hanger

Edition size undisclosed, limited by announced period of issue

Numbered with certificate

**84-E74-1.1**
1981 *Stop and Smell the Roses*
Issue price: $24.50

**84-E74-1.2**
1982 *Home by Lunch*
Issue price: $24.50

**84-E74-1.3**
1982 *Lisa's Creek*
Issue price: $24.50

**84-E74-1.4**
1983 *It's Got My Name on It*
Issue price: $24.50

**84-E74-1.5**
1984 *My Magic Hat*
Issue price: $24.50

**84-E74-1.6**
1984 *Little Prince*
Issue price: $24.50
*Series Closed*

*Fairmont*

Perfect Porcelain

## FAIRMONT
Pasadena, California

Fairmont China was established in 1976 to produce limited-edition plates. Two series began that year: the *Holiday* series with artwork by Ted DeGrazia and the *Famous Clowns* series by comedian Red Skelton. The *Famous Clowns* series ended in 1979 and the *Holiday* series closed in 1985. In 1978, Fairmont issued the third plate in the *DeGrazia Children* series, originally started by Gorham (see United States, GORHAM). This series ended in 1985. In 1979, Fairmont started the *Classical American Beauties* series by artist Vincent, which closed in 1981, and, in 1981, began the *Playful Memories* series with artwork by Sue Etém. This series ended in 1983.

In 1985, Fairmont introduced the *DeGrazia's Children at Play* series. In 1986, the *DeGrazia's Western* series began. All these DeGrazia series are produced under the auspices of Artists of the World (see United States, ARTISTS OF THE WORLD).

### DeGrazia Holiday Series

Artist: Ted DeGrazia. Artist's signature appears on front; first 500 autographed on back

China banded in gold

Diameter: 26 centimeters (10¼ inches)

No hanger

Edition size limited to 10,000

Numbered since 1977, without certificate

**84-F4-1.1**
1976 *The Festival of Lights*
Issue price: $45.00

**84-F4-1.2**
1977 *The Bell of Hope*
Issue price: $45.00

**84-F4-1.3**
1978 *Little Madonna*
Issue price: $45.00

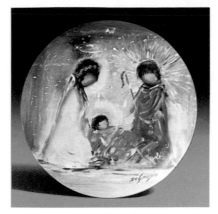

**84-F4-1.4**
1979 *The Nativity*
Issue price: $50.00

**84-F4-1.5**
1980 *Little Pima Indian Drummer Boy*
Issue price: $50.00

**84-F4-1.6**
1981 *Little Prayer—The Christmas Angel*
Issue price: $55.00

**84-F4-1.7**
1982 *The Blue Boy*
Issue price: $60.00

**84-F4-1.8**
1983 *Heavenly Blessings*
Issue price: $65.00

**84-F4-1.9**
1984 *Navajo Madonna*
Issue price: $65.00

**84-F4-1.10**
1985 *Saguaro Dance*
Issue price: $65.00
*Series Closed*

# UNITED STATES
## FAIRMONT

### 84-F4-2.1

*Famous Clowns Series*

Artist: Red Skelton. Artist's signature appears on front

China banded in gold

Diameter: 21.6 centimeters (8½ inches)

No hanger

Edition size limited to 10,000

Numbered without certificate

**84-F4-2.1**
1976 *Freddie the Freeloader*
Issue price: $55.00

**84-F4-2.2**
1977 *W. C. Fields*
Issue price: $55.00

**84-F4-2.3**
1978 *Happy*
Issue price: $55.00

**84-F4-2.4**
1979 *The Pledge*
Issue price: $55.00
*Series Closed*

*DeGrazia Children Series*

Artist: Ted DeGrazia. Artist's signature appears on front; first 500 autographed on back

China banded in gold

Diameter: 26 centimeters (10¼ inches)

No hanger

Edition size limited to 10,000

Numbered without certificate

**84-F4-4.1**
1978 *Flower Girl*
Issue price: $45.00

**84-F4-4.2**
1979 *Flower Boy*
Issue price: $45.00

**84-F4-4.3**
1980 *Little Cocopah Indian Girl*
Issue price: $50.00

**84-F4-4.4**
1981 *Beautiful Burden*
Issue price: $50.00

**84-F4-4.5**
1982 *Merry Little Indian*
Issue price: $55.00

**84-F4-4.6**
1983 *Wondering*
Issue price: $60.00

**84-F4-4.7**
1984 *Pink Papoose*
Issue price: $65.00

**84-F4-4.8**
1985 *Sunflower Boy*
Issue price: $65.00
*Series Closed*

## Classical American Beauties Series

Artist: Vincent. Artist's signature appears on front

China banded in gold

Diameter: 26 centimeters (10¼ inches)

No hanger

Edition size limited to 7,500

Numbered without certificate

**84-F4-8.1**
1979 *Colleen*
Issue price: $60.00

**84-F4-8.2**
1979 *Heather*
Issue price: $60.00

# UNITED STATES
## FAIRMONT

### 84-F4-8.3

**84-F4-8.3**
1980 *Dawn*
Issue price: $60.00

**84-F4-8.4**
1981 *Eve*
Issue price: $60.00
*Series Closed*

## *Playful Memories Series*

Artist: Sue Etém. Artist's signature appears on front

China banded in gold

Diameter: 22.3 centimeters (8¾ inches)

No hanger

Edition size limited to 10,000

Numbered without certificate

**84-F4-10.1**
1981 *Renee*
Issue price: $39.50

**84-F4-10.2**
1982 *Jeremy*
Issue price: $42.50

**84-F4-10.3**
1983 *Jamie*
Issue price: $42.50

**84-F4-10.4**
1983 *Randy*
Issue price: $45.00
*Series Closed*

## DeGrazia's Children at Play Series

Artist: Ted DeGrazia. Artist's signature appears on front

China banded in gold

Diameter: 26 centimeters (10¼ inches)

No hanger

Edition size limited to 15,000

Numbered without certificate

**84-F4-27.1**
1985 *My First Horse*
Issue price: $65.00

**84-F4-27.2**
1986 *Girl with Sewing Machine*
Issue price: $65.00

**84-F4-27.3**
1987 *Love Me*
Issue price: $65.00

## DeGrazia's Western Series

Artist: Ted DeGrazia. Artist's signature appears on front

China banded in gold

Diameter: 26 centimeters (10¼ inches)

No hanger

Edition limited to 7,500

Numbered, without certificate

**84-F4-30.1**
1986 *Morning Ride*
Issue price: $65.00

# UNITED STATES
## FRANKLIN MINT

**84-F64-0.0**

## FRANKLIN MINT
### Franklin Center, Pennsylvania

The Franklin Mint, the world's largest private mint, was established in 1965 in the Philadelphia area by Joseph Segel. The firm specializes in porcelain collectibles, sculptures, fine art prints, jewelry and has several international subsidiaries and branches.

The Franklin Mint entered the limited-edition plate field in 1970 with the six-plate *Rockwell Christmas* series, crafted in sterling silver.

The *Rockwell Christmas* series is the only one to be designed especially for the collector's plate market by the artist, Norman Rockwell.

## Rockwell Christmas Series

Artist: Norman Rockwell. Artist's signature appears on front

Etched sterling silver

Diameter: 20.3 centimeters (8 inches)

No hanger

Edition size: as indicated

Numbered, with certificate since 1972

**84-F64-1.1**
1970 *Bringing Home the Tree*
Edition: 18,321
Issue price: $100.00

**84-F64-1.2**
1971 *Under the Mistletoe*
Edition: 24,792
Issue price: $100.00

**84-F64-1.3**
1972 *The Carolers*
Edition: 29,074
Issue price: $125.00

**84-F64-1.4**
1973 *Trimming the Tree*
Edition: 18,010
Issue price: $125.00

**84-F64-1.5**
1974 *Hanging the Wreath*
Edition: 12,822
Issue price: $175.00

**84-F64-1.6**
1975 *Home for Christmas*
Edition: 11,059
Issue price: $180.00
*Series Closed*

*W. S. George*
**FINE CHINA**

## W. S. GEORGE POTTERY CO.
East Liverpool, Ohio

The W. S. George Pottery Company carries on a tradition of fine china established many years ago by the grandfather of its founder, William S. George. Born in 1865 in the Ohio River Valley, an area famous for its deposits of fine china clay, Mr. George learned the potter's craft "from the bottom up" in the china manufactories of East Liverpool, Ohio. In 1902, he launched his own company, fulfilling a lifelong dream.

During the years that followed the company prospered, becoming known for its exceptionally high standards in everything from its secret family formulas for china to its advanced ceramics technology.

Today, the standards of excellence of the original W. S. George China Company are carried forward through an affiliation with The Bradford Exchange. A new company with W. S. George's grandson as founding member carries on the tradition, once again establishing the W. S. George name as a pre-eminent purveyor of "works of art in china."

W. S. George's first contribution to the collector's plate field was the long-awaited series to commemorate the 50th anniversary of the film classic, Gone With the Wind, which will occur in 1989. Titled *Gone With the Wind: Golden Anniversary Series*, the series was introduced in 1987. It is the only plate issue authorized by Metro-Goldwyn-Mayer to celebrate the film as it enters its second half-decade of popularity.

*Gone With the Wind:
Golden Anniversary Series*

Artist: Howard Rogers. Artist's signature appears on front

China banded in gold

Diameter: 21.6 centimeters (8½ inches)

No hanger

Edition size undisclosed, limited by announced period of issue

Numbered, with certificate

**84-W60-1.1**
1987 *Scarlett and Her Suitors*
Issue price: $24.50

## GORHAM
Providence, Rhode Island

In 1831, silversmith Jabez Gorham, established the Gorham Corporation. Today a division of Textron, the firm is one of the world's largest producers of sterling and hollowware, figurines and ornaments.

Gorham Corporation acquired crystal and china manufacturing companies in 1970, enabling it to produce limited-edition plates in china as well as silver.

Gorham's *Rockwell Four Seasons* series, which began in 1971 and ended in 1980, was comprised of four plates each year (spring, summer, fall, and winter). A *Christmas* series, also with artwork by Norman Rockwell, was started in 1974. The *DeGrazia Children* series and the *Sugar and Spice* series, with artwork by Leo Jansen, began in 1976 with the former ending in 1977 and the latter ending in 1979.

Since 1978, Fairmont China has made the *DeGrazia Children* plates (see United States, FAIRMONT). The *Sugar and Spice* series is produced for Kern Collectibles by Gorham (see United States, KERN COLLECTIBLES).

## Rockwell Four Seasons Series

Artist: Norman Rockwell. Artist's signature appears on front

China banded in 24k gold

Diameter: 26.7 centimeters (10½ inches)

No hanger

Edition size undisclosed, limited by year of issue

Not numbered, without certificate

Issued in sets of four

**84-G58-1.1-1**
1971 *A Boy and His Dog;*
*A Boy Meets His Dog*
Issue price: $50.00

**84-G58-1.1-2**
1971 *Adventurers Between Adventures*

**84-G58-1.1-3**
1971 *A Mysterious Malady*

**84-G58-1.1-4**
1971 *Pride of Parenthood*

**84-G58-1.2-1**
1972 *Young Love; Flying Colors*
Issue price: $60.00

**84-G58-1.2-2**
1972 *Beguiling Buttercup*

**84-G58-1.2-3**
1972 *A Scholarly Pace*

**84-G58-1.2-4**
1972 *Downhill Daring*

**84-G58-1.3-1**
1973 *The Ages of Love;*
*Sweet Song So Young*
Issue price: $60.00

**84-G58-1.3-2**
1973 *Flowers in Tender Bloom*

**84-G58-1.3-3**
1973 *Fondly Do We Remember*

**84-G58-1.3-4**
1973 *Gaily Sharing Vintage*

**84-G58-1.4-1**
1974 *Grandpa and Me; Day Dreamers*
Issue price: $60.00

**84-G58-1.4-2**
1974 *Goin' Fishin'*

**84-G58-1.4-3**
1974 *Pensive Pals*

**84-G58-1.4-4**
1974 *Gay Blades*

**84-G58-1.5-1**
1975 *Me and My Pal;*
*Young Man's Fancy*
Issue price: $70.00

**84-G58-1.5-2**
1975 *Fisherman's Paradise*

**84-G58-1.5-3**
1975 *Disastrous Daring*

**84-G58-1.5-4**
1975 *A Lickin' Good Bath*

**84-G58-1.6-1**
1976 *Grand Pals; Soaring Spirits*
Issue price: $70.00

**84-G58-1.6-2**
1976 *Fish Finders*

**84-G58-1.6-3**
1976 *Ghostly Gourds*

**84-G58-1.6-4**
1976 *Snow Sculpture*

**84-G58-1.7-1**
1977 *Going on Sixteen; Sweet Serenade*
Issue price: $75.00

**84-G58-1.7-2**
1977 *Shear Agony*

# UNITED STATES
## GORHAM

**84-G58-1.7-3**

**84-G58-1.7-3**
1977 *Pilgrimage*

**84-G58-1.7-4**
1977 *Chilling Chore*

**84-G58-1.8-1**
1978 *The Tender Years; Spring Tonic*
Issue price: $100.00

**84-G58-1.8-2**
1978 *Cool Aid*

**84-G58-1.8-3**
1978 *Chilly Reception*

**84-G58-1.8-4**
1978 *New Year Look*

**84-G58-1.9-1**
1979 *A Helping Hand;*
*Closed for Business*
Issue price: $100.00

**84-G58-1.9-2**
1979 *Swatter's Rights*

**84-G58-1.9-3**
1979 *The Coal Season's Coming*

**84-G58-1.9-4**
*1979 Year End Count*

**84-G58-1.10-1**
*1980 Dad's Boy; In His Spirit*
Issue price: $135.00
*Series Closed*

**84-G58-1.10-2**
*1980 Trout Dinner*

**84-G58-1.10-3**
*1980 Careful Aim*

**84-G58-1.10-4**
*1980 Ski Skills*
*Series Closed*

## Rockwell Christmas Series

Artist: Norman Rockwell. Artist's signature appears on front

China banded in 24k gold

Diameter: 21.6 centimeters (8½ inches)

No hanger

Edition size undisclosed, limited by year of issue

Not numbered, without certificate

**84-G58-3.1**
*1974 Tiny Tim*
Issue price: $12.50

**84-G58-3.2**
*1975 Good Deeds*
Issue price: $17.50

# UNITED STATES
## GORHAM

**84-G58-3.3**

**84-G58-3.3**
1976 *Christmas Trio*
Issue price: $19.50

**84-G58-3.4**
1977 *Yuletide Reckoning*
Issue price: $19.50

**84-G58-3.5**
1978 *Planning Christmas Visits*
Issue price: $24.50

**84-G58-3.6**
1979 *Santa's Helpers*
Issue price: $24.50

**84-G58-3.7**
1980 *Letter to Santa*
Issue price: $27.50

**84-G58-3.8**
1981 *Santa Plans His Visit*
Issue price: $29.50

**84-G58-3.9**
1982 *The Jolly Coachman*
Issue price: $29.50

**84-G58-3.10**
1983 *Christmas Dancers*
Issue price: $29.50

**84-G58-3.11**
1984 *Christmas Medley*
Issue price: $29.50

**84-G58-3.12**
1985 *Home for the Holidays*
Issue price: $29.50

**84-G58-3.13**
1986 *Merry Christmas, Grandma*
Issue price: $29.50

## DeGrazia Children Series

Artist: Ted DeGrazia. Artist's signature appears on front

China banded in 24k gold

Diameter: 26.7 centimeters (10½ inches)

No hanger

Edition size: as indicated

Not numbered, without certificate

**84-G58-5.1**
1976 *Los Niños*
Edition: 5,000
Issue price: $35.00

**84-G58-5.2**
1977 *The White Dove*
Edition: 10,000
Issue price: $40.00
*Series Closed*

## Sugar and Spice Series

Artist: Leo Jansen. Artist's signature appears on front

China banded in 24k gold

Diameter: 21.6 centimeters (8½ inches)

No hanger

Edition size limited to 7,500

Numbered without certificate

**84-G58-6.1**
1976 *Dana and Debbie*
Issue price: $40.00

**84-G58-6.2**
1977 *Becky and Baby*
Issue price: $42.50

# UNITED STATES
## GORHAM

**84-G58-6.3**

**84-G58-6.3**
1978 *Jeanette and Julie*
Issue price: $47.50

**84-G58-6.4**
1979 *Ramona and Rachel*
Issue price: $50.00
*Series Closed*

**84-I31-1.1** "She Walks in Beauty"
1977 Incolay *Romantic Poets*
The first Incolay stone collector's plate.
The sculptural technique closely resembles
high-relief cameo carving.

289

## 84-I31-1.1

# Incolay Studios
of California

## INCOLAY
San Fernando, California

Incolay Studios has been creating cameo *objets d'art* in Incolay stone since 1965. The manufacturing process by which Incolay stone is created is a closely guarded secret, but it is acknowledged that the process includes the addition of a range of quartz-based minerals to replicate the coloring and weight of semi-precious stone cameos of the past.

Incolay Studios began its first series of collector's plates, the *Romantic Poets Collection,* in 1977. The series is inspired by the poetry of early 19th-century poets and it closed in 1985. In 1979, a second series of cameo plates, the *Great*

*Romances of History Collection,* began. This series ended in 1982. The *Voyage of Ulysses* series began in 1984.

Gayle Bright Appleby was the designer of the first four issues in the *Romantic Poets Collection.* Roger Akers completed the collection. Carl Romanelli was the sculptor for the *Great Romances of History* series and Alan Brunettin is the creator of *Voyage of Ulysses.* In 1987, Roger Akers created his first independent series for Incolay, the *Love Sonnets of Shakespeare* series. Alan Brunettin began his *The Fall of Troy* series, a sequel to the *Ulysses* series, in the same year.

## *Romantic Poets Collection*

Artist: as indicated. Artist's signature appears on front

Incolay stone with high relief cameos

Diameter: 26 centimeters (10¼ inches)

Attached back hanger

Edition size undisclosed, limited by announced period of issue

Numbered with certificate

**84-I31-1.1**
1977 *She Walks in Beauty*
Artist: Gayle Bright Appleby
Issue price: $60.00

**84-I31-1.2**
1978 *A Thing of Beauty Is a Joy Forever*
Artist: Gayle Bright Appleby
Issue price: $60.00

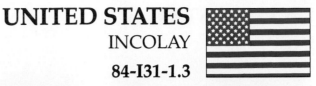

**84-I31-1.3**
1979 *To a Skylark*
Artist: Gayle Bright Appleby
Issue price: $65.00

**84-I31-1.4**
1980 *She Was a Phantom of Delight*
Artist: Gayle Bright Appleby
Issue price: $65.00

**84-I31-1.5**
1981 *The Kiss*
Artist: Roger Akers
Issue price: $65.00

**84-I31-1.6**
1982 *My Heart Leaps Up When I Behold*
Artist: Roger Akers
Issue price: $70.00

**84-I31-1.7**
1983 *I Stood Tiptoe*
Artist: Roger Akers
Issue price: $70.00

**84-I31-1.8**
1984 *The Dream*
Artist: Roger Akers
Issue price: $70.00

**84-I31-1.9**
1985 *The Recollection*
Artist: Roger Akers
Issue price: $70.00
*Series Closed*

# UNITED STATES
## INCOLAY

### 84-I31-3.1

*Great Romances of History Collection*

Artist: Carl Romanelli. Artist's signature appears on front

Incolay stone with high relief cameos

Diameter: 26 centimeters (10¼ inches)

Attached back hanger

Edition size undisclosed, limited by announced period of issue

Numbered with certificate

**84-I31-3.1**
*1979 Antony and Cleopatra*
Issue price: $65.00

**84-I31-3.2**
*1980 The Taj Mahal Lovers*
Issue price: $65.00

**84-I31-3.3**
*1981 Lancelot and Guinevere*
Issue price: $65.00

**84-I31-3.4**
*1982 Lord Nelson and Lady Hamilton*
Issue price: $70.00
*Series Closed*

*Voyage of Ulysses Series*

Artist: Alan Brunettin. Artist's signature appears on front

Incolay stone with high-relief cameos

Diameter: 21.6 centimeters (8½ inches)

Pierced foot rim

Edition size undisclosed, limited by year of issue

Numbered with certificate

**84-I31-4.1**
*1984 The Isle of Circe*
Issue price: $50.00

**84-I31-4.2**
*1985 The Sirens*
Issue price: $50.00

**84-I31-4.3**
1985 *The Isle of Calypso*
Issue price: $55.00

**84-I31-4.4**
1986 *The Land of the Phaeacians*
Issue price: $55.00

**84-I31-4.5**
1986 *The Return of Ulysses*
Issue price: $55.00

**84-I31-4.6**
1986 *Penelope and Ulysses: The Reunion*
Issue price: $55.00
*Series Closed*

## *Love Sonnets of Shakespeare Series*

Artist: Roger Akers. Artist's signature incised on front

Incolay stone with high-relief cameos

Diameter: 27 centimeters (9¼ inches)

Pierced foot rim

Edition size undisclosed, limited by announced period of issue

Numbered, with certificate

**84-I31-6.1**
1987 *Shall I Compare Thee to a Summer's Day?*
Issue price: $55.00

**84-I31-6.2**
1987 *Thou Art Too Dear for My Possessing*
Issue price: $55.00

# UNITED STATES
## INCOLAY

### 84-I31-7.1

*The Fall of Troy Series*

Artist: Alan Brunettin. Artist's signature incised on front

Incolay stone with high-relief cameos

Diameter: 21.6 centimeters (8½ inches)

Pierced foot rim

Edition size undisclosed, limited by announced period of issue

Numbered, with certificate

**84-I31-7.1**
1987 *The Judgment of Paris*
Issue price unavailable
at press time

**84-K20-7.4** "Future Teacher"
1983 Kern Collectibles *Leaders of Tomorrow*
Artist Leo Jansen earned a position of respect among collectors before his untimely death at the age of 50. One of the last series created before his death was this one, *Leaders of Tomorrow,* in which he mirrored the fortunes of adults in the innocent activities of childhood.

## KERN COLLECTIBLES
Stillwater, Minnesota

The story of Kern Collectibles dates to 1969 when Oscar L. Kern founded Commemorative Imports, a distributor of limited-edition collectibles. Kern expanded his business one step further in 1972 with the establishment of Kern Collectibles. In 1984, Kern Collectibles was purchased by the Consumer Products Division of 3M Company. After Kern's death in 1986, the company was transferred back to the ownership of Commemorative Editions, which is now continuing several of the firm's existing series.

Kern Collectibles issues limited-edition plates produced especially for the company by several of the world's fine china manufacturers. *Leaders of Tomorrow* began in 1980 and comprised four issues by the late Leo Jansen.

## *Leaders of Tomorrow Series*

Artist: Leo Jansen. Artist's signature appears on front

China banded in gold

Diameter: 21.6 centimeters (8½ inches)

No hanger

Edition size limited to 9,800

Numbered without certificate

**84-K20-7.1**
1980 *Future Physician*
Issue price: $50.00

**84-K20-7.2**
1981 *Future Farmer*
Issue price: $50.00

**84-K20-7.3**
1982 *Future Florist*
Issue price: $50.00

**84-K20-7.4**
1983 *Future Teacher*
Issue price: $50.00
*Series Closed*

# UNITED STATES
## EDWIN M. KNOWLES

84-K41-0.0

## EDWIN M. KNOWLES
Newell, West Virginia

The Edwin M. Knowles heritage of fine china can be traced to the early 19th century when Isaac Knowles, father of Edwin, established the family firm—Knowles, Taylor and Knowles—in East Liverpool, Ohio. The site was chosen for its proximity to deposits of high-quality kaolin clay. The firm became well known for its delicate Lotus ware.

After apprenticing with his father's firm, Edwin established his own company in Newell, West Virginia, and became a pre-eminent force in American china, honored by election to the presidency of the United States Potters Association.

After his death, the company ceased operations for a time until entering into an affiliation with The Bradford Exchange to preserve its time-honored name.

The Edwin M. Knowles name has appeared on both the firm's own series, beginning with the *Wizard of Oz* in 1977 (which closed in 1980) and also on issues certified by the Rockwell Society of America since 1975 (See United States, ROCKWELL SOCIETY).

The *Americana Holidays* series, by Don Spaulding, and the landmark *Gone With the Wind* series, by Raymond Kursár, both began in 1978. The former closed in 1984 and the latter in 1986. Knowles introduced the *Csatari Grandparents* series in 1980.

The *Annie Collector's Plate* series, by William Chambers, began in 1983 and closed in 1987. The *Biblical Mothers* series, with art by Eve Licea, also began in 1983 but ended in 1986, as did the Jeanne Down's *Friends I Remember* series.

The year 1984 saw the introduction of the *Four Ancient Elements* series, *A Father's Love* and *Hibel Mother's Day*. Both the *Ancient Elements* series and *Father's Love* closed in 1985.

Also appearing in 1984 was the first of the new series based on the musical masterworks of Rodgers and Hammerstein: *The King and I*, by William Chambers. This was followed in 1985 by a second series, *Oklahoma!*, by Mort Künstler and in 1986 by *The Sound of Music* by Tony Crnkovich.

The first series ever sponsored by the *Encyclopaedia Britannica*, entitled *Birds of Your Garden*, was introduced in 1985 with art by Kevin Daniel. That year also saw the creation of the first Knowles series by

the late Frances Hook, the *Legacy* series.

In 1986, besides *The Sound of Music* series, Knowles introduced two new wildlife series: *Living with Nature: Jerner's Ducks* by Bart Jerner, and the *Upland Birds of North America* by Wayne Anderson. The *American Innocents* series, designed by Barbara Marsten and Valentin Mandrajji, also appeared in 1986 and closed in 1987. Knowles also introduced the *Jessie Willcox Smith Childhood Holiday Memories* series in 1986.

In 1987, Knowles began two new series by William Chambers, *Portraits of Motherhood* and *Tom Sawyer*. Also new this year in the Rodgers and Hammerstein cycle was *South Pacific*, by Elaine Gignilliat.

Two other popular Knowles artists debuted second series: Eve Licea, with her *Licea's Christmas* series, and Mort Künstler, with *Lincoln, Man of America*. New also was *A Swan is Born*, by Lu Ann Roberts. Finally, two new animal series, *Friends in the Forest* by Kevin Daniel and *Amy Brackenbury's Cat Tales*, were also introduced.

## Wizard of Oz Series

Artist: James Auckland. Artist's signature appears on front

China

Diameter: 21.6 centimeters (8½ inches) through 1979; 25.4 centimeters (10 inches) for 1980 plate

No hanger

Edition size undisclosed, limited by announced period of issue

Numbered with certificate

**84-K41-1.1**
*1977 Over the Rainbow*
Issue price: $19.00

**84-K41-1.2**
*1978 If I Only Had a Brain*
Issue price: $19.00

**84-K41-1.3**
*1978 If I Only Had a Heart*
Issue price: $19.00

**84-K41-1.4**
*1978 If I Were King of the Forest*
Issue price: $19.00

**84-K41-1.5**
*1979 The Wicked Witch of the West*
Issue price: $19.00

**84-K41-1.6**
*1979 Follow the Yellow Brick Road*
Issue price: $19.00

**84-K41-1.7**
*1979 Wonderful Wizard of Oz*
Issue price: $19.00

**84-K41-1.8**
*1980 The Grand Finale*
*(We're Off to See the Wizard)*
Issue price: $24.00
*Series Closed*

# UNITED STATES

## EDWIN M. KNOWLES

### 84-K41-2.1

*Americana Holidays Series*

Artist: Don Spaulding. Artist's signature appears on front

China

Diameter: 21.6 centimeters (8½ inches)

No hanger

Edition size undisclosed, limited by announced period of issue

Numbered with certificate

**84-K41-2.1**
1978 *Fourth of July*
Issue price: $26.00

**84-K41-2.2**
1979 *Thanksgiving*
Issue price: $26.00

**84-K41-2.3**
1980 *Easter*
Issue price: $26.00

**84-K41-2.4**
1981 *Valentine's Day*
Issue price: $26.00

**84-K41-2.5**
1982 *Father's Day*
Issue price: $26.00

**84-K41-2.6**
1983 *Christmas*
Issue price: $26.00

**84-K41-2.7**
1984 *Mother's Day*
Issue price: $26.00
*Series Closed*

## Gone With the Wind Series

Artist: Raymond Kursár. Artist's signature appears on front

China

Diameter: 21.6 centimeters (8½ inches) through 1985; 25.7 centimeters (10⅛ inches) for 1986 plate

No hanger

Edition size undisclosed, limited by announced period of issue

Numbered with certificate

**84-K41-3.1**
1978 *Scarlett*
Issue price: $21.50

**84-K41-3.2**
1979 *Ashley*
Issue price: $21.50

**84-K41-3.3**
1980 *Melanie*
Issue price: $21.50

**84-K41-3.4**
1981 *Rhett*
Issue price: $23.50

**84-K41-3.5**
1982 *Mammy Lacing Scarlett*
Issue price: $23.50

**84-K41-3.6**
1983 *Melanie Gives Birth*
Issue price: $23.50

**84-K41-3.7**
1984 *Scarlett's Green Dress*
Issue price: $25.50

**84-K41-3.8**
1985 *Rhett and Bonnie*
Issue price: $25.50

# UNITED STATES
## EDWIN M. KNOWLES

### 84-K41-3.9

**84-K41-3.9**
1986 *Scarlett and Rhett: The Finale*
Issue price: $29.50
*Series Closed*

## Csatari Grandparent Plate Series

Artist: Joseph Csatari. Artist's signature appears on front

China

Diameter: 21.6 centimeters (8½ inches)

No hanger

Edition size undisclosed, limited by announced period of issue

Numbered with certificate

**84-K41-4.1**
1980 *Bedtime Story*
Issue price: $18.00

**84-K41-4.2**
1981 *The Skating Lesson*
Issue price: $20.00

**84-K41-4.3**
1982 *The Cookie Tasting*
Issue price: $20.00

**84-K41-4.4**
1983 *The Swinger*
Issue price: $20.00

**84-K41-4.5**
1984 *The Skating Queen*
Issue price: $22.00

**84-K41-4.6**
1985 *The Patriots' Parade*
Issue price: $22.00

**84-K41-4.7**
1986 *The Home Run*
Issue price: $22.00

**84-K41-4.8**
1987 *The Sneak Preview*
Issue price: $22.00

## *Annie Collector's Plate Series*

Artist: William Chambers. Artist's signature appears on front

China

Diameter: 21.6 centimeters (8½ inches)

No hanger

Edition size undisclosed, limited by announced period of issue

Numbered with certificate

**84-K41-5.1**
1983 *Annie and Sandy*
Issue price: $19.00

**84-K41-5.2**
1983 *Daddy Warbucks*
Issue price: $19.00

**84-K41-5.3**
1983 *Annie and Grace*
Issue price: $19.00

**84-K41-5.4**
1984 *Annie and the Orphans*
Issue price: $21.00

**84-K41-5.5**
1985 *Tomorrow*
Issue price: $21.00

**84-K41-5.6**
1986 *Annie and Miss Hannigan*
Issue price: $21.00

**84-K41-5.7**
1986 *Annie, Lily and Rooster*
Issue price: $24.00

**84-K41-5.8**
1986 *Grand Finale*
Issue price: $24.00
*Series Closed*

## Biblical Mothers Series

Artist: Eve Licea. Artist's signature appears on front

China banded in 24k gold

Diameter: 26 centimeters (10¼ inches)

No hanger

Edition size undisclosed, limited by announced period of issue

Numbered with certificate

**84-K41-6.1**
1983 *Bathsheba and Solomon*
Issue price: $39.50

**84-K41-6.2**
1984 *The Judgment of Solomon*
Issue price: $39.50

**84-K41-6.3**
1984 *Pharoah's Daughter and Moses*
Issue price: $39.50

**84-K41-6.4**
1984 *Mary and Jesus*
Issue price: $39.50

**84-K41-6.5**
1985 *Sarah and Isaac*
Issue price: $44.50

**84-K41-6.6**
1986 *Rebekah, Jacob and Esau*
Issue price: $44.50
*Series Closed*

## Jeanne Down's Friends I Remember Series

Artist: Jeanne Down. Artist's signature appears on front

China

Diameter: 21.6 centimeters (8½ inches)

No hanger

Edition size undisclosed, limited by announced period of issue

Numbered with certificate

**84-K41-7.1**
1983 *Fish Story*
Issue price: $17.50

**84-K41-7.2**
1984 *Office Hours*
Issue price: $17.50

**84-K41-7.3**
1984 *A Coat of Paint*
Issue price: $17.50

**84-K41-7.4**
1985 *Here Comes the Bride*
Issue price: $19.50

**84-K41-7.5**
1985 *Fringe Benefits*
Issue price: $19.50

# UNITED STATES
## EDWIN M. KNOWLES

**84-K41-7.6**

**84-K41-7.6**
1985 *High Society*
Issue price: $19.50

**84-K41-7.7**
1986 *The Flower Arrangement*
Issue price: $21.50

**84-K41-7.8**
1986 *The Taste Test*
Issue price: $21.50
*Series Closed*

## Four Ancient Elements Series

Artist: Georgia Lambert. Artist's signature appears on front

China

Diameter: 23.5 centimeters (9¼ inches)

No hanger

Edition size undisclosed, limited by announced period of issue

Numbered with certificate

**84-K41-8.1**
1984 *Earth*
Issue price: $27.50

**84-K41-8.2**
1984 *Water*
Issue price: $27.50

**84-K41-8.3**
1985 *Air*
Issue price: $29.50

**84-K41-8.4**
1985 *Fire*
Issue price: $29.50
*Series Closed*

## Hibel Mother's Day Series

Artist: Edna Hibel. Artist's signature appears on front

China banded in burnished gold

Diameter: 21.6 centimeters (8½ inches)

No hanger

Edition size undisclosed, limited by year of issue

Numbered with certificate

**84-K41-9.1**
*1984 Abby and Lisa*
Issue $29.50

**84-K41-9.2**
*1985 Erica and Jamie*
Issue price: $29.50

**84-K41-9.3**
*1986 Emily and Jennifer*
Issue price: $29.50

**84-K41-9.4**
*1987 Catherine and Heather*
Issue price: $34.50

## A Father's Love Series

Artist: Betsey Bradley. Artist's signature appears on front

China

Diameter: 21.6 centimeters (8½ inches)

No hanger

Edition size undisclosed, limited by announced period of issue

Numbered with certificate

**84-K41-10.1**
*1984 Open Wide*
Issue price: $19.50

**84-K41-10.2**
*1984 Batter Up*
Issue price: $19.50

# UNITED STATES
## EDWIN M. KNOWLES

### 84-K41-10.3

**84-K41-10.3**
1985 *Little Shaver*
Issue price: $19.50

**84-K41-10.4**
1985 *Swing Time*
Issue price: $22.50
*Series Closed*

### The King and I Series

Artist: William Chambers. Artist's signature appears on front

China

Diameter: 21.6 centimeters (8½ inches)

No hanger

Edition size undisclosed, limited by announced period of issue

Numbered with certificate

**84-K41-11.1**
1984 *A Puzzlement*
Issue price: $19.50

**84-K41-11.2**
1985 *Shall We Dance?*
Issue price: $19.50

**84-K41-11.3**
1985 *Getting to Know You*
Issue price: $19.50

**84-K41-11.4**
1985 *We Kiss in a Shadow*
Issue price: $19.50
*Series Closed*

## Birds of Your Garden Series

Artist: Kevin Daniel. Artist's signature appears on front

China

Diameter: 21.6 centimeters (8½ inches)

No hanger

Edition size undisclosed, limited by announced period of issue

Numbered with certificate

**84-K41-12.1**
1985 *The Cardinal*
Issue price: $19.50

**84-K41-12.2**
1985 *The Blue Jay*
Issue price: $19.50

**84-K41-12.3**
1985 *The Baltimore Oriole*
Issue price: $22.50

**84-K41-12.4**
1986 *The Chickadee*
Issue price: $22.50

**84-K41-12.5**
1986 *The Bluebird*
Issue price: $22.50

**84-K41-12.6**
1986 *The Robin*
Issue price: $22.50

**84-K41-12.7**
1986 *The Hummingbird*
Issue price: $22.50

**84-K41-12.8**
1987 *The Goldfinch*
Issue price: $24.50

# UNITED STATES
## EDWIN M. KNOWLES

### 84-K41-13.1

*Frances Hook Legacy Series*

Artist: Frances Hook. Artist's signature appears on front

China

Diameter: 21.6 centimeters (8½ inches)

No hanger

Edition size undisclosed, limited by announced period of issue

Numbered with certificate

**84-K41-13.1**
1985 *Fascination*
Issue price: $19.50

**84-K41-13.2**
1985 *Daydream*
Issue price: $19.50

**84-K41-13.3**
1986 *Discovery*
Issue price: $22.50

**84-K41-13.4**
1986 *Disappointment*
Issue price: $22.50

**84-K41-13.5**
1987 *Wonderment*
Issue price: $22.50

**84-K41-13.6**
1987 *Expectation*
Issue price: $22.50

## Edna Hibel Christmas Series

Artist: Edna Hibel. Artist's signature appears on front

China banded in 22k gold

Diameter: 26 centimeters (10¼ inches)

No hanger

Edition size undisclosed, limited by year of issue

Numbered with certificate

**84-K41-15.1**
1985 *The Angels' Message*
Issue price: $45.00

**84-K41-15.2**
1986 *The Gifts of the Magi*
Issue price: $45.00

**84-K41-15.3**
1987 *The Flight Into Egypt*
Issue price: $45.00

## A Swan is Born Series

Artist: Lu Ann Roberts. Artist's signature appears on front

Overglaze-decorated china

Diameter: 21.6 centimeters (8½ inches)

No hanger

Edition size undisclosed, limited by period of issue

Numbered, with certificate

**84-K41-16.1**
1986 *Hopes and Dreams*
Issue price: $24.50

# UNITED STATES
## EDWIN M. KNOWLES

## 84-K41-17.1

### Oklahoma! Series

Artist: Mort Künstler. Artist's signature appears on front

China

Diameter: 21.6 centimeters (8½ inches)

No hanger

Edition size undisclosed, limited by announced period of issue

Numbered with certificate

**84-K41-17.1**
1985 *Oh, What a Beautiful Mornin'*
Issue price: $19.50

**84-K41-17.2**
1986 *The Surrey With the Fringe on Top*
Issue price: $19.50

**84-K41-17.3**
1986 *I Cain't Say No*
Issue price: $19.50

**84-K41-17.4**
1986 *Oklahoma!*
Issue price: $19.50
*Series Closed*

### The Sound of Music Series

Artist: Tony Crnkovich. Artist's signature appears on front

China

Diameter: 21.6 centimeters (8½ inches)

No hanger

Edition size undisclosed, limited by announced period of issue

Numbered with certificate

**84-K41-18.1**
1986 *The Sound of Music*
Issue price: $19.50

**84-K41-18.2**
1986 *Do-Re-Mi*
Issue price: $19.50

**84-K41-18.3**
1986 *My Favorite Things*
Issue price: $22.50

**84-K41-18.4**
1986 *Laendler*
Issue price: $22.50

**84-K41-18.5**
1987 *Edelweiss*
Issue price: $22.50

## Upland Birds of North America Series

Artist: Wayne Anderson. Artist's signature appears on front

China

Diameter: 21.6 centimeters (8½ inches)

No hanger

Edition size undisclosed, limited by announced period of issue

Numbered with certificate

**84-K41-20.1**
1986 *The Pheasant*
Issue price: $24.50

**84-K41-20.2**
1986 *The Grouse*
Issue price: $24.50

**84-K41-20.3**
1987 *The Quail*
Issue price: $27.50

# UNITED STATES
## EDWIN M. KNOWLES

### 84-K41-21.1

#### American Innocents Series

Artist: Barbara Marsten and Valentin Mandrajji. Artists' signatures appear on front

China

Diameter: 21.6 centimeters (8½ inches)

No hanger

Edition size undisclosed, limited by announced period of issue

Numbered with certificate

**84-K41-21.1**
1986 *Abigail in the Rose Garden*
Issue price: $19.50

**84-K41-21.2**
1986 *Ann by the Terrace*
Issue price: $19.50

**84-K41-21.3**
1987 *Ellen and John in the Parlor*
Issue price: $19.50

**84-K41-21.4**
1987 *William on the Rocking Horse*
Issue price: $19.50
*Series Closed*

#### Jessie Willcox Smith Childhood Holiday Memories Series

Artist: Jessie Willcox Smith. Artist's signature appears on front

China

Diameter: 21.6 centimeters (8½ inches)

No hanger

Edition size undisclosed, limited by announced period of issue

Numbered with certificate

**84-K41-22.1**
1986 *Easter*
Issue price: $19.50

**84-K41-22.2**
1986 *Thanksgiving*
Issue price: $19.50

**84-K41-22.3**
1986 *Christmas*
Issue price: $22.50

**84-K41-22.4**
1986 *Valentine's Day*
Issue price: $22.50

**84-K41-22.5**
1987 *Mother's Day*
Issue price: $22.50

**84-K41-22.6**
1987 *Fourth of July*
Issue price: $22.50

## *Living With Nature: Jerner's Ducks Series*

Artist: Bart Jerner. Artist's signature appears on front

China banded in gold

Diameter: 21.6 centimeters (8½ inches)

No hanger

Edition size undisclosed, limited by announced period of issue

Numbered with certificate

**84-K41-23.1**
1986 *The Pintail*
Issue price: $19.50

**84-K41-23.2**
1986 *The Mallard*
Issue price: $19.50

# UNITED STATES
## EDWIN M. KNOWLES

**84-K41-23.3**

**84-K41-23.3**
1987 *The Wood Duck*
Issue price: $22.50

## South Pacific Series

Artist: Elaine Gignilliat. Artist's
signature appears on front

Overglaze-decorated china

Diameter: 21.6 centimeters
(8½ inches)

No hanger

Edition size undisclosed, limited
by announced period of issue

Numbered, with certificate

**84-K41-26.1**
1987 *Some Enchanted Evening*
Issue price unavailable
at press time

## Eve Licea Christmas Series

Artist: Eve Licea. Artist's signature
appears on front

Overglaze-decorated china

Diameter: 26 centimeters
(10¼ inches)

No hanger

Edition size undisclosed, limited
by announced period of issue

Numbered, with certificate

**84-K41-32.1**
1987 *The Annunciation*
Issue price unavailable
at press time

## Tom Sawyer Series

Artist: William Chambers. Artist's signature appears on front

Overglaze-decorated china

Diameter: 21.6 centimeters (8½ inches)

No hanger

Edition size undisclosed, limited to announced period of issue

Numbered, with certificate

**84-K41-38.1**
1987 *Whitewashing the Fence*
Issue price unavailable
at press time

## Lincoln, Man of America Series

Artist: Mort Künstler. Artist's signature appears on front

Overglaze-decorated china

Diameter: 21.6 centimeters (8½ inches)

No hanger

Edition size undisclosed, limited by announced period of issue

Numbered, with certificate

**84-K41-42.1**
1987 *The Gettysburg Address*
Issue price: $24.50

# UNITED STATES
## EDWIN M. KNOWLES

### 84-K41-44.1

*Portraits of Motherhood Series*

Artist: William Chambers. Artist's signature appears on front

China with gold overlay border

Diameter: 21.6 centimeters (8½ inches)

No hanger

Edition size undisclosed, limited by announced period of issue

Numbered, with certificate

**84-K41-44.1**
1987 *Mother's Here*
Issue price: $29.50

*Friends of the Forest Series*

Artist: Kevin Daniel. Artist's signature appears on front

China

Diameter: 21.6 centimeters (8½ inches)

No hanger

Edition size undisclosed, limited by announced period of issue

Numbered, with certificate

**84-K41-45.1**
1987 *The Rabbit*
Issue price unavailable
at press time

## *Amy Brackenbury's Cat Tales Series*

Artist: Amy Brackenbury. Artist's signature appears on front

China

Diameter: 21.6 centimeters (8½ inches)

No hanger

Edition size undisclosed, limited by announced period of issue

Numbered, with certificate

**84-K41-47.1**
1987 *A Chance Meeting: American White Shorthairs*
Issue price: $21.50

# LENOX

## LENOX
Lawrenceville, New Jersey

Walter Scott Lenox and his partner, Jonathan Coxon, Sr., established the Ceramic Art Company in 1889 in Trenton, New Jersey. Their goal was to produce an American china surpassing the finest in Europe. In 1895, Lenox bought out Coxon and operated the business alone until it was reorganized in 1906 as Lenox, Inc. The plant later moved to Pomona. The firm's early products were bowls, vases, figurines, and later, tableware. All were made in "American Belleek," named for the town in Ireland where this creamy, ivory-tinted ware was first produced.

In 1918, Lenox was commissioned to supply President Wilson with a complete 1,700-piece dinner service, the first wholly American china ever used in the White House. Later, both Presidents Franklin Roosevelt and Harry Truman commissioned Lenox to make sets of dinnerware. In 1981, the Reagan administration commissioned Lenox to create a 4,372-piece dinnerware set for the White House.

Today, in its facilities in Pomona, New Jersey, and Oxford, North Carolina, Lenox still handcrafts dinnerware, china gifts and collectibles with the same meticulous care as the early thimbles, inkstands and parasol handles.

In 1970, Lenox introduced its *Boehm Bird* series using paintings by artist Edward Marshall Boehm. The series ended in 1981. The company also has several other series listed in the OVER-THE-COUNTER section of this book.

## Boehm Bird Series

Artist: Edward Marshall Boehm.
Artist's name appears on back

China with 24k gold design on border

Diameter: 26.7 centimeters (10½ inches)

No hanger

Edition size undisclosed

Not numbered, without certificate

**84-L18-1.1**
1970 *Wood Thrush*
Issue price: $35.00

**84-L18-1.2**
1971 *Goldfinch*
Issue price: $35.00

**84-L18-1.3**
1972 *Mountain Bluebird*
Issue price: $37.50

**84-L18-1.4**
1973 *Meadowlark*
Issue price: $41.00

**84-L18-1.5**
1974 *Rufous Hummingbird*
Issue price: $45.00

**84-L18-1.6**
1975 *American Redstart*
Issue price: $50.00

**84-L18-1.7**
1976 *Cardinal*
Issue price: $53.00

**84-L18-1.8**
1977 *Robins*
Issue price: $55.00

**84-L18-1.9**

**84-L18-1.9**
1978 *Mockingbirds*
Issue price: $58.00

**84-L18-1.10**
1979 *Golden-Crowned Kinglets*
Issue price: $65.00

**84-L18-1.11**
1980 *Black-Throated Blue Warblers*
Issue price: $80.00

**84-L18-1.12**
1981 *Eastern Phoebes*
Issue price: $90.00
*Series Closed*

**84-M58-1.3** "Heather"
**1983 Morgantown Crystal**
*Yates' Country Ladies*
Because there is so much hand-craftsmanship involved in the production of crystal plates, there are very few crystal series in today's market. This one, from Morgantown Crystal, is *double-intaglio carved* on both the front and back of the plate. The result is a fascinating illusion of depth and a subtle interplay of light and shadow.

*Morgantown Crystal*

## MORGANTOWN CRYSTAL
Morgantown, West Virginia

Floyd Jones and his father founded the Monongahela Valley Cut Glass Company in 1912 in Morgantown, West Virginia. Their most famous design was an elegant pattern known as "Morgantown Rose." The company flourished under the direction of the Jones family for four generations. In 1977, John Heiner purchased the firm and renamed it Morgantown Crystal, which re-cently expanded operations to include glass etching and engraving as well as cutting.

The first limited-edition collector's plate series to bear the Morgantown Crystal hallmark, *Yates' Country Ladies*, began in 1981 and closed in 1984.

Designs for issues in the series were by Michael Yates.

## Michael Yates' Country Ladies Series

Artist: Michael Yates. Artist's signature appears on front

Full-lead crystal

Diameter: 22.6 centimeters (8⅞ inches)

No hanger

Edition size limited to 30,000

Numbered with certificate

**84-M58-1.1**
1981 *Angelica*
Issue price: $75.00

**84-M58-1.2**
1982 *Violet*
Issue price: $75.00

**84-M58-1.3**
1983 *Heather*
Issue price: $75.00

**84-M58-1.4**
1984 *Laurel*
Issue price: $75.00
*Series Closed*

## NEWELL POTTERY
### Newell, West Virginia

The Newell Pottery Company is a division of the Edwin M. Knowles China Company. The firm is best known for its Newellware, a variety of earthenware.

After having first produced the *Rockwell on Tour* series for the Rockwell Society of America in 1984, the Newell Pottery Company entered the limited-edition plate market under its own name with its *Sarah Stilwell Weber Calendar* series.

### *Sarah Stilwell Weber Calendar Series*

Artist: Sarah Stilwell Weber

Newellware

Diameter: 18.4 centimeters (7¼ inches)

No hanger

Edition size undisclosed, limited by announced period of issue

Numbered with certificate

© 1984 SEPCO

**84-N18-1.1**
1984 *June*
Issue price: $19.00

**84-N18-1.2**
1985 *July*
Issue price: $19.00

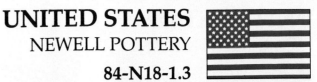

**84-N18-1.3**
1985 *August*
Issue price: $19.00

**84-N18-1.4**
1985 *September*
Issue price: $19.00

**84-N18-1.5**
1985 *October*
Issue price: $19.00

**84-N18-1.6**
1985 *November*
Issue price: $19.00

**84-N18-1.7**
1986 *December*
Issue price: $19.00

**84-N18-1.8**
1986 *January*
Issue price: $19.00

**84-N18-1.9**
1986 *February*
Issue price: $19.00

**84-N18-1.10**
1987 *March*
Issue price: $19.00

**84-N18-1.11**
1987 *April*
Issue price: $19.00

## PEMBERTON & OAKES
Santa Barbara, California

Pemberton & Oakes was founded in 1977. Originally located in Evanston, Illinois, the firm moved to Santa Barbara, California, in 1979 and opened a gallery for the display of original art works from its proprietary plate series.

The first two Bradex-listed series produced by the company, *Zolan's Children* and the *Nutcracker Ballet Plate Collection*, were introduced in 1978. They are listed under the maker's name, Viletta China Co. (see United States, VILETTA). The three most recent Bradex-listed series from the company are listed under the Pemberton & Oakes name. The *Children at Christmas Collection*, introduced in 1981, *Wonder of Childhood Collection*, introduced in 1982 and *Children and Pets* series, introduced in 1984, all feature the work of Donald Zolan, already well known to collectors for his earlier *Zolan's Children* series.

## Wonder of Childhood Collection

Artist: Donald Zolan. Artist's signature appears on front

China

Diameter: 21.6 centimeters (8½ inches)

No hanger

Edition size undisclosed, limited by announced period of issue

Numbered with certificate

**84-P19-1.1**
1982 *Touching the Sky*
Issue price: $19.00

**84-P19-1.2**
1983 *Spring Innocence*
Issue price: $19.00

**84-P19-1.3**
1984 *Winter Angel*
Issue price: $22.00

**84-P19-1.4**
1985 *Small Wonder*
Issue price: $22.00

**84-P19-1.5**
1986 *Grandma's Garden*
Issue price: $22.00

**84-P19-1.6**
1987 *Daydreamer*
Issue price: $24.00

# UNITED STATES
## PEMBERTON & OAKES

### 84-P19-2.1

*Children at Christmas Collection*

Artist: Donald Zolan. Artist's signature appears on front

China banded in gold

Diameter: 26 centimeters (10¼ inches)

No hanger

Edition size limited to 15,000

Numbered with certificate

**84-P19-2.1**
1981 *A Gift for Laurie*
Issue price: $48.00

**84-P19-2.2**
1982 *A Christmas Prayer*
Issue price: $48.00

**84-P19-2.3**
1983 *Erik's Delight*
Issue price: $48.00

**84-P19-2.4**
1984 *Christmas Secret*
Issue price: $48.00

**84-P19-2.5**
1985 *Christmas Kitten*
Issue price: $48.00

**84-P19-2.6**
1986 *Laurie and the Creche*
Issue price: $48.00
*Series Closed*

## Children and Pets Series

Artist: Donald Zolan. Artist's signature appears on front

China

Diameter: 19 centimeters (7½ inches)

No hanger

Edition size undisclosed, limited by announced period of issue

Numbered with certificate

**84-P19-3.1**
1984 *Tender Moment*
Issue price: $19.00

**84-P19-3.2**
1985 *Golden Moment*
Issue price: $19.00

**84-P19-3.3**
1985 *Making Friends*
Issue price: $19.00

**84-P19-3.4**
1985 *Tender Beginning*
Issue price: $19.00

**84-P19-3.5**
1986 *Backyard Discovery*
Issue price: $19.00

**84-P19-3.6**
1986 *Waiting to Play*
Issue price: $19.00
*Series Closed*

*Pickard*
The fine art of collecting.

## PICKARD

Antioch, Illinois

Pickard was established in Edgerton, Wisconsin, in 1894 by Wilder Austin Pickard, then moved to Chicago in 1897. For some 40 years the Pickard China Studio, as the firm was then known, was a decorating company employing artists to hand-paint white blanks of bowls, pitchers, and other items obtained from factories in Europe.

In 1920, Pickard was incorporated and in 1938 moved to Antioch, Illinois, the site of the present pottery. Here the firm began making its own fine china. Today Pickard, Inc. is headed by Henry A. Pickard, a third generation descendant of the founder, making it the only American china company in the hands of the founding family.

In 1970, Pickard introduced its *Lockhart Wildlife* series, with artwork by James Lockhart. These plates were issued in pairs during the first four years of the series, but from 1974 individual plates were issued. The series ended in 1980. The *Christmas* series began in 1976 and closed in 1981, and in 1978 Pickard began the *Children of Renoir* series, which ended in 1980. Pickard began its *Mother's Love* series in 1980 with artwork by Irene Spencer. This series ended in 1983. In 1981, Pickard introduced *Oleg Cassini's Most Beautiful Women of All Time Collection*. This series closed in 1984. In 1982, the *Symphony of Roses* series began with artwork by Irene Spencer. This series ended in 1985.

## Lockhart Wildlife Series

Artist: James Lockhart. Artist's signature appears on front

China banded in 24k gold

Diameter: as indicated

No hanger

Edition size: as indicated

Numbered with certificate

**84-P29-1.1-1**
1970 *Woodcock*
Edition: 2,000
Diameter: 26.7 cm. (10½ in.)
Pair Issue price: $150.00

**84-P29-1.1-2**
1970 *Ruffed Grouse*

**84-P29-1.2-1**
1971 *Green-Winged Teal*
Edition: 2,000
Diameter: 26.7 cm. (10½ in.)
Pair Issue price: $150.00

**84-P29-1.2-2**
1971 *Mallard*

**84-P29-1.3-1**
1972 *Mockingbird*
Edition: 2,000
Diameter: 26.7 cm. (10½ in.)
Pair Issue price: $162.50

**84-P29-1.3-2**
1972 *Cardinal*

**84-P29-1.4-1**
1973 *Wild Turkey*
Edition: 2,000
Diameter: 26.7 cm. (10½ in.)
Pair Issue price: $162.50

**84-P29-1.4-2**
1973 *Ring-Necked Pheasant*

**84-P29-1.5**
1974 *American Bald Eagle*
Edition: 2,000
Diameter: 33 cm. (13 in.)
Issue price: $150.00

**84-P29-1.6**
1975 *White-Tailed Deer*
Edition: 2,500
Diameter: 27.9 cm. (11 in.)
Issue price: $100.00

**84-P29-1.7**
1976 *American Buffalo*
Edition: 2,500
Diameter: 33 cm. (13 in.)
Issue price: $165.00

**84-P29-1.8**
1977 *Great Horned Owl*
Edition:. 2,500
Diameter: 27.9 cm. (11 in.)
Issue price: $100.00

**84-P29-1.9**
1978 *American Panther*
Edition: 2,000
Diameter: 33 cm. (13 in.)
Issue price: $175.00

**84-P29-1.10**
1979 *Red Fox*
Edition: 2,500
Diameter: 27.9 cm. (11 in.)
Issue price: $120.00

**84-P29-1.11**
1980 *Trumpeter Swan*
Edition: 2,000
Diameter: 33 cm. (13 in.)
Issue price: $200.00
*Series Closed*

## Christmas Series

Artist: as indicated

China with 24k gold design on border

Diameter: 21 centimeters (8¼ inches)

No hanger

Edition size: as indicated

Numbered without certificate

**84-P29-2.1**
1976 *The Alba Madonna*
Artist: Raphael/Edition: 7,500
Issue price: $60.00

**84-P29-2.2**
1977 *The Nativity*
Artist: Lorenzo Lotto/Edition: 7,500
Issue price: $65.00

**84-P29-2.3**
1978 *The Rest on the Flight into Egypt*
Artist: Gerard David/Edition: 10,000
Issue price: $65.00

**84-P29-2.4**
1979 *Adoration of the Magi*
Artist: Botticelli/Edition: 10,000
Issue price: $70.00

**84-P29-2.5**
1980 *Madonna and Child with the Infant Saint John*
Artist: Sodoma/Edition: 10,000
Issue price: $80.00

**84-P29-2.6**
1981 *Madonna and Child with Angels*
Artist: Hans Memling/Edition: 10,000
Issue price: $90.00
*Series Closed*

# UNITED STATES
## PICKARD

### 84-P29-4.1

*Children of Renoir Series*

Artist: Pierre Auguste Renoir. Artist's signature appears on front

China banded in 24k gold

Diameter: 21 centimeters (8¼ inches)

No hanger

Edition size limited to 5,000. Two annual issues

Numbered without certificate

**84-P29-4.1**
1978 *A Girl with a Watering Can*
Issue price: $50.00

**84-P29-4.2**
1978 *Child in White*
Issue price: $50.00

**84-P29-4.3**
1979 *Girl with Hoop*
Issue price: $55.00

**84-P29-4.4**
1979 *At the Piano*
Issue price: $55.00

**84-P29-4.5**
1980 *Two Little Circus Girls*
Issue price: $60.00

**84-P29-4.6**
1980 *The Artist's Son Jean*
Issue price: $60.00
*Series Closed*

## Oleg Cassini's Most Beautiful Women of All Time Collection

Artist: Oleg Cassini. Artist's signature appears on front

China banded in 24k gold

Diameter: 26.7 centimeters (10½ inches)

No hanger

Edition size undisclosed, limited by year of issue

Numbered with certificate

**84-P29-5.1**
1981 *Helen of Troy*
Issue price: $75.00

**84-P29-5.2**
1982 *Marie Antoinette*
Issue price: $75.00

**84-P29-5.3**
1983 *Lillie Langtry*
Issue price: $75.00

**84-P29-5.4**
1984 *Salomé*
Issue price: $75.00
*Series Closed*

## Mother's Love Series

Artist: Irene Spencer. Artist's signature appears on front

China banded in 24k gold

Diameter: 23.8 centimeters (9⅜ inches)

No hanger

Edition size limited to 7,500

Numbered without certificate

**84-P29-6.1**
1980 *Miracle*
Issue price: $95.00

**84-P29-6.2**
1981 *Story Time*
Issue price: $110.00

**84-P29-6.3**

**84-P29-6.3**
1982 *First Edition*
Issue price: $115.00

**84-P29-6.4**
1983 *Precious Moment*
Issue price: $120.00
*Series Closed*

## *Symphony of Roses Series*

Artist: Irene Spencer. Artist's signature appears on front

China with scalloped, gold-rimmed border

Diameter: 23.8 centimeters (9⅜ inches)

No hanger

Edition size limited to 10,000

Numbered without certificate

**84-P29-8.1**
1982 *Wild Irish Rose*
Issue price: $85.00

**84-P29-8.2**
1983 *Yellow Rose of Texas*
Issue price: $90.00

**84-P29-8.3**
1984 *Honeysuckle Rose*
Issue price: $95.00

**84-P29-8.4**
1985 *Rose of Washington Square*
Issue price: $100.00
*Series Closed*

**84-R60-2.1** "Mary, Mary"
1979 Reco International *McClelland's Mother Goose*
Although the *Mother Goose* series was not artist John McClelland's first plate series, it is certainly the best-known among collectors. "Mary, Mary," the first plate in the series, quickly won collectors' hearts with its charming depiction of a favorite nursery rhyme, and apparently, it has never lost them. In today's market, "Mary, Mary" regularly sells for eight to 10 times its issue price.

## RECO INTERNATIONAL
Port Washington, New York

Reco International was founded in 1967 by Heio W. Reich who continues as its president. From the beginning the firm has been an importer and maker of limited-edition plates. The firm has won numerous awards from the National Association of Limited Edition Dealers, and in 1986, Mr. Reich received the coveted Lee Benson Award from this organization for his service to the collectibles industry.

*World of Children*, Reco International's first U.S. proprietary series, was introduced in 1977, with designs by John McClelland. The series ended in 1980. A second series with designs by the same artist, *McClelland's Mother Goose* series, was introduced in 1979. In 1981, Reco International began a third series, the *McClelland Children's Circus Collection* which ended in 1983. The *Days Gone By* series, with award-winning artwork by Sandra Kuck, began in 1983 and closed in 1985. The *Becky's Day* series, with artwork by John McClelland, began in 1985 and ended in 1987.

## *World of Children Series*

Artist: John McClelland. Artist's signature appears on front

China banded in 24k gold

Diameter: 26.7 centimeters (10½ inches)

No hanger

Edition size limited to 10,000 in 1977; 15,000 thereafter

Numbered with certificate since 1978

**84-R60-1.1**
*1977 Rainy Day Fun*
Issue price: $50.00

**84-R60-1.2**
*1978 When I Grow Up*
Issue price: $50.00

**84-R60-1.3**
*1979 You're Invited*
Issue price: $50.00

**84-R60-1.4**
*1980 Kittens for Sale*
Issue price: $50.00
*Series Closed*

## *McClelland's Mother Goose Series*

Artist: John McClelland. Artist's signature appears on front

China

Diameter: 21.6 centimeters (8½ inches)

No hanger

Edition size undisclosed, limited by year of issue

Numbered with certificate

**84-R60-2.1**
*1979 Mary, Mary*
Issue price: $22.50

**84-R60-2.2**
*1980 Little Boy Blue*
Issue price: $22.50

# UNITED STATES
## RECO INTERNATIONAL

**84-R60-2.3**

**84-R60-2.3**
1981 *Little Miss Muffet*
Issue price: $24.50

**84-R60-2.4**
1982 *Little Jack Horner*
Issue price: $24.50

**84-R60-2.5**
1983 *Little Bo Peep*
Issue price: $24.50

**84-R60-2.6**
1984 *Diddle, Diddle Dumpling*
Issue price: $24.50

**84-R60-2.7**
1985 *Mary Had a Little Lamb*
Issue price: $27.50

**84-R60-2.8**
1986 *Jack and Jill*
Issue price: $27.50

## McClelland Children's Circus Collection

Artist: John McClelland. Artist's signature appears on front

China

Diameter: 23.5 centimeters (9¼ inches)

No hanger

Edition size undisclosed, limited by announced period of issue

Numbered with certificate

**84-R60-3.1**
1981 *Tommy the Clown*
Issue price: $29.50

**84-R60-3.2**
1982 *Katie the Tightrope Walker*
Issue price: $29.50

**84-R60-3.3**
1983 *Johnny the Strongman*
Issue price: $29.50

**84-R60-3.4**
1983 *Maggie the Animal Trainer*
Issue price: $29.50
*Series Closed*

## Days Gone By Series

Artist: Sandra Kuck. Artist's signature appears on front

China banded in 23k gold

Diameter: 23.5 centimeters (9¼ inches)

No hanger

Edition size undisclosed, limited by announced period of issue

Numbered with certificate

**84-R60-8.1**
1983 *Sunday Best*
Issue price: $29.50

**84-R60-8.2**
1983 *Amy's Magic Horse*
Issue price: $29.50

**84-R60-8.3**
1984 *Little Anglers*
Issue price: $29.50

**84-R60-8.4**
1984 *Afternoon Recital*
Issue price: $29.50

**84-R60-8.5**
1984 *Little Tutor*
Issue price: $29.50

# UNITED STATES
## RECO INTERNATIONAL
### 84-R60-8.6

**84-R60-8.6**
1984 *Easter at Grandma's*
Issue price: $29.50

**84-R60-8.7**
1985 *Morning Song*
Issue price: $29.50

**84-R60-8.8**
1985 *Surrey Ride*
Issue price: $29.50
*Series Closed*

## *Becky's Day Series*

Artist: John McClelland. Artist's signature appears on front

China

Diameter: 21.6 centimeters (8½ inches)

No hanger

Edition size undisclosed, limited by announced period of issue

Numbered with certificate

**84-R60-10.1**
1985 *Awakening*
Issue price: $24.50

**84-R60-10.2**
1985 *Getting Dressed*
Issue price: $24.50

**84-R60-10.3**
1986 *Breakfast*
Issue price: $27.50

**84-R60-10.4**
1986 *Learning Is Fun*
Issue price: $27.50

**84-R60-10.5**
1986 *Muffin Making*
Issue price: $27.50

**84-R60-10.6**
1986 *Tub Time*
Issue price: $27.50

**84-R60-10.7**
1986 *Evening Prayer*
Issue price: $27.50
*Series Closed*

## REED & BARTON
Taunton, Massachusetts

Reed & Barton Silversmiths traces its origin to a factory established by Isaac Babbitt in the early 19th century. In 1824, Babbitt developed an alloy, harder and more lustrous than pewter, which he named Britannia metal. Henry G. Reed and Charles E. Barton, artists working for Babbitt, acquired the firm in the 1830s and continued to manufacture Brittania ware. In the late 1840s, the factory began to produce plated silverware. Reed & Barton was incorporated in 1888 and started producing solid silver services. Sterling flatware and hollowware soon replaced plated ware as their largest line. In 1903, the firm began reproducing colonial pewter ware.

In 1970 Reed & Barton began its *Christmas* series, which changed theme every three years. The first three plates are based on Christmas carols; the second three are based on 15th-century altar art; the next are based on American Christmas scenes; and the next depict 19th-century American illustrations. The series ended in 1981.

Artist Robert Johnson, whose works are in private collections throughout the United States, Europe and the Far East, developed the patented electroplating process used in the creation of the Reed & Barton *Christmas* series. The medium, known as Damascene silver, combines silver, gold, copper and bronze. The electroplating process is derived from a hand-craft method perfected at Damascus in the middle ages.

## Christmas Series

Artist: as indicated

Damascene silver

Diameter: 27.9 centimeters (11 inches) through 1978; 20.3 centimeters (8 inches) thereafter

No hanger

Edition size: as indicated

Numbered without certificate through 1978; numbered with certificate thereafter

**84-R18-2.1**
1970 *A Partridge in a Pear Tree*
Artist: Robert Johnson/Edition: 2,500
Issue price: $55.00

**84-R18-2.2**
1971 *We Three Kings of Orient Are*
Artist: Robert Johnson/Edition: 7,500
Issue price: $60.00

**84-R18-2.3**
1972 *Hark! The Herald Angels Sing*
Artist: Robert Johnson/Edition: 7,500
Issue price: $60.00

**84-R18-2.4**
1973 *Adoration of the Kings*
Artist: Rogier van der Weyden
Edition: 7,500
Issue price: $60.00

**84-R18-2.5**
1974 *The Adoration of the Magi*
Artist: Fra Angelico and Fra Lippi
Edition: 7,500
Issue price: $65.00

**84-R18-2.6**
1975 *Adoration of the Kings*
Artist: Steven Lochner/Edition: 7,500
Issue price: $65.00

**84-R18-2.7**
1976 *Morning Train*
Artist: Maxwell Mays/Edition: 7,500
Issue price: $65.00

**84-R18-2.8**
1977 *Decorating the Church*
Artist: Maxwell Mays/Edition: 7,500
Issue price: $65.00

**84-R18-2.9**
1978 *The General Store at Christmas Time*
Artist: Maxwell Mays/Edition: 7,500
Issue price: $65.00

**84-R18-2.10**
1979 *Merry Old Santa Claus*
Artist: Thomas Nast/Edition: 2,500
Issue price: $55.00

**84-R18-2.11**
1980 *Gathering Christmas Greens*
Artist: unknown/Edition: 2,500
Issue price: $65.00

**84-R18-2.12**
1981 *The Shopkeeper at Christmas*
Artist: W. L. Sheppard/Edition: 2,500
Issue price: $75.00
*Series Closed*

**84-R30-1.1** "Moses and the Ten Commandments"
1986 Rhodes Studios *Treasures of the Doré Bible*
Sculptor Merri Roderick translates the power and drama of the most famous Bible illustrations of the 19th century—the works of Gustave Doré—into the medium of fused bronze. This plate is the first among Bradex-listed editions to use this material.

## RHODES STUDIOS
Chicago, Illinois

Rhodes Studios searches the world to bring under its aegis the perfect union of artist and maker, to create limited editions of unusual and distinctive appeal. The firm's hallmark—the sign of the griffin—represents a mythical beast with the body of a lion and the head and wings of an eagle, which in medieval heraldry was a guardian of treasure. Today, this hallmark serves as a symbol of Rhodes Studios' dedication to the creation of "art that endures."

After first commissioning artist and sculptor Merri Roderick's work for the *Treasures of the Doré Bible* series, Rhodes located an American maker who was capable of producing her sculpture in the unique medium of hand-cast hand-finished fused bronze. This series was introduced in 1986.

## The Treasures of the Doré Bible Series

Artist: Merri Roderick. Artist's signature incised on front

Hand-cast fused bronze

Diameter: 21 centimeters (8¼ inches)

No hanger

Edition size undisclosed, limited by announced period of issue

Numbered, with certificate

**84-R30-1.1**
1986 *Moses and the Ten Commandments*
Issue price: $59.00

*River Shore, Ltd.*®

*Museum Quality Limited Editions*

## RIVER SHORE
Caledonia, Michigan

River Shore, Ltd. was established in 1975 to market limited-edition collectibles.

In 1976, River Shore began its *Famous Americans* series, the first collector's plates crafted in copper. This series, based on artwork by Norman Rockwell and sculpted by Roger Brown, ended in 1979. River Shore introduced its *Signs of Love* series in 1981 with artwork by Yin-Rei Hicks.

The company ceased production of collector's plates upon the completion of the *Signs of Love* series in 1985.

## Famous Americans Series

Artist: Roger Brown (after works by Norman Rockwell). Artist's signature appears on front along with name of Norman Rockwell

Copper

Diameter: 20.3 centimeters (8 inches)

No hanger

Edition size limited to 9,500

Numbered with certificate

**84-R69-1.1**
1976 *Lincoln*
Issue price: $40.00

**84-R69-1.2**
1977 *Rockwell*
Issue price: $45.00

**84-R69-1.3**
1978 *Peace Corps*
Issue price: $45.00

**84-R69-1.4**
1979 *Spirit of Lindbergh*
Issue price: $50.00
*Series Closed*

## Signs of Love Series

Artist: Yin-Rei Hicks. Artist's signature appears on front

China

Diameter: 21.6 centimeters (8½ inches)

No hanger

Edition size undisclosed, limited by announced period of issue

Numbered with certificate

**84-R69-2.1**
1981 *A Kiss for Mother*
Issue price: $18.50

**84-R69-2.2**
1981 *A Watchful Eye*
Issue price: $21.50

**84-R69-2.3**
1982 *A Gentle Persuasion*
Issue price: $21.50

**84-R69-2.4**
1983 *A Protective Embrace*
Issue price: $23.50

**84-R69-2.5**
1983 *A Tender Coaxing*
Issue price: $23.50

**84-R69-2.6**
1984 *A Reassuring Touch*
Issue price: $23.50

**84-R69-2.7**
1985 *A Trusting Hug*
Issue price: $26.50

**84-R69-2.8**
1985 *A Loving Guidance*
Issue price: $26.50
*Series Closed*

**84-R70-1.8** "Wrapped Up in Christmas"
1981 Rockwell Society *Christmas*
The Rockwell Society of America is recognized for its efforts to renew collector interest in obscure-but-worthy Rockwell works. Here, the simple elements of the overburdened boy and the playful dog demonstrate Rockwell's astounding story-telling ability and his gift for capturing the American character on canvas.

## ROCKWELL SOCIETY
Ardsley, New York

The Rockwell Society of America is a chartered non-profit organization devoted to the study and appreciation of the works of Norman Rockwell. The Society's *Christmas* series began in 1974, with the first issue manufactured by Ridgewood. Subsequent issues have been made by the Edwin M. Knowles China Company (see United States, KNOWLES). The *Mother's Day* series started in 1976 and the *Rockwell Heritage* series began in 1977. The *Rockwell's Rediscovered Women* series was introduced in 1981. It ended in 1984. The *Rockwell on Tour Collection* and *Rockwell's Light Campaign* series both started in 1983 and closed in 1984.

In 1985, the Rockwell Society introduced the first Rockwell series to earn recognition and endorsement by the Norman Rockwell Family Trust, comprised of Norman Rockwell's heirs. The first series to bear the seals of the Rockwell Society, Knowles and the Rockwell Family Trust is entitled *Rockwell's American Dream.*

*Rockwell's Colonials: The Rarest Rockwells* series, a tribute to the Colonial era of American history and a personal favorite of Norman Rockwell, followed in 1986. *A Mind of Her Own: Rockwell's Studies of Girlhood* series was also begun in 1986.

In 1987, the Rockwell Society introduced a series showing Norman Rockwell's insight into the "golden years" of adult life, titled *Rockwell's Golden Moments.*

## Christmas Series

Artist: Norman Rockwell. Artist's signature appears on front

China

Diameter: 21 centimeters
(8¼ inches)

No hanger

Edition size undisclosed, limited by announced period of issue

Numbered with certificate

**84-R70-1.1**
1974 *Scotty Gets His Tree*
Issue price: $24.50

**84-R70-1.2**
1975 *Angel with a Black Eye*
Issue price: $24.50

**84-R70-1.3**
1976 *Golden Christmas*
Issue price: $24.50

**84-R70-1.4**
1977 *Toy Shop Window*
Issue price: $24.50

**84-R70-1.5**
1978 *Christmas Dream*
Issue price: $24.50

**84-R70-1.6**
1979 *Somebody's Up There*
Issue price: $24.50

**84-R70-1.7**
1980 *Scotty Plays Santa*
Issue price: $24.50

**84-R70-1.8**
1981 *Wrapped Up in Christmas*
Issue price: $25.50

# UNITED STATES
## ROCKWELL SOCIETY

**84-R70-1.9**

**84-R70-1.9**
1982 *Christmas Courtship*
Issue price: $25.50

**84-R70-1.10**
1983 *Santa in the Subway*
Issue price: $25.50

**84-R70-1.11**
1984 *Santa in His Workshop*
Issue price: $27.50

**84-R70-1.12**
1985 *Grandpa Plays Santa*
Issue price: $27.50

**84-R70-1.13**
1986 *Deer Santy Claus*
Issue price: $27.90

**84-R70-1.14**
1987 *Santa's Golden Gift*
Issue price: $29.90

## Mother's Day Series

Artist: Norman Rockwell. Artist's signature appears on front

China

Diameter: 21.6 centimeters (8½ inches)

No hanger

Edition size undisclosed, limited by announced period of issue

Numbered with certificate

**84-R70-2.1**
1976 *A Mother's Love*
Issue price: $24.50

**84-R70-2.2**
1977 *Faith*
Issue price: $24.50

**84-R70-2.3**
1978 *Bedtime*
Issue price: $24.50

**84-R70-2.4**
1979 *Reflections*
Issue price: $24.50

**84-R70-2.5**
1980 *A Mother's Pride*
Issue price: $24.50

**84-R70-2.6**
1981 *After the Party*
Issue price: $24.50

**84-R70-2.7**
1982 *The Cooking Lesson*
Issue price: $25.50

**84-R70-2.8**
1983 *Add Two Cups and a Measure of Love*
Issue price: $25.50

**84-R70-2.9**
1984 *Grandma's Courting Dress*
Issue price: $25.50

**84-R70-2.10**
1985 *Mending Time*
Issue price: $27.50

**84-R70-2.11**
1986 *Pantry Raid*
Issue price: $27.90

# UNITED STATES
## ROCKWELL SOCIETY

## 84-R70-3.1

### *Rockwell Heritage Series*

Artist: Norman Rockwell. Artist's signature appears on front

China

Diameter: 21.6 centimeters (8½ inches)

No hanger

Edition size undisclosed, limited by announced period of issue

Numbered with certificate

**84-R70-3.1**
1977 *The Toy Maker*
Issue price: $14.50

**84-R70-3.2**
1978 *The Cobbler*
Issue price: $19.50

**84-R70-3.3**
1979 *The Lighthouse Keeper's Daughter*
Issue price: $19.50

**84-R70-3.4**
1980 *The Ship Builder*
Issue price: $19.50

**84-R70-3.5**
1981 *The Music Maker*
Issue price: $19.50

**84-R70-3.6**
1982 *The Tycoon*
Issue price: $19.50

**84-R70-3.7**
1983 *The Painter*
Issue price: $19.50

**84-R70-3.8**
1984 *The Storyteller*
Issue price: $19.50

**84-R70-3.9**
1985 *The Gourmet*
Issue price: $19.50

**84-R70-3.10**
1986 *The Professor*
Issue price: $22.90

**84-R70-3.11**
1987 *The Shadow Artist*
Issue price: $22.90

## Rockwell's Rediscovered Women Series

Artist: Norman Rockwell. Artist's signature appears on front

China

Diameter: 21.6 centimeters (8½ inches)

No hanger

Edition size undisclosed, limited by announced period of issue

Numbered with certificate

**84-R70-4.1**
1981 *Dreaming in the Attic*
Issue price: $19.50

**84-R70-4.2**
1982 *Waiting on the Shore*
Issue price: $22.50

**84-R70-4.3**
1983 *Pondering on the Porch*
Issue price: $22.50

**84-R70-4.4**
1983 *Making Believe at the Mirror*
Issue price: $22.50

**84-R70-4.5**
1983 *Waiting at the Dance*
Issue price: $22.50

**84-R70-4.6**
1983 *Gossiping in the Alcove*
Issue price: $22.50

**84-R70-4.7**
1983 *Standing in the Doorway*
Issue price: $22.50

**84-R70-4.8**
1983 *Flirting in the Parlor*
Issue price: $22.50

**84-R70-4.9**
1984 *Working in the Kitchen*
Issue price: $22.50

**84-R70-4.10**
1984 *Meeting on the Path*
Issue price: $22.50

**84-R70-4.11**
1984 *Confiding in the Den*
Issue price: $22.50

**84-R70-4.12**
1984 *Reminiscing in the Quiet*
Issue price: $22.50
*Series Closed*

## Rockwell on Tour Collection

Artist: Norman Rockwell. Artist's signature appears on front

Newellware with raised border

Diameter: 19.7 centimeters (7¾ inches)

No hanger

Edition size undisclosed, limited by announced period of issue

Numbered with certificate

**84-R70-5.1**
1983 *Walking through Merrie Englande*
Issue price: $16.00

**84-R70-5.2**
1983 *Promenade à Paris*
Issue price: $16.00

**84-R70-5.3**
1983 *When in Rome—*
Issue price: $16.00

**84-R70-5.4**
1984 *Die Walk am Rhein*
Issue price: $16.00
*Series Closed*

## Rockwell's Light Campaign Series

Artist: Norman Rockwell. Artist's signature appears on front

China banded in 14k gold

Diameter: 21.6 centimeters (8½ inches)

No hanger

Edition size undisclosed, limited by announced period of issue

Numbered with certificate

**84-R70-6.1**
1983 *This Is the Room That Light Made*
Issue price: $19.50

**84-R70-6.2**
1984 *Grandpa's Treasure Chest*
Issue price: $19.50

**84-R70-6.3**
1984 *Father's Help*
Issue price: $19.50

**84-R70-6.4**
1984 *Evening's Ease*
Issue price: $19.50

**84-R70-6.5**
1984 *Close Harmony*
Issue price: $21.50

**84-R70-6.6**
1984 *The Birthday Wish*
Issue price: $21.50
*Series Closed*

## Rockwell's American Dream Series

Artist: Norman Rockwell. Artist's signature appears on front

China banded in 14k gold

Diameter: 21.6 centimeters (8½ inches)

No hanger

Edition size undisclosed, limited by announced period of issue

Numbered with certificate

**84-R70-7.1**
1985 *A Young Girl's Dream*
Issue price: $19.90

**84-R70-7.2**
1985 *A Couple's Commitment*
Issue price: $19.90

**84-R70-7.3**
1985 *A Family's Full Measure*
Issue price: $22.90

**84-R70-7.4**
1986 *A Mother's Welcome*
Issue price: $22.90

**84-R70-7.5**
1986 *A Young Man's Dream*
Issue price: $22.90

**84-R70-7.6**
1986 *The Musician's Magic*
Issue price: $22.90

**84-R70-7.7**
1986 *An Orphan's Hope*
Issue price: $24.90

**84-R70-7.8**
1986 *Love's Reward*
Issue price: $24.90
*Series Closed*

## Rockwell's Colonials: The Rarest Rockwells Series

Artist: Norman Rockwell. Artist's signature appears on front

China banded in gold

Diameter: 23.5 centimeters (9¼ inches)

No hanger

Edition size undisclosed, limited by announced period of issue

Numbered with certificate

**84-R70-8.1**
1986 *The Unexpected Proposal*
Issue price: $27.90

**84-R70-8.2**
1986 *Words of Comfort*
Issue price: $27.90

**84-R70-8.3**
1986 *Light for the Winter*
Issue price: $30.90

**84-R70-8.4**
1987 *Portrait for a Bridegroom*
Issue price: $30.90

## *A Mind of Her Own Series*

Artist: Norman Rockwell. Artist's signature appears on front

China banded in gold

Diameter: 21.6 centimeters (8½ inches)

No hanger

Edition size undisclosed, limited by announced period of issue

Numbered with certificate

**84-R70-9.1**
1986 *Sitting Pretty*
Issue price: $19.90

**84-R70-9.2**
1987 *Serious Business*
Issue price: $24.90

*Rockwell's Golden
Moments Series*

Artist: Norman Rockwell. Artist's
signature appears on front

China banded in 22k gold

Diameter: 21.6 centimeters
(8½ inches)

No hanger

Edition size undisclosed, limited
by announced period of issue

Numbered, with certificate

**84-R70-10.1**
1987 *Grandpa's Gift*
Issue price: $19.90

# UNITED STATES
ROMAN

**84-R53-0.0**

## ROMAN
Roselle, Illinois

Founded in 1963 by Ronald T. Jedlinski, Roman concentrated its initial efforts on religious articles and giftware. Its first venture into the collectors' market was the Ceramica Excelsis line of limited-edition porcelains, which focussed on Biblical and inspirational subjects. Later, the company entered into association with the well-known illustrator Frances Hook, who worked closely with the firm to translate her illustrations of children into three-dimensional sculptures and plates. Mrs. Hook created Roman's first Bradex-listed series, *A Child's Play,* in 1982.

In 1986, Roman introduced the first collector's plate series created in the same indestructible polymer material as the famous Fontanini creche figures, for which it is the exclusive North American importer. The series, titled Fontanini Christmas Story, is deeply undersculpted, hand-painted and patinaed to a warm amber tone to give it the appearance of hand-carved wood.

## A Child's Play Series

Artist: Frances Hook. Artist's signature appears on front

China banded in 24k gold

Diameter: 21.6 centimeters (8½ inches)

No hanger

Edition size undisclosed, limited by announced period of issue

Numbered with certificate

**84-R53-1.1**
1982 *Kite Flying*
Issue price: $29.95

**84-R53-1.2**
1982 *Breezy Day*
Issue price: $29.95

**84-R53-1.3**
1984 *First Snow*
Issue price: $29.95

**84-R53-1.4**
1984 *Bathtub Sailor*
Issue price: $29.95
*Series Closed*

## Fontanini Christmas Story Series

Artist: Elio Simonetti. Artist's signature incised on front

Molded polymer material, hand-painted and patinaed

Diameter: 22 centimters (9 inches)

No hanger

Edition size undisclosed, limited to announced period of issue

Numbered, with certificate

**84-R53-12.1**
1986 *A King is Born*
Issue price: $60.00

**84-R53-12.2**
1987 *Oh Come, Let Us Adore Him*
Issue price: $60.00

**84-R61-0.0**

## ROYAL DEVON
Providence, Rhode Island

Royal Devon plates were manufactured by the Gorham Company (see United States, GORHAM). Both the *Christmas* series and *Mother's Day* series, bearing artwork by Norman Rockwell, began in 1975. Both series ended in 1980.

## Christmas Series

Artist: Norman Rockwell. Artist's signature appears on front

China banded in gold

Diameter: 21.6 centimeters (8½ inches)

No hanger

Edition size undisclosed, limited by year of issue

Not numbered, without certificate

**84-R61-1.1**
1975 *Downhill Daring*
Issue price: $24.50

**84-R61-1.2**
1976 *The Christmas Gift*
Issue price: $24.50

**84-R61-1.3**
1977 *The Big Moment*
Issue price: $27.50

**84-R61-1.4**
1978 *Puppets for Christmas*
Issue price: $27.50

**84-R61-1.5**
1979 *One Present Too Many*
Issue price: $31.50

**84-R61-1.6**
1980 *Gramps Meets Gramps*
Issue price: $33.00
*Series Closed*

# UNITED STATES
## ROYAL DEVON

### 84-R61-2.1

*Mother's Day Series*

Artist: Norman Rockwell. Artist's signature appears on front

China banded in gold

Diameter: 21.6 centimeters (8½ inches)

No hanger

Edition size undisclosed, limited by year of issue

Not numbered, without certificate

**84-R61-2.1**
1975 *Doctor and the Doll*
Issue price: $23.50

**84-R61-2.2**
1976 *Puppy Love*
Issue price: $24.50

**84-R61-2.3**
1977 *The Family*
Issue price: $24.50

**84-R61-2.4**
1978 *Mother's Day Off*
Issue price: $27.00

**84-R61-2.5**
1979 *Mother's Evening Out*
Issue price: $30.00

**84-R61-2.6**
1980 *Mother's Treat*
Issue price: $32.50
*Series Closed*

**84-V3-2.1** "Chief Sitting Bull"
1979 Vague Shadows *The Chieftains I*
This first issue by artist Gregory Perillo established him as a master of Western art in the eyes of plate collectors everywhere. Eagerly sought on the secondary market, "Sitting Bull" commands lofty prices whenever it is traded.

## VAGUE SHADOWS
Staten Island, New York

Vague Shadows, currently a division of Artaffects, Ltd., was established in 1977 to produce limited-edition works by artist Gregory Perillo. His *Chieftain I* series was introduced in 1979 and closed in 1981.

Mr. Perillo has won several awards for his limited-edition work, including a 1987 Silver Chalice Award for "Plate of the Year." Several other plate series with Indian themes—or covering such subjects as wildlife and children—are listed in the OVER-THE-COUNTER SECTION of this book under the Vague Shadows name.

## The Chieftains I Series

Artist: Gregory Perillo. Artist's signature appears on front

Overglaze-decorated porcelain banded in 24k gold

Diameter: 26 centimeters (10¼ inches)

No hanger

Edition size limited to 7,500

Numbered with certificate

**84-V3-2.1**
1979 *Chief Sitting Bull*
Issue price: $65.00

**84-V3-2.2**
1979 *Chief Joseph*
Issue price: $65.00

**84-V3-2.3**
1980 *Chief Red Cloud*
Issue price: $65.00

**84-V3-2.4**
1980 *Chief Geronimo*
Issue price: $65.00

**84-V3-2.5**
1981 *Chief Crazy Horse*
Issue price: $65.00
*Series Closed*

## VILETTA
Houston, Texas

Viletta China Company was started in 1959 in Roseberg, Oregon by Viletta West, who hand-painted china and sold it through stores in the Pacific Northwest. The firm is involved in many areas of the giftware and fine china field, including commemorative china items and limited-edition collector's plates.

In 1979, Viletta China moved from Roseberg to Houston, Texas.

The *Zolan's Children* series, by Donald Zolan, began in 1978 and was completed in 1981. The *Nutcracker Ballet Plate Collection* began in 1978 and ended in 1980. The artist for the series was Shell Fisher.

## Zolan's Children Series

Artist: Donald Zolan. Artist's signature appears on front

China

Diameter: 21.6 centimeters (8½ inches)

No hanger

Edition size undisclosed, limited by announced period of issue

Numbered with certificate

**84-V36-1.1**
1978 *Erik and Dandelion*
Issue price: $19.00

**84-V36-1.2**
1979 *Sabina in the Grass*
Issue price: $22.00

**84-V36-1.3**
1980 *By Myself*
Issue price: $24.00

**84-V36-1.4**
1981 *For You*
Issue price: $24.00
*Series Closed*

## Nutcracker Ballet Plate Collection

Artist: Shell Fisher. Artist's signature appears on front

China

Diameter: 21.6 centimeters (8½ inches)

No hanger

Edition size undisclosed, limited by announced period of issue

Numbered with certificate

**84-V36-2.1**
1978 *Clara and Nutcracker*
Issue price: $19.50

**84-V36-2.2**
1979 *A Gift from Godfather*
Issue price: $19.50

**84-V36-2.3**

**84-V36-2.3**
1979 *The Sugarplum Fairy*
Issue price: $19.50

**84-V36-2.4**
1979 *The Snow King and Queen*
Issue price: $19.50

**84-V36-2.5**
1980 *The Waltz of the Flowers*
Issue price: $19.50

**84-V36-2.6**
1980 *Clara and the Prince*
Issue price: $19.50
*Series Closed*

# The Bradford Exchange Current Quotations

All prices are in U.S. dollars; prices in other countries to be at the dollar buying rate in New York on the day of transaction. Every effort is made to maintain a uniform international open market with the most precise quotations of actual available prices which are subject to market demand.

### All Prices other than Issue Prices Subject to Daily Market Fluctuations

<table>
<tr><td>U.S. EDITION<br>PRICES AT<br>PRESS TIME</td><td>MARKET BRADEX 323<br>The Market Bradex is the Bradford Index based on current quote-price/issue-price ratio of 12 significant plate series.</td><td>Advances 258<br>Declines 420<br>Unchanged 652<br>New Listings 31<br>Total Listings 1479</td></tr>
</table>

| BRADEX NO. | | ISSUE PRICE | CLOSE | QUOTE | CHANGE |
|---|---|---|---|---|---|
| **CANADA** | | | | | |
| **Christian Bell Age of Steam** (8-C30-1) | | | | | |
| 8-C30-1.1 | 81 Symphony in Steam | 65.00 | 200.00 | 250.00 | −15.00 |
| 8-C30-1.2 | 82 Brief Encounter | 65.00 | 82.00 | 85.00 | +2.00 |
| 8-C30-1.3 | 83 No Contest | 65.00 | 160.00 | 163.00 | −1.00 |
| 8-C30-1.4 | 84 Timber Country | 65.00 | 75.00 | 115.00 | −4.00 |
| 8-C30-1.5 | 85 White Pass in Yukon | 65.00 | 65.00 | 70.00 | 0.00 |
| **Christian Bell Yesterday's Memories** (8-C30-8) | | | | | |
| 8-C30-8.1 | 84 Ice | 45.00 | 45.00 | 46.00 | 0.00 |
| 8-C30-8.2 | 84 Milk | 45.00 | 45.00 | 47.00 | +2.00 |
| **Dominion China, Ltd. Wings Upon the Wind** (8-D52-1) | | | | | |
| 8-D52-1.1 | 86 The Landing | 21.80 | 43.00 | 74.00 | 0.00 |
| 8-D52-1.2 | 86 The Nesting | 21.80 | 21.80 | 21.80◊ | 0.00 |
| 8-D52-1.3 | 86 The Courtship | 24.80 | 24.80 | 24.80◊ | 0.00 |
| 8-D52-1.4 | 87 The Family | 24.80 | 24.80 | 24.80◊ | 0.00 |
| 8-D52-1.5 | 87 Southward Bound | 24.80 | 24.80 | 24.80◊ | 0.00 |
| 8-D52-1.6 | 87 Winter Home | 24.80 | 24.80 | 24.80◊ | 0.00 |
| **Dominion China, Ltd. Reflections of Canadian Childhood** (8-D52-2) | | | | | |
| 8-D52-2.1 | 86 Dreams of Glory | 24.80 | 24.80 | 24.80◊ | 0.00 |
| 8-D52-2.2 | 86 Quiet Moment | 24.80 | 24.80 | 24.80◊ | 0.00 |
| **CHINA, THE PEOPLE'S REPUBLIC OF** | | | | | |
| **Imperial Ching-te Chen Beauties of the Red Mansion** (10-I50-1) | | | | | |
| 10-I50-1.1 | 86 Pao-chai | 27.92 | 27.92 | 27.92◊ | 0.00 |
| 10-I50-1.2 | 86 Yuan-chun | 27.92 | 27.92 | 27.92◊ | 0.00 |
| **TAIWAN, REPUBLIC OF CHINA** | | | | | |
| **Pavilion of T'sang Ying-Hsüan Chinese Childrens Games** (10-P8-1) | | | | | |
| 10-P8-1.1 | 86 Chinese Chess | 29.00 | 29.00 | 29.00◊ | 0.00 |
| 10-P8-1.2 | 86 Kite Flying | 29.00 | 29.00 | 29.00◊ | 0.00 |
| 10-P8-1.3 | 86 Spinning Tops | 32.00 | 32.00 | 32.00◊ | 0.00 |
| **DENMARK** | | | | | |
| **Bing & Grøndahl Christmas** (14-B36-1) | | | | | |
| 14-B36-1.1 | 95 Frozen Window | .50 | 3200.00 | 3400.00 | 0.00 |
| 14-B36-1.2 | 96 New Moon | .50 | 1680.00 | 1680.00 | +80.00 |
| 14-B36-1.3 | 97 Sparrows | .75 | 900.00 | 1000.00 | 0.00 |
| 14-B36-1.4 | 98 Roses and Star | .75 | 500.00 | 520.00 | +20.00 |
| 14-B36-1.5 | 99 Crows | .75 | 600.00 | 800.00 | 0.00 |
| 14-B36-1.6 | 00 Church Bells | .75 | 800.00 | 730.00 | +30.00 |
| 14-B36-1.7 | 01 Three Wise Men | 1.00 | 279.00 | 280.00 | 0.00 |
| 14-B36-1.8 | 02 Gothic Church Interior | 1.00 | 349.00 | 350.00 | +1.00 |
| 14-B36-1.9 | 03 Happy Expectation | 1.00 | 130.00 | 200.00 | 0.00 |
| 14-B36-1.10 | 04 Frederiksberg Hill | 1.00 | 123.00 | 124.00 | 0.00 |
| 14-B36-1.11 | 05 Christmas Night | 1.00 | 130.00 | 160.00 | +8.00 |
| 14-B36-1.12 | 06 Sleighing to Church | 1.00 | 87.00 | 90.00 | 0.00 |
| 14-B36-1.13 | 07 Little Match Girl | 1.00 | 133.00 | 125.00 | +5.00 |
| 14-B36-1.14 | 08 St. Petri Church | 1.00 | 65.00 | 80.00 | −1.00 |
| 14-B36-1.15 | 09 Yule Tree | 1.50 | 94.00 | 85.00 | +10.00 |
| 14-B36-1.16 | 10 The Old Organist | 1.50 | 109.00 | 100.00 | −9.00 |
| 14-B36-1.17 | 11 Angels and Shepherds | 1.50 | 84.00 | 85.00 | +1.00 |
| 14-B36-1.18 | 12 Going to Church | 1.50 | 79.00 | 70.00 | 0.00 |
| 14-B36-1.19 | 13 Bringing Home the Tree | 1.50 | 69.00 | 70.00 | 0.00 |
| 14-B36-1.20 | 14 Amalienborg Castle | 1.50 | 65.00 | 65.00 | +3.00 |
| 14-B36-1.21 | 15 Dog Outside Window | 1.50 | 125.00 | 130.00 | 0.00 |
| 14-B36-1.22 | 16 Sparrows at Christmas | 1.50 | 88.00 | 89.00 | 0.00 |
| 14-B36-1.23 | 17 Christmas Boat | 1.50 | 74.00 | 74.00 | 0.00 |
| 14-B36-1.24 | 18 Fishing Boat | 1.50 | 75.00 | 93.00 | −2.00 |
| 14-B36-1.25 | 19 Outside the Window | 2.00 | 70.00 | 70.00 | 0.00 |
| 14-B36-1.26 | 20 Hare in the Snow | 2.00 | 85.00 | 70.00 | 0.00 |
| 14-B36-1.27 | 21 Pigeons | 2.00 | 60.00 | 70.00 | 0.00 |
| 14-B36-1.28 | 22 Star of Bethlehem | 2.00 | 77.00 | 75.00 | +5.00 |
| 14-B36-1.29 | 23 The Ermitage | 2.00 | 69.00 | 69.00 | 0.00 |
| 14-B36-1.30 | 24 Lighthouse | 2.50 | 69.00 | 69.00 | 0.00 |
| 14-B36-1.31 | 25 Child's Christmas | 2.50 | 79.00 | 79.00 | 0.00 |
| 14-B36-1.32 | 26 Churchgoers | 2.50 | 98.00 | 90.00 | 0.00 |
| 14-B36-1.33 | 27 Skating Couple | 2.50 | 75.00 | 107.00 | 0.00 |
| 14-B36-1.34 | 28 Eskimos | 2.50 | 55.00 | 55.00 | 0.00 |
| 14-B36-1.35 | 29 Fox Outside Farm | 2.50 | 74.00 | 80.00 | 0.00 |
| 14-B36-1.36 | 30 Town Hall Square | 2.50 | 99.00 | 98.00 | +3.00 |
| 14-B36-1.37 | 31 Christmas Train | 2.50 | 70.00 | 80.00 | 0.00 |
| 14-B36-1.38 | 32 Lifeboat | 2.50 | 70.00 | 80.00 | −2.00 |
| 14-B36-1.39 | 33 Korsor Nyborg Ferry | 3.00 | 85.00 | 75.00 | −5.00 |
| 14-B36-1.40 | 34 Church Bell in Tower | 3.00 | 72.00 | 72.00 | 0.00 |
| 14-B36-1.41 | 35 Lillebelt Bridge | 3.00 | 85.00 | 85.00 | 0.00 |
| 14-B36-1.42 | 36 Royal Guard | 3.00 | 65.00 | 75.00 | 0.00 |
| 14-B36-1.43 | 37 Arrival of Christmas Guests | 3.00 | 99.00 | 99.00 | +14.00 |
| 14-B36-1.44 | 38 Lighting the Candles | 3.00 | 114.00 | 114.00 | +3.00 |
| 14-B36-1.45 | 39 Ole Lock-Eye, the Sandman | 3.00 | 165.00 | 150.00 | +10.00 |
| 14-B36-1.46 | 40 Christmas Letters | 4.00 | 135.00 | 135.00 | 0.00 |
| 14-B36-1.47 | 41 Horses Enjoying Meal | 4.00 | 250.00 | 288.00 | 0.00 |
| 14-B36-1.48 | 42 Danish Farm | 4.00 | 175.00 | 172.00 | +3.00 |
| 14-B36-1.49 | 43 Ribe Cathedral | 5.00 | 120.00 | 120.00 | 0.00 |
| 14-B36-1.50 | 44 Sorgenfri Castle | 5.00 | 104.00 | 110.00 | 0.00 |
| 14-B36-1.51 | 45 The Old Water Mill | 5.00 | 140.00 | 140.00 | 0.00 |
| 14-B36-1.52 | 46 Commemoration Cross | 5.00 | 91.00 | 90.00 | 0.00 |
| 14-B36-1.53 | 47 Dybbol Mill | 5.00 | 108.00 | 105.00 | 0.00 |
| 14-B36-1.54 | 48 Watchman | 5.50 | 75.00 | 75.00 | −4.00 |
| 14-B36-1.55 | 49 Landsoldaten | 5.50 | 75.00 | 75.00 | 0.00 |
| 14-B36-1.56 | 50 Kronborg Castle | 5.50 | 100.00 | 100.00 | 0.00 |
| 14-B36-1.57 | 51 Jens Bang | 6.00 | 96.00 | 100.00 | +3.00 |
| 14-B36-1.58 | 52 Thorvaldsen Museum | 6.00 | 81.00 | 90.00 | −2.00 |
| 14-B36-1.59 | 53 Royal Boat | 7.00 | 95.00 | 99.00 | 0.00 |
| 14-B36-1.60 | 54 Snowman | 7.50 | 105.00 | 105.00 | +8.00 |
| 14-B36-1.61 | 55 Kalundborg Church | 8.00 | 95.00 | 103.00 | 0.00 |
| 14-B36-1.62 | 56 Christmas in Copenhagen | 8.50 | 110.00 | 130.00 | 0.00 |
| 14-B36-1.63 | 57 Christmas Candles | 9.00 | 127.00 | 128.00 | 0.00 |
| 14-B36-1.64 | 58 Santa Claus | 9.50 | 76.00 | 99.00 | 0.00 |
| 14-B36-1.65 | 59 Christmas Eve | 10.00 | 80.00 | 90.00 | 0.00 |
| 14-B36-1.66 | 60 Village Church | 10.00 | 134.00 | 140.00 | 0.00 |
| 14-B36-1.67 | 61 Winter Harmony | 10.50 | 80.00 | 95.00 | 0.00 |
| 14-B36-1.68 | 62 Winter Night | 11.00 | 59.00 | 60.00 | 0.00 |
| 14-B36-1.69 | 63 The Christmas Elf | 11.00 | 85.00 | 85.00 | 0.00 |
| 14-B36-1.70 | 64 The Fir Tree and Hare | 11.50 | 40.00 | 50.00 | 0.00 |
| 14-B36-1.71 | 65 Bringing Home the Tree | 12.00 | 40.00 | 53.00 | −5.00 |
| 14-B36-1.72 | 66 Home for Christmas | 12.00 | 38.00 | 45.00 | 0.00 |
| 14-B36-1.73 | 67 Sharing the Joy | 13.00 | 34.00 | 40.00 | 0.00 |
| 14-B36-1.74 | 68 Christmas in Church | 14.00 | 25.00 | 25.00 | 0.00 |
| 14-B36-1.75 | 69 Arrival of Guests | 14.00 | 14.00 | 15.00 | 0.00 |
| 14-B36-1.76 | 70 Pheasants in Snow | 14.50 | 14.00 | 15.00 | 0.00 |
| 14-B36-1.77 | 71 Christmas at Home | 15.00 | 12.00 | 15.00 | 0.00 |
| 14-B36-1.78 | 72 Christmas in Greenland | 16.50 | 10.00 | 12.00 | 0.00 |
| 14-B36-1.79 | 73 Country Christmas | 19.50 | 19.00 | 21.00 | +2.00 |
| 14-B36-1.80 | 74 Christmas in the Village | 22.00 | 14.00 | 18.00 | 0.00 |
| 14-B36-1.81 | 75 Old Water Mill | 27.50 | 15.00 | 15.00 | 0.00 |
| 14-B36-1.82 | 76 Christmas Welcome | 27.50 | 22.00 | 22.00 | 0.00 |
| 14-B36-1.83 | 77 Copenhagen Christmas | 29.50 | 15.00 | 15.00 | 0.00 |
| 14-B36-1.84 | 78 Christmas Tale | 32.00 | 24.00 | 25.00 | −5.00 |
| 14-B36-1.85 | 79 White Christmas | 36.50 | 29.00 | 32.00 | 0.00 |
| 14-B36-1.86 | 80 Christmas in Woods | 42.50 | 24.00 | 29.00 | 0.00 |
| 14-B36-1.87 | 81 Christmas Peace | 49.50 | 20.00 | 45.00 | 0.00 |
| 14-B36-1.88 | 82 Christmas Tree | 54.50 | 26.00 | 30.00 | −1.00 |
| 14-B36-1.89 | 83 Christmas in Old Town | 54.50 | 34.00 | 43.00 | −2.00 |
| 14-B36-1.90 | 84 Christmas Letter | 54.50 | 40.00 | 44.00 | −1.00 |
| 14-B36-1.91 | 85 Christmas Eve at the Farmhouse | 54.50 | 34.00 | 40.00 | −4.00 |
| 14-B36-1.92 | 86 Silent Night | 54.50 | 45.00 | 50.00 | −4.50 |
| 14-B36-1.93 | 87 Snowman's Christmas | 59.50 | 59.50 | 59.50◊ | 0.00 |
| **Bing & Grøndahl Mother's Day** (14-B36-3) | | | | | |
| 14-B36-3.1 | 69 Dog and Puppies | 9.75 | 300.00 | 400.00 | 0.00 |
| 14-B36-3.2 | 70 Bird and Chicks | 10.00 | 18.00 | 20.00 | 0.00 |
| 14-B36-3.3 | 71 Cat and Kitten | 11.00 | 8.00 | 11.00 | 0.00 |

**Price Explanation: ISSUE:** Price when first issued. **CLOSE:** Last traded price on the Exchange. **QUOTE:** The Exchange's best estimate of market price in the current bi-monthly trading period. **CHANGE:** Increase or decrease in QUOTE price since previous bi-monthly trading period. **NOTE:** Plates identified with this diamond symbol ◊ are quoted at issue price. All prices are subject to daily fluctuation.

| BRADEX NO. | | ISSUE PRICE | CLOSE | QUOTE | CHANGE |
|---|---|---|---|---|---|
| **14-B36-3.4** | 72 Mare and Foal | 12.00 | 9.00 | **10.00** | 0.00 |
| **14-B36-3.5** | 73 Duck and Ducklings | 13.00 | 10.00 | **12.00** | 0.00 |
| **14-B36-3.6** | 74 Bear and Cubs | 16.50 | 14.00 | **14.00** | −2.00 |
| **14-B36-3.7** | 75 Doe and Fawns | 19.50 | 11.00 | **13.00** | 0.00 |
| **14-B36-3.8** | 76 Swan and Cygnets | 22.50 | 18.00 | **20.00** | 0.00 |
| **14-B36-3.9** | 77 Squirrel and Young | 23.50 | 18.00 | **22.00** | 0.00 |
| **14-B36-3.10** | 78 Heron | 24.50 | 15.00 | **17.00** | −2.00 |
| **14-B36-3.11** | 79 Fox and Cubs | 27.50 | 25.00 | **29.00** | −1.00 |
| **14-B36-3.12** | 80 Woodpecker and Young | 29.50 | 30.00 | **33.00** | −3.00 |
| **14-B36-3.13** | 81 Hare and Young | 36.50 | 27.00 | **34.00** | 0.00 |
| **14-B36-3.14** | 82 Lioness and Cubs | 39.50 | 22.00 | **30.00** | 0.00 |
| **14-B36-3.15** | 83 Raccoon and Young | 39.50 | 29.00 | **30.00** | −2.00 |
| **14-B36-3.16** | 84 Stork and Her Nestlings | 39.50 | 28.00 | **32.00** | −4.00 |
| **14-B36-3.17** | 85 Bear and Cubs | 39.50 | 29.00 | **36.00** | −1.00 |
| **14-B36-3.18** | 86 Elephant with Calf | 39.50 | 65.00 | **65.00** | +25.50 |
| **14-B36-3.19** | 87 Sheep and Lamb | 42.50 | 43.00 | **42.50** | 0.00 |
| **Bing & Grøndahl Moments of Truth** (14-B36-7) | | | | | |
| **14-B36-7.1** | 84 Home is Best | 29.50 | 30.00 | **34.00** | +2.00 |
| **14-B36-7.2** | 84 Road to Virtuosity | 29.50 | 30.00 | **40.00** | +6.00 |
| **14-B36-7.3** | 85 First Things First | 29.50 | 30.00 | **36.00** | 0.00 |
| **14-B36-7.4** | 85 Unfair Competition | 29.50 | 30.00 | **32.00** | 0.00 |
| **14-B36-7.5** | 86 Bored Sick | 29.50 | 32.00 | **36.00** | 0.00 |
| **14-B36-7.6** | 86 First Crush | 29.50 | 34.00 | **33.00** | +3.00 |
| **Bing & Grøndahl Children's Day** (14-B36-13) | | | | | |
| **14-B36-13.1** | 85 The Magical Tea Party | 24.50 | 17.00 | **20.00** | −5.00 |
| **14-B36-13.2** | 86 A Joyful Flight | 26.50 | 24.00 | **27.00** | 0.00 |
| **Bing & Grøndahl Family Portraits** (14-B36-20) | | | | | |
| **14-B36-20.1** | 86 The Card Sharks | 35.50 | 35.50 | **35.50**◊ | 0.00 |
| **14-B36-20.2** | 87 The Intruder | 35.50 | 35.50 | **35.50**◊ | 0.00 |
| **Bing & Grøndahl Summer at Skagen** (14-B36-22) | | | | | |
| **14-B36-22.1** | 86 Summer Evening/Artists Wife | 34.50 | 50.00 | **43.00** | +8.00 |
| **14-B36-22.2** | 87 Luncheon at Kroyer's | 34.50 | 34.50 | **34.50**◊ | 0.00 |
| **14-B36-22.3** | 87 Hip, Hip, Hurrah | 34.50 | 34.50 | **34.50**◊ | 0.00 |
| **Grande Copenhagen Christmas** (14-G65-1) | | | | | |
| **14-G65-1.1** | 75 Alone Together | 24.50 | 25.00 | **25.00** | 0.00 |
| **14-G65-1.2** | 76 Christmas Wreath | 24.50 | 25.00 | **25.00** | 0.00 |
| **14-G65-1.3** | 77 Fishwives at Gammelstrand | 26.50 | 27.00 | **30.00** | 0.00 |
| **14-G65-1.4** | 78 Hans Christian Andersen | 32.50 | 33.00 | **37.00** | +2.00 |
| **14-G65-1.5** | 79 Pheasants | 34.50 | 51.00 | **51.00** | 0.00 |
| **14-G65-1.6** | 80 Snow Queen in the Tivoli | 39.50 | 40.00 | **40.00** | 0.00 |
| **14-G65-1.7** | 81 Little Match Girl in Nyhavn | 42.50 | 43.00 | **45.00** | 0.00 |
| **14-G65-1.8** | 82 Shepherdess/Chimney Sweep | 45.00 | 45.00 | **50.00** | 0.00 |
| **14-G65-1.9** | 83 Little Mermaid Near Kronborg | 45.00 | 125.00 | **130.00** | +5.00 |
| **14-G65-1.10** | 84 Sandman at Amalienborg | 45.00 | 62.00 | **62.00** | −2.00 |
| **Grande Copenhagen Ugly Duckling** (14-G65-2) | | | | | |
| **14-G65-2.1** | 85 Not Like the Others | 29.00 | 20.00 | **30.00** | −2.00 |
| **14-G65-2.2** | 86 He Will Grow Up Strong | 29.00 | 29.00 | **33.00** | +4.00 |
| **14-G65-2.3** | 86 Come With Us | 32.00 | 35.00 | **35.00** | +3.00 |
| **14-G65-2.4** | 86 You Don't Understand Me | 32.00 | 40.00 | **35.00** | +3.00 |
| **14-G65-2.5** | 86 What Beautiful Birds | 32.00 | 32.00 | **32.00**◊ | 0.00 |
| **14-G65-2.6** | 86 Most Beautiful of All | 32.00 | 32.00 | **32.00**◊ | 0.00 |
| | Complete Collection | 186.00 | 188.00 | **197.00** | +8.00 |
| **Royal Copenhagen Christmas** (14-R59-1) | | | | | |
| **14-R59-1.1** | 08 Madonna and Child | 1.00 | 1900.00 | **1900.00** | 0.00 |
| **14-R59-1.2** | 09 Danish Landscape | 1.00 | 169.00 | **169.00** | 0.00 |
| **14-R59-1.3** | 10 The Magi | 1.00 | 140.00 | **140.00** | 0.00 |
| **14-R59-1.4** | 11 Danish Landscape | 1.00 | 174.00 | **180.00** | 0.00 |
| **14-R59-1.5** | 12 Christmas Tree | 1.00 | 134.00 | **135.00** | 0.00 |
| **14-R59-1.6** | 13 Frederik's Church Spire | 1.50 | 125.00 | **125.00** | 0.00 |
| **14-R59-1.7** | 14 Holy Spirit Church | 1.50 | 120.00 | **125.00** | +5.00 |
| **14-R59-1.8** | 15 Danish Landscape | 1.50 | 0.00 | **194.00** | 0.00 |
| **14-R59-1.9** | 16 Shepherd on Christmas Night | 1.50 | 90.00 | **103.00** | +3.00 |
| **14-R59-1.10** | 17 Our Savior's Church Tower | 2.00 | 70.00 | **75.00** | 0.00 |
| **14-R59-1.11** | 18 Sheep and Shepherds | 2.00 | 80.00 | **80.00** | 0.00 |
| **14-R59-1.12** | 19 In the Park | 2.00 | 108.00 | **108.00** | 0.00 |
| **14-R59-1.13** | 20 Mary with Child Jesus | 2.00 | 70.00 | **83.00** | −3.00 |
| **14-R59-1.14** | 21 Aabenraa Marketplace | 2.00 | 70.00 | **90.00** | 0.00 |
| **14-R59-1.15** | 22 Three Singing Angels | 2.00 | 65.00 | **65.00** | 0.00 |
| **14-R59-1.16** | 23 Danish Landscape | 2.00 | 80.00 | **80.00** | 0.00 |
| **14-R59-1.17** | 24 Christmas Star and Sailing Ship | 2.00 | 78.00 | **105.00** | +5.00 |
| **14-R59-1.18** | 25 Christianshavn Street Scene | 2.00 | 90.00 | **90.00** | 0.00 |
| **14-R59-1.19** | 26 Christianshavn Canal | 2.00 | 75.00 | **75.00** | 0.00 |
| **14-R59-1.20** | 27 Ship's Boy at Tiller | 2.00 | 130.00 | **135.00** | 0.00 |
| **14-R59-1.21** | 28 Vicar's Family | 2.00 | 60.00 | **63.00** | +3.00 |
| **14-R59-1.22** | 29 Grundtvig Church | 2.00 | 98.00 | **98.00** | +6.00 |
| **14-R59-1.23** | 30 Fishing Boats | 2.50 | 129.00 | **115.00** | +7.00 |
| **14-R59-1.24** | 31 Mother and Child | 2.50 | 115.00 | **115.00** | 0.00 |
| **14-R59-1.25** | 32 Frederiksberg Gardens | 2.50 | 125.00 | **125.00** | 0.00 |
| **14-R59-1.26** | 33 Great Belt Ferry | 2.50 | 117.00 | **117.00** | 0.00 |
| **14-R59-1.27** | 34 The Hermitage Castle | 2.50 | 120.00 | **98.00** | +10.00 |
| **14-R59-1.28** | 35 Kronborg Castle | 2.50 | 140.00 | **143.00** | +3.00 |
| **14-R59-1.29** | 36 Roskilde Cathedral | 2.50 | 148.00 | **155.00** | +7.00 |
| **14-R59-1.30** | 37 Main Street Copenhagen | 2.50 | 150.00 | **159.00** | 0.00 |
| **14-R59-1.31** | 38 Round Church Osterlars | 3.00 | 184.00 | **190.00** | +6.00 |
| **14-R59-1.32** | 39 Greenland Pack-Ice | 3.00 | 200.00 | **163.00** | 0.00 |
| **14-R59-1.33** | 40 The Good Shepherd | 3.00 | 90.00 | **300.00** | 0.00 |
| **14-R59-1.34** | 41 Danish Village Church | 3.00 | 299.00 | **299.00** | 0.00 |
| **14-R59-1.35** | 42 Bell Tower | 4.00 | 250.00 | **250.00** | 0.00 |
| **14-R59-1.36** | 43 Flight Into Egypt | 4.00 | 400.00 | **450.00** | 0.00 |
| **14-R59-1.37** | 44 Danish Winter Scene | 4.00 | 195.00 | **203.00** | +4.00 |
| **14-R59-1.38** | 45 A Peaceful Motif | 4.00 | 302.00 | **300.00** | 0.00 |
| **14-R59-1.39** | 46 Zealand Village Church | 4.00 | 145.00 | **150.00** | 0.00 |
| **14-R59-1.40** | 47 The Good Shepherd | 4.50 | 194.00 | **205.00** | +5.00 |
| **14-R59-1.41** | 48 Nodebo Church | 4.50 | 165.00 | **165.00** | 0.00 |
| **14-R59-1.42** | 49 Our Lady's Cathedral | 5.00 | 125.00 | **125.00** | 0.00 |
| **14-R59-1.43** | 50 Boeslunde Church | 5.00 | 175.00 | **170.00** | +5.00 |
| **14-R59-1.44** | 51 Christmas Angel | 5.00 | 220.00 | **246.00** | −4.00 |
| **14-R59-1.45** | 52 Christmas in Forest | 5.00 | 123.00 | **105.00** | +10.00 |
| **14-R59-1.46** | 53 Frederiksberg Castle | 6.00 | 70.00 | **106.00** | +3.00 |
| **14-R59-1.47** | 54 Amalienborg Palace | 6.00 | 90.00 | **125.00** | +2.00 |
| **14-R59-1.48** | 55 Fano Girl | 7.00 | 185.00 | **210.00** | 0.00 |
| **14-R59-1.49** | 56 Rosenborg Castle | 7.00 | 125.00 | **125.00** | 0.00 |
| **14-R59-1.50** | 57 The Good Shepherd | 8.00 | 75.00 | **83.00** | −2.00 |
| **14-R59-1.51** | 58 Sunshine over Greenland | 9.00 | 100.00 | **103.00** | 0.00 |
| **14-R59-1.52** | 59 Christmas Night | 9.00 | 85.00 | **90.00** | 0.00 |
| **14-R59-1.53** | 60 The Stag | 10.00 | 110.00 | **130.00** | 0.00 |
| **14-R59-1.54** | 61 Training Ship Danmark | 10.00 | 118.00 | **120.00** | 0.00 |
| **14-R59-1.55** | 62 The Little Mermaid | 11.00 | 160.00 | **190.00** | +10.00 |
| **14-R59-1.56** | 63 Hojsager Mill | 11.00 | 35.00 | **75.00** | 0.00 |
| **14-R59-1.57** | 64 Fetching the Christmas Tree | 11.00 | 45.00 | **53.00** | −2.00 |
| **14-R59-1.58** | 65 Little Skaters | 12.00 | 45.00 | **45.00** | 0.00 |
| **14-R59-1.59** | 66 Blackbird at Christmas | 12.00 | 27.00 | **30.00** | 0.00 |

| BRADEX NO. | | ISSUE PRICE | CLOSE | QUOTE | CHANGE |
|---|---|---|---|---|---|
| **14-R59-1.60** | 67 The Royal Oak | 13.00 | 25.00 | **32.00** | −2.00 |
| **14-R59-1.61** | 68 The Last Umiak | 13.00 | 20.00 | **23.00** | +3.00 |
| **14-R59-1.62** | 69 The Old Farmyard | 14.00 | 25.00 | **25.00** | −3.00 |
| **14-R59-1.63** | 70 Christmas Rose and Cat | 14.00 | 39.00 | **40.00** | 0.00 |
| **14-R59-1.64** | 71 Hare in Winter | 15.00 | 15.00 | **15.00** | 0.00 |
| **14-R59-1.65** | 72 In the Desert | 16.00 | 20.00 | **20.00** | 0.00 |
| **14-R59-1.66** | 73 Train Homeward Bound | 22.00 | 18.00 | **22.00** | −2.00 |
| **14-R59-1.67** | 74 Winter Twilight | 22.00 | 21.00 | **23.00** | 0.00 |
| **14-R59-1.68** | 75 Queen's Palace | 27.50 | 13.00 | **13.00** | 0.00 |
| **14-R59-1.69** | 76 Danish Watermill | 27.50 | 35.00 | **35.00** | +5.00 |
| **14-R59-1.70** | 77 Immervad Bridge | 32.00 | 28.00 | **29.00** | +3.00 |
| **14-R59-1.71** | 78 Greenland Scenery | 35.00 | 19.00 | **25.00** | 0.00 |
| **14-R59-1.72** | 79 Choosing Christmas Tree | 42.50 | 69.00 | **66.00** | +1.00 |
| **14-R59-1.73** | 80 Bringing Home the Tree | 49.50 | 29.00 | **31.00** | −4.00 |
| **14-R59-1.74** | 81 Admiring Christmas Tree | 52.50 | 29.00 | **35.00** | 0.00 |
| **14-R59-1.75** | 82 Waiting For Christmas | 54.50 | 40.00 | **54.00** | −1.00 |
| **14-R59-1.76** | 83 Merry Christmas | 54.50 | 34.00 | **38.00** | 0.00 |
| **14-R59-1.77** | 84 Jingle Bells | 54.50 | 30.00 | **36.00** | 0.00 |
| **14-R59-1.78** | 85 Snowman | 54.50 | 50.00 | **51.00** | −3.00 |
| **14-R59-1.79** | 86 Wait For Me | 54.50 | 59.00 | **64.00** | +9.50 |
| **14-R59-1.80** | 87 Winter Birds | 59.50 | 59.50 | **59.50**◊ | 0.00 |
| **Royal Copenhagen Motherhood** (14-R59-4) | | | | | |
| **14-R59-4.1** | 82 Mother Robin and Babies | 29.50 | 25.00 | **28.00** | 0.00 |
| **14-R59-4.2** | 83 Mother Cat and Kitten | 29.50 | 32.00 | **32.00** | 0.00 |
| **14-R59-4.3** | 84 Mare and Foal | 29.50 | 26.00 | **26.00** | −1.00 |
| **14-R59-4.4** | 85 Rabbit and Bunny | 29.50 | 32.00 | **34.00** | +1.00 |
| **14-R59-4.5** | 86 Dog and Puppies | 32.50 | 35.00 | **38.00** | 0.00 |
| **14-R59-4.6** | 87 Goat and Kid | 37.50 | 44.00 | **40.00** | +2.50 |

## FINLAND

| BRADEX NO. | | ISSUE PRICE | CLOSE | QUOTE | CHANGE |
|---|---|---|---|---|---|
| **Arabia Kalevala** (16-A69-1) | | | | | |
| **16-A69-1.1** | 76 Vainamoinen's Sowing | 30.00 | 250.00 | **255.00** | −5.00 |
| **16-A69-1.2** | 77 Aino's Fate | 30.00 | 20.00 | **30.00** | 0.00 |
| **16-A69-1.3** | 78 Lemminkainen's Chase | 39.00 | 38.00 | **40.00** | 0.00 |
| **16-A69-1.4** | 79 Kullervo's Revenge | 39.50 | 30.00 | **35.00** | +2.00 |
| **16-A69-1.5** | 80 Vainamoinen's Rescue | 45.00 | 60.00 | **65.00** | 0.00 |
| **16-A69-1.6** | 81 Vainamoinen's Magic | 49.50 | 40.00 | **43.00** | +3.00 |
| **16-A69-1.7** | 82 Joukahainen Shoots Horse | 55.50 | 35.00 | **47.00** | +3.00 |
| **16-A69-1.8** | 83 Lemminkainen's Escape | 60.00 | 90.00 | **85.00** | −5.00 |
| **16-A69-1.9** | 84 Lemminkainen's Magic Feathers | 60.00 | 90.00 | **90.00** | +1.00 |
| **16-A69-1.10** | 85 Vainamoinen's Grief | 60.00 | 88.00 | **85.00** | −3.00 |
| **16-A69-1.11** | 86 Osmatar creating Ale | 60.00 | 75.00 | **72.00** | +2.00 |

## FRANCE

| BRADEX NO. | | ISSUE PRICE | CLOSE | QUOTE | CHANGE |
|---|---|---|---|---|---|
| **Georges Boyer Alice in Wonderland** (18-B61-1) | | | | | |
| **18-B61-1.1** | 82 Alice and the White Rabbit | 36.96 | 37.00 | **37.00** | 0.00 |
| **18-B61-1.2** | 83 Alice and the Caterpillar | 36.96 | 37.00 | **37.00** | 0.00 |
| **18-B61-1.3** | 83 Alice and the Cheshire Cat | 36.96 | 37.00 | **37.00** | 0.00 |
| **18-B61-1.4** | 83 Alice and the Mad Hatter | 36.96 | 44.00 | **47.00** | −3.00 |
| **18-B61-1.5** | 84 Painting the Roses | 36.96 | 37.00 | **40.00** | 0.00 |
| **18-B61-1.6** | 84 Alice and the Croquet Game | 36.96 | 37.00 | **40.00** | 0.00 |
| **18-B61-1.7** | 84 The Gryphon and Mock Turtle | 36.96 | 37.00 | **40.00** | 0.00 |
| **18-B61-1.8** | 84 The Knave of Hearts | 36.96 | 52.00 | **53.00** | 0.00 |
| | Complete Collection | 295.68 | 318.00 | **331.00** | −3.00 |
| **D'Arceau-Limoges Lafayette Legacy** (18-D15-1) | | | | | |
| **18-D15-1.1** | 73 The Secret Contract | 14.82 | 15.00 | **15.00** | 0.00 |
| **18-D15-1.2** | 73 North Island Landing | 19.82 | 20.00 | **20.00** | 0.00 |
| **18-D15-1.3** | 74 City Tavern Meeting | 19.82 | 20.00 | **20.00** | 0.00 |
| **18-D15-1.4** | 74 Battle of Brandywine | 19.82 | 20.00 | **20.00** | 0.00 |
| **18-D15-1.5** | 75 Messages to Franklin | 19.82 | 20.00 | **20.00** | 0.00 |
| **18-D15-1.6** | 75 Siege at Yorktown | 19.82 | 20.00 | **20.00** | 0.00 |
| | Complete Collection | 113.92 | 115.00 | **115.00** | 0.00 |
| **D'Arceau-Limoges Noël Vitrail** (18-D15-2) | | | | | |
| **18-D15-2.1** | 75 La Fuite en Egypte | 24.32 | 25.00 | **25.00** | 0.00 |
| **18-D15-2.2** | 76 Dans la Creche | 24.32 | 25.00 | **30.00** | 0.00 |
| **18-D15-2.3** | 77 Refus d'Hebergement | 24.32 | 25.00 | **28.00** | −2.00 |
| **18-D15-2.4** | 78 La Purification | 26.81 | 27.00 | **30.00** | 0.00 |
| **18-D15-2.5** | 79 L'Adoration des Rois | 26.81 | 27.00 | **29.00** | −2.00 |
| **18-D15-2.6** | 80 Joyeuse Nouvelle | 28.74 | 29.00 | **29.00** | 0.00 |
| **18-D15-2.7** | 81 Guidès par l'Etoile | 28.74 | 29.00 | **29.00** | 0.00 |
| **18-D15-2.8** | 82 L'Annonciation | 30.74 | 31.00 | **33.00** | 0.00 |
| | Complete Collection | 214.80 | 218.00 | **233.00** | −4.00 |
| **D'Arceau-Limoges Les Femmes du Siècle** (18-D15-3) | | | | | |
| **18-D15-3.1** | 76 Scarlet en Crinoline | 17.67 | 24.00 | **30.00** | +6.00 |
| **18-D15-3.2** | 76 Sarah en Tournure | 22.74 | 25.00 | **25.00** | +2.00 |
| **18-D15-3.3** | 76 Colette | 22.74 | 25.00 | **25.00** | +2.00 |
| **18-D15-3.4** | 76 Léa | 22.74 | 25.00 | **25.00** | +2.00 |
| **18-D15-3.5** | 77 Albertine | 22.74 | 23.00 | **23.00** | 0.00 |
| **18-D15-3.6** | 77 Edith | 22.74 | 23.00 | **23.00** | 0.00 |
| **18-D15-3.7** | 77 Daisy | 22.74 | 23.00 | **23.00** | 0.00 |
| **18-D15-3.8** | 77 Marlène | 22.74 | 23.00 | **23.00** | 0.00 |
| **18-D15-3.9** | 78 Hélène | 22.74 | 23.00 | **23.00** | 0.00 |
| **18-D15-3.10** | 78 Sophie | 22.74 | 23.00 | **23.00** | 0.00 |
| **18-D15-3.11** | 79 Françoise | 22.74 | 23.00 | **24.00** | 0.00 |
| **18-D15-3.12** | 79 Brigitte | 22.74 | 23.00 | **23.00** | 0.00 |
| | Complete Collection | 267.81 | 283.00 | **290.00** | +12.00 |
| **D'Arceau-Limoges Les Jeunes Filles des Saisons** (18-D15-4) | | | | | |
| **18-D15-4.1** | 78 La Jeune Fille d'Eté | 105.00 | 105.00 | **105.00** | 0.00 |
| **18-D15-4.2** | 79 La Jeune Fille d'Hiver | 105.00 | 105.00 | **105.00** | 0.00 |
| **18-D15-4.3** | 80 La Jeune Fille du Printemps | 105.00 | 105.00 | **105.00** | −5.00 |
| **18-D15-4.4** | 81 La Jeune Fille d'Automne | 105.00 | 105.00 | **105.00** | 0.00 |
| | Complete Collection | 420.00 | 420.00 | **420.00** | −5.00 |
| **D'Arceau-Limoges Les Très Riches Heures** (18-D15-5) | | | | | |
| **18-D15-5.1** | 79 Janvier | 75.48 | 76.00 | **76.00** | 0.00 |
| **18-D15-5.2** | 80 Avril | 75.48 | 78.00 | **80.00** | 0.00 |
| **18-D15-5.3** | 81 Août | 75.48 | 80.00 | **80.00** | −2.00 |
| **18-D15-5.4** | 82 Juin | 75.48 | 150.00 | **150.00** | 0.00 |
| **18-D15-5.5** | 83 Mai | 75.48 | 110.00 | **115.00** | −5.00 |
| **18-D15-5.6** | 84 Octobre | 75.48 | 90.00 | **97.00** | −3.00 |
| **18-D15-5.7** | 87 February | 75.48 | 75.48 | **75.48** | 0.00 |
| **D'Arceau-Limoges Les Douze Sites Parisiens de Louis Dali** (18-D15-6) | | | | | |
| **18-D15-6.1** | 80 L'Arc de Triomphe | 22.94 | 23.00 | **23.00** | 0.00 |
| **18-D15-6.2** | 81 La Cathédrale Notre Dame | 24.94 | 25.00 | **25.00** | 0.00 |
| **18-D15-6.3** | 81 La Place de la Concorde | 24.94 | 25.00 | **27.00** | 0.00 |
| **18-D15-6.4** | 82 L'Eglise Saint Pierre | 26.83 | 27.00 | **27.00** | 0.00 |
| **18-D15-6.5** | 82 Le Marché aux Fleurs | 26.83 | 27.00 | **27.00** | 0.00 |
| **18-D15-6.6** | 82 La Pointe du Vert Galant | 26.83 | 27.00 | **27.00** | 0.00 |
| **18-D15-6.7** | 83 Le Jardin des Tuileries | 26.83 | 26.83 | **26.83**◊ | 0.00 |

| BRADEX NO. | | ISSUE PRICE | CLOSE | QUOTE | CHANGE |
|---|---|---|---|---|---|
| **18-D15-6.8** | 83 Le Moulin Rouge | 26.83 | 26.83 | **26.83**◊ | 0.00 |
| **18-D15-6.9** | 83 Le Pont Alexandre | 26.83 | 26.83 | **26.83**◊ | 0.00 |
| **18-D15-6.10** | 83 L'Opéra | 26.83 | 26.83 | **26.83**◊ | 0.00 |
| **18-D15-6.11** | 83 La Tour Eiffel | 26.83 | 26.83 | **26.83**◊ | 0.00 |
| **18-D15-6.12** | 83 L'Hôtel de Ville de Paris | 26.83 | 26.83 | **26.83**◊ | 0.00 |
| | Complete Collection | 314.29 | 314.98 | **316.98** | 0.00 |
| **D'Arceau-Limoges Joséphine et Napoléon** (18-D15-7) | | | | | |
| **18-D15-7.1** | 84 L'impératrice Joséphine | 29.32 | 30.00 | **33.00** | −2.00 |
| **18-D15-7.2** | 84 Bonaparte Traversant les Alpes | 29.32 | 30.00 | **33.00** | −2.00 |
| **18-D15-7.3** | 84 La Rencontre | 29.32 | 25.00 | **35.00** | 0.00 |
| **18-D15-7.4** | 85 Sacre de Napoléon | 29.32 | 33.00 | **35.00** | −5.00 |
| **18-D15-7.5** | 85 Le Divorce | 34.32 | 35.00 | **35.00** | 0.00 |
| **18-D15-7.6** | 86 Le Souvenir | 34.32 | 35.00 | **35.00** | 0.00 |
| | Complete Collection | 185.92 | 188.00 | **206.00** | −9.00 |
| **D'Arceau-Limoges Cambier Mother's Day** (18-D15-8) | | | | | |
| **18-D15-8.1** | 83 Michèle and Sylvie | 32.84 | 33.00 | **33.00** | 0.00 |
| **18-D15-8.2** | 84 Marie and Jacqueline | 32.84 | 33.00 | **33.00** | 0.00 |
| **18-D15-8.3** | 85 Monique and François | 32.84 | 33.00 | **33.00** | 0.00 |
| **18-D15-8.4** | 86 Marianne and Thérèse | 35.84 | 36.00 | **38.00** | +2.00 |
| | Complete Collection | 134.36 | 135.00 | **137.00** | +2.00 |
| **D'Arceau-Limoges Gigi** (18-D15-9) | | | | | |
| **18-D15-9.1** | 85 Gigi | 24.73 | 26.00 | **26.00** | 0.00 |
| **18-D15-9.2** | 85 Night They Invented Champagne | 24.73 | 31.00 | **25.00** | 0.00 |
| **18-D15-9.3** | 86 I Remember it Well | 24.73 | 25.00 | **25.00** | 0.00 |
| **18-D15-9.4** | 86 Gigi is in Love | 24.73 | 25.00 | **25.00** | 0.00 |
| | Complete Collection | 98.92 | 107.00 | **101.00** | 0.00 |
| **D'Arceau-Limoges Women of LaBelle Epoque** (18-D15-10) | | | | | |
| **18-D15-10.1** | 86 Sarah Bernhardt | 24.96 | 31.00 | **33.00** | 0.00 |
| **18-D15-10.2** | 86 Liane De Pougy | 24.96 | 48.00 | **50.00** | +15.00 |
| **18-D15-10.3** | 86 Caroline Otero | 24.96 | 24.96 | **25.00** | +0.04 |
| **18-D15-10.4** | 87 Anna Pavlova | 24.96 | 24.96 | **25.00** | +0.04 |
| | Complete Collection | 99.84 | 128.92 | **133.00** | +15.08 |
| **D'Arceau-Limoges Christmas in France** (18-D15-11) | | | | | |
| **18-D15-11.1** | 86 The Magical Window | 28.47 | 43.00 | **55.00** | −5.00 |
| **D'Arceau-Limoges French Country Landscapes** (18-D15-12) | | | | | |
| **18-D15-12.1** | 87 Along the Riverside | 33.87 | 33.87 | **33.87**◊ | 0.00 |
| **Haviland Christmas** (18-H6-1) | | | | | |
| **18-H6-1.1** | 70 Partridge | 25.00 | 99.00 | **104.00** | 0.00 |
| **18-H6-1.2** | 71 Two Turtle Doves | 25.00 | 17.00 | **17.00** | −1.00 |
| **18-H6-1.3** | 72 Three French Hens | 27.50 | 10.00 | **10.00** | −2.00 |
| **18-H6-1.4** | 73 Four Colly Birds | 28.50 | 9.00 | **20.00** | 0.00 |
| **18-H6-1.5** | 74 Five Golden Rings | 30.00 | 14.00 | **15.00** | −3.00 |
| **18-H6-1.6** | 75 Six Geese A'Laying | 32.50 | 13.00 | **15.00** | −4.00 |
| **18-H6-1.7** | 76 Seven Swans | 38.00 | 13.00 | **15.00** | 0.00 |
| **18-H6-1.8** | 77 Eight Maids | 40.00 | 35.00 | **40.00** | 0.00 |
| **18-H6-1.9** | 78 Nine Ladies Dancing | 45.00 | 45.00 | **45.00** | 0.00 |
| **18-H6-1.10** | 79 Ten Lords A'Leaping | 50.00 | 20.00 | **25.00** | −3.00 |
| **18-H6-1.11** | 80 Eleven Pipers Piping | 55.00 | 35.00 | **42.00** | −2.00 |
| **18-H6-1.12** | 81 Twelve Drummers Drumming | 60.00 | 35.00 | **35.00** | −2.00 |
| | Complete Collection | 456.50 | 345.00 | **383.00** | −17.00 |
| **Haviland 1001 Arabian Nights** (18-H6-4) | | | | | |
| **18-H6-4.1** | 79 The Magic Horse | 54.50 | 20.00 | **30.00** | 0.00 |
| **18-H6-4.2** | 80 Aladdin and the Lamp | 54.50 | 58.00 | **60.00** | 0.00 |
| **18-H6-4.3** | 81 Scheherazade | 54.50 | 80.00 | **100.00** | 0.00 |
| **18-H6-4.4** | 82 Sinbad the Sailor | 54.50 | 80.00 | **85.00** | −4.00 |
| | Complete Collection | 218.00 | 238.00 | **275.00** | −4.00 |
| **Haviland & Parlon Tapestry** (18-H8-1) | | | | | |
| **18-H8-1.1** | 71 Unicorn in Captivity | 35.00 | 98.00 | **103.00** | −2.00 |
| **18-H8-1.2** | 72 Start of the Hunt | 35.00 | 31.00 | **34.00** | 0.00 |
| **18-H8-1.3** | 73 Chase of the Unicorn | 35.00 | 80.00 | **90.00** | 0.00 |
| **18-H8-1.4** | 74 End of the Hunt | 37.50 | 79.00 | **80.00** | 0.00 |
| **18-H8-1.5** | 75 Unicorn Surrounded | 40.00 | 40.00 | **40.00** | 0.00 |
| **18-H8-1.6** | 76 Brought to the Castle | 42.50 | 30.00 | **40.00** | 0.00 |
| | Complete Collection | 225.00 | 358.00 | **387.00** | −2.00 |
| **Haviland & Parlon Christmas** (18-H8-2) | | | | | |
| **18-H8-2.1** | 72 Madonna by Raphael | 35.00 | 65.00 | **65.00** | +5.00 |
| **18-H8-2.2** | 73 Madonnina by Feruzzi | 40.00 | 70.00 | **97.00** | −3.00 |
| **18-H8-2.3** | 74 Madonna by Raphael | 42.50 | 43.00 | **50.00** | 0.00 |
| **18-H8-2.4** | 75 Madonna by Murillo | 42.50 | 20.00 | **27.00** | −3.00 |
| **18-H8-2.5** | 76 Madonna by Botticelli | 45.50 | 44.00 | **47.00** | −2.00 |
| **18-H8-2.6** | 77 Madonna by Bellini | 48.00 | 50.00 | **50.00** | −2.00 |
| **18-H8-2.7** | 78 Madonna by Lippi | 48.00 | 52.00 | **65.00** | −5.00 |
| **18-H8-2.8** | 79 Madonna of the Eucharist | 49.50 | 100.00 | **100.00** | 0.00 |
| | Complete Collection | 351.00 | 444.00 | **501.00** | −10.00 |
| **Haviland & Parlon The Lady and the Unicorn** (18-H8-4) | | | | | |
| **18-H8-4.1** | 77 To My Only Desire | 45.00 | 30.00 | **35.00** | −3.00 |
| **18-H8-4.2** | 78 Sight | 45.00 | 27.00 | **30.00** | 0.00 |
| **18-H8-4.3** | 79 Sound | 47.50 | 29.00 | **33.00** | −2.00 |
| **18-H8-4.4** | 80 Touch | 52.50 | 60.00 | **60.00** | 0.00 |
| **18-H8-4.5** | 81 Scent | 59.00 | 40.00 | **45.00** | 0.00 |
| **18-H8-4.6** | 82 Taste | 59.00 | 38.00 | **43.00** | −2.00 |
| | Complete Collection | 308.00 | 224.00 | **246.00** | −7.00 |
| **Lalique Annual** (18-L3-1) | | | | | |
| **18-L3-1.1** | 65 Deux Oiseaux (Two Birds) | 25.00 | 1000.00 | **1000.00** | 0.00 |
| **18-L3-1.2** | 66 Rose de Songerie (Dream Rose) | 25.00 | 110.00 | **130.00** | −5.00 |
| **18-L3-1.3** | 67 Ballet de Poisson (Fish Ballet) | 25.00 | 92.00 | **95.00** | −3.00 |
| **18-L3-1.4** | 68 Gazelle Fantaisie | 25.00 | 60.00 | **60.00** | 0.00 |
| **18-L3-1.5** | 69 Papillon (Butterfly) | 30.00 | 55.00 | **65.00** | −5.00 |
| **18-L3-1.6** | 70 Paon (Peacock) | 30.00 | 53.00 | **60.00** | +7.00 |
| **18-L3-1.7** | 71 Hibou (Owl) | 35.00 | 43.00 | **48.00** | 0.00 |
| **18-L3-1.8** | 72 Coquillage (Shell) | 40.00 | 45.00 | **55.00** | −3.00 |
| **18-L3-1.9** | 73 Petit Geai (Jayling) | 42.50 | 39.00 | **45.00** | +5.00 |
| **18-L3-1.10** | 74 Sous d'Argent (Silver Pennies) | 47.50 | 38.00 | **45.00** | 0.00 |
| **18-L3-1.11** | 75 Duo de Poisson (Fish Duet) | 50.00 | 60.00 | **60.00** | 0.00 |
| **18-L3-1.12** | 76 Aigle (Eagle) | 60.00 | 100.00 | **120.00** | +20.00 |
| | Complete Collection | 435.00 | 1,695.00 | **1,783.00** | +16.00 |
| **Limoges-Turgot Les Enfants de Durand** (18-L52-1) | | | | | |
| **18-L52-1.1** | 78 Marie-Ange | 36.40 | 37.00 | **37.00** | 0.00 |
| **18-L52-1.2** | 79 Emilie et Philippe | 36.40 | 37.00 | **37.00** | 0.00 |
| **18-L52-1.3** | 80 Christiane et Fifi | 36.40 | 37.00 | **37.00** | 0.00 |
| **18-L52-1.4** | 80 Cecile et Raoul | 36.40 | 37.00 | **37.00** | 0.00 |
| | Complete Collection | 145.60 | 148.00 | **148.00** | 0.00 |
| **Limoges-Turgot Quellier's Morals of Perrault** (18-L52-2) | | | | | |
| **18-L52-2.1** | 83 Cinderella | 28.67 | 29.00 | **30.00** | −5.00 |
| **18-L52-2.2** | 84 Little Tom Thumb | 28.67 | 29.00 | **30.00** | 0.00 |
| **18-L52-2.3** | 84 Little Red Riding Hood | 28.67 | 29.00 | **29.00** | 0.00 |
| **18-L52-2.4** | 84 Sleeping Beauty | 28.67 | 29.00 | **36.00** | −1.00 |
| | Complete Collection | 114.68 | 116.00 | **125.00** | −6.00 |

| BRADEX NO. | | ISSUE PRICE | CLOSE | QUOTE | CHANGE |
|---|---|---|---|---|---|
| **Limoges-Turgot Peltriaux's Children of the Turn of the Century** (18-L52-3) | | | | | |
| **18-L52-3.1** | 85 Patinage au Trocadéro | 24.82 | 25.00 | **25.00** | 0.00 |
| **18-L52-3.2** | 85 Petits Voiliers au bassin des Tuileries | 29.82 | 43.00 | **43.00** | 0.00 |
| **18-L52-3.3** | 85 Guignol au Luxembourg | 29.82 | 43.00 | **42.00** | −3.00 |
| **18-L52-3.4** | 86 Manege aux Champs Elysées | 29.82 | 31.00 | **31.00** | −1.00 |
| | Complete Collection | 114.28 | 142.00 | **141.00** | −4.00 |

## GERMANY

| BRADEX NO. | | ISSUE PRICE | CLOSE | QUOTE | CHANGE |
|---|---|---|---|---|---|
| **Anna-Perenna Triptych** (22-A3-3) | | | | | |
| **22-A3-3.1** | 79 Byzantine Triptych | 325.00 | 125.00 | **110.00** | +10.00 |
| **22-A3-3.2** | 80 Jerusalem Triptych | 350.00 | 150.00 | **150.00** | 0.00 |
| | Complete Collection | 675.00 | 275.00 | **260.00** | +10.00 |
| **Anna-Perenna Romantic Loves** (22-A3-4) | | | | | |
| **22-A3-4.1** | 79 Romeo and Juliet | 95.00 | 34.00 | **35.00** | 0.00 |
| **22-A3-4.2** | 80 Lancelot and Guinevere | 95.00 | 47.00 | **47.00** | −2.00 |
| **22-A3-4.3** | 81 Helen and Paris | 95.00 | 41.00 | **54.00** | 0.00 |
| **22-A3-4.4** | 82 Lovers of Taj Mahal | 95.00 | 81.00 | **83.00** | +4.00 |
| | Complete Collection | 380.00 | 203.00 | **219.00** | +2.00 |
| **Anna-Perenna Uncle Tad's Cats** (22-A3-5) | | | | | |
| **22-A3-5.1** | 79 Oliver's Birthday | 75.00 | 190.00 | **205.00** | +6.00 |
| **22-A3-5.2** | 80 Peaches and Cream | 75.00 | 60.00 | **75.00** | −5.00 |
| **22-A3-5.3** | 81 Princess Aurora | 80.00 | 50.00 | **60.00** | 0.00 |
| **22-A3-5.4** | 81 Walter's Window | 85.00 | 50.00 | **80.00** | +1.00 |
| | Complete Collection | 315.00 | 350.00 | **420.00** | +2.00 |
| **Anna-Perenna Uncle Tad's Golden Oldies** (22-A3-26) | | | | | |
| **22-A3-26.1** | 86 My Merry Oldsmobile | 39.50 | 26.00 | **37.00** | −3.00 |
| **22-A3-26.2** | 86 Down by the Old Mill Stream | 39.50 | 39.50 | **39.50** | 0.00 |
| **22-A3-26.3** | 86 Ramona | 39.50 | 39.50 | **39.50** | 0.00 |
| **22-A3-26.4** | 87 Paddlin' Madeline Home | 39.50 | 39.50 | **39.50** | 0.00 |
| | Complete Collection | 158.00 | 144.50 | **155.50** | −3.00 |
| **Bareuther Christmas** (22-B7-1) | | | | | |
| **22-B7-1.1** | 67 Stiftskirche | 12.00 | 85.00 | **90.00** | 0.00 |
| **22-B7-1.2** | 68 Kappl | 12.00 | 30.00 | **30.00** | 0.00 |
| **22-B7-1.3** | 69 Christkindlesmarkt | 12.00 | 11.00 | **15.00** | 0.00 |
| **22-B7-1.4** | 70 Chapel in Oberndorf | 12.50 | 8.00 | **10.00** | 0.00 |
| **22-B7-1.5** | 71 Toys for Sale | 12.75 | 12.00 | **15.00** | 0.00 |
| **22-B7-1.6** | 72 Christmas in Munich | 14.50 | 22.00 | **25.00** | 0.00 |
| **22-B7-1.7** | 73 Sleigh Ride | 15.00 | 30.00 | **20.00** | 0.00 |
| **22-B7-1.8** | 74 Black Forest Church | 19.00 | 17.00 | **18.00** | 0.00 |
| **22-B7-1.9** | 75 Snowman | 21.50 | 18.00 | **18.00** | 0.00 |
| **22-B7-1.10** | 76 Chapel in the Hills | 23.50 | 18.00 | **20.00** | +1.00 |
| **22-B7-1.11** | 77 Story Time | 24.50 | 37.00 | **33.00** | +3.00 |
| **22-B7-1.12** | 78 Mittenwald | 27.50 | 30.00 | **33.00** | +3.00 |
| **22-B7-1.13** | 79 Winter Day | 35.00 | 17.00 | **20.00** | 0.00 |
| **22-B7-1.14** | 80 Mittenberg | 37.50 | 35.00 | **33.00** | +3.00 |
| **22-B7-1.15** | 81 Walk in the Forest | 39.50 | 35.00 | **34.00** | +4.00 |
| **22-B7-1.16** | 82 Bad Wimpfen | 39.50 | 33.00 | **35.00** | 0.00 |
| **22-B7-1.17** | 83 The Night Before Christmas | 39.50 | 30.00 | **33.00** | +3.00 |
| **22-B7-1.18** | 84 Zeil on the River Main | 42.50 | 42.00 | **42.00** | 0.00 |
| **22-B7-1.19** | 85 Winter Wonderland | 42.50 | 38.00 | **40.00** | +2.00 |
| **22-B7-1.20** | 86 Christmas in Forchhe | 42.50 | 47.00 | **50.00** | +7.00 |
| **Bareuther Father's Day** (22-B7-2) | | | | | |
| **22-B7-2.1** | 69 Castle Neuschwanstein | 10.50 | 50.00 | **50.00** | +5.00 |
| **22-B7-2.2** | 70 Castle Pfalz | 12.50 | 10.00 | **12.00** | −2.00 |
| **22-B7-2.3** | 71 Castle Heidelberg | 12.75 | 17.00 | **20.00** | −2.00 |
| **22-B7-2.4** | 72 Castle Hohenschwangau | 14.50 | 27.00 | **27.00** | −2.00 |
| **22-B7-2.5** | 73 Castle Katz | 15.00 | 20.00 | **20.00** | 0.00 |
| **22-B7-2.6** | 74 Wurzburg Castle | 19.00 | 30.00 | **30.00** | 0.00 |
| **22-B7-2.7** | 75 Castle Lichtenstein | 21.50 | 20.00 | **20.00** | 0.00 |
| **22-B7-2.8** | 76 Castle Hohenzollern | 23.50 | 25.00 | **30.00** | 0.00 |
| **22-B7-2.9** | 77 Castle Eltz | 24.50 | 24.00 | **24.00** | 0.00 |
| **22-B7-2.10** | 78 Castle Falkenstein | 27.50 | 18.00 | **24.00** | 0.00 |
| **22-B7-2.11** | 79 Castle Rheinstein | 35.00 | 20.00 | **20.00** | −4.00 |
| **22-B7-2.12** | 80 Castle Cochum | 37.50 | 17.00 | **27.00** | +2.00 |
| **22-B7-2.13** | 81 Castle Gutenfels | 39.50 | 40.00 | **40.00** | 0.00 |
| **22-B7-2.14** | 82 Castle Zwingenberg | 39.50 | 30.00 | **32.00** | −3.00 |
| **22-B7-2.15** | 83 Castle Lauenstein | 39.50 | 40.00 | **40.00** | 0.00 |
| **22-B7-2.16** | 84 Castle Neuenstein | 42.50 | 43.00 | **43.00** | 0.00 |
| **22-B7-2.17** | 85 Castle Wartburg | 42.50 | 43.00 | **43.00** | 0.00 |
| **Berlin Design Christmas** (22-B20-1) | | | | | |
| **22-B20-1.1** | 70 Christmas in Bernkastel | 14.50 | 130.00 | **140.00** | 0.00 |
| **22-B20-1.2** | 71 Christmas in Rothenburg | 14.50 | 25.00 | **25.00** | −1.00 |
| **22-B20-1.3** | 72 Christmas in Michelstadt | 15.00 | 44.00 | **45.00** | 0.00 |
| **22-B20-1.4** | 73 Christmas in Wendelstein | 20.00 | 35.00 | **39.00** | +1.00 |
| **22-B20-1.5** | 74 Christmas in Bremen | 25.00 | 18.00 | **18.00** | 0.00 |
| **22-B20-1.6** | 75 Christmas in Dortland | 30.00 | 24.00 | **24.00** | −2.00 |
| **22-B20-1.7** | 76 Christmas in Augsburg | 32.00 | 18.00 | **18.00** | 0.00 |
| **22-B20-1.8** | 77 Christmas in Hamburg | 32.00 | 35.00 | **35.00** | 0.00 |
| **22-B20-1.9** | 78 Christmas Market at Berlin | 36.00 | 38.00 | **38.00** | −1.00 |
| **22-B20-1.10** | 79 Christmas in Greetsiel | 47.50 | 48.00 | **52.00** | 0.00 |
| **22-B20-1.11** | 80 Christmas Eve in Miltenberg | 55.00 | 60.00 | **60.00** | 0.00 |
| **22-B20-1.12** | 81 Christmas Eve in Hahnenklee | 55.00 | 44.00 | **45.00** | 0.00 |
| **22-B20-1.13** | 82 Christmas Eve in Wasserberg | 55.00 | 59.00 | **60.00** | 0.00 |
| **22-B20-1.14** | 83 Chapel in Oberndorf | 55.00 | 53.00 | **55.00** | 0.00 |
| **22-B20-1.15** | 84 Christmas in Ramsau | 55.00 | 49.00 | **55.00** | 0.00 |
| **22-B20-1.16** | 85 Christmas Eve in Bad Wimpfen | 55.00 | 53.00 | **55.00** | 0.00 |
| **22-B20-1.17** | 86 Christmas Eve in Gelnhaus | 65.00 | 65.00 | **70.00** | +4.00 |
| **Berlin Design Holiday Week of the Family Kappelmann** (22-B20-4) | | | | | |
| **22-B20-4.1** | 84 Monday | 33.00 | 33.00 | **33.00** | 0.00 |
| **22-B20-4.2** | 84 Tuesday | 33.00 | 33.00 | **33.00** | 0.00 |
| **22-B20-4.3** | 85 Wednesday | 33.00 | 34.00 | **35.00** | 0.00 |
| **22-B20-4.4** | 85 Thursday | 35.00 | 36.00 | **40.00** | 0.00 |
| **22-B20-4.5** | 86 Friday | 35.00 | 35.00 | **45.00** | −5.00 |
| **22-B20-4.6** | 86 Saturday | 35.00 | 36.00 | **38.00** | +3.00 |
| **22-B20-4.7** | 86 Sunday | 35.00 | 36.00 | **36.00** | +1.00 |
| | Complete Collection | 239.00 | 243.00 | **260.00** | −1.00 |
| **Christian Seltmannn Lückel's Idyllic Village Life** (22-C32-1) | | | | | |
| **22-C32-1.1** | 86 Blacksmith | 24.50 | 27.00 | **30.00** | 0.00 |
| **22-C32-1.2** | 86 The Arrival of the Stagecoach | 24.50 | 20.20 | **30.00** | +5.50 |
| **22-C32-1.3** | 87 Stop at the Village Inn | 27.50 | 27.50 | **27.50**◊ | 0.00 |
| **22-C32-1.4** | 87 In the Fields at Harvest Time | 27.50 | 27.50 | **27.50**◊ | 0.00 |
| **22-C32-1.5** | 87 On the Way to the Market | 27.50 | 27.50 | **27.50**◊ | 0.00 |
| **Fürstenberg Muninger's Romantic Winter Impressions** (22-F82-6) | | | | | |
| **22-F82-6.1** | 87 Ice Skaters in Evening Sun | 34.50 | 34.50 | **34.50**◊ | 0.00 |
| **Goebel Hummel Annual** (22-G54-1) | | | | | |
| **22-G54-1.1** | 71 Heavenly Angel | 25.00 | 600.00 | **650.00** | 0.00 |
| **22-G54-1.2** | 72 Hear Ye, Hear Ye | 30.00 | 40.00 | **45.00** | 0.00 |

| BRADEX NO. | | ISSUE PRICE | CLOSE | QUOTE | CHANGE |
|---|---|---|---|---|---|
| 22-G54-1.3 | 73 Globe Trotter | 32.50 | 100.00 | **100.00** | 0.00 |
| 22-G54-1.4 | 74 Goose Girl | 40.00 | 49.00 | **55.00** | −5.00 |
| 22-G54-1.5 | 75 Ride into Christmas | 50.00 | 50.00 | **60.00** | 0.00 |
| 22-G54-1.6 | 76 Apple Tree Girl | 50.00 | 45.00 | **55.00** | 0.00 |
| 22-G54-1.7 | 77 Apple Tree Boy | 50.00 | 74.00 | **75.00** | −4.00 |
| 22-G54-1.8 | 78 Happy Pastime | 65.00 | 45.00 | **50.00** | 0.00 |
| 22-G54-1.9 | 79 Singing Lesson | 90.00 | 34.00 | **39.00** | +4.00 |
| 22-G54-1.10 | 80 School Girl | 100.00 | 40.00 | **48.00** | −2.00 |
| 22-G54-1.11 | 81 Umbrella Boy | 100.00 | 49.00 | **55.00** | −5.00 |
| 22-G54-1.12 | 82 Umbrella Girl | 100.00 | 130.00 | **134.00** | +4.00 |
| 22-G54-1.13 | 83 The Postman | 108.00 | 130.00 | **190.00** | −20.00 |
| 22-G54-1.14 | 84 Little Helper | 108.00 | 72.00 | **73.00** | +9.00 |
| 22-G54-1.15 | 85 Chick Girl | 110.00 | 80.00 | **90.00** | −5.00 |
| 22-G54-1.16 | 86 Playmates | 125.00 | 121.00 | **125.00** | 0.00 |
| 22-G54-1.17 | 87 Feeding Time | 125.00 | 115.00 | **125.00** | 0.00 |
| **Goebel Hummel Anniversary** (22-G54-3) | | | | | |
| 22-G54-3.1 | 75 Stormy Weather | 100.00 | 90.00 | **130.00** | 0.00 |
| 22-G54-3.2 | 80 Spring Dance | 225.00 | 75.00 | **80.00** | 0.00 |
| 22-G54-3.3 | 85 Auf Wiedersehen | 225.00 | 162.00 | **174.00** | −10.00 |
| **Heinrich/Villeroy & Boch Russian Fairy Tales** (22-H18-1) | | | | | |
| 22-H18-1.1 | 80 Snow Maiden | 70.00 | 273.00 | **240.00** | +20.00 |
| 22-H18-1.2 | 80 Court of Tsar Berendei | 70.00 | 70.00 | **70.00** | 0.00 |
| 22-H18-1.3 | 80 Lel the Shepherd Boy | 70.00 | 70.00 | **89.00** | +4.00 |
| 22-H18-1.4 | 81 The Red Knight | 70.00 | 69.00 | **75.00** | +5.00 |
| 22-H18-1.5 | 81 Vassilissa and Stepsisters | 70.00 | 75.00 | **75.00** | 0.00 |
| 22-H18-1.6 | 81 Vassilissa Presented to Tsar | 70.00 | 70.00 | **70.00** | 0.00 |
| 22-H18-1.7 | 82 Search of the Firebird | 70.00 | 70.00 | **74.00** | 0.00 |
| 22-H18-1.8 | 82 Ivan/Tsarevna on Wolf | 70.00 | 70.00 | **70.00** | −4.00 |
| 22-H18-1.9 | 82 Wedding of Tsarevna | 70.00 | 70.00 | **70.00** | 0.00 |
| 22-H18-1.10 | 83 Maria Morevna/Tsarevna Ivan | 70.00 | 70.00 | **70.00** | 0.00 |
| 22-H18-1.11 | 83 Koshey Carries Maria Morevna | 70.00 | 71.00 | **73.00** | −2.00 |
| 22-H18-1.12 | 83 Tsarvich Ivan and Castle | 70.00 | 70.00 | **70.00** | 0.00 |
| | Complete Collection | 840.00 | 1048.00 | **1046.00** | +23.00 |
| **Heinrich/Villeroy & Boch Fairies of the Fields and Flowers** (22-H18-3) | | | | | |
| 22-H18-3.1 | 82 Ragged Robin | 49.00 | 49.00 | **50.00** | 0.00 |
| 22-H18-3.2 | 83 Willow | 49.00 | 50.00 | **50.00** | 0.00 |
| 22-H18-3.3 | 84 Elderberry | 49.00 | 49.00 | **49.00** | −1.00 |
| 22-H18-3.4 | 84 Vetch | 49.00 | 55.00 | **60.00** | 0.00 |
| 22-H18-3.5 | 84 Narcissus | 49.00 | 52.00 | **54.00** | 0.00 |
| 22-H18-3.6 | 84 Nasturtium | 49.00 | 55.00 | **56.00** | 0.00 |
| 22-H18-3.7 | 85 Phlox | 49.00 | 54.00 | **55.00** | 0.00 |
| 22-H18-3.8 | 85 Gorse | 49.00 | 54.00 | **54.00** | 0.00 |
| | Complete Collection | 392.00 | 418.00 | **428.00** | −1.00 |
| **Heinrich/Villeroy & Boch Once Upon a Rhyme** (22-H18-8) | | | | | |
| 22-H18-8.1 | 84 Roses Are Red | 35.00 | 24.00 | **30.00** | −2.00 |
| 22-H18-8.2 | 84 A Tisket, A Tasket | 35.00 | 32.00 | **35.00** | −5.00 |
| 22-H18-8.3 | 84 Mary Had a Little Lamb | 35.00 | 32.00 | **39.00** | −3.00 |
| 22-H18-8.4 | 85 Star Light, Star Bright | 35.00 | 35.00 | **44.00** | −1.00 |
| 22-H18-8.5 | 86 Tom Tom Pipers Son | 35.00 | 34.00 | **35.00** | 0.00 |
| 22-H18-8.6 | 86 Over the River/Woods | 35.00 | 35.00 | **35.00◊** | 0.00 |
| | Complete Collection | 210.00 | 192.00 | **218.00** | −11.00 |
| **Heinrich/Villeroy & Boch Dreams of Katharina** (22-H18-12) | | | | | |
| 22-H18-12.1 | 86 Katharina Receives a Promise | 75.00 | 75.00 | **75.00◊** | 0.00 |
| **Hibel Studio David** (22-H31-1) | | | | | |
| 22-H31-1.1 | 79 Wedding/David-Bathsheba | 250.00 | 250.00 | **265.00** | 0.00 |
| 22-H31-1.2 | 80 David, Bathsheba, Solomon | 275.00 | 275.00 | **345.00** | +10.00 |
| 22-H31-1.3 | 82 King David | 275.00 | 250.00 | **275.00** | 0.00 |
| 22-H31-1.4 | 83 Bathsheba | 275.00 | 290.00 | **290.00** | 0.00 |
| | Complete Collection | 1075.00 | 1065.00 | **1175.00** | +10.00 |
| **Hutschenreuther Love for All Seasons** (22-H82-6) | | | | | |
| 22-H82-6.1 | 82 The Minstrel Song | 125.00 | 50.00 | **85.00** | −5.00 |
| 22-H82-6.2 | 82 Affection | 125.00 | 90.00 | **124.00** | −1.00 |
| 22-H82-6.3 | 82 The Tournament | 125.00 | 110.00 | **123.00** | −2.00 |
| 22-H82-6.4 | 83 The Falcon Hunt | 125.00 | 130.00 | **130.00** | 0.00 |
| 22-H82-6.5 | 83 Winter Romance | 125.00 | 101.00 | **125.00** | 0.00 |
| 22-H82-6.6 | 83 The Ride Out | 125.00 | 101.00 | **130.00** | 0.00 |
| | Complete Collection | 750.00 | 582.00 | **717.00** | −8.00 |
| **Hutschenreuther Bouquets of the Seasons** (22-H82-26) | | | | | |
| 22-H82-26.1 | 87 Spring Morning | 24.50 | 24.50 | **24.50◊** | 0.00 |
| 22-H82-26.2 | 87 Easter Bouquet | 24.50 | 24.50 | **24.50◊** | 0.00 |
| **Kaiser Christmas** (22-K4-1) | | | | | |
| 22-K4-1.1 | 70 Waiting for Santa Claus | 12.50 | 22.00 | **25.00** | −4.00 |
| 22-K4-1.2 | 71 Silent Night | 13.50 | 15.00 | **17.00** | −3.00 |
| 22-K4-1.3 | 72 Welcome Home | 16.50 | 18.00 | **17.00** | −3.00 |
| 22-K4-1.4 | 73 Holy Night | 18.00 | 27.00 | **30.00** | +2.00 |
| 22-K4-1.5 | 74 Christmas Carolers | 25.00 | 12.00 | **26.00** | −4.00 |
| 22-K4-1.6 | 75 Bringing Home the Tree | 25.00 | 10.00 | **18.00** | −2.00 |
| 22-K4-1.7 | 76 Christ the Savior | 25.00 | 23.00 | **26.00** | −4.00 |
| 22-K4-1.8 | 77 Three Kings | 25.00 | 15.00 | **17.00** | −1.00 |
| 22-K4-1.9 | 78 Shepherds in the Field | 30.00 | 10.00 | **14.00** | 0.00 |
| 22-K4-1.10 | 79 Christmas Eve | 32.00 | 25.00 | **25.00** | 0.00 |
| 22-K4-1.11 | 80 Joys of Winter | 40.00 | 12.00 | **25.00** | 0.00 |
| 22-K4-1.12 | 81 Most Holy Night | 40.00 | 12.00 | **39.00** | −2.00 |
| 22-K4-1.13 | 82 Bringing Home the Tree | 40.00 | 12.00 | **40.00** | −5.00 |
| | Complete Collection | 342.50 | 213.00 | **319.00** | −26.00 |
| **Kaiser Mother's Day** (22-K4-2) | | | | | |
| 22-K4-2.1 | 71 Mare and Foal | 13.00 | 20.00 | **25.00** | 0.00 |
| 22-K4-2.2 | 72 Flowers for Mother | 16.50 | 10.00 | **13.00** | −1.00 |
| 22-K4-2.3 | 73 Cats | 17.00 | 23.00 | **25.00** | −4.00 |
| 22-K4-2.4 | 74 Fox | 22.00 | 38.00 | **48.00** | −2.00 |
| 22-K4-2.5 | 75 German Shepherd | 25.00 | 45.00 | **50.00** | 0.00 |
| 22-K4-2.6 | 76 Swan and Cygnets | 25.00 | 15.00 | **15.00** | 0.00 |
| 22-K4-2.7 | 77 Mother Rabbit and Young | 25.00 | 25.00 | **33.00** | −2.00 |
| 22-K4-2.8 | 78 Hen and Chicks | 30.00 | 30.00 | **37.00** | 0.00 |
| 22-K4-2.9 | 79 A Mother's Devotion | 32.00 | 16.00 | **16.00** | 0.00 |
| 22-K4-2.10 | 80 Raccoon Family | 40.00 | 39.00 | **39.00** | 0.00 |
| 22-K4-2.11 | 81 Safe Near Mother | 40.00 | 20.00 | **40.00** | 0.00 |
| 22-K4-2.12 | 82 Pheasant Family | 40.00 | 40.00 | **40.00** | −1.00 |
| 22-K4-2.13 | 83 Tender Care | 40.00 | 60.00 | **65.00** | 0.00 |
| | Complete Collection | 365.50 | 381.00 | **446.00** | −10.00 |
| **Kaiser Classic Fairy Tales** (22-K4-5) | | | | | |
| 22-K4-5.1 | 82 The Frog King | 39.50 | 40.00 | **40.00** | 0.00 |
| 22-K4-5.2 | 83 Puss in Boots | 39.50 | 40.00 | **40.00** | 0.00 |
| 22-K4-5.3 | 83 Little Red Riding Hood | 39.50 | 40.00 | **40.00** | 0.00 |
| 22-K4-5.4 | 83 Hansel and Gretel | 39.50 | 40.00 | **40.00** | 0.00 |
| 22-K4-5.5 | 84 Cinderella | 39.50 | 40.00 | **40.00** | 0.00 |
| 22-K4-5.6 | 84 Sleeping Beauty | 39.50 | 40.00 | **40.00** | 0.00 |
| | Complete Collection | 237.00 | 240.00 | **240.00** | 0.00 |
| **Kaiser Classic Lullabies of the World** (22-K4-22) | | | | | |
| 22-K4-22.1 | 85 Sleep, Baby, Sleep | 39.50 | 37.00 | **48.00** | 0.00 |
| 22-K4-22.2 | 86 Rock a Bye Baby | 39.50 | 39.50 | **39.50** | 0.00 |
| 22-K4-22.3 | 86 The Mockingbird | 39.50 | 39.50 | **39.50◊** | 0.00 |
| 22-K4-22.4 | 86 Au Clair de la Lune | 39.50 | 39.50 | **39.50◊** | 0.00 |
| 22-K4-22.5 | 87 All Through the Night | 39.50 | 39.50 | **39.50◊** | 0.00 |
| 22-K4-22.6 | 87 Brahms Lullaby | 39.50 | 39.50 | **39.50◊** | 0.00 |
| | Complete Collection | 237.00 | 234.50 | **245.50** | 0.00 |
| **Königszelt Bayern Hedi Keller Christmas** (22-K46-1) | | | | | |
| 22-K46-1.1 | 79 The Adoration | 29.50 | 30.00 | **32.00** | 0.00 |
| 22-K46-1.2 | 80 Flight into Egypt | 29.50 | 30.00 | **30.00** | 0.00 |
| 22-K46-1.3 | 81 Return into Galilee | 29.50 | 30.00 | **30.00** | 0.00 |
| 22-K46-1.4 | 82 Following the Star | 29.50 | 30.00 | **30.00** | 0.00 |
| 22-K46-1.5 | 83 Rest on the Flight | 29.50 | 30.00 | **35.00** | 0.00 |
| 22-K46-1.6 | 84 The Nativity | 29.50 | 35.00 | **40.00** | 0.00 |
| 22-K46-1.7 | 85 Gift of the Magi | 34.50 | 43.00 | **49.00** | +6.00 |
| 22-K46-1.8 | 86 Annunciation | 34.50 | 35.00 | **50.00** | 0.00 |
| | Complete Collection | 246.00 | 263.00 | **296.00** | +6.00 |
| **Königszelt Bayern Grimm's Fairy Tales** (22-K46-2) | | | | | |
| 22-K46-2.1 | 81 Rumpelstilzchen | 23.00 | 23.00 | **23.00** | 0.00 |
| 22-K46-2.2 | 82 Rapunzel | 25.00 | 25.00 | **31.00** | 0.00 |
| 22-K46-2.3 | 82 Hansel and Gretel | 25.00 | 36.00 | **35.00** | +4.00 |
| 22-K46-2.4 | 83 Shoemaker and Elves | 25.00 | 23.00 | **25.00** | 0.00 |
| 22-K46-2.5 | 84 Golden Goose | 29.00 | 29.00 | **29.00** | −2.00 |
| 22-K46-2.6 | 85 Shoes That Were Danced | 29.00 | 35.00 | **45.00** | 0.00 |
| 22-K46-2.7 | 86 Sleeping Beauty | 29.00 | 36.00 | **40.00** | +11.00 |
| 22-K46-2.8 | 87 Snow White | 29.00 | 29.00 | **29.00◊** | 0.00 |
| | Complete Collection | 214.00 | 236.00 | **257.00** | +13.00 |
| **Königszelt Bayern Sulamith's Love Song** (22-K46-3) | | | | | |
| 22-K46-3.1 | 82 The Music | 29.00 | 29.00 | **32.00** | 0.00 |
| 22-K46-3.2 | 83 The Pledge | 29.00 | 29.00 | **30.00** | 0.00 |
| 22-K46-3.3 | 83 The Vision | 29.00 | 29.00 | **29.00** | 0.00 |
| 22-K46-3.4 | 83 The Gift | 29.00 | 37.00 | **39.00** | 0.00 |
| 22-K46-3.5 | 84 The Circle | 29.00 | 36.00 | **39.00** | 0.00 |
| 22-K46-3.6 | 84 The Centre | 29.00 | 29.00 | **40.00** | −4.00 |
| 22-K46-3.7 | 84 The Journey | 29.00 | 33.00 | **35.00** | 0.00 |
| 22-K46-3.8 | 84 The Completion | 29.00 | 28.00 | **45.00** | 0.00 |
| | Complete Collection | 232.00 | 250.00 | **289.00** | −4.00 |
| **Königszelt Bayern Deutsches Fachwerk (German Half-Timbered Houses)** (22-K46-4) | | | | | |
| 22-K46-4.1 | 84 Bauernhaus in Fronhausen | 24.00 | 24.00 | **26.00** | 0.00 |
| 22-K46-4.2 | 84 Niedersachsenhaus | 24.00 | 26.00 | **29.00** | 0.00 |
| 22-K46-4.3 | 85 Moselhaus | 27.00 | 30.00 | **37.00** | −3.00 |
| 22-K46-4.4 | 85 Westfalenhaus aus Delbrueck | 27.00 | 37.00 | **43.00** | −2.00 |
| 22-K46-4.5 | 85 Mittelfrankenhaus/Ernhofen | 27.00 | 43.00 | **50.00** | −2.00 |
| 22-K46-4.6 | 86 Bodenseehaus | 27.00 | 55.00 | **60.00** | +5.00 |
| | Complete Collection | 156.00 | 215.00 | **245.00** | −2.00 |
| **Königszelt Bayern Sulamith's Christmas** (22-K46-5) | | | | | |
| 22-K46-5.1 | 85 The Angels' Vigil | 35.00 | 35.00 | **41.00** | −3.00 |
| 22-K46-5.2 | 86 Christmas Child | 35.00 | 42.00 | **52.00** | −3.00 |
| **Königszelt Bayern A Woman's Love and Life** (22-K46-6) | | | | | |
| 22-K46-6.1 | 86 Since I First Saw Him | 29.85 | 29.85 | **29.85◊** | 0.00 |
| 22-K46-6.2 | 86 He, Noblest of All | 29.85 | 29.85 | **29.85◊** | 0.00 |
| 22-K46-6.3 | 86 I Can't Understand It | 29.85 | 29.85 | **29.85◊** | 0.00 |
| 22-K46-6.4 | 87 You, Ring on My Finger | 32.85 | 32.85 | **32.85◊** | 0.00 |
| **Sulamith Wulfing Mother's Day** (22-K46-8) | | | | | |
| 22-K46-8.1 | 87 Springs New Life | 32.85 | 32.85 | **32.85◊** | 0.00 |
| **Rosenthal Traditional Classic Rose Christmas** (22-R55-1) | | | | | |
| 22-R55-1.62 | 71 Christmas in Garmisch | 66.00 | 90.00 | **95.00** | +1.00 |
| 22-R55-1.63 | 72 Christmas in Franconia | 66.00 | 94.00 | **96.00** | −4.00 |
| 22-R55-1.64 | 73 Lubeck-Holstein | 84.00 | 84.00 | **100.00** | −8.00 |
| 22-R55-1.65 | 74 Christmas in Wurzburg | 85.00 | 100.00 | **100.00** | 0.00 |
| 22-R55-1.66 | 74 Memorial Church in Berlin | 75.00 | 200.00 | **200.00** | 0.00 |
| 22-R55-1.67 | 75 Freiburg Cathedral | 75.00 | 100.00 | **100.00** | 0.00 |
| 22-R55-1.68 | 76 Castle of Cochem | 95.00 | 78.00 | **78.00** | 0.00 |
| 22-R55-1.69 | 77 Hannover Town Hall | 125.00 | 110.00 | **100.00** | −10.00 |
| 22-R55-1.70 | 78 Cathedral at Aachen | 150.00 | 140.00 | **140.00** | 0.00 |
| 22-R55-1.71 | 79 Cathedral in Luxemburg | 165.00 | 120.00 | **120.00** | 0.00 |
| 22-R55-1.72 | 80 Christmas in Brussels | 190.00 | 190.00 | **175.00** | 0.00 |
| 22-R55-1.73 | 81 Christmas in Trier | 190.00 | 70.00 | **70.00** | 0.00 |
| 22-R55-1.74 | 82 Milan Cathedral | 190.00 | 190.00 | **190.00** | 0.00 |
| 22-R55-1.75 | 83 Church at Castle Wittenberg | 195.00 | 195.00 | **190.00** | −5.00 |
| 22-R55-1.76 | 84 City Hall of Stockholm | 195.00 | 195.00 | **195.00** | 0.00 |
| 22-R55-1.77 | 85 Christmas in Augsburg | 195.00 | 195.00 | **195.00** | 0.00 |
| **Rosenthal Wiinblad Christmas** (22-R55-2) | | | | | |
| 22-R55-2.1 | 71 Maria and Child | 100.00 | 900.00 | **980.00** | +30.00 |
| 22-R55-2.2 | 72 Caspar | 100.00 | 300.00 | **420.00** | −5.00 |
| 22-R55-2.3 | 73 Melchior | 125.00 | 400.00 | **500.00** | 0.00 |
| 22-R55-2.4 | 74 Balthazar | 125.00 | 375.00 | **400.00** | 0.00 |
| 22-R55-2.5 | 75 The Annunciation | 195.00 | 169.00 | **177.00** | −3.00 |
| 22-R55-2.6 | 76 Angel with Trumpet | 195.00 | 140.00 | **140.00** | 0.00 |
| 22-R55-2.7 | 77 Adoration of Shepherds | 225.00 | 149.00 | **170.00** | −10.00 |
| 22-R55-2.8 | 78 Angel with Harp | 278.00 | 240.00 | **249.00** | −1.00 |
| 22-R55-2.9 | 79 Exodus from Egypt | 310.00 | 240.00 | **280.00** | −10.00 |
| 22-R55-2.10 | 80 Angel with Glockenspiel | 360.00 | 125.00 | **245.00** | −5.00 |
| 22-R55-2.11 | 81 Christ Child Visits Temple | 375.00 | 350.00 | **345.00** | −5.00 |
| 22-R55-2.12 | 82 Christening of Christ | 375.00 | 400.00 | **360.00** | +10.00 |
| | Complete Collection | 2763.00 | 3788.00 | **4266.00** | +1.00 |
| **Rosenthal Nobility of Children** (22-R55-6) | | | | | |
| 22-R55-6.1 | 76 La Contessa Isabella | 120.00 | 85.00 | **95.00** | −3.00 |
| 22-R55-6.2 | 77 Le Marquis Maurice-Pierre | 120.00 | 77.00 | **80.00** | 0.00 |
| 22-R55-6.3 | 78 Baronesse Johanna-Maryke | 130.00 | 127.00 | **140.00** | −10.00 |
| 22-R55-6.4 | 79 Chief Red Feather | 140.00 | 120.00 | **125.00** | +10.00 |
| | Complete Collection | 510.00 | 409.00 | **440.00** | −3.00 |
| **Rosenthal Oriental Gold** (22-R55-8) | | | | | |
| 22-R55-8.1 | 76 Yasuko | 275.00 | 600.00 | **900.00** | −100.00 |
| 22-R55-8.2 | 77 Mr. Obata | 275.00 | 350.00 | **470.00** | 0.00 |
| 22-R55-8.3 | 78 Sakura | 295.00 | 350.00 | **540.00** | 0.00 |
| 22-R55-8.4 | 79 Michio | 325.00 | 325.00 | **350.00** | 0.00 |
| | Complete Collection | 1170.00 | 1625.00 | **2260.00** | −100.00 |
| **Royal Bayreuth Mother's Day** (22-R58-2) | | | | | |
| 22-R58-2.1 | 73 Consolation | 16.50 | 20.00 | **23.00** | 0.00 |
| 22-R58-2.2 | 74 Young Americans | 25.00 | 100.00 | **125.00** | +10.00 |
| 22-R58-2.3 | 75 Young Americans II | 25.00 | 74.00 | **85.00** | 0.00 |
| 22-R58-2.4 | 76 Young Americans III | 30.00 | 49.00 | **60.00** | 0.00 |
| 22-R58-2.5 | 77 Young Americans IV | 40.00 | 38.00 | **40.00** | −2.00 |
| 22-R58-2.6 | 78 Young Americans V | 45.00 | 18.00 | **21.00** | −4.00 |
| 22-R58-2.7 | 79 Young Americans VI | 60.00 | 74.00 | **75.00** | −5.00 |
| 22-R58-2.8 | 80 Young Americans VII | 65.00 | 60.00 | **60.00** | 0.00 |
| 22-R58-2.9 | 81 Young Americans VIII | 65.00 | 27.00 | **30.00** | 0.00 |

| BRADEX NO. | | ISSUE PRICE | CLOSE | QUOTE | CHANGE |
|---|---|---|---|---|---|
| **22-R58-2.10** | 82 Young Americans IX | 65.00 | 35.00 | **40.00** | −4.00 |
| | Complete Collection | 436.50 | 495.00 | **559.00** | −5.00 |
| **Schmid Hummel Christmas** (22-S12-1) | | | | | |
| **22-S12-1.1** | 71 Angel | 15.00 | 20.00 | **20.00** | 0.00 |
| **22-S12-1.2** | 72 Angel with Flute | 15.00 | 11.00 | **12.00** | −1.00 |
| **22-S12-1.3** | 73 The Nativity | 15.00 | 100.00 | **120.00** | −2.00 |
| **22-S12-1.4** | 74 The Guardian Angel | 18.50 | 10.00 | **10.00** | 0.00 |
| **22-S12-1.5** | 75 Christmas Child | 25.00 | 11.00 | **14.00** | 0.00 |
| **22-S12-1.6** | 76 Sacred Journey | 27.50 | 15.00 | **17.00** | −1.00 |
| **22-S12-1.7** | 77 Herald Angel | 27.50 | 7.00 | **13.00** | 0.00 |
| **22-S12-1.8** | 78 Heavenly Trio | 32.50 | 9.00 | **13.00** | 0.00 |
| **22-S12-1.9** | 79 Starlight Angel | 38.00 | 10.00 | **13.00** | 0.00 |
| **22-S12-1.10** | 80 Parade into Toyland | 45.00 | 25.00 | **28.00** | +2.00 |
| **22-S12-1.11** | 81 A Time to Remember | 45.00 | 9.00 | **12.00** | −2.00 |
| **22-S12-1.12** | 82 Angelic Procession | 45.00 | 20.00 | **25.00** | 0.00 |
| **22-S12-1.13** | 83 Angelic Messenger | 45.00 | 28.00 | **35.00** | +7.00 |
| **22-S12-1.14** | 84 A Gift from Heaven | 45.00 | 32.00 | **34.00** | 0.00 |
| **22-S12-1.15** | 85 Heavenly Light | 45.00 | 31.00 | **33.00** | −1.00 |
| **22-S12-1.16** | 86 Tell the Heavens | 45.00 | 44.00 | **47.00** | −2.00 |
| **Schmid Hummel Mother's Day** (22-S12-2) | | | | | |
| **22-S12-2.1** | 72 Playing Hooky | 15.00 | 9.00 | **12.00** | −1.00 |
| **22-S12-2.2** | 73 Little Fisherman | 15.00 | 38.00 | **40.00** | 0.00 |
| **22-S12-2.3** | 74 Bumblebee | 18.50 | 17.00 | **20.00** | 0.00 |
| **22-S12-2.4** | 75 Message of Love | 25.00 | 19.00 | **20.00** | 0.00 |
| **22-S12-2.5** | 76 Devotion for Mother | 27.50 | 8.00 | **12.00** | 0.00 |
| **22-S12-2.6** | 77 Moonlight Return | 27.50 | 27.00 | **30.00** | 0.00 |
| **22-S12-2.7** | 78 Afternoon Stroll | 32.50 | 9.00 | **10.00** | 0.00 |
| **22-S12-2.8** | 79 Cherub's Gift | 38.00 | 8.00 | **14.00** | 0.00 |
| **22-S12-2.9** | 80 Mother's Little Helpers | 45.00 | 17.00 | **19.00** | −2.00 |
| **22-S12-2.10** | 81 Playtime | 45.00 | 15.00 | **26.00** | 0.00 |
| **22-S12-2.11** | 82 The Flower Basket | 45.00 | 44.00 | **44.00** | +17.00 |
| **22-S12-2.12** | 83 Spring Bouquet | 45.00 | 40.00 | **43.00** | +4.00 |
| **22-S12-2.13** | 84 A Joy to Share | 45.00 | 23.00 | **28.00** | −2.00 |
| **22-S12-2.14** | 85 A Mother's Journey | 45.00 | 28.00 | **32.00** | −1.00 |
| **22-S12-2.15** | 86 Home From School | 45.00 | 35.00 | **42.00** | −3.00 |
| **22-S12-2.16** | 87 Mother's Little Learner | 45.00 | 45.00 | **45.00** | 0.00 |
| **Tirschenreuth Band's Songbirds of Europe** (22-T40-1) | | | | | |
| **22-T40-1.1** | 85 Blue Titmouse | 19.50 | 19.50 | **19.50◊** | 0.00 |
| **22-T40-1.2** | 86 Firecrest | 19.50 | 19.50 | **19.50◊** | 0.00 |
| **22-T40-1.3** | 86 Corsican Nuthatch | 22.50 | 22.50 | **22.50◊** | 0.00 |
| **22-T40-1.4** | 86 Golden Oriole | 22.50 | 22.50 | **22.50◊** | 0.00 |
| **22-T40-1.5** | 86 Great Titmouse | 22.50 | 22.50 | **22.50◊** | 0.00 |
| **22-T40-1.6** | 86 Red Robin | 22.50 | 22.50 | **22.50◊** | 0.00 |
| **22-T40-1.7** | 87 Chaffinch | 24.50 | 24.50 | **24.50◊** | 0.00 |
| **22-T40-1.8** | 87 Redstart | 24.50 | 24.50 | **24.50◊** | 0.00 |
| | Complete Collection | 178.00 | 178.00 | **178.00** | 0.00 |

## GREAT BRITAIN

| BRADEX NO. | | ISSUE PRICE | CLOSE | QUOTE | CHANGE |
|---|---|---|---|---|---|
| **Belleek Christmas** (26-B18-1) | | | | | |
| **26-B18-1.1** | 70 Castle Caldwell | 25.00 | 75.00 | **80.00** | 0.00 |
| **26-B18-1.2** | 71 Celtic Cross | 25.00 | 35.00 | **35.00** | 0.00 |
| **26-B18-1.3** | 72 Flight of the Earls | 30.00 | 30.00 | **35.00** | −3.00 |
| **26-B18-1.4** | 73 Tribute to Yeats | 38.50 | 55.00 | **55.00** | 0.00 |
| **26-B18-1.5** | 74 Devenish Island | 45.00 | 245.00 | **230.00** | +5.00 |
| **26-B18-1.6** | 75 The Celtic Cross | 48.00 | 60.00 | **60.00** | 0.00 |
| **26-B18-1.7** | 76 Dove of Peace | 55.00 | 29.00 | **29.00** | −1.00 |
| **26-B18-1.8** | 77 Wren | 55.00 | 45.00 | **50.00** | −2.00 |
| | Complete Collection | 321.50 | 574.00 | **574.00** | −1.00 |
| **Belleek Irish Wildlife Christmas** (26-B18-2) | | | | | |
| **26-B18-2.1** | 78 A Leaping Salmon | 55.00 | 40.00 | **60.00** | −5.00 |
| **26-B18-2.2** | 79 Hare at Rest | 58.50 | 60.00 | **60.00** | 0.00 |
| **26-B18-2.3** | 80 The Hedgehog | 66.50 | 48.00 | **60.00** | −5.00 |
| **26-B18-2.4** | 81 Red Squirrel | 78.00 | 55.00 | **60.00** | −5.00 |
| **26-B18-2.5** | 82 Irish Seal | 78.00 | 70.00 | **70.00** | 0.00 |
| **26-B18-2.6** | 83 Red Fox | 85.00 | 75.00 | **80.00** | 0.00 |
| | Complete Collection | 421.00 | 348.00 | **390.00** | −15.00 |
| **Davenport Pottery The Toby Plate Collection** (26-D8-1) | | | | | |
| **26-D8-1.1** | 84 Toby Fillpot | 35.00 | 35.00 | **35.00** | 0.00 |
| **26-D8-1.2** | 84 Falstaff | 35.00 | 42.00 | **47.00** | −3.00 |
| **26-D8-1.3** | 85 Jack Tar | 40.00 | 40.00 | **40.00** | 0.00 |
| **26-D8-1.4** | 86 Mr. Pickwick | 40.00 | 40.00 | **45.00** | +5.00 |
| **26-D8-1.5** | 86 Friar Tuck | 40.00 | 40.00 | **40.00◊** | 0.00 |
| **26-D8-1.6** | 86 Long John Silver | 40.00 | 40.00 | **40.00◊** | 0.00 |
| | Complete Collection | 230.00 | 237.00 | **247.00** | +2.00 |
| **Davenport Pottery Treasury of Classic Children's Verses** (26-D8-2) | | | | | |
| **26-D8-2.1** | 86 All Things Bright and Beautiful | 29.00 | 29.00 | **35.00** | +6.00 |
| **26-D8-2.2** | 86 Pirate Story | 29.00 | 29.00 | **29.00◊** | 0.00 |
| **26-D8-2.3** | 87 The Star | 29.00 | 29.00 | **29.00◊** | 0.00 |
| **Longton Crown Pottery Canterbury Tales** (26-L46-1) | | | | | |
| **26-L46-1.1** | 81 Man of Law's Tale | 29.80 | 30.00 | **30.00** | 0.00 |
| **26-L46-1.2** | 82 Franklin's Tale | 29.80 | 30.00 | **30.00** | 0.00 |
| **26-L46-1.3** | 82 Knight's Tale | 31.80 | 32.00 | **32.00** | 0.00 |
| **26-L46-1.4** | 82 Wife of Bath's Tale | 31.80 | 33.00 | **35.00** | −2.00 |
| | Complete Collection | 123.20 | 125.00 | **127.00** | −2.00 |
| **Royal Doulton Beswick Christmas** (26-R62-1) | | | | | |
| **26-R62-1.1** | 72 Christmas in England | 35.00 | 30.00 | **43.00** | −2.00 |
| **26-R62-1.2** | 73 Christmas in Mexico | 37.50 | 19.00 | **20.00** | +1.00 |
| **26-R62-1.3** | 74 Christmas in Bulgaria | 37.50 | 50.00 | **50.00** | 0.00 |
| **26-R62-1.4** | 75 Christmas in Norway | 45.00 | 45.00 | **45.00** | +5.00 |
| **26-R62-1.5** | 76 Christmas in Holland | 50.00 | 48.00 | **48.00** | 0.00 |
| **26-R62-1.6** | 77 Christmas in Poland | 50.00 | 35.00 | **60.00** | −10.00 |
| **26-R62-1.7** | 78 Christmas in America | 55.00 | 20.00 | **50.00** | 0.00 |
| | Complete Collection | 310.00 | 247.00 | **316.00** | −6.00 |
| **Royal Doulton Mother and Child** (26-R62-2) | | | | | |
| **26-R62-2.1** | 73 Colette and Child | 40.00 | 275.00 | **300.00** | +15.00 |
| **26-R62-2.2** | 74 Sayuri and Child | 40.00 | 70.00 | **100.00** | −15.00 |
| **26-R62-2.3** | 75 Kristina and Child | 50.00 | 40.00 | **45.00** | −6.00 |
| **26-R62-2.4** | 76 Marilyn and Child | 55.00 | 60.00 | **65.00** | +7.00 |
| **26-R62-2.5** | 77 Lucia and Child | 70.00 | 60.00 | **60.00** | 0.00 |
| **26-R62-2.6** | 78 Kathleen and Child | 85.00 | 60.00 | **65.00** | 0.00 |
| | Complete Collection | 340.00 | 565.00 | **635.00** | +1.00 |
| **Royal Doulton Commedia Dell' Arte** (26-R62-3) | | | | | |
| **26-R62-3.1** | 74 Harlequin | 50.00 | 53.00 | **55.00** | −5.00 |
| **26-R62-3.2** | 75 Pierrot | 60.00 | 50.00 | **50.00** | 0.00 |
| **26-R62-3.3** | 77 Columbine | 70.00 | 75.00 | **75.00** | 0.00 |
| **26-R62-3.4** | 78 Punchinello | 70.00 | 75.00 | **75.00** | +5.00 |
| | Complete Collection | 250.00 | 253.00 | **255.00** | 0.00 |

| BRADEX NO. | | ISSUE PRICE | CLOSE | QUOTE | CHANGE |
|---|---|---|---|---|---|
| **Royal Doulton Log of the "Dashing Wave"** (26-R62-6) | | | | | |
| **26-R62-6.1** | 76 Sailing with the Tide | 65.00 | 65.00 | **70.00** | −5.00 |
| **26-R62-6.2** | 77 Running Free | 70.00 | 125.00 | **133.00** | +5.00 |
| **26-R62-6.3** | 78 Rounding the Horn | 70.00 | 60.00 | **90.00** | −10.00 |
| **26-R62-6.4** | 79 Hong Kong | 75.00 | 105.00 | **105.00** | 0.00 |
| **26-R62-6.5** | 81 Bora Bora | 95.00 | 68.00 | **70.00** | −2.00 |
| **26-R62-6.6** | 82 Journey's End | 95.00 | 75.00 | **98.00** | −2.00 |
| | Complete Collection | 470.00 | 498.00 | **566.00** | −14.00 |
| **Royal Doulton Valentine's Day** (26-R62-7) | | | | | |
| **26-R62-7.1** | 76 Victorian Boy and Girl | 25.00 | 22.00 | **30.00** | +8.00 |
| **26-R62-7.2** | 77 My Sweetest Friend | 25.00 | 10.00 | **12.00** | +1.00 |
| **26-R62-7.3** | 78 If I Loved You | 25.00 | 23.00 | **23.00** | −2.00 |
| **26-R62-7.4** | 79 My Valentine | 29.95 | 10.00 | **11.00** | 0.00 |
| **26-R62-7.5** | 80 On a Swing | 32.95 | 29.00 | **30.00** | +5.00 |
| **26-R62-7.6** | 81 Sweet Music | 35.00 | 29.00 | **29.00** | −4.00 |
| **26-R62-7.7** | 82 From My Heart | 40.00 | 35.00 | **42.00** | −3.00 |
| **26-R62-7.8** | 83 Cherub's Song | 40.00 | 35.00 | **35.00** | +1.00 |
| **26-R62-7.9** | 84 Love in Bloom | 40.00 | 40.00 | **55.00** | −5.00 |
| **26-R62-7.10** | 85 With Loving Care | 39.95 | 43.00 | **48.00** | +7.00 |
| | Complete Collection | 332.85 | 276.00 | **315.00** | +8.00 |
| **Royal Doulton Portraits of Innocence** (26-R62-11) | | | | | |
| **26-R62-11.1** | 80 Panchito | 75.00 | 95.00 | **110.00** | +11.00 |
| **26-R62-11.2** | 81 Adrien | 85.00 | 40.00 | **47.00** | 0.00 |
| **26-R62-11.3** | 82 Angelica | 95.00 | 58.00 | **58.00** | +4.00 |
| **26-R62-11.4** | 83 Juliana | 95.00 | 40.00 | **50.00** | −5.00 |
| | Complete Collection | 350.00 | 233.00 | **265.00** | +10.00 |
| **Spode Christmas** (26-S63-1) | | | | | |
| **26-S63-1.1** | 70 Partridge | 35.00 | 30.00 | **30.00** | −3.00 |
| **26-S63-1.2** | 71 Angels Singing | 35.00 | 15.00 | **18.00** | +3.00 |
| **26-S63-1.3** | 72 Three Ships A'Sailing | 35.00 | 35.00 | **35.00** | 0.00 |
| **26-S63-1.4** | 73 Three Kings of Orient | 35.00 | 55.00 | **55.00** | 0.00 |
| **26-S63-1.5** | 74 Deck the Halls | 35.00 | 40.00 | **40.00** | 0.00 |
| **26-S63-1.6** | 75 Christbaum | 45.00 | 35.00 | **35.00** | 0.00 |
| **26-S63-1.7** | 76 Good King Wenceslas | 45.00 | 35.00 | **35.00** | 0.00 |
| **26-S63-1.8** | 77 Holly and Ivy | 45.00 | 35.00 | **35.00** | 0.00 |
| **26-S63-1.9** | 78 While Shepherds Watched | 45.00 | 40.00 | **40.00** | 0.00 |
| **26-S63-1.10** | 79 Away in a Manger | 50.00 | 30.00 | **30.00** | 0.00 |
| **26-S63-1.11** | 80 Bringing in the Boar's Head | 60.00 | 40.00 | **51.00** | +1.00 |
| **26-S63-1.12** | 81 Make We Merry | 65.00 | 50.00 | **55.00** | +5.00 |
| | Complete Collection | 530.00 | 440.00 | **459.00** | +6.00 |
| **Wedgwood Christmas** (26-W90-1) | | | | | |
| **26-W90-1.1** | 69 Windsor Castle | 25.00 | 175.00 | **190.00** | +5.00 |
| **26-W90-1.2** | 70 Trafalgar Square | 30.00 | 12.00 | **12.00** | 0.00 |
| **26-W90-1.3** | 71 Piccadilly Circus | 30.00 | 25.00 | **26.00** | 0.00 |
| **26-W90-1.4** | 72 St. Paul's Cathedral | 35.00 | 24.00 | **24.00** | +1.00 |
| **26-W90-1.5** | 73 Tower of London | 40.00 | 35.00 | **38.00** | +3.00 |
| **26-W90-1.6** | 74 Houses of Parliament | 40.00 | 25.00 | **27.00** | −3.00 |
| **26-W90-1.7** | 75 Tower Bridge | 45.00 | 19.00 | **22.00** | +1.00 |
| **26-W90-1.8** | 76 Hampton Court | 50.00 | 25.00 | **25.00** | 0.00 |
| **26-W90-1.9** | 77 Westminster Abbey | 55.00 | 28.00 | **28.00** | 0.00 |
| **26-W90-1.10** | 78 Horse Guards | 60.00 | 22.00 | **24.00** | −5.00 |
| **26-W90-1.11** | 79 Buckingham Palace | 65.00 | 25.00 | **25.00** | −5.00 |
| **26-W90-1.12** | 80 St. James Palace | 70.00 | 34.00 | **40.00** | −3.00 |
| **26-W90-1.13** | 81 Marble Arch | 75.00 | 34.00 | **40.00** | −3.00 |
| **26-W90-1.14** | 82 Lambeth Palace | 80.00 | 100.00 | **90.00** | +10.00 |
| **26-W90-1.15** | 83 All Souls, Langham Palace | 80.00 | 60.00 | **60.00** | 0.00 |
| **26-W90-1.16** | 84 Constitutional Hill | 80.00 | 55.00 | **56.00** | 0.00 |
| **26-W90-1.17** | 85 Tate Gallery | 80.00 | 78.00 | **80.00** | 0.00 |
| **26-W90-1.18** | 86 Albert Memorial | 80.00 | 87.00 | **92.00** | +12.00 |
| **Wedgwood Mothers** (26-W90-2) | | | | | |
| **26-W90-2.1** | 71 Sportive Love | 20.00 | 14.00 | **15.00** | 0.00 |
| **26-W90-2.2** | 72 The Sewing Lesson | 20.00 | 18.00 | **18.00** | −1.00 |
| **26-W90-2.3** | 73 Baptism of Achilles | 25.00 | 12.00 | **13.00** | 0.00 |
| **26-W90-2.4** | 74 Domestic Employment | 30.00 | 30.00 | **33.00** | −3.00 |
| **26-W90-2.5** | 75 Mother and Child | 35.00 | 34.00 | **34.00** | −1.00 |
| **26-W90-2.6** | 76 The Spinner | 35.00 | 25.00 | **25.00** | −2.00 |
| **26-W90-2.7** | 77 Leisure Time | 35.00 | 20.00 | **20.00** | 0.00 |
| **26-W90-2.8** | 78 Swan and Cygnets | 40.00 | 28.00 | **28.00** | −3.00 |
| **26-W90-2.9** | 79 Deer and Fawn | 45.00 | 30.00 | **32.00** | −2.00 |
| **26-W90-2.10** | 80 Birds | 47.50 | 36.00 | **38.00** | −2.00 |
| **26-W90-2.11** | 81 Mare and Foal | 50.00 | 40.00 | **49.00** | +1.00 |
| **26-W90-2.12** | 82 Cherubs with Swing | 55.00 | 55.00 | **55.00** | 0.00 |
| **26-W90-2.13** | 83 Cupid and Butterfly | 55.00 | 55.00 | **55.00** | 0.00 |
| **26-W90-2.14** | 84 Cupid and Music | 55.00 | 55.00 | **60.00** | +15.00 |
| **26-W90-2.15** | 85 Cupid and Doves | 55.00 | 53.00 | **53.00** | −9.00 |
| **26-W90-2.16** | 86 Cupids at Play | 55.00 | 55.00 | **55.00** | 0.00 |
| **Wedgwood Blossoming of Suzanne** (26-W90-4) | | | | | |
| **26-W90-4.1** | 77 Innocence | 60.00 | 22.00 | **25.00** | −3.00 |
| **26-W90-4.2** | 78 Cherish | 60.00 | 25.00 | **29.00** | −3.00 |
| **26-W90-4.3** | 79 Daydream | 65.00 | 39.00 | **44.00** | −5.00 |
| **26-W90-4.4** | 80 Wistful | 70.00 | 30.00 | **44.00** | −3.00 |
| | Complete Collection | 255.00 | 116.00 | **142.00** | −14.00 |
| **Wedgwood Mary Vickers My Memories** (26-W90-5) | | | | | |
| **26-W90-5.1** | 81 Be My Friend | 27.00 | 27.00 | **27.00** | 0.00 |
| **26-W90-5.2** | 82 Playtime | 27.00 | 27.00 | **27.00** | 0.00 |
| **26-W90-5.3** | 83 Our Garden | 27.00 | 27.00 | **30.00** | −5.00 |
| **26-W90-5.4** | 84 The Recital | 27.00 | 27.00 | **29.00** | −3.00 |
| **26-W90-5.5** | 85 Mother's Treasures | 29.00 | 29.00 | **29.00** | −1.00 |
| **26-W90-5.6** | 86 Riding High | 29.00 | 47.00 | **49.00** | +20.00 |
| | Complete Collection | 166.00 | 184.00 | **191.00** | +11.00 |
| **Wedgwood The Street Sellers of London** (26-W90-10) | | | | | |
| **26-W90-10.1** | 86 The Baked Potato Man | 25.00 | 134.00 | **120.00** | +30.00 |
| **26-W90-10.2** | 86 Street Seller of Hot Elder Wine | 25.00 | 100.00 | **110.00** | +85.00 |
| **26-W90-10.3** | 87 Ginger Beer Fountain | 25.00 | 25.00 | **25.00◊** | 0.00 |
| **26-W90-10.4** | 86 Hot Green Peas | 25.00 | 25.00 | **25.00◊** | 0.00 |
| **Wedgwood Legends of King Arthur** (26-W90-17) | | | | | |
| **26-W90-17.1** | 86 Arthur Draws Sword | 39.00 | 39.00 | **45.00** | 0.00 |
| **26-W90-17.2** | 87 Arthur Crowned King | 39.00 | 39.00 | **39.00◊** | 0.00 |
| **26-W90-17.3** | 87 Excalibur | 42.00 | 42.00 | **42.00◊** | 0.00 |
| **Wedgwood Mary Vickers Portraits of First Love** (26-W90-18) | | | | | |
| **26-W90-18.1** | 86 Love Letter | 27.00 | 41.00 | **42.00** | −3.00 |
| **26-W90-18.2** | 86 The Ring | 27.00 | 27.00 | **27.00◊** | 0.00 |
| **26-W90-18.3** | 87 The Gift | 27.00 | 27.00 | **27.00◊** | 0.00 |
| **Wedgwood Colin Newman's Country Panorama** (26-W90-27) | | | | | |
| **26-W90-27.1** | 87 Meadows and Wheatfields | 29.00 | 29.00 | **29.00◊** | 0.00 |

## ITALY

| BRADEX NO. | | ISSUE PRICE | CLOSE | QUOTE | CHANGE |
|---|---|---|---|---|---|
| **Anri Christmas** (38-A54-1) | | | | | |
| **38-A54-1.1** | 71 St. Jakob in Groden | 37.50 | 55.00 | **55.00** | 0.00 |
| **38-A54-1.2** | 72 Pipers at Alberobello | 45.00 | 84.00 | **84.00** | 0.00 |

| BRADEX NO. | | ISSUE PRICE | CLOSE | QUOTE | CHANGE |
|---|---|---|---|---|---|
| **38-A54-1.3** | 73 Alpine Horn | 45.00 | 350.00 | **335.00** | +10.00 |
| **38-A54-1.4** | 74 Young Man and Girl | 50.00 | 50.00 | **70.00** | −9.00 |
| **38-A54-1.5** | 75 Christmas in Ireland | 60.00 | 50.00 | **52.00** | 0.00 |
| **38-A54-1.6** | 76 Alpine Christmas | 65.00 | 185.00 | **185.00** | −5.00 |
| **38-A54-1.7** | 77 Heiligenblut | 65.00 | 109.00 | **110.00** | −10.00 |
| **38-A54-1.8** | 78 Klockler Singers | 80.00 | 49.00 | **50.00** | −5.00 |
| **38-A54-1.9** | 79 Moss Gatherers | 135.00 | 39.00 | **45.00** | −4.00 |
| **38-A54-1.10** | 80 Wintry Church-going | 165.00 | 124.00 | **124.00** | 0.00 |
| **38-A54-1.11** | 81 Santa Claus in Tyrol | 165.00 | 77.00 | **118.00** | 0.00 |
| **38-A54-1.12** | 82 The Star Singers | 165.00 | 134.00 | **134.00** | 0.00 |
| **38-A54-1.13** | 83 Unto Us a Child Is Born | 165.00 | 191.00 | **196.00** | +6.00 |
| **38-A54-1.14** | 84 Yuletide in the Valley | 165.00 | 165.00 | **165.00** | 0.00 |
| **38-A54-1.15** | 85 Good Morning, Good Cheer | 165.00 | 150.00 | **155.00** | −10.00 |
| **King's Flowers of America** (38-K32-2) | | | | | |
| **38-K32-2.1** | 73 Pink Carnation | 85.00 | 94.00 | **95.00** | 0.00 |
| **38-K32-2.2** | 74 Red Roses | 100.00 | 140.00 | **140.00** | −5.00 |
| **38-K32-2.3** | 75 Yellow Dahlia | 110.00 | 155.00 | **155.00** | 0.00 |
| **38-K32-2.4** | 76 Bluebells | 130.00 | 160.00 | **160.00** | −5.00 |
| **38-K32-2.5** | 77 Anemones | 130.00 | 175.00 | **175.00** | 0.00 |
| | Complete Collection | 555.00 | 724.00 | **725.00** | −10.00 |
| **Le Porcellane Fontana dei Medici Le Donne Di Puccini (Puccini's Women)** (38-P63-1) | | | | | |
| **38-P63-1.1** | 86 Musetta | 39.00 | 35.00 | **40.00** | −5.00 |
| **38-P63-1.2** | 86 Mimi | 39.00 | 46.00 | **47.00** | +2.00 |
| **38-P63-1.3** | 86 Manon | 39.00 | 39.00 | **39.00** | 0.00 |
| **38-P63-1.4** | 87 Madame Butterfly | 39.00 | 39.00 | **39.00**◊ | 0.00 |
| **38-P63-1.5** | 87 Tosca | 39.00 | 39.00 | **39.00**◊ | 0.00 |
| **Veneto Flair Bellini** (38-V22-1) | | | | | |
| **38-V22-1.1** | 71 Madonna | 45.00 | 385.00 | **385.00** | 0.00 |
| **Veneto Flair Last Supper** (38-V22-6) | | | | | |
| **38-V22-6.1** | 72 Three Apostles (Scene I) | 100.00 | 100.00 | **100.00** | 0.00 |
| **38-V22-6.2** | 73 Three Apostles (Scene II) | 70.00 | 78.00 | **78.00** | 0.00 |
| **38-V22-6.3** | 74 Three Apostles (Scene III) | 70.00 | 73.00 | **78.00** | +3.00 |
| **38-V22-6.4** | 75 Three Apostles (Scene IV) | 70.00 | 125.00 | **135.00** | +10.00 |
| **38-V22-6.5** | 76 Christ (Scene V) | 70.00 | 60.00 | **60.00** | 0.00 |
| | Complete Collection | 380.00 | 436.00 | **451.00** | +13.00 |
| **Veneto Flair St. Mark's of Venice** (38-V22-15) | | | | | |
| **38-V22-15.1** | 84 Noah and the Dove | 60.00 | 60.00 | **60.00** | 0.00 |
| **38-V22-15.2** | 85 Moses and the Burning Bush | 60.00 | 60.00 | **60.00** | 0.00 |
| **38-V22-15.3** | 86 Abraham and the Journey | 60.00 | 65.00 | **70.00** | −6.00 |
| **38-V22-15.4** | 86 Joseph and Coat | 63.00 | 65.00 | **85.00** | 0.00 |
| | Complete Collection | 243.00 | 250.00 | **275.00** | −6.00 |
| **Studio Dante di Volteradici Grand Opera** (38-V90-1) | | | | | |
| **38-V90-1.1** | 76 Rigoletto | 35.00 | 35.00 | **37.00** | −3.00 |
| **38-V90-1.2** | 77 Madama Butterfly | 35.00 | 35.00 | **35.00** | 0.00 |
| **38-V90-1.3** | 78 Carmen | 40.00 | 40.00 | **40.00** | 0.00 |
| **38-V90-1.4** | 79 Aida | 40.00 | 40.00 | **40.00** | 0.00 |
| **38-V90-1.5** | 80 Barber of Seville | 40.00 | 40.00 | **40.00** | 0.00 |
| **38-V90-1.6** | 81 Tosca | 40.00 | 40.00 | **43.00** | −2.00 |
| **38-V90-1.7** | 82 Pagliacci | 40.00 | 70.00 | **100.00** | 0.00 |
| | Complete Collection | 270.00 | 300.00 | **335.00** | −5.00 |
| **Studio Dante di Volteradici Living Madonnas** (38-V90-2) | | | | | |
| **38-V90-2.1** | 78 The Pensive Madonna | 45.00 | 45.00 | **45.00** | 0.00 |
| **38-V90-2.2** | 79 The Serene Madonna | 45.00 | 45.00 | **45.00** | 0.00 |
| **38-V90-2.3** | 80 The Beatific Madonna | 45.00 | 45.00 | **45.00** | −2.00 |
| **38-V90-2.4** | 81 The Prophetic Madonna | 45.00 | 45.00 | **50.00** | 0.00 |
| **38-V90-2.5** | 82 The Demure Madonna | 45.00 | 60.00 | **65.00** | −4.00 |
| **38-V90-2.6** | 83 The Wise Madonna | 45.00 | 70.00 | **75.00** | 0.00 |
| **38-V90-2.7** | 84 The Tender Madonna | 45.00 | 47.00 | **60.00** | 0.00 |
| | Complete Collection | 315.00 | 357.00 | **375.00** | −6.00 |
| **Studio Dante di Volteradici Ghiberti Doors** (38-V90-3) | | | | | |
| **38-V90-3.1** | 83 Adoration of the Magi | 50.00 | 110.00 | **130.00** | −25.00 |
| **38-V90-3.2** | 84 The Nativity | 50.00 | 50.00 | **60.00** | −5.00 |
| **38-V90-3.3** | 85 The Annunciation | 50.00 | 50.00 | **55.00** | −5.00 |
| **38-V90-3.4** | 86 Christ and Doctors | 55.00 | 55.00 | **60.00** | −4.00 |
| **38-V90-3.5** | 86 Christ Walks on the Water | 55.00 | 70.00 | **82.00** | −5.00 |
| **38-V90-3.6** | 86 Expulsion of Money Changers | 55.00 | 55.00 | **60.00** | +5.00 |
| **38-V90-3.7** | 87 Entry Into Jerusalem | 55.00 | 55.00 | **55.00**◊ | 0.00 |
| **Studio Dante di Volteradici Benvenuti's Muses** (38-V90-4) | | | | | |
| **38-V90-4.1** | 85 Erato | 50.00 | 50.00 | **56.00** | 0.00 |
| **38-V90-4.2** | 85 Cleo | 50.00 | 50.00 | **55.00** | −8.00 |
| **38-V90-4.3** | 86 Terpsichore | 55.00 | 75.00 | **75.00** | +20.00 |
| **38-V90-4.4** | 87 Euterpe | 55.00 | 55.00 | **55.00**◊ | 0.00 |
| | Complete Collection | 210.00 | 230.00 | **241.00** | +12.00 |
| **Studio Dante di Volteradici Renaissance Madonnas: Gifts of Maternal Love** (38-V90-5) | | | | | |
| **38-V90-5.1** | 86 The Gift of Wisdom | 65.00 | 65.00 | **65.00**◊ | 0.00 |
| **38-V90-5.2** | 87 Gift of Faith | 65.00 | 65.00 | **65.00**◊ | 0.00 |
| **Studio Dante di Volteradici Christmas Creche** (38-V90-7) | | | | | |
| **38-V90-7.1** | 87 Joy to the World | 55.00 | 55.00 | **55.00**◊ | 0.00 |

## JAPAN

| BRADEX NO. | | ISSUE PRICE | CLOSE | QUOTE | CHANGE |
|---|---|---|---|---|---|
| **Fukagawa Haiku About Children** (42-F78-1) | | | | | |
| **42-F78-1.1** | 77 Beneath the Plum Branch | 38.00 | 38.00 | **38.00** | 0.00 |
| **42-F78-1.2** | 78 Child of Straw | 42.00 | 42.00 | **42.00** | 0.00 |
| **42-F78-1.3** | 79 Dragon Dance | 42.00 | 48.00 | **53.00** | +8.00 |
| **42-F78-1.4** | 80 Mask Dancing | 42.00 | 115.00 | **125.00** | +25.00 |
| | Complete Collection | 164.00 | 243.00 | **258.00** | +33.00 |
| **Schmid Peanuts Christmas** (42-S12-1) | | | | | |
| **42-S12-1.1** | 72 Snoopy Guides the Sleigh | 10.00 | 68.00 | **70.00** | −4.00 |
| **42-S12-1.2** | 73 Christmas Eve at Doghouse | 10.00 | 170.00 | **175.00** | −5.00 |
| **42-S12-1.3** | 74 Christmas at Fireplace | 10.00 | 28.00 | **31.00** | 0.00 |
| **42-S12-1.4** | 75 Woodstock, Santa Claus | 12.50 | 12.00 | **12.00** | 0.00 |
| **42-S12-1.5** | 76 Woodstock's Christmas | 13.00 | 18.00 | **19.00** | 0.00 |
| **42-S12-1.6** | 77 Deck the Doghouse | 13.00 | 13.00 | **15.00** | 0.00 |
| **42-S12-1.7** | 78 Filling the Stocking | 15.00 | 25.00 | **25.00** | 0.00 |
| **42-S12-1.8** | 79 Christmas at Hand | 17.50 | 18.00 | **18.00** | 0.00 |
| **42-S12-1.9** | 80 Waiting for Santa | 17.50 | 35.00 | **42.00** | 0.00 |
| **42-S12-1.10** | 81 A Christmas Wish | 17.50 | 12.00 | **12.00** | 0.00 |
| **42-S12-1.11** | 82 A Perfect Performance | 18.50 | 22.00 | **22.00** | 0.00 |
| | Complete Collection | 154.50 | 421.00 | **441.00** | −9.00 |
| **Schmid Disney Christmas** (42-S12-3) | | | | | |
| **42-S12-3.1** | 73 Sleigh Ride | 10.00 | 150.00 | **260.00** | −20.00 |
| **42-S12-3.2** | 74 Decorating the Tree | 10.00 | 60.00 | **60.00** | −5.00 |
| **42-S12-3.3** | 75 Caroling | 12.50 | 11.00 | **12.00** | −3.00 |
| **42-S12-3.4** | 76 Building a Snowman | 13.00 | 12.00 | **15.00** | −1.00 |
| **42-S12-3.5** | 77 Down the Chimney | 13.00 | 21.00 | **25.00** | +3.00 |
| **42-S12-3.6** | 78 Night Before Christmas | 15.00 | 20.00 | **20.00** | −4.00 |
| **42-S12-3.7** | 79 Santa's Surprise | 17.50 | 14.00 | **15.00** | 0.00 |
| **42-S12-3.8** | 80 Sleigh Ride | 17.50 | 27.00 | **28.00** | 0.00 |
| **42-S12-3.9** | 81 Happy Holidays | 17.50 | 10.00 | **12.00** | −3.00 |
| **42-S12-3.10** | 82 Winter Games | 18.50 | 19.00 | **19.00** | 0.00 |
| | Complete Collection | 144.50 | 344.00 | **466.00** | −33.00 |
| **Schmid Disney Mother's Day** (42-S12-4) | | | | | |
| **42-S12-4.1** | 74 Flowers for Mother | 10.00 | 30.00 | **39.00** | −3.00 |
| **42-S12-4.2** | 75 Snow White and Dwarfs | 12.50 | 19.00 | **25.00** | −4.00 |
| **42-S12-4.3** | 76 Minnie Mouse | 13.00 | 11.00 | **11.00** | 0.00 |
| **42-S12-4.4** | 77 Pluto's Pals | 13.00 | 14.00 | **16.00** | 0.00 |
| **42-S12-4.5** | 78 Flowers for Bambi | 15.00 | 12.00 | **12.00** | −3.00 |
| **42-S12-4.6** | 79 Happy Feet | 17.50 | 17.00 | **18.00** | 0.00 |
| **42-S12-4.7** | 80 Minnie's Surprise | 17.50 | 12.00 | **12.00** | 0.00 |
| **42-S12-4.8** | 81 Playmates | 17.50 | 14.00 | **15.00** | 0.00 |
| **42-S12-4.9** | 82 A Dream Come True | 18.50 | 24.00 | **25.00** | +1.00 |
| | Complete Collection | 134.50 | 153.00 | **173.00** | −9.00 |

## NORWAY

| BRADEX NO. | | ISSUE PRICE | CLOSE | QUOTE | CHANGE |
|---|---|---|---|---|---|
| **Porsgrund Christmas** (54-P62-1) | | | | | |
| **54-P62-1.1** | 68 Church Scene | 12.00 | 150.00 | **125.00** | +25.00 |
| **54-P62-1.2** | 69 Three Kings | 12.00 | 9.00 | **9.00** | 0.00 |
| **54-P62-1.3** | 70 Road to Bethlehem | 12.00 | 8.00 | **10.00** | 0.00 |
| **54-P62-1.4** | 71 A Child is Born | 12.00 | 10.00 | **12.00** | 0.00 |
| **54-P62-1.5** | 72 Hark the Herald Angels | 12.00 | 12.00 | **12.00** | 0.00 |
| **54-P62-1.6** | 73 Promise of the Savior | 15.00 | 24.00 | **28.00** | −4.00 |
| **54-P62-1.7** | 74 The Shepherds | 15.00 | 50.00 | **50.00** | +3.00 |
| **54-P62-1.8** | 75 Road to Temple | 19.50 | 10.00 | **10.00** | −4.00 |
| **54-P62-1.9** | 76 Jesus and the Elders | 22.00 | 12.00 | **12.00** | 0.00 |
| **54-P62-1.10** | 77 Draught of the Fish | 24.00 | 12.00 | **12.00** | 0.00 |
| | Complete Collection | 155.50 | 297.00 | **280.00** | +20.00 |
| **Porsgrund Mother's Day** (54-P62-2) | | | | | |
| **54-P62-2.1** | 70 Mare and Foal | 7.50 | 7.00 | **9.00** | 0.00 |
| **54-P62-2.2** | 71 Boy and Geese | 7.50 | 5.00 | **7.00** | 0.00 |
| **54-P62-2.3** | 72 Doe and Fawn | 10.00 | 5.00 | **9.00** | 0.00 |
| **54-P62-2.4** | 73 Cat and Kittens | 10.00 | 10.00 | **19.00** | 0.00 |
| **54-P62-2.5** | 74 Boy and Goats | 10.00 | 25.00 | **25.00** | 0.00 |
| **54-P62-2.6** | 75 Dog and Puppies | 12.50 | 32.00 | **33.00** | 0.00 |
| **54-P62-2.7** | 76 Girl and Calf | 15.00 | 28.00 | **28.00** | +3.00 |
| **54-P62-2.8** | 77 Boy and Chickens | 16.50 | 28.00 | **28.00** | −1.00 |
| **54-P62-2.9** | 78 Girl and Pigs | 17.50 | 27.00 | **27.00** | 0.00 |
| **54-P62-2.10** | 79 Boy and Reindeer | 19.50 | 19.50 | **20.00** | 0.00 |
| **54-P62-2.11** | 80 Girl and Lambs | 21.50 | 29.00 | **29.00** | 0.00 |
| **54-P62-2.12** | 81 Boy and Birds | 24.00 | 25.00 | **25.00** | 0.00 |
| **54-P62-2.13** | 82 Child with Rabbit | 26.00 | 25.00 | **25.00** | 0.00 |
| **54-P62-2.14** | 83 Mother and Kittens | 26.00 | 26.00 | **26.00** | 0.00 |
| **54-P62-2.15** | 84 By the Pond | 25.00 | 27.00 | **27.00** | 0.00 |
| **54-P62-2.16** | 85 Mother's Day | 26.00 | 26.00 | **50.00** | 0.00 |
| **54-P62-2.17** | 86 First Feeding | 27.00 | 27.00 | **27.00** | 0.00 |
| **Porsgrund Traditional Norwegian Christmas** (54-P62-5) | | | | | |
| **54-P62-5.1** | 78 Guests Are Coming | 27.00 | 20.00 | **20.00** | −5.00 |
| **54-P62-5.2** | 79 Home for Christmas | 30.00 | 20.00 | **20.00** | 0.00 |
| **54-P62-5.3** | 80 Preparing for Christmas | 34.00 | 40.00 | **34.00** | 0.00 |
| **54-P62-5.4** | 81 Christmas Skating | 38.00 | 35.00 | **35.00** | 0.00 |
| **54-P62-5.5** | 82 White Christmas | 42.00 | 45.00 | **45.00** | 0.00 |
| | Complete Collection | 171.00 | 160.00 | **154.00** | −5.00 |

## SPAIN

| BRADEX NO. | | ISSUE PRICE | CLOSE | QUOTE | CHANGE |
|---|---|---|---|---|---|
| **Lladro Mother's Day** (72-L41-2) | | | | | |
| **72-L41-2.1** | 71 Kiss of the Child | 27.50 | 50.00 | **54.00** | +10.00 |
| **72-L41-2.2** | 72 Bird and Chicks | 27.50 | 25.00 | **27.00** | −3.00 |
| **72-L41-2.3** | 73 Mother and Children | 35.00 | 39.00 | **40.00** | +4.00 |
| **72-L41-2.4** | 74 Mother Nursing | 45.00 | 100.00 | **116.00** | −9.00 |
| **72-L41-2.5** | 75 Mother and Child | 60.00 | 50.00 | **55.00** | 0.00 |
| **72-L41-2.6** | 76 Tender Vigil | 60.00 | 50.00 | **50.00** | −5.00 |
| **72-L41-2.7** | 77 Mother and Daughter | 67.50 | 51.00 | **53.00** | −2.00 |
| **72-L41-2.8** | 78 New Arrival | 80.00 | 85.00 | **70.00** | +10.00 |
| **72-L41-2.9** | 79 Off to School | 90.00 | 80.00 | **80.00** | +20.00 |
| **72-L41-2.10** | 80 Mother and Children | 95.00 | 95.00 | **95.00** | 0.00 |
| | Complete Collection | 587.50 | 625.00 | **640.00** | +25.00 |

## SWEDEN

| BRADEX NO. | | ISSUE PRICE | CLOSE | QUOTE | CHANGE |
|---|---|---|---|---|---|
| **Orrefors Annual Cathedral** (76-074-1) | | | | | |
| **76-074-1.1** | 70 Notre Dame Cathedral | 50.00 | 55.00 | **50.00** | +5.00 |
| **76-074-1.2** | 71 Westminster Abbey | 50.00 | 50.00 | **50.00** | +15.00 |
| **76-074-1.3** | 72 Basilica di San Marco | 50.00 | 57.00 | **57.00** | 0.00 |
| **76-074-1.4** | 73 Cologne Cathedral | 50.00 | 70.00 | **80.00** | +10.00 |
| **76-074-1.5** | 74 Rue de la Victoire | 60.00 | 80.00 | **85.00** | +10.00 |
| **76-074-1.6** | 75 Basilica di San Pietro | 85.00 | 80.00 | **80.00** | 0.00 |
| **76-074-1.7** | 76 Christ Church | 85.00 | 65.00 | **65.00** | +5.00 |
| **76-074-1.8** | 77 Masjid-E-Shah | 90.00 | 130.00 | **130.00** | +12.00 |
| **76-074-1.9** | 78 Santiago de Compostela | 95.00 | 110.00 | **115.00** | +5.00 |
| | Complete Collection | 615.00 | 697.00 | **712.00** | +62.00 |
| **Rorstrand Christmas** (76-R54-1) | | | | | |
| **76-R54-1.1** | 68 Bringing Home the Tree | 12.00 | 300.00 | **300.00** | 0.00 |
| **76-R54-1.2** | 69 Fisherman Sailing Home | 13.50 | 26.00 | **26.00** | −4.00 |
| **76-R54-1.3** | 70 Nils with His Geese | 13.50 | 15.00 | **15.00** | −3.00 |
| **76-R54-1.4** | 71 Nils in Lapland | 15.00 | 15.00 | **15.00** | 0.00 |
| **76-R54-1.5** | 72 Dalecarlian Fiddler | 15.00 | 18.00 | **20.00** | +2.00 |
| **76-R54-1.6** | 73 Farm in Smaland | 16.00 | 50.00 | **50.00** | 0.00 |
| **76-R54-1.7** | 74 Vadstena | 19.00 | 40.00 | **40.00** | 0.00 |
| **76-R54-1.8** | 75 Nils in Vastmanland | 20.00 | 15.00 | **15.00** | −3.00 |
| **76-R54-1.9** | 76 Nils in Uppland | 20.00 | 30.00 | **35.00** | +5.00 |
| **76-R54-1.10** | 77 Nils in Varmland | 29.50 | 12.00 | **12.00** | −3.00 |
| **76-R54-1.11** | 78 Nils in Fjallbacka | 32.50 | 18.00 | **18.00** | −5.00 |
| **76-R54-1.12** | 79 Nils in Vaestergoetland | 38.50 | 38.00 | **38.00** | 0.00 |
| **76-R54-1.13** | 80 Nils in Halland | 55.00 | 45.00 | **45.00** | 0.00 |
| **76-R54-1.14** | 81 Nils in Gotland | 55.00 | 18.00 | **30.00** | −10.00 |
| **76-R54-1.15** | 82 Nils at Skansen | 47.50 | 45.00 | **45.00** | −5.00 |
| **76-R54-1.16** | 83 Nils in Oland | 42.50 | 43.00 | **43.00** | 0.00 |
| **76-R54-1.17** | 84 Angermanland | 42.50 | 38.00 | **38.00** | −4.00 |
| **76-R54-1.18** | 85 Christmas | 42.50 | 42.00 | **42.00** | −2.00 |
| **76-R54-1.19** | 86 Nils in Karlskr | 42.50 | 45.00 | **43.00** | −2.00 |

## SWITZERLAND

| BRADEX NO. | | ISSUE PRICE | CLOSE | QUOTE | CHANGE |
|---|---|---|---|---|---|
| **Langenthal Swiss China Anker Heritage** (78-L5-1) | | | | | |
| **78-L5-1.1** | 86 Grandfather Tells a Story | 34.86 | 30.00 | **35.00** | 0.00 |
| **78-L5-1.2** | 87 The First Smile | 34.86 | 34.86 | **34.86**◊ | 0.00 |
| **78-L5-1.3** | 87 Girl Feeding Chickens | 34.86 | 34.86 | **34.86**◊ | 0.00 |

# UNITED STATES

| BRADEX NO. | | ISSUE PRICE | CLOSE | QUOTE | CHANGE |
|---|---|---|---|---|---|
| **Artists of the World Children of Aberdeen** (84-A72-1) | | | | | |
| **84-A72-1.1** | 79 Girl with Little Brother | 50.00 | 25.00 | **30.00** | −5.00 |
| **84-A72-1.2** | 80 Sampan Girl | 50.00 | 48.00 | **48.00** | +8.00 |
| **84-A72-1.3** | 81 Girl with Little Sister | 55.00 | 37.00 | **40.00** | 0.00 |
| **84-A72-1.4** | 82 Girl with Seashells | 60.00 | 60.00 | **63.00** | +3.00 |
| **84-A72-1.5** | 83 Girl with Seabirds | 60.00 | 65.00 | **65.00** | 0.00 |
| **84-A72-1.6** | 84 Brother and Sister | 60.00 | 45.00 | **47.00** | −3.00 |
| | Complete Collection | 335.00 | 280.00 | **293.00** | +3.00 |
| **Crown Parian Freddie the Freeloader** (84-C72-1) | | | | | |
| **84-C72-1.1** | 79 Freddie in the Bathtub | 55.00 | 199.00 | **205.00** | −14.00 |
| **84-C72-1.2** | 80 Freddie's Shack | 55.00 | 87.00 | **60.00** | −4.00 |
| **84-C72-1.3** | 81 Freddie on the Green | 60.00 | 47.00 | **49.00** | 0.00 |
| **84-C72-1.4** | 82 Love That Freddie | 60.00 | 34.00 | **37.00** | −3.00 |
| | Complete Collection | 230.00 | 367.00 | **351.00** | −21.00 |
| **Crown Parian American Folk Heroes** (84-C72-2) | | | | | |
| **84-C72-2.1** | 83 Johnny Appleseed | 35.00 | 35.00 | **35.00** | 0.00 |
| **84-C72-2.2** | 84 Davy Crockett | 35.00 | 35.00 | **35.00** | 0.00 |
| **84-C72-2.3** | 85 Betsy Ross | 35.00 | 35.00 | **39.00** | −3.00 |
| **84-C72-2.4** | 85 Buffalo Bill | 35.00 | 42.00 | **45.00** | 0.00 |
| **84-C72-2.5** | 86 Casey Jones | 40.00 | 65.00 | **70.00** | +30.00 |
| **84-C72-2.6** | 86 Sacajawea | 40.00 | 58.00 | **60.00** | +20.00 |
| **Crown Parian Freddie's Adventures** (84-C72-3) | | | | | |
| **84-C72-3.1** | 82 Captain Freddie | 60.00 | 43.00 | **44.00** | +4.00 |
| **84-C72-3.2** | 82 Bronco Freddie | 60.00 | 25.00 | **24.00** | −2.00 |
| **84-C72-3.3** | 83 Sir Freddie | 62.50 | 30.00 | **32.00** | 0.00 |
| **84-C72-3.4** | 84 Gertrude and Heathcliffe | 62.50 | 68.00 | **70.00** | −5.00 |
| | Complete Collection | 245.00 | 166.00 | **170.00** | −3.00 |
| **Ernst Enterprises Seems Like Yesterday** (84-E74-1) | | | | | |
| **84-E74-1.1** | 81 Stop and Smell the Roses | 24.50 | 8.00 | **10.00** | −2.00 |
| **84-E74-1.2** | 82 Home by Lunch | 24.50 | 17.00 | **18.00** | −2.00 |
| **84-E74-1.3** | 82 Lisa's Creek | 24.50 | 20.00 | **20.00** | −2.00 |
| **84-E74-1.4** | 83 It's Got My Name on It | 24.50 | 20.00 | **21.00** | 0.00 |
| **84-E74-1.5** | 84 My Magic Hat | 24.50 | 19.00 | **20.00** | 0.00 |
| **84-E74-1.6** | 84 Little Prince | 24.50 | 17.00 | **18.00** | −2.00 |
| | Complete Collection | 147.00 | 101.00 | **107.00** | −8.00 |
| **Fairmont Artists of the World DeGrazia Holiday** (84-F4-1) | | | | | |
| **84-F4-1.1** | 76 Festival of Lights | 45.00 | 195.00 | **220.00** | 0.00 |
| **84-F4-1.2** | 77 Bell of Hope | 45.00 | 90.00 | **80.00** | −10.00 |
| **84-F4-1.3** | 78 Little Madonna | 45.00 | 125.00 | **115.00** | −10.00 |
| **84-F4-1.4** | 79 The Nativity | 50.00 | 120.00 | **125.00** | −5.00 |
| **84-F4-1.5** | 80 Pima Indian Drummer | 50.00 | 79.00 | **90.00** | −12.00 |
| **84-F4-1.6** | 81 Little Prayer-Angel | 55.00 | 89.00 | **98.00** | 0.00 |
| **84-F4-1.7** | 82 Blue Boy | 60.00 | 75.00 | **80.00** | −5.00 |
| **84-F4-1.8** | 83 Heavenly Blessings | 65.00 | 65.00 | **68.00** | −5.00 |
| **84-F4-1.9** | 84 Navajo Madonna | 65.00 | 69.00 | **78.00** | −2.00 |
| **84-F4-1.10** | 85 Saguaro Dance | 65.00 | 98.00 | **100.00** | 0.00 |
| | Complete Collection | 545.00 | 1005.00 | **1054.00** | −49.00 |
| **Fairmont Famous Clowns** (84-F4-2) | | | | | |
| **84-F4-2.1** | 76 Freddie the Freeloader | 55.00 | 500.00 | **515.00** | 0.00 |
| **84-F4-2.2** | 77 W. C. Fields | 55.00 | 60.00 | **61.00** | 0.00 |
| **84-F4-2.3** | 78 Happy | 55.00 | 54.00 | **55.00** | +5.00 |
| **84-F4-2.4** | 79 The Pledge | 55.00 | 60.00 | **68.00** | +3.00 |
| | Complete Collection | 220.00 | 674.00 | **699.00** | +8.00 |
| **Fairmont Artists of the World DeGrazia Children** (84-F4-4) | | | | | |
| **84-F4-4.1** | 78 Flower Girl | 45.00 | 170.00 | **155.00** | +15.00 |
| **84-F4-4.2** | 79 Flower Boy | 45.00 | 100.00 | **125.00** | 0.00 |
| **84-F4-4.3** | 80 Little Cocopah Indian Girl | 50.00 | 91.00 | **91.00** | −4.00 |
| **84-F4-4.4** | 81 Beautiful Burden | 50.00 | 85.00 | **95.00** | −5.00 |
| **84-F4-4.5** | 82 Merry Little Indian | 55.00 | 100.00 | **133.00** | −6.00 |
| **84-F4-4.6** | 83 Wondering | 60.00 | 66.00 | **66.00** | −3.00 |
| **84-F4-4.7** | 84 Pink Papoose | 65.00 | 71.00 | **71.00** | +1.00 |
| **84-F4-4.8** | 84 Sunflower Boy | 65.00 | 64.00 | **65.00** | −5.00 |
| | Complete Collection | 435.00 | 747.00 | **801.00** | −7.00 |
| **Fairmont/Hackett Classical American Beauties** (84-F4-8) | | | | | |
| **84-F4-8.1** | 78 Colleen | 60.00 | 60.00 | **65.00** | +5.00 |
| **84-F4-8.2** | 79 Heather | 60.00 | 40.00 | **46.00** | −4.00 |
| **84-F4-8.3** | 80 Dawn | 60.00 | 50.00 | **65.00** | 0.00 |
| **84-F4-8.4** | 81 Eve | 60.00 | 60.00 | **65.00** | +10.00 |
| | Complete Collection | 240.00 | 210.00 | **241.00** | +11.00 |
| **Fairmont/Hackett Playful Memories** (84-F4-10) | | | | | |
| **84-F4-10.1** | 81 Renee | 39.50 | 65.00 | **75.00** | 0.00 |
| **84-F4-10.2** | 82 Jeremy | 42.50 | 30.00 | **38.00** | −2.00 |
| **84-F4-10.3** | 83 Jamie | 42.50 | 29.00 | **30.00** | −3.00 |
| **84-F4-10.4** | 83 Randy | 45.00 | 17.00 | **20.00** | −2.00 |
| | Complete Collection | 169.50 | 141.00 | **163.00** | −7.00 |
| **Fairmont/Artists of the World DeGrazia Children at Play** (84-F4-27) | | | | | |
| **84-F4-27.1** | 85 My First Horse | 65.00 | 34.00 | **55.00** | −10.00 |
| **84-F4-27.2** | 86 Girl at Sewing Machine | 65.00 | 65.00 | **65.00**◊ | 0.00 |
| **Fairmont/Artists of the World DeGrazia Western** ((84-F4-3) | | | | | |
| **84-F4-30.1** | 86 Morning Ride | 65.00 | 65.00 | **65.00**◊ | 0.00 |
| **Franklin Mint Rockwell Christmas** (84-F64-1) | | | | | |
| **84-F64-1.1** | 70 Bringing Home the Tree | 100.00 | 120.00 | **145.00** | 0.00 |
| **84-F64-1.2** | 71 Under the Mistletoe | 100.00 | 90.00 | **100.00** | 0.00 |
| **84-F64-1.3** | 72 The Carolers | 125.00 | 125.00 | **140.00** | −10.00 |
| **84-F64-1.4** | 73 Trimming the Tree | 125.00 | 120.00 | **120.00** | +10.00 |
| **84-F64-1.5** | 74 Hanging the Wreath | 175.00 | 100.00 | **100.00** | 0.00 |
| **84-F64-1.6** | 75 Home for Christmas | 180.00 | 155.00 | **160.00** | −10.00 |
| | Complete Collection | 805.00 | 710.00 | **765.00** | −10.00 |
| **Gorham Rockwell Four Seasons (4 pc. set)** (84-G58-1) | | | | | |
| **84-G58-1.1** | 71 Boy and His Dog | 50.00 | 195.00 | **220.00** | −5.00 |
| **84-G58-1.2** | 72 Young Love | 60.00 | 125.00 | **125.00** | 0.00 |
| **84-G58-1.3** | 73 Ages of Love | 60.00 | 325.00 | **260.00** | +35.00 |
| **84-G58-1.4** | 74 Grandpa and Me | 60.00 | 140.00 | **150.00** | +10.00 |
| **84-G58-1.5** | 75 Me and My Pal | 70.00 | 95.00 | **105.00** | 0.00 |
| **84-G58-1.6** | 76 Grand Pals | 70.00 | 220.00 | **250.00** | 0.00 |
| **84-G58-1.7** | 77 Going on Sixteen | 75.00 | 100.00 | **115.00** | 0.00 |
| **84-G58-1.8** | 78 Tender Years | 100.00 | 70.00 | **71.00** | +1.00 |
| **84-G58-1.9** | 79 A Helping Hand | 100.00 | 48.00 | **51.00** | 0.00 |
| **84-G58-1.10** | 80 Dad's Boy | 135.00 | 135.00 | **120.00** | +25.00 |
| | Complete Collection | 780.00 | 1453.00 | **1467.00** | +66.00 |
| **Gorham Rockwell Christmas** (84-G58-3) | | | | | |
| **84-G58-3.1** | 74 Tiny Tim | 12.50 | 24.00 | **25.00** | 0.00 |
| **84-G58-3.2** | 75 Good Deeds | 17.50 | 50.00 | **40.00** | +10.00 |
| **84-G58-3.3** | 76 Christmas Trio | 19.50 | 19.00 | **20.00** | 0.00 |
| **84-G58-3.4** | 77 Yuletide Reckoning | 19.50 | 24.00 | **25.00** | 0.00 |
| **84-G58-3.5** | 78 Planning Christmas Visits | 24.50 | 17.00 | **17.00** | −1.00 |
| **84-G58-3.6** | 79 Santa's Helpers | 24.50 | 18.00 | **18.00** | 0.00 |
| **84-G58-3.7** | 80 Letter to Santa | 27.50 | 15.00 | **16.00** | −3.00 |
| **84-G58-3.8** | 81 Santa Plans His Visit | 29.50 | 15.00 | **15.00** | −4.00 |
| **84-G58-3.9** | 82 The Jolly Coachman | 29.50 | 17.00 | **20.00** | −2.00 |
| **84-G58-3.10** | 83 Christmas Dancers | 29.50 | 24.00 | **25.00** | 0.00 |
| **84-G58-3.11** | 84 Christmas Medley | 29.50 | 26.00 | **28.00** | 0.00 |
| **84-G58-3.12** | 85 Home for the Holidays | 29.50 | 24.00 | **24.00** | −4.00 |
| **84-G58-3.13** | 86 Merry Christmas Grandma | 29.50 | 65.00 | **76.00** | 0.00 |
| **Gorham DeGrazia Children** (84-G58-5) | | | | | |
| **84-G58-5.1** | 76 Los Ninos | 35.00 | 1200.00 | **1200.00** | −100.00 |
| **84-G58-5.2** | 77 White Dove | 40.00 | 140.00 | **150.00** | −20.00 |
| | Complete Collection | 75.00 | 1340.00 | **1350.00** | −120.00 |
| **Gorham Jansen Sugar & Spice** (84-G58-6) | | | | | |
| **84-G58-6.1** | 76 Dana and Debbie | 40.00 | 62.00 | **75.00** | −9.00 |
| **84-G58-6.2** | 77 Becky and Baby | 42.50 | 30.00 | **35.00** | −3.00 |
| **84-G58-6.3** | 78 Jeanette and Julie | 47.50 | 30.00 | **40.00** | 0.00 |
| **84-G58-6.4** | 79 Ramona and Rachel | 50.00 | 90.00 | **93.00** | −3.00 |
| | Complete Collection | 180.00 | 212.00 | **243.00** | −15.00 |
| **Incolay Romantic Poets** (84-I31-1) | | | | | |
| **84-I31-1.1** | 77 She Walks in Beauty | 60.00 | 68.00 | **75.00** | 0.00 |
| **84-I31-1.2** | 78 A Thing of Beauty | 60.00 | 60.00 | **60.00** | 0.00 |
| **84-I31-1.3** | 79 To a Skylark | 65.00 | 65.00 | **65.00** | 0.00 |
| **84-I31-1.4** | 80 Phantom of Delight | 65.00 | 65.00 | **65.00** | 0.00 |
| **84-I31-1.5** | 81 The Kiss | 65.00 | 65.00 | **65.00** | 0.00 |
| **84-I31-1.6** | 82 My Heart Leaps Up | 70.00 | 70.00 | **70.00** | 0.00 |
| **84-I31-1.7** | 83 I Stood Tiptoe | 70.00 | 70.00 | **70.00** | 0.00 |
| **84-I31-1.8** | 84 The Dream | 70.00 | 70.00 | **70.00** | 0.00 |
| **84-I31-1.9** | 85 The Recollection | 70.00 | 70.00 | **70.00** | 0.00 |
| | Complete Collection | 595.00 | 603.00 | **610.00** | 0.00 |
| **Incolay Great Romances of History** (84-I31-3) | | | | | |
| **84-I31-3.1** | 79 Antony and Cleopatra | 65.00 | 24.00 | **25.00** | −5.00 |
| **84-I31-3.2** | 80 The Taj Mahal Lovers | 65.00 | 32.00 | **37.00** | −3.00 |
| **84-I31-3.3** | 81 Lancelot and Guinevere | 65.00 | 42.00 | **45.00** | −5.00 |
| **84-I31-3.4** | 82 Lord Nelson/Lady Hamilton | 70.00 | 67.00 | **70.00** | 0.00 |
| | Complete Collection | 265.00 | 165.00 | **177.00** | −13.00 |
| **Incolay Voyage of Ulysses** (84-I31-4) | | | | | |
| **84-I31-4.1** | 84 The Isle of Circe | 50.00 | 50.00 | **55.00** | −5.00 |
| **84-I31-4.2** | 85 The Sirens | 50.00 | 50.00 | **50.00** | −3.00 |
| **84-I31-4.3** | 85 Oygia, Isle of Calypso | 55.00 | 55.00 | **58.00** | −2.00 |
| **84-I31-4.4** | 86 Land of Phaecians | 55.00 | 55.00 | **55.00** | −3.00 |
| **84-I31-4.5** | 86 Return of Ulysses | 55.00 | 55.00 | **55.00** | 0.00 |
| **84-I31-4.6** | 86 The Reunion: Penelope and Ulysses | 55.00 | 64.00 | **74.00** | +19.00 |
| | Complete Collection | 320.00 | 329.00 | **347.00** | +6.00 |
| **Incolay Love Sonnets of Shakespeare** (84-I31-6) | | | | | |
| **84-I31-6.1** | 86 Shall I Compare Thee | 55.00 | 55.00 | **55.00**◊ | 0.00 |
| **84-I31-6.2** | 87 Thou Art Too Dear | 55.00 | 55.00 | **55.00**◊ | 0.00 |
| **Kern Leaders of Tomorrow** (84-K20-7) | | | | | |
| **84-K20-7.1** | 80 Future Physician | 50.00 | 25.00 | **25.00** | −3.00 |
| **84-K20-7.2** | 81 Future Farmer | 50.00 | 25.00 | **27.00** | +2.00 |
| **84-K20-7.3** | 82 Future Florist | 50.00 | 36.00 | **33.00** | +3.00 |
| **84-K20-7.4** | 83 Future Teacher | 50.00 | 27.00 | **28.00** | −1.00 |
| | Complete Collection | 200.00 | 113.00 | **113.00** | +1.00 |
| **Edwin M. Knowles Wizard of Oz** (84-K41-1) | | | | | |
| **84-K41-1.1** | 77 Over the Rainbow | 19.00 | 59.00 | **65.00** | −3.00 |
| **84-K41-1.2** | 78 If I Only Had a Brain | 19.00 | 28.00 | **30.00** | 0.00 |
| **84-K41-1.3** | 78 If I Only Had a Heart | 19.00 | 30.00 | **35.00** | 0.00 |
| **84-K41-1.4** | 78 If I Were King of the Forest | 19.00 | 28.00 | **30.00** | 0.00 |
| **84-K41-1.5** | 79 Wicked Witch of the West | 19.00 | 32.00 | **40.00** | 0.00 |
| **84-K41-1.6** | 79 Follow the Yellow Brick Road | 19.00 | 31.00 | **35.00** | −2.00 |
| **84-K41-1.7** | 79 Wonderful Wizard of Oz | 19.00 | 56.00 | **65.00** | +13.00 |
| **84-K41-1.8** | 80 The Grand Finale | 24.00 | 59.00 | **60.00** | 0.00 |
| | Complete Collection | 157.00 | 323.00 | **360.00** | +8.00 |
| **Edwin M. Knowles Americana Holidays** (84-K41-2) | | | | | |
| **84-K41-2.1** | 78 Fourth of July | 26.00 | 28.00 | **30.00** | −5.00 |
| **84-K41-2.2** | 79 Thanksgiving | 26.00 | 30.00 | **35.00** | 0.00 |
| **84-K41-2.3** | 80 Easter | 26.00 | 26.00 | **26.00** | −2.00 |
| **84-K41-2.4** | 81 Valentine's Day | 26.00 | 26.00 | **26.00** | 0.00 |
| **84-K41-2.5** | 82 Father's Day | 26.00 | 26.00 | **26.00** | 0.00 |
| **84-K41-2.6** | 83 Christmas | 26.00 | 26.00 | **26.00** | 0.00 |
| **84-K41-2.7** | 84 Mother's Day | 26.00 | 26.00 | **26.00** | 0.00 |
| | Complete Collection | 182.00 | 188.00 | **195.00** | −7.00 |
| **Edwin M. Knowles Gone with the Wind** (84-K41-3) | | | | | |
| **84-K41-3.1** | 78 Scarlett | 21.50 | 275.00 | **280.00** | −20.00 |
| **84-K41-3.2** | 79 Ashley | 21.50 | 220.00 | **225.00** | −5.00 |
| **84-K41-3.3** | 80 Melanie | 21.50 | 85.00 | **95.00** | +20.00 |
| **84-K41-3.4** | 81 Rhett | 23.50 | 49.00 | **50.00** | 0.00 |
| **84-K41-3.5** | 82 Mammy Lacing Scarlett | 23.50 | 50.00 | **60.00** | −4.00 |
| **84-K41-3.6** | 83 Melanie Gives Birth | 23.50 | 80.00 | **92.00** | +2.00 |
| **84-K41-3.7** | 84 Scarlett's Green Dress | 25.50 | 70.00 | **72.00** | +22.00 |
| **84-K41-3.8** | 85 Rhett and Bonnie | 25.50 | 37.00 | **37.00** | −1.00 |
| **84-K41-3.9** | 85 Scarlett and Rhett: The Finale | 29.50 | 30.00 | **32.00** | −7.00 |
| | Complete Collection | 215.50 | 896.00 | **943.00** | +7.00 |
| **Edwin M. Knowles Csatari Grandparent** (84-K41-4) | | | | | |
| **84-K41-4.1** | 80 Bedtime Story | 18.00 | 19.00 | **23.00** | −4.00 |
| **84-K41-4.2** | 81 The Skating Lesson | 20.00 | 15.00 | **22.00** | −4.00 |
| **84-K41-4.3** | 82 The Cookie Tasting | 20.00 | 20.00 | **23.00** | −5.00 |
| **84-K41-4.4** | 83 The Swinger | 20.00 | 20.00 | **20.00** | 0.00 |
| **84-K41-4.5** | 84 The Skating Queen | 22.00 | 22.00 | **23.00** | −2.00 |
| **84-K41-4.6** | 85 The Patriot's Parade | 22.00 | 22.00 | **23.00** | −3.00 |
| **84-K41-4.7** | 86 The Home Run | 22.00 | 22.00 | **25.00** | −5.00 |
| **Edwin M. Knowles Annie** (84-K41-5) | | | | | |
| **84-K41-5.1** | 83 Annie and Sandy | 19.00 | 24.00 | **25.00** | 0.00 |
| **84-K41-5.2** | 83 Daddy Warbucks | 19.00 | 24.00 | **26.00** | 0.00 |
| **84-K41-5.3** | 83 Annie and Grace | 19.00 | 39.00 | **41.00** | +4.00 |
| **84-K41-5.4** | 84 Annie and the Orphans | 21.00 | 29.00 | **30.00** | −2.00 |
| **84-K41-5.5** | 85 Tomorrow | 21.00 | 26.00 | **27.00** | −3.00 |
| **84-K41-5.6** | 86 Annie and Miss Hannigan | 21.00 | 21.00 | **25.00** | +1.00 |
| **84-K41-5.7** | 86 Annie, Lily and Rooster | 24.00 | 33.00 | **30.00** | +5.00 |
| **84-K41-5.8** | 86 Grand Finale | 24.00 | 32.00 | **34.00** | +4.00 |
| | Complete Collection | 168.00 | 228.00 | **238.00** | +9.00 |
| **Edwin M. Knowles Biblical Mothers** (84-K41-6) | | | | | |
| **84-K41-6.1** | 83 Bathsheba and Solomon | 39.50 | 90.00 | **95.00** | −5.00 |
| **84-K41-6.2** | 84 Judgment of Solomon | 39.50 | 65.00 | **75.00** | 0.00 |
| **84-K41-6.3** | 84 Pharaoh's Daughter and Moses | 39.50 | 54.00 | **55.00** | −5.00 |
| **84-K41-6.4** | 84 Mary and Jesus | 39.50 | 40.00 | **45.00** | −5.00 |
| **84-K41-6.5** | 85 Sarah and Isaac | 44.50 | 45.00 | **50.00** | −5.00 |

| BRADEX NO. | | ISSUE PRICE | CLOSE | QUOTE | CHANGE |
|---|---|---|---|---|---|
| 84-K41-6.6 | 86 Rebekah, Jacob and Esau | 44.50 | 47.00 | 55.00 | +9.00 |
| | Complete Collection | 247.00 | 341.00 | 375.00 | −11.00 |
| **Edwin M. Knowles Jeanne Down's Friends I Remember** (84-K41-7) | | | | | |
| 84-K41-7.1 | 83 Fish Story | 17.50 | 23.00 | 28.00 | −4.00 |
| 84-K41-7.2 | 84 Office Hours | 17.50 | 18.00 | 22.00 | −3.00 |
| 84-K41-7.3 | 84 A Coat of Paint | 17.50 | 20.00 | 23.00 | −2.00 |
| 84-K41-7.4 | 85 Here Comes the Bride | 19.50 | 24.00 | 25.00 | −4.00 |
| 84-K41-7.5 | 85 Fringe Benefits | 19.50 | 20.00 | 25.00 | −5.00 |
| 84-K41-7.6 | 85 High Society | 19.50 | 21.00 | 25.00 | −3.00 |
| 84-K41-7.7 | 86 Flower Arrangement | 21.50 | 24.00 | 28.00 | −6.00 |
| 84-K41-7.8 | 86 Taste Test | 21.50 | 35.00 | 38.00 | −6.00 |
| | Complete Collection | 154.00 | 185.00 | 214.00 | −33.00 |
| **Edwin M. Knowles The Four Ancient Elements** (84-K41-8) | | | | | |
| 84-K41-8.1 | 84 Earth | 27.50 | 31.00 | 31.00 | −2.00 |
| 84-K41-8.2 | 84 Water | 27.50 | 28.00 | 30.00 | −2.00 |
| 84-K41-8.3 | 85 Air | 29.50 | 30.00 | 32.00 | −3.00 |
| 84-K41-8.4 | 85 Fire | 29.50 | 41.00 | 45.00 | +6.00 |
| | Complete Collection | 114.00 | 130.00 | 138.00 | −1.00 |
| **Edwin M. Knowles Hibel Mother's Day** (84-K41-9) | | | | | |
| 84-K41-9.1 | 84 Abby and Lisa | 29.50 | 50.00 | 50.00 | 0.00 |
| 84-K41-9.2 | 85 Erica and Jamie | 29.50 | 38.00 | 40.00 | +5.00 |
| 84-K41-9.3 | 86 Emily and Jennifer | 29.50 | 49.00 | 49.00 | +14.00 |
| 84-K41-9.4 | 87 Catherine and Heather | 34.50 | 38.00 | 40.00 | +5.50 |
| **Edwin M. Knowles Father's Love** (84-K41-10) | | | | | |
| 84-K41-10.1 | 84 Open Wide | 19.50 | 20.00 | 20.00 | −2.00 |
| 84-K41-10.2 | 84 Batter Up | 19.50 | 20.00 | 20.00 | −5.00 |
| 84-K41-10.3 | 85 Little Shaver | 19.50 | 24.00 | 26.00 | 0.00 |
| 84-K41-10.4 | 85 Swing Time | 22.50 | 24.00 | 24.00 | −3.00 |
| | Complete Collection | 81.00 | 88.00 | 90.00 | −10.00 |
| **Edwin M. Knowles The King and I** (84-K41-11) | | | | | |
| 84-K41-11.1 | 84 A Puzzlement | 19.50 | 50.00 | 51.00 | −4.00 |
| 84-K41-11.2 | 85 Shall We Dance? | 19.50 | 40.00 | 42.00 | +2.00 |
| 84-K41-11.3 | 85 Getting to Know You | 19.50 | 22.00 | 30.00 | +1.00 |
| 84-K41-11.4 | 85 We Kiss in a Shadow | 19.50 | 19.50 | 19.50◊ | 0.00 |
| | Complete Collection | 78.00 | 131.50 | 142.50 | −1.00 |
| **Edwin M. Knowles Encyclopaedia Britannica's Birds of Your Garden** (84-K41-12) | | | | | |
| 84-K41-12.1 | 85 Cardinal | 19.50 | 31.00 | 33.00 | +1.00 |
| 84-K41-12.2 | 85 Blue Jay | 19.50 | 19.50 | 19.50◊ | 0.00 |
| 84-K41-12.3 | 85 Oriole | 22.50 | 22.50 | 22.50◊ | 0.00 |
| 84-K41-12.4 | 86 Chickadees | 22.50 | 22.50 | 22.50◊ | 0.00 |
| 84-K41-12.5 | 86 Bluebird | 22.50 | 22.50 | 22.50◊ | 0.00 |
| 84-K41-12.6 | 86 Robin | 22.50 | 22.50 | 22.50◊ | 0.00 |
| 84-K41-12.7 | 86 Hummingbird | 24.50 | 24.50 | 24.50◊ | 0.00 |
| 84-K41-12.8 | 87 Goldfinch | 24.50 | 24.50 | 24.50◊ | 0.00 |
| **Edwin M. Knowles Frances Hook Legacy** (84-K41-13) | | | | | |
| 84-K41-13.1 | 85 Fascination | 19.50 | 20.00 | 20.00 | −1.00 |
| 84-K41-13.2 | 85 Daydreaming | 19.50 | 20.00 | 21.00 | −4.00 |
| 84-K41-13.3 | 86 Discovery | 22.50 | 22.50 | 22.50◊ | 0.00 |
| 84-K41-13.4 | 86 Disappointment | 22.50 | 22.50 | 22.50◊ | 0.00 |
| 84-K41-13.5 | 86 Wonderment | 22.50 | 22.50 | 22.50◊ | 0.00 |
| 84-K41-13.6 | 87 Expectation | 22.50 | 22.50 | 22.50◊ | 0.00 |
| | Complete Collection | 129.00 | 130.00 | 131.00 | −5.00 |
| **Edwin M. Knowles Hibel Christmas** (84-K41-15) | | | | | |
| 84-K41-15.1 | 85 The Angel's Message | 45.00 | 45.00 | 45.00 | −1.00 |
| 84-K41-15.2 | 86 The Gifts of the Magi | 45.00 | 50.00 | 50.00 | 0.00 |
| **Edwin M. Knowles A Swan is Born** (84-K41-16) | | | | | |
| 84-K41-16.1 | 87 Hopes and Dreams | 24.50 | 24.50 | 24.50◊ | 0.00 |
| **Edwin M. Knowles Oklahoma!** (84-K41-17) | | | | | |
| 84-K41-17.1 | 85 Oh, What a Beautiful Mornin' | 19.50 | 19.50 | 19.50◊ | 0.00 |
| 84-K41-17.2 | 86 Surrey With the Fringe on Top | 19.50 | 19.50 | 19.50◊ | 0.00 |
| 84-K41-17.3 | 86 I Cain't Say No | 19.50 | 19.50 | 19.50◊ | 0.00 |
| 84-K41-17.4 | 86 Oklahoma! | 19.50 | 19.50 | 19.50◊ | 0.00 |
| | Complete Collection | 78.00 | 78.00 | 78.00 | 0.00 |
| **Edwin M. Knowles Sound of Music** (84-K41-18) | | | | | |
| 84-K41-18.1 | 86 Sound of Music | 19.50 | 19.50 | 19.50◊ | 0.00 |
| 84-K41-18.2 | 86 Do-Re-Mi | 19.50 | 19.50 | 19.50◊ | 0.00 |
| 84-K41-18.3 | 86 My Favorite Things | 22.50 | 22.50 | 22.50◊ | 0.00 |
| 84-K41-18.4 | 86 Laendler Waltz | 22.50 | 22.50 | 22.50◊ | 0.00 |
| 84-K41-18.5 | 87 Edelweiss | 22.50 | 22.50 | 22.50◊ | 0.00 |
| **Edwin M. Knowles Upland Birds of North America** (84-K41-20) | | | | | |
| 84-K41-20.1 | 86 The Pheasant | 24.50 | 24.50 | 24.50◊ | 0.00 |
| 84-K41-20.2 | 86 The Grouse | 24.50 | 24.50 | 24.50◊ | 0.00 |
| 84-K41-20.3 | 87 The Quail | 27.50 | 27.50 | 27.50◊ | 0.00 |
| 84-K41-20.4 | 87 The Wild Turkey | 27.50 | 27.50 | 27.50◊ | 0.00 |
| **Edwin M. Knowles American Innocents** (84-K41-21) | | | | | |
| 84-K41-21.1 | 86 Abigail in the Rose Garden | 19.50 | 19.50 | 19.50◊ | 0.00 |
| 84-K41-21.2 | 86 Ann by the Terrace | 19.50 | 19.50 | 19.50◊ | 0.00 |
| 84-K41-21.3 | 86 Ellen and John in the Parlor | 19.50 | 19.50 | 19.50◊ | 0.00 |
| 84-K41-21.4 | 87 William on the Rocking Horse | 19.50 | 19.50 | 19.50◊ | 0.00 |
| **Edwin M. Knowles Jessie Willcox Smith Childhood Holiday Memories** (84-K41-22) | | | | | |
| 84-K41-22.1 | 86 Easter | 19.50 | 25.00 | 28.00 | +7.00 |
| 84-K41-22.2 | 86 Thanksgiving | 19.50 | 19.50 | 19.50◊ | 0.00 |
| 84-K41-22.3 | 86 Christmas | 19.50 | 19.50 | 19.50◊ | 0.00 |
| 84-K41-22.4 | 86 Valentine's Day | 22.50 | 22.50 | 22.50◊ | 0.00 |
| 84-K41-22.5 | 87 Mother's Day | 22.50 | 22.50 | 22.50◊ | 0.00 |
| 84-K41-22.6 | 87 Fourth of July | 22.50 | 22.50 | 22.50◊ | 0.00 |
| | Complete Collection | 126.00 | 131.50 | 134.50 | +7.00 |
| **Edwin M. Knowles Living With Nature: Jerner's Ducks** (84-K41-23) | | | | | |
| 84-K41-23.1 | 86 The Pintail | 19.50 | 19.50 | 19.50◊ | 0.00 |
| 84-K41-23.2 | 86 The Mallard | 19.50 | 19.50 | 19.50◊ | 0.00 |
| 84-K41-23.3 | 87 The Wood Duck | 22.50 | 22.50 | 22.50◊ | 0.00 |
| **Edwin M. Knowles South Pacific** (84-K41-26) | | | | | |
| 84-K41-26.1 | 86 Some Enchanted Evening | 24.50 | 24.50 | 24.50◊ | 0.00 |
| **Edwin M. Knowles Tom Sawyer** (84-K41-38) | | | | | |
| 84-K41-38.1 | 87 Whitewashing the Fence | 27.50 | 27.50 | 27.50◊ | 0.00 |
| **Edwin M. Knowles Lincoln Man of America** (84-K41-42) | | | | | |
| 84-K41-42.1 | 86 The Gettysburg Address | 24.50 | 24.50 | 24.50◊ | 0.00 |
| 84-K41-42.2 | 87 The Inauguration | 24.50 | 24.50 | 24.50◊ | 0.00 |
| **Edwin M. Knowles Portraits of Motherhood** (84-K41-44) | | | | | |
| 84-K41-44.1 | 87 Mother's Here | 29.50 | 30.00 | 38.00 | +8.50 |
| **Edwin M. Knowles Friends of the Forest** (84-K41-45) | | | | | |
| 84-K41-45.1 | 87 The Rabbit | 24.50 | 24.50 | 24.50◊ | 0.00 |
| **Edwin M. Knowles Amy Brackenbury's Cat Tales** (84-K41-47) | | | | | |
| 84-K41-47.1 | 87 A Chance Meeting | 21.50 | 21.50 | 21.50◊ | 0.00 |

| BRADEX NO. | | ISSUE PRICE | CLOSE | QUOTE | CHANGE |
|---|---|---|---|---|---|
| **Lenox Boehm Bird** (84-L18-1) | | | | | |
| 84-L18-1.1 | 70 Wood Thrush | 35.00 | 200.00 | 205.00 | −5.00 |
| 84-L18-1.2 | 71 Goldfinch | 35.00 | 100.00 | 100.00 | +45.00 |
| 84-L18-1.3 | 72 Mountain Bluebird | 37.50 | 50.00 | 55.00 | +9.00 |
| 84-L18-1.4 | 73 Meadowlark | 41.00 | 40.00 | 45.00 | +10.00 |
| 84-L18-1.5 | 74 Rufous Hummingbird | 45.00 | 44.00 | 44.00 | −1.00 |
| 84-L18-1.6 | 75 American Redstart | 50.00 | 34.00 | 35.00 | 0.00 |
| 84-L18-1.7 | 76 Cardinals | 53.00 | 45.00 | 50.00 | 0.00 |
| 84-L18-1.8 | 77 Robins | 55.00 | 49.00 | 50.00 | 0.00 |
| 84-L18-1.9 | 78 Mockingbirds | 58.00 | 53.00 | 55.00 | 0.00 |
| 84-L18-1.10 | 79 Golden-Crowned Kinglets | 65.00 | 49.00 | 49.00 | 0.00 |
| 84-L18-1.11 | 80 Black-Throated Blue Warblers | 80.00 | 60.00 | 75.00 | 0.00 |
| 84-L18-1.12 | 81 Eastern Phoebes | 90.00 | 80.00 | 95.00 | 0.00 |
| | Complete Collection | 644.50 | 804.00 | 858.00 | +58.00 |
| **Morgantown Crystal Yates' Country Ladies** (84-M58-1) | | | | | |
| 84-M58-1.1 | 81 Angelica | 75.00 | 75.00 | 75.00 | 0.00 |
| 84-M58-1.2 | 82 Violet | 75.00 | 75.00 | 75.00 | 0.00 |
| 84-M58-1.3 | 83 Heather | 75.00 | 85.00 | 85.00 | −20.00 |
| 84-M58-1.4 | 84 Laurel | 75.00 | 85.00 | 100.00 | 0.00 |
| | Complete Collection | 300.00 | 320.00 | 335.00 | −20.00 |
| **Newell Sarah Stilwell Weber's Calendar** (84-N18-1) | | | | | |
| 84-N18-1.1 | 84 June | 19.00 | 19.00 | 20.00 | 0.00 |
| 84-N18-1.2 | 85 July | 19.00 | 19.00 | 20.00 | 0.00 |
| 84-N18-1.3 | 85 August | 19.00 | 19.00 | 20.00 | 0.00 |
| 84-N18-1.4 | 85 September | 19.00 | 34.00 | 40.00 | 0.00 |
| 84-N18-1.5 | 85 October | 19.00 | 31.00 | 40.00 | 0.00 |
| 84-N18-1.6 | 85 November | 19.00 | 30.00 | 30.00 | +11.00 |
| 84-N18-1.7 | 86 December | 19.00 | 35.00 | 35.00 | +1.00 |
| 84-N18-1.8 | 86 January | 19.00 | 36.00 | 36.00 | +17.00 |
| 84-N18-1.9 | 86 February | 19.00 | 19.00 | 30.00 | +11.00 |
| 84-N18-1.10 | 86 March | 19.00 | 19.00 | 19.00◊ | 0.00 |
| 84-N18-1.11 | 86 April | 19.00 | 19.00 | 19.00◊ | 0.00 |
| 84-N18-1.12 | 87 May | 19.00 | 19.00 | 19.00◊ | 0.00 |
| | Complete Collection | 228.00 | 299.00 | 328.00 | +40.00 |
| **Pemberton & Oakes Wonder of Childhood** (84-P19-1) | | | | | |
| 84-P19-1.1 | 82 Touching the Sky | 19.00 | 28.00 | 33.00 | 0.00 |
| 84-P19-1.2 | 83 Spring Innocence | 19.00 | 40.00 | 40.00 | +3.00 |
| 84-P19-1.3 | 84 Winter Angel | 22.00 | 50.00 | 53.00 | +9.00 |
| 84-P19-1.4 | 85 Small Wonder | 22.00 | 36.00 | 37.00 | +3.00 |
| 84-P19-1.5 | 85 Grandma's Garden | 22.00 | 36.00 | 37.00 | +15.00 |
| 84-P19-1.6 | 86 Daydreamer | 22.00 | 22.00 | 22.00◊ | 0.00 |
| **Pemberton & Oakes Children at Christmas** (84-P19-2) | | | | | |
| 84-P19-2.1 | 81 Gift for Laurie | 48.00 | 83.00 | 85.00 | +5.00 |
| 84-P19-2.2 | 82 Christmas Prayer | 48.00 | 90.00 | 90.00 | +10.00 |
| 84-P19-2.3 | 83 Erik's Delight | 48.00 | 50.00 | 55.00 | −8.00 |
| 84-P19-2.4 | 84 Christmas Secret | 48.00 | 63.00 | 64.00 | 0.00 |
| 84-P19-2.5 | 85 Christmas Kitten | 48.00 | 61.00 | 62.00 | −2.00 |
| 84-P19-2.6 | 86 Laurie and the Creche | 48.00 | 60.00 | 62.00 | +14.00 |
| **Pemberton & Oakes Children and Pets** (84-P19-3) | | | | | |
| 84-P19-3.1 | 84 Tender Moment | 19.00 | 50.00 | 78.00 | −2.00 |
| 84-P19-3.2 | 84 Golden Moment | 19.00 | 31.00 | 35.00 | 0.00 |
| 84-P19-3.3 | 85 Making Friends | 19.00 | 34.00 | 35.00 | −4.00 |
| 84-P19-3.4 | 85 Tender Beginning | 19.00 | 45.00 | 49.00 | +4.00 |
| 84-P19-3.5 | 86 Backyard Discovery | 19.00 | 19.00 | 27.00 | −6.00 |
| 84-P19-3.6 | 86 Waiting to Play | 19.00 | 25.00 | 40.00 | +21.00 |
| **Pickard Lockhart Wildlife** (84-P29-1) | | | | | |
| 84-P29-1.1 | 70 Woodcock-Grouse | 150.00 | 275.00 | 275.00 | −25.00 |
| 84-P29-1.2 | 71 Teal-Mallard | 150.00 | 190.00 | 190.00 | 0.00 |
| 84-P29-1.3 | 72 Mockingbird-Cardinal | 162.50 | 125.00 | 125.00 | −25.00 |
| 84-P29-1.4 | 73 Turkey-Pheasant | 162.50 | 85.00 | 150.00 | −30.00 |
| 84-P29-1.5 | 74 American Bald Eagle | 150.00 | 650.00 | 850.00 | −70.00 |
| 84-P29-1.6 | 75 White-Tailed Deer | 100.00 | 80.00 | 85.00 | −5.00 |
| 84-P29-1.7 | 76 American Buffalo | 165.00 | 105.00 | 110.00 | +5.00 |
| 84-P29-1.8 | 77 Great Horned Owl | 100.00 | 76.00 | 100.00 | 0.00 |
| 84-P29-1.9 | 78 American Panther | 175.00 | 109.00 | 120.00 | −10.00 |
| 84-P29-1.10 | 79 Red Foxes | 120.00 | 80.00 | 90.00 | −15.00 |
| 84-P29-1.11 | 80 Trumpeter Swan | 200.00 | 135.00 | 165.00 | 0.00 |
| | Complete Collection | 1635.00 | 1910.00 | 2260.00 | −175.00 |
| **Pickard Annual Christmas** (84-P29-2) | | | | | |
| 84-P29-2.1 | 76 Alba Madonna | 60.00 | 100.00 | 104.00 | +4.00 |
| 84-P29-2.2 | 77 Nativity | 65.00 | 50.00 | 55.00 | −5.00 |
| 84-P29-2.3 | 78 Rest on Flight into Egypt | 65.00 | 21.00 | 25.00 | −5.00 |
| 84-P29-2.4 | 79 Adoration of the Magi | 70.00 | 25.00 | 25.00 | 0.00 |
| 84-P29-2.5 | 80 Madonna and Child | 80.00 | 50.00 | 50.00 | +11.00 |
| 84-P29-2.6 | 81 Madonna and Child | 90.00 | 31.00 | 40.00 | +8.00 |
| | Complete Collection | 430.00 | 277.00 | 299.00 | +13.00 |
| **Pickard Children of Renoir** (84-P29-4) | | | | | |
| 84-P29-4.1 | 78 Girl with Watering Can | 50.00 | 75.00 | 80.00 | 0.00 |
| 84-P29-4.2 | 78 Child in White | 50.00 | 34.00 | 34.00 | 0.00 |
| 84-P29-4.3 | 79 Girl with Hoop | 55.00 | 30.00 | 30.00 | −3.00 |
| 84-P29-4.4 | 79 At the Piano | 55.00 | 35.00 | 36.00 | −7.00 |
| 84-P29-4.5 | 80 Two Little Circus Girls | 60.00 | 22.00 | 24.00 | 0.00 |
| 84-P29-4.6 | 80 Artist's Son Jean | 60.00 | 19.00 | 20.00 | −5.00 |
| | Complete Collection | 330.00 | 215.00 | 224.00 | −15.00 |
| **Pickard Oleg Cassini's Most Beautiful Women of All Time** (84-P29-5) | | | | | |
| 84-P29-5.1 | 81 Helen of Troy | 75.00 | 19.00 | 25.00 | −5.00 |
| 84-P29-5.2 | 82 Marie Antoinette | 75.00 | 50.00 | 50.00 | 0.00 |
| 84-P29-5.3 | 83 Lillie Langtry | 75.00 | 70.00 | 80.00 | 0.00 |
| 84-P29-5.4 | 84 Salome | 75.00 | 100.00 | 100.00 | 0.00 |
| | Complete Collection | 300.00 | 239.00 | 255.00 | −5.00 |
| **Pickard Mother's Love** (84-P29-6) | | | | | |
| 84-P29-6.1 | 80 Miracle | 95.00 | 97.00 | 100.00 | 0.00 |
| 84-P29-6.2 | 81 Story Time | 110.00 | 40.00 | 45.00 | −5.00 |
| 84-P29-6.3 | 82 First Edition | 115.00 | 44.00 | 53.00 | +3.00 |
| 84-P29-6.4 | 83 Precious Moment | 120.00 | 97.00 | 100.00 | −5.00 |
| | Complete Collection | 440.00 | 278.00 | 298.00 | −7.00 |
| **Pickard Symphony of Roses** (84-P29-8) | | | | | |
| 84-P29-8.1 | 82 Wild Irish Rose | 85.00 | 69.00 | 70.00 | 0.00 |
| 84-P29-8.2 | 83 The Yellow Rose of Texas | 90.00 | 90.00 | 90.00 | +20.00 |
| 84-P29-8.3 | 84 Honeysuckle Rose | 95.00 | 85.00 | 95.00 | 0.00 |
| 84-P29-8.4 | 85 Rose of Washington Square | 100.00 | 100.00 | 100.00 | −10.00 |
| | Complete Collection | 370.00 | 344.00 | 355.00 | +10.00 |
| **Reco World of Children** (84-R60-1) | | | | | |
| 84-R60-1.1 | 77 Rainy Day Fun | 50.00 | 60.00 | 60.00 | −5.00 |
| 84-R60-1.2 | 78 When I Grow Up | 50.00 | 40.00 | 43.00 | +3.00 |
| 84-R60-1.3 | 79 You're Invited | 50.00 | 35.00 | 35.00 | 0.00 |
| 84-R60-1.4 | 80 Kittens for Sale | 50.00 | 20.00 | 25.00 | −3.00 |
| | Complete Collection | 200.00 | 155.00 | 163.00 | −5.00 |

| BRADEX NO. | | ISSUE PRICE | CLOSE | QUOTE | CHANGE |
|---|---|---|---|---|---|
| **Reco McClelland's Mother Goose** (84-R60-2) | | | | | |
| **84-R60-2.1** | 79 Mary, Mary | 22.50 | 195.00 | **205.00** | −5.00 |
| **84-R60-2.2** | 80 Little Boy Blue | 22.50 | 75.00 | **85.00** | −5.00 |
| **84-R60-2.3** | 81 Little Miss Muffet | 24.50 | 25.00 | **30.00** | −3.00 |
| **84-R60-2.4** | 82 Little Jack Horner | 24.50 | 25.00 | **30.00** | −3.00 |
| **84-R60-2.5** | 83 Little Bo Peep | 24.50 | 29.00 | **35.00** | −7.00 |
| **84-R60-2.6** | 84 Diddle, Diddle Dumpling | 24.50 | 35.00 | **39.00** | +13.00 |
| **84-R60-2.7** | 85 Mary Had a Little Lamb | 27.50 | 28.00 | **28.00** | −2.00 |
| **84-R60-2.8** | 86 Jack and Jill | 27.50 | 30.00 | **30.00** | 0.00 |
| | Complete Collection | 198.00 | 442.00 | **482.00** | −12.00 |
| **Reco McClelland's Children's Circus** (84-R60-3) | | | | | |
| **84-R60-3.1** | 81 Tommy the Clown | 29.50 | 30.00 | **32.00** | +2.00 |
| **84-R60-3.2** | 82 Katie the Tightrope Walker | 29.50 | 29.00 | **30.00** | 0.00 |
| **84-R60-3.3** | 83 Johnny the Strongman | 29.50 | 25.00 | **30.00** | 0.00 |
| **84-R60-3.4** | 83 Maggie the Animal Trainer | 29.50 | 30.00 | **34.00** | 0.00 |
| | Complete Collection | 118.00 | 114.00 | **126.00** | +2.00 |
| **Reco Days Gone By** (84-R60-8) | | | | | |
| **84-R60-8.1** | 83 Sunday Best | 29.50 | 75.00 | **80.00** | −5.00 |
| **84-R60-8.2** | 83 Amy's Magic Horse | 29.50 | 50.00 | **51.00** | +1.00 |
| **84-R60-8.3** | 84 Little Anglers | 29.50 | 50.00 | **55.00** | +5.00 |
| **84-R60-8.4** | 84 Afternoon Recital | 29.50 | 60.00 | **70.00** | +15.00 |
| **84-R60-8.5** | 84 Little Tutor | 29.50 | 24.00 | **27.00** | −4.00 |
| **84-R60-8.6** | 84 Easter at Grandma's | 29.50 | 23.00 | **27.00** | −4.00 |
| **84-R60-8.7** | 85 Morning Song | 29.50 | 19.00 | **25.00** | −5.00 |
| **84-R60-8.8** | 85 Surrey Ride | 29.50 | 24.00 | **28.00** | −2.00 |
| | Complete Collection | 236.00 | 325.00 | **363.00** | +1.00 |
| **Reco Becky's Day** (84-R60-10) | | | | | |
| **84-R60-10.1** | 85 Awakening | 24.50 | 25.00 | **26.00** | 0.00 |
| **84-R60-10.2** | 85 Getting Dressed | 24.50 | 25.00 | **26.00** | 0.00 |
| **84-R60-10.3** | 86 Breakfast | 27.50 | 28.00 | **29.00** | −4.00 |
| **84-R60-10.4** | 86 Learning Is Fun | 27.50 | 29.00 | **33.00** | −5.00 |
| **84-R60-10.5** | 86 Muffin Making | 27.50 | 32.00 | **33.00** | −3.00 |
| **84-R60-10.6** | 86 Tub Time | 27.50 | 33.00 | **33.00** | +5.50 |
| **84-R60-10.7** | 87 Evening Prayer | 27.50 | 27.50 | **27.50◊** | 0.00 |
| | Complete Collection | 186.50 | 199.50 | **207.50** | −6.50 |
| **Reed & Barton Christmas** (84-R18-2) | | | | | |
| **84-R18-2.1** | 70 Partridge | 55.00 | 125.00 | **130.00** | −5.00 |
| **84-R18-2.2** | 71 We Three Kings | 60.00 | 45.00 | **45.00** | 0.00 |
| **84-R18-2.3** | 72 Herald Angels | 60.00 | 37.00 | **37.00** | −3.00 |
| **84-R18-2.4** | 73 Adoration of Kings | 60.00 | 45.00 | **50.00** | −5.00 |
| **84-R18-2.5** | 74 Adoration of Magi | 65.00 | 58.00 | **58.00** | 0.00 |
| **84-R18-2.6** | 75 Adoration of Kings | 65.00 | 65.00 | **65.00** | 0.00 |
| **84-R18-2.7** | 76 Morning Train | 65.00 | 62.00 | **60.00** | 0.00 |
| **84-R18-2.8** | 77 Decorating the Church | 65.00 | 60.00 | **60.00** | 0.00 |
| **84-R18-2.9** | 78 General Store | 65.00 | 66.00 | **66.00** | 0.00 |
| **84-R18-2.10** | 79 Merry Old Santa Claus | 55.00 | 63.00 | **63.00** | 0.00 |
| **84-R18-2.11** | 80 Gathering Christmas Greens | 65.00 | 75.00 | **75.00** | 0.00 |
| **84-R18-2.12** | 81 Shopkeeper at Christmas | 75.00 | 75.00 | **75.00** | 0.00 |
| | Complete Collection | 755.00 | 776.00 | **784.00** | −13.00 |
| **Rhodes Treasures of the Doré Bible** (84-R30-1) | | | | | |
| **84-R30-1.1** | 87 Moses and the Ten Commandments | 59.00 | 59.00 | **59.00◊** | 0.00 |
| **River Shore Famous Americans** (84-R69-1) | | | | | |
| **84-R69-1.1** | 76 Brown's Lincoln | 40.00 | 47.00 | **49.00** | 0.00 |
| **84-R69-1.2** | 77 Brown's Rockwell | 45.00 | 35.00 | **40.00** | −5.00 |
| **84-R69-1.3** | 78 Brown's Peace Corps | 45.00 | 26.00 | **45.00** | −10.00 |
| **84-R69-1.4** | 79 Spirit of Lindbergh | 50.00 | 42.00 | **45.00** | −5.00 |
| | Complete Collection | 180.00 | 150.00 | **179.00** | −20.00 |
| **River Shore Signs of Love** (84-R69-2) | | | | | |
| **84-R69-2.1** | 81 A Kiss for Mother | 18.50 | 19.00 | **19.00** | 0.00 |
| **84-R69-2.2** | 81 A Watchful Eye | 21.50 | 22.00 | **22.00** | 0.00 |
| **84-R69-2.3** | 82 A Gentle Persuasion | 21.50 | 22.00 | **22.00** | 0.00 |
| **84-R69-2.4** | 83 A Protective Embrace | 23.50 | 24.00 | **26.00** | −4.00 |
| **84-R69-2.5** | 83 A Tender Coaxing | 23.50 | 38.00 | **40.00** | 0.00 |
| **84-R69-2.6** | 84 A Reassuring Touch | 23.50 | 27.00 | **30.00** | −2.00 |
| **84-R69-2.7** | 85 A Trusting Hug | 26.50 | 33.00 | **33.00** | −2.00 |
| **84-R69-2.8** | 85 A Loving Guidance | 26.50 | 30.00 | **33.00** | 0.00 |
| | Complete Collection | 185.00 | 215.00 | **225.00** | −8.00 |
| **Rockwell Society Christmas** (84-R70-1) | | | | | |
| **84-R70-1.1** | 74 Scotty Gets His Tree | 24.50 | 115.00 | **119.00** | +4.00 |
| **84-R70-1.2** | 75 Angel with Black Eye | 24.50 | 52.00 | **60.00** | 0.00 |
| **84-R70-1.3** | 76 Golden Christmas | 24.50 | 40.00 | **50.00** | −5.00 |
| **84-R70-1.4** | 77 Toy Shop Window | 24.50 | 30.00 | **35.00** | −3.00 |
| **84-R70-1.5** | 78 Christmas Dream | 24.50 | 27.00 | **34.00** | −4.00 |
| **84-R70-1.6** | 79 Somebody's Up There | 24.50 | 25.00 | **26.00** | 0.00 |
| **84-R70-1.7** | 80 Scotty Plays Santa | 24.50 | 25.00 | **26.00** | 0.00 |
| **84-R70-1.8** | 81 Wrapped Up in Christmas | 25.50 | 26.00 | **27.00** | 0.00 |
| **84-R70-1.9** | 82 Christmas Courtship | 25.50 | 26.00 | **28.00** | 0.00 |
| **84-R70-1.10** | 83 Santa in the Subway | 25.50 | 26.00 | **27.00** | −3.00 |
| **84-R70-1.11** | 84 Santa in His Workshop | 27.50 | 28.00 | **28.00** | −15.00 |
| **84-R70-1.12** | 85 Grandpa Plays Santa | 27.50 | 28.00 | **30.00** | 0.00 |
| **84-R70-1.13** | 86 Deer Santy Claus | 27.90 | 38.00 | **40.00** | +12.00 |
| **Rockwell Society Mother's Day** (84-R70-2) | | | | | |
| **84-R70-2.1** | 76 A Mother's Love | 24.50 | 99.00 | **105.00** | 0.00 |
| **84-R70-2.2** | 77 Faith | 24.50 | 75.00 | **79.00** | −6.00 |
| **84-R70-2.3** | 78 Bedtime | 24.50 | 65.00 | **75.00** | −3.00 |
| **84-R70-2.4** | 79 Reflections | 24.50 | 28.00 | **30.00** | +1.00 |
| **84-R70-2.5** | 80 A Mother's Pride | 24.50 | 30.00 | **32.00** | +2.00 |
| **84-R70-2.6** | 81 After the Party | 24.50 | 25.00 | **30.00** | 0.00 |
| **84-R70-2.7** | 82 The Cooking Lesson | 25.50 | 30.00 | **32.00** | +2.00 |
| **84-R70-2.8** | 83 Add Two Cups and Love | 25.50 | 37.00 | **38.00** | +1.00 |
| **84-R70-2.9** | 84 Grandma's Courting Dress | 25.50 | 26.00 | **26.00** | −2.00 |
| **84-R70-2.10** | 85 Mending Time | 27.50 | 30.00 | **33.00** | 0.00 |
| **84-R70-2.11** | 86 Pantry Raid | 27.90 | 27.00 | **28.00** | 0.00 |
| **84-R70-2.12** | 87 Grandma's Surprise | 29.90 | 29.90 | **29.90** | 0.00 |
| **Rockwell Society Rockwell Heritage** (84-R70-3) | | | | | |
| **84-R70-3.1** | 77 Toy Maker | 14.50 | 160.00 | **170.00** | +10.00 |
| **84-R70-3.2** | 78 Cobbler | 19.50 | 119.00 | **125.00** | −3.00 |
| **84-R70-3.3** | 79 Lighthouse Keeper's Daughter | 19.50 | 55.00 | **58.00** | +3.00 |
| **84-R70-3.4** | 80 Ship Builder | 19.50 | 40.00 | **42.00** | +2.00 |
| **84-R70-3.5** | 81 Music Maker | 19.50 | 21.00 | **24.00** | 0.00 |
| **84-R70-3.6** | 82 Tycoon | 19.50 | 25.00 | **27.00** | +2.00 |
| **84-R70-3.7** | 83 Painter | 19.50 | 22.00 | **28.00** | 0.00 |
| **84-R70-3.8** | 84 Storyteller | 19.50 | 25.00 | **30.00** | −8.00 |
| **84-R70-3.9** | 85 Gourmet | 19.50 | 30.00 | **35.00** | −5.00 |
| **84-R70-3.10** | 86 Professor | 22.90 | 24.00 | **27.00** | −2.00 |
| **84-R70-3.11** | 87 Shadow Artist | 22.90 | 22.90 | **22.90◊** | 0.00 |
| **Rockwell Society Rockwell's Rediscovered Women** (84-R70-4) | | | | | |
| **84-R70-4.1** | 81 Dreaming in the Attic | 19.50 | 32.00 | **34.00** | +1.00 |
| **84-R70-4.2** | 82 Waiting on the Shore | 22.50 | 26.00 | **27.00** | 0.00 |
| **84-R70-4.3** | 83 Pondering on the Porch | 22.50 | 24.00 | **27.00** | −3.00 |
| **84-R70-4.4** | 83 Making Believe at the Mirror | 22.50 | 25.00 | **25.00** | −7.00 |
| **84-R70-4.5** | 83 Waiting at the Dance | 22.50 | 29.00 | **30.00** | −5.00 |
| **84-R70-4.6** | 83 Gossiping in the Alcove | 22.50 | 23.00 | **26.00** | −4.00 |
| **84-R70-4.7** | 83 Standing in the Doorway | 22.50 | 33.00 | **38.00** | −6.00 |
| **84-R70-4.8** | 83 Flirting in the Parlor | 22.50 | 22.50 | **22.50◊** | 0.00 |
| **84-R70-4.9** | 84 Working in the Kitchen | 22.50 | 22.50 | **22.50◊** | 0.00 |
| **84-R70-4.10** | 84 Meeting on the Path | 22.50 | 22.50 | **22.50◊** | 0.00 |
| **84-R70-4.11** | 84 Confiding in the Den | 22.50 | 22.50 | **22.50◊** | 0.00 |
| **84-R70-4.12** | 84 Reminiscing In the Quiet | 22.50 | 22.50 | **22.50◊** | 0.00 |
| | Complete Collection | 267.00 | 304.50 | **319.50** | −24.00 |
| **Rockwell Society Rockwell on Tour** (84-R70-5) | | | | | |
| **84-R70-5.1** | 83 Walking through Merrie Englande | 16.00 | 27.00 | **30.00** | −5.00 |
| **84-R70-5.2** | 83 Promenade a Paris | 16.00 | 16.00 | **20.00** | −2.00 |
| **84-R70-5.3** | 83 When in Rome— | 16.00 | 17.00 | **20.00** | −2.00 |
| **84-R70-5.4** | 84 Die Walk am Rhein | 16.00 | 19.00 | **25.00** | −4.00 |
| | Complete Collection | 64.00 | 79.00 | **95.00** | −13.00 |
| **Rockwell Society Rockwell's Light Campaign** (84-R70-6) | | | | | |
| **84-R70-6.1** | 83 This Is the Room That Light Made | 19.50 | 50.00 | **65.00** | 0.00 |
| **84-R70-6.2** | 84 Grandpa's Treasure Chest | 19.50 | 26.00 | **29.00** | +9.00 |
| **84-R70-6.3** | 84 Father's Help | 19.50 | 20.00 | **22.00** | +2.00 |
| **84-R70-6.4** | 84 Evening's Ease | 19.50 | 22.00 | **23.00** | 0.00 |
| **84-R70-6.5** | 84 Close Harmony | 21.50 | 22.00 | **22.00** | 0.00 |
| **84-R70-6.6** | 84 The Birthday Wish | 21.50 | 22.00 | **25.00** | 0.00 |
| | Complete Collection | 121.00 | 162.00 | **186.00** | +11.00 |
| **Rockwell Society Rockwell's American Dream** (84-R70-7) | | | | | |
| **84-R70-7.1** | 85 A Young Girl's Dream | 19.90 | 19.90 | **19.90◊** | 0.00 |
| **84-R70-7.2** | 85 A Couple's Commitment | 19.90 | 19.90 | **19.90◊** | 0.00 |
| **84-R70-7.3** | 85 A Family's Full Measure | 22.90 | 22.90 | **22.90◊** | 0.00 |
| **84-R70-7.4** | 86 A Mother's Welcome | 22.90 | 22.90 | **22.90◊** | 0.00 |
| **84-R70-7.5** | 86 Young Man's Dream | 22.90 | 22.90 | **22.90◊** | 0.00 |
| **84-R70-7.6** | 86 The Musician's Magic | 22.90 | 22.90 | **22.90◊** | 0.00 |
| **84-R70-7.7** | 87 An Orphan's Hope | 24.90 | 24.90 | **24.90◊** | 0.00 |
| **84-R70-7.8** | 87 Love's Reward | 24.90 | 24.90 | **24.90◊** | 0.00 |
| | Complete Collection | 181.20 | 181.20 | **181.20** | 0.00 |
| **Rockwell Society Rockwell's Colonials—The Rarest Rockwells** (84-R70-8) | | | | | |
| **84-R70-8.1** | 85 Unexpected Proposal | 27.90 | 27.90 | **27.90◊** | 0.00 |
| **84-R70-8.2** | 86 Words of Comfort | 27.90 | 27.90 | **27.90◊** | 0.00 |
| **84-R70-8.3** | 86 Light for the Winter | 30.90 | 30.90 | **30.90◊** | 0.00 |
| **84-R70-8.4** | 87 Portrait for a Bridegroom | 30.90 | 30.90 | **30.90◊** | 0.00 |
| **Rockwell Society A Mind of Her Own** (84-R70-9) | | | | | |
| **84-R70-9.1** | 86 Sitting Pretty | 24.90 | 24.90 | **24.90◊** | 0.00 |
| **84-R70-9.2** | 87 Serious Business | 24.90 | 24.90 | **24.90◊** | 0.00 |
| **Rockwell Society Rockwells Golden Moments** (84-R70-10) | | | | | |
| **84-R70-10.1** | 87 Grandpa's Gift | 19.90 | 19.90 | **19.90◊** | 0.00 |
| **Roman Inc. A Child's Play** (84-R53-1) | | | | | |
| **84-R53-1.1** | 82 Kite Flying | 29.95 | 22.00 | **25.00** | −5.00 |
| **84-R53-1.2** | 82 Breezy Day | 29.95 | 24.00 | **25.00** | −5.00 |
| **84-R53-1.3** | 84 First Snow | 29.95 | 25.00 | **27.00** | −3.00 |
| **84-R53-1.4** | 84 Bathtub Sailor | 29.95 | 21.00 | **25.00** | −5.00 |
| | Complete Collection | 119.80 | 92.00 | **102.00** | −18.00 |
| **Roman Inc. Fontanini Christmas Story** (84-R53-14) | | | | | |
| **84-R53-12.1** | 86 A King is Born | 60.00 | 58.00 | **60.00** | −4.00 |
| **Royal Devon Christmas** (84-R61-1) | | | | | |
| **84-R61-1.1** | 75 Downhill Daring | 24.50 | 34.00 | **35.00** | +16.00 |
| **84-R61-1.2** | 76 The Christmas Gift | 24.50 | 54.00 | **55.00** | −5.00 |
| **84-R61-1.3** | 77 The Big Moment | 27.50 | 50.00 | **55.00** | +8.00 |
| **84-R61-1.4** | 78 Puppets for Christmas | 27.50 | 26.00 | **28.00** | 0.00 |
| **84-R61-1.5** | 79 One Present Too Many | 31.50 | 25.00 | **25.00** | 0.00 |
| **84-R61-1.6** | 80 Gramps Meets Gramps | 33.00 | 30.00 | **35.00** | 0.00 |
| | Complete Collection | 168.50 | 219.00 | **233.00** | +19.00 |
| **Royal Devon Mother's Day** (84-R61-2) | | | | | |
| **84-R61-2.1** | 75 Doctor and Doll | 23.50 | 59.00 | **60.00** | +10.00 |
| **84-R61-2.2** | 76 Puppy Love | 24.50 | 63.00 | **65.00** | +7.00 |
| **84-R61-2.3** | 77 The Family | 24.50 | 50.00 | **50.00** | 0.00 |
| **84-R61-2.4** | 78 Mother's Day Off | 27.00 | 25.00 | **28.00** | −5.00 |
| **84-R61-2.5** | 79 Mother's Evening Out | 30.00 | 21.00 | **21.00** | −2.00 |
| **84-R61-2.6** | 80 Mother's Treat | 32.50 | 30.00 | **30.00** | 0.00 |
| | Complete Collection | 162.00 | 248.00 | **254.00** | +10.00 |
| **Vague Shadows The Chieftains I** (84-V3-2) | | | | | |
| **84-V3-2.1** | 79 Chief Sitting Bull | 65.00 | 525.00 | **575.00** | +25.00 |
| **84-V3-2.2** | 79 Chief Joseph | 65.00 | 97.00 | **105.00** | +15.00 |
| **84-V3-2.3** | 80 Chief Red Cloud | 65.00 | 145.00 | **150.00** | 0.00 |
| **84-V3-2.4** | 80 Geronimo | 65.00 | 64.00 | **65.00** | 0.00 |
| **84-V3-2.5** | 81 Chief Crazy Horse | 65.00 | 126.00 | **135.00** | +10.00 |
| | Complete Collection | 325.00 | 957.00 | **1030.00** | +50.00 |
| **Viletta Zolan's Children** (84-V36-1) | | | | | |
| **84-V36-1.1** | 78 Erik and Dandelion | 19.00 | 220.00 | **240.00** | −10.00 |
| **84-V36-1.2** | 79 Sabina in the Grass | 22.00 | 199.00 | **205.00** | −5.00 |
| **84-V36-1.3** | 80 By Myself | 24.00 | 40.00 | **43.00** | −2.00 |
| **84-V36-1.4** | 81 For You | 24.00 | 38.00 | **39.00** | +4.00 |
| | Complete Collection | 89.00 | 497.00 | **527.00** | −13.00 |
| **Viletta Nutcracker Ballet** (84-V36-2) | | | | | |
| **84-V36-2.1** | 78 Clara and Nutcracker | 19.50 | 18.00 | **20.00** | +1.00 |
| **84-V36-2.2** | 79 Gift from Godfather | 19.50 | 10.00 | **13.00** | 0.00 |
| **84-V36-2.3** | 79 The Sugarplum Fairy | 19.50 | 20.00 | **23.00** | +3.00 |
| **84-V36-2.4** | 79 Snow King and Queen | 19.50 | 30.00 | **30.00** | 0.00 |
| **84-V36-2.5** | 80 Waltz of the Flowers | 19.50 | 19.00 | **20.00** | 0.00 |
| **84-V36-2.6** | 80 Clara and the Prince | 19.50 | 26.00 | **27.00** | 0.00 |
| | Complete Collection | 117.00 | 123.00 | **133.00** | +4.00 |

# BRADEX-LISTED
# PLATE ARTIST INFORMATION

**AKERS, Roger** (1940–    ) Roger Aker's artwork ranges from massive wooden sculpture to the delicately rendered cameos of Incolay's *Romantic Poets Collection*. Akers was educated at the Cooper School of Art in Cleveland, the Art Institute of Chicago and the American Academy of Art in Chicago. Akers' awards include Best of Show at the Excellence in Woodcarving Show in 1981. The American Numismatic Association commissioned him for "Coin of the Year" in 1974. He is a freelance artist in Chicago and his works hang in midwestern galleries and have been selected for permanent museum display by the Illinois Arts Council. He was born and raised in Cleveland.

**ALLINGHAM, Helen** (1848–1920?) Helen Allingham was born in Barton, Trent in the Victorian era. Rejecting the confines of Victorian life, she was determined to support herself, and won admission to the Royal Academy of Art in London through sheer stubborness of effort. After working in oils her first year as a student, she decided she could express herself better in watercolors, but brought some of the techniques and disciplines of oil painting to the new medium. As a result, she managed to create watercolors of such unique and original quality that her name ranked with the major male artists of the period. She began her commercial career as a free-lance illustrator for the *London Graphic*, and also illustrated a number of books and magazines, with her first work done mostly in black ink on wood. She also did portraits, mostly at the request of friends.

A highly prolific painter, Mrs. Allingham turned our nearly a thousand completed works in her lifetime, many inspired by the rolling hills and trees of southeast England where she and her husband lived. In 1987, her artwork was the basis of the *Happy England* plate series from Royal Worcester.

**ANDERSON, Wayne** (1951–    ) Wayne Anderson, a native of Wisconsin, earned a degree in fine art from the University of Wisconsin at Stevens Point. Since then, he has had extensive commissions and has been represented in numerous shows. His oil paintings are in many private collections across the United States and Canada, and he has participated in the prestigious National Exhibition of Alaskan Wildlife at Anchorage. Anderson, who grew up with a love of nature, is best-known for his wildlife art, which he says is influenced by the work of realist painter Richard Estes and wildlife artists John James Audobon and J. Fenwick Lansdowne. In 1986, Anderson created his first collector's plate series for the Knowles China Company, titled *The Upland Birds of North America*.

**ANKER, Albert** (1831–1910) Albert Anker was born and raised in the small French town of Ins, near Bern, midway between French- and German-speaking Switzerland. He was ordained a minister before turning to painting as his life's work. Anker studied in Paris and became a student of classic French realism while attending the famous studio of Charles Gleyre and the prestigious Ecole des Beaux Arts. He is said to belong to the school of Realist "genre" painters, whose art depicted everyday people and scenes. Anker was a much-honored artist in his lifetime and a civic leader widely known for his successful effort to persuade the Swiss government to encourage the arts. He also participated in the planning of a museum which would later house the largest collection of his work—the Neuchâtel Museum of Fine Arts. In 1986, the Langenthal Swiss China Works introduced the *Anker's Heritage* series, which features scenes from Swiss village life in the nineteenth century. It is the first series based on this artist's work.

**APPLEBY, Gayle Bright** (1949–      ) Gayle Bright Appleby is designer of the first four issues in Incolay's *Romantic Poets Collection*. She studied at San Fernando Valley State College in California and at Otis Art School. Her works have appeared in exhibits at Mari's of Hawaii in Lahaina and Alchemists Garden, Kihei, Hawaii. She is widely known for the intricate detail of her sculptures in bronze, silver and gold.

**ARD, Kurt** (1925–      ) Kurt Ard's career got off to an inauspicious start when a bomb in wartime Denmark destroyed both his artwork and the publisher for his first major commission. But Ard has enjoyed international success in the four decades since. His illustrations have appeared in virtually every printed form, including magazines, posters, greeting cards and calendars. His credits include cover and story illustrations in such magazines as *The Saturday Evening Post, Redbook, McCalls, Modern Maturity* and equally prestigious publications in Germany, France and Scandinavia. He shares with Norman Rockwell an uncanny ability to capture the trauma and adventure of growing up, as shown in his *Moments of Truth* series for Bing & Grøndahl. Ard is a self-taught artist.

**AUCKLAND, James** (1946–      ) James Auckland, creator of the *Wizard of Oz* series produced by Edwin M. Knowles, was copying Van Gogh prints at the age of six, using his mother's palette and brushes. He studied at the Art Center College of Design in Los Angeles and privately with Richard Huebnes, Lorser Feitelson, Joe Hehnigar and Harry Carmen.

**BAHNSEN, Frode** (1923–1983) Frode Bahnsen's training in sculpture, ceramics and drawing is evident in the plates he designed for Grande Copenhagen's *Christmas* series, with bas-relief scenes from the fairy tales of Hans Christian Andersen. He studied at the Copenhagen Royal Academy of Art and subsequently worked for the Royal Mint in Copenhagen, rising to the position of head sculptor in 1968. His works hang in the Denmark National Museum and have been exhibited in many places, including the Charlottenborg Art Exhibition in Copenhagen and F.I.D.M.E. (Federal International

Danish Medal Exhibitions). The Queen of Denmark titled him knight of Dannebrog in 1978.

**BAND, Ursula** (1937–     ) Born in Meissen, Germany, Alt Tirschenreuth artist Ursula Band displayed talent for painting and drawing in her early childhood. As a young woman she attended the Painting and Drawing School of the Meissen State Porcelain Manufactury. After her rigorous training she was selected to be among the handful of people who hand-paint Meissen china. In 1964, she established her own atelier. She portrayed the songbirds of the woodlands surrounding her home in Germany in her first collector's plate series, *Songbirds of Europe*.

**BARKER, Cicely Mary** (1895–1973) Heinrich/Villeroy & Boch artist Cicely Mary Barker published the first of her numerous Flower Fairy books in 1923. A largely self-taught artist, she also had formal training at the Croyden School of Art. A stained glass window of her design hangs in St. Andrew's Church in Croyden. Her works have been exhibited at the Royal Institute and are in the collection of the British royal family.

**BARRER, Gertrude** (1921–     ) With her husband Frank Russell, Gertrude Barrer has produced art displayed in some of the United States' most prestigious museums, including the Whitney Museum of American Art and the Art Institute of Chicago, and in the private collections of Cyrus Vance and Helmut Schmidt and the United Nations Interfaith Chapel in New York. Together they created the *Triptych* and *Romantic Love* series for Anna-Perenna. Barrer and Russell first met at the Art Student's League in New York. Five years later, they reunited in New York's art center, Greenwich Village, to work jointly on photographs, lithographs, frescoes, serigraphs and sculpture.

**BEDAL, Karl** (1914–     ) The man whose illustrations of West Germany's classic half-timbered farmhouses appear on *Deutsches Fachwerk* plates is well-known throughout Bavaria for his architecture research and literature on German folk history. His artistic creations range from wall-size paintings to delicate water colors and linocut book illustrations. Bedal has been a freelance artist since 1958. He travels throughout Germany in search of his country's finest regional architecture, making his sketches on the spot to capture the patterns of wooden beams and braces on houses built centuries ago.

**BENVENUTI, Riccardo** (1939–     ) Riccardo Benvenuti was born in Lucca, the same town that produced one of Italy's greatest operatic composers, Giacomo Puccini. (He is the brother of Sergio Benvenuti, the sculptor of the *Benvenuti's Muses* series.) Raised in Puccini's shadow, Riccardo Benvenuti eventually developed an artistic style that reflects the great romantic themes of that composer. Benvenuti's paintings speak of the immortal power of passionate women and the joys and sorrows of unrequited love. The artist has explored these themes in three major exhibitions honoring the 50th anniversary of Puccini's death. In 1985, Le Porcellane Fontana Dei Medici commissioned Benvenuti to create *The Women of Puccini*, a series of haunting portraits of Puccini's great heroines.

**BENVENUTI, Sergio** (1940– )
The designer of the *Muses* plate series for Studio Dante di Volteradici is an Italian master who gained international prominence in 1984 with two important commissions for bronze sculptures. He created his Beato Angelico statue at the request of the Dominican monks for the Church of San Marco in Florence. Italian National Television covered the statue's unveiling, which was attended by His Eminence, the Archbishop of Florence. Americans were introduced to Benvenuti with the critically acclaimed fountain he executed for the First International Bank Plaza in San Diego, California. Benvenuti has won numerous awards in his thirty-year career.

**BLANDFORD, W.A.** (1915– )
W.A. Blandford's career in the British ceramics industry began in the 1930s, when he was apprenticed to Wood & Sons, the Staffordshire ceramics house that produced many of the earliest Toby jugs. Since then he has modeled thousands of intricate ceramic pieces. In order to create the "Toby Fillpot" collector's plate for Davenport Pottery, Blandford spent hours examining antique Toby pieces before sketching his own design, true to the eighteenth century ceramics that inspired it.

**BOEHM, Edward Marshall** (1914–1969) From a background as farmer and veterinarian, the artist for Lenox's *Boehm Bird* series became a full-time sculptor in 1949. The self-taught Boehm was recognized as one of America's greatest wildlife artists. His faithful replication of nature scenes won a substantial following and his work has appeared in the collections of Dwight D. Eisenhower, John F. Kennedy, Lyndon B. Johnson, Queen Elizabeth II and Pope John XXIII. Boehm won numerous awards and his art is displayed in the Smithsonian Institution, the Metropolitan Museum of Art and other museums.

**BORNHOLT, Karen** (1957– )
Although she is an American artist and illustrator, Karen Bornholt drew on her Scandinavian heritage to create *The Ugly Duckling* series, the first full-color plate series from Grande Copenhagen Porcelain. The series, introduced in 1985, is based on one of the most famous tales of Denmark's greatest storyteller, Hans Christian Andersen. The whisper-soft pastel colors of Bornholt's palette capture both the natural beauty and the subtle moral lesson of this beloved children's story.

**BOULMÉ, Claude** (1930– )
When Gerard Boyer of D'Arceau-Limoges approached the great porcelain artist Claude Boulmé about a plate series capturing the porcelain style of the Sèvres Empire, Boulmé knew the subject of the plates must be the Emperor Napoléon, whose patronage permitted the Sèvres art to flower. In the *Joséphine et Napoléon* series, he portrays, in neo-Classical style, the passion of Napoléon for his Empress Joséphine.

**BOYER, Gene** (1948– ) Crown Parian artist Gene Boyer is best known for more than 45 illustrations that appeared in the *Saturday Evening Post* between 1975 and 1978. Boyer got his first big break when Norman Rockwell awarded him second place in a cover contest for the new magazine. Although his portrait assignments for the Post included such contemporary celebrities as Elizabeth Taylor and Jimmy Carter, Boyer was attracted

to the history and integrity offered by the past. In his portraits of such legends as Johnny Appleseed and Davy Crockett in the *American Folk Heroes* plate series, Boyer strives to capture with almost photographic realism the courage and qualities of heroes. Self-taught Boyer has done numerous portrait commissions and exhibited primarily in the Denver, Colorado and Washington, D.C. areas.

**BRACKENBURY, Amy**
(1953–    ) Amy Brackenbury's work has been included for three years in the exclusive and prestigious Leigh Yawkey Woodson Birds in Art Museum in Wisconsin, in a show for new and unusual bird art, and has twice been selected to participate in the museum's world tour. Her inspiration for her animal art comes from the family ranch, located in the foothills of northern Colorado where she lives with her husband and two children.

Ms. Brackenbury first studied art and painting at Colorado State University. She admires Oriental art, but chooses realism to depict the animals she portrays, preferring to paint them as close to life-size as possible. She keeps many pets on her ranch—including geckos and tree frogs. In her free time she likes to cross-country ski and run sled dogs; she also teaches dog obedience classes for 4-H.

**BRADLEY, Betsey** (1949–    )
Edwin M. Knowles artist Betsey Bradley first realized she had talent when her fifth grade profiles of classmates showed a striking likeness to their subjects. She has been doing portraits ever since in pastels, pencil, acrylic and oils, and more recently began doing landscapes and still lifes. Bradley studied art at Smith College for Women in Massachusetts, the Minneapolis School of Art and the Rocky Mountain School of Art. Her paintings have been shown in several exhibitions. To her collector's plate series *A Father's Love* Bradley brings a softer version of her strikingly realistic artwork, inspiration from her own happy family, and support for the increasingly active role today's fathers take with their children.

**BRAITHWAITE, Derek**
(1929–    ) After an art college education at Harrogate in England, Derek Braithwaite spent a great portion of his career as the art director of a large advertising studio (he is a member of the Society of Illustrators). But while pursuing his profession in the commercial world, he always retained an avid interest in his personal artistic passion—landscape painting and wildlife art. Far from the hectic pace of the advertising world, the wilderness landscape teeming with life presented a compelling artistic challenge as well as a place of solace and refuge. Braithwaites's refined artistic sensibility, combined with his rare command of technique and patient study, brings a unique quality to his work. This is evident in the *Braithwaite Game Birds Collection*, his first series by Royal Grafton.

Braithwaite was born in Folifoot near Knaresborough, North Yorkshire, England. He and his wife live in England. They have two children; his daughter Ann is also an illustrator. For relaxation he enjoys walking and photography.

**BRATLIE, Gunnar** (1918–    )
Born in Fredrikstad, Norway, Gunnar Bratlie is a master of the traditional Norwegian folk art known as "rosemaling." He has worked in such diverse styles as oil, tempera, aquarelle and etching. Among his many awards are the Scandinavian book prize for illustration, a contest-winning design for Fredrikstad's 400th-year jubilee and a special stipend from the Norwegian Design Organization. His work is represented in many museums around the world, most notably at the Commune of Oslo, the Art Society of Fredrikstad and the Museo del Arte in Pisoia, Italy. Sole artist since 1967 for Porsgrund Pottery, his plates in the *Christmas, Mother's Day* and *Traditional Norwegian Christmas* series primarily depict Norwegian country scenes.

**BRENOT, Pierre- Laurent**
(1913–      ) A Parisian by birth, Pierre-Laurent Brenot studied at the Ecole Estienne in Paris and finished in first place at the end of his schooling. As one of France's leading interpreters of women, he uses a technique called *une realité poetique*. Brenot has worked on fashion illustrations for such magazines as *Elle* and *Vogue*. He was a medalist at the *Salon des Artistes Français* in 1965 and 1966, and received the *Prix Henner* in Paris in 1971. He also won the *Grand Prix de Tour* in 1975. Brenot is a permanent exhibitor at the prestigious *Galleria d'Arte Firenze* in Florence, Italy. He is also a member of the *Jury des Artistes Française*, and exhibits in galleries throughout the world. In 1985, D'Arceau-Limoges introduced his first plate series, *The Women of the Belle Epoque*, a historic tribute to the glamorous women of Paris at the turn of the century.

**BROWN, Roger** (1933–      ) Roger Brown studied under Dorothea Denslow at the New York Sculpture Center and is a member of the New York Sculpture Center and the National Sculpture Center. Brown's works are in the collections of the Whitney Museum of American Art and the Remington Museum in New York, the Studebaker Museum in South Bend, Indiana, the Lyndon Baines Johnson Memorial Library and the Teterboro Aviation Museum, among others. He is sculptor of the *Famous Americans* series for River Shore, Ltd.

**BRUNETTIN, Alan** (1954–      )
Incolay artist Alan Brunettin mastered the art of traditional sculpture in a nine-year apprenticeship to his father, internationally celebrated sculptor Alfred Brunettin. Today his art in several media ranges from striking photorealism to cartoon-like surrealism. In *Voyage of Ulysses*, his first collector's plate series, Brunettin uses traditional sculptural techniques to render scenes from the Greek epic in cameo-carved high relief. Brunettin earned a Bachelor of Fine Arts degree with an emphasis in painting at Northern Illinois University and also studied at the American Academy of Art in Chicago. He has exhibited at Chicago-area art fairs and won prizes two consecutive years at the National Exhibit of Italian-American Art in Chicago.

**CAMBIER, Guy** (1923–      ) Self-taught artist Guy Cambier had his first one-man show at age 19 and has been exhibiting ever since in Belgium, France and at the Zantman Art Galleries in Carmel, California. He has won numerous awards and honors through the years, from the *Prix de la Jeune Peinture Méditerranée* in 1955 to the *Laureate de la Médaille International des Artes* in 1977. He designed the *Girls of the Seasons* and *Cambier Mother's Day* series in a neo-Classical style for D'Arceau-Limoges.

**CASSINI, Oleg** (1913–      ) Oleg Cassini is one of the best-known names in contemporary fashion—his name has appeared on everything from sunglasses to perfume—as well as an accomplished artist. Born to Countess Loiewski Cassini in Paris, Cassini renounced his right to the title of Count to become an American citizen after immigrating to the United States in the late 1930s. He designed film costumes in Hollywood for such celebrities as Gene Tierney and Grace Kelly before going to New York to put his name on a par with Dior and Cardin. Jacqueline Kennedy named Cassini her official couturier during her White House years. He received a law degree from the University of Florence and graduated from Florence's prestigious Academia delle Belle Artes. For *Oleg Cassini's Most Beautiful Women of All Time Collection* for Pickard, Cassini explored the historical and cultural aspects of the lives of women such as Helen of Troy.

**CHAMBERS, William**
(1940–     ) William Chambers came to the plate world almost by accident and became an overnight success in the midst of his career as a well-known illustrator and prize-winning portraitist. He had never heard of collector's plates when he got a letter from an Edwin M. Knowles art representative inviting him to discuss the *Annie Collector's Plate* series. Soon afterwards his debut plate, "Annie and Sandy," made history when it walked off with two of the most coveted awards, Plate of the Year and New Edition of the Year for 1983—the first time a single plate has won both honors. Chambers paid his dues as an illustrator and photographer before he came to the realization that he could both make a living and satisfy his artistic needs painting portraits. He has exhibited in the American Society of Illustrators' annual show, The American Show at Marshall Field's and the Mongerson Galleries (both in Chicago), and won first prize in the John Howard Sanden portrait competition. His works hang in various homes and businesses and at Ron De Bouver Fine Arts in Chicago. Chambers studied at Northeastern Illinois University and the American Academy of Art in Chicago.

**CRNKOVICH, Tony** (1962–     ) While other youngsters played baseball after school, Tony Crnkovich taught himself to draw. He watched old films on TV, and then recreated what he saw on the screen—including portraits of many famous film characters. Born in Chicago, Illinois, Crnkovich eventually enrolled at the American Academy of Art in that city, where he received his professional art training. From there, he developed his two loves—art and classic movies—into a respected body of work that captures not only the details of great films, but also the mood of a film and its important characters. His first series is *The Sound of Music* for the Knowles China Company, in which he recreates the musical highlights of the film.

**CSATARI, Joseph** (1929–     ) Joseph Csatari, long-time friend and protégé of the late master of realism Norman Rockwell, is one of the most highly regarded realist painters of today. He and Rockwell collaborated on the annual calendars published by the Boy Scouts of America for a decade until 1975, when Rockwell turned the calendar commission over to Csatari, who has continued it. Edwin M. Knowles commissioned him for the *Csatari Grandparent Plate* series. His other important recent commissions include cover illustrations for numerous books and a commemorative stamp for the U.S. Postal Service. Csatari studied at the

Academy of Art in Newark, New Jersey and the Pratt Institute in New York City. His awards include a Gold Medal from the Society of Illustrators.

**DALI, Louis** (1906–     ) A noted Impressionist, Louis Dali is a Fellow of the *Salon de l'Ecole Française* and of the *Salon des Indépendants*, and winner of the *Prix Dessin de Briton*. Dali is a self-taught artist whose works hang in many private collections and salons, including the *Salon de la Marine*, *Salon de la Nationale des Beaux-Artes*, and the *Salon de l'Ecole Française des Indépendants*. Dali designed his *Twelve Parisian Places of Louis Dali* for D'Arceau-Limoges.

**DANIEL, Kevin** (1951–     ) For Edwin M. Knowles artist Kevin Daniel, painting is a way of preserving wildlife. He used to hunt with a gun; now he combs the wilds with his camera, collecting

photographs from which to paint highly accurate, detailed portrayals of animals from pheasants to fishes. For his *Birds of Your Garden* series, Daniel erected a camera on the birdfeeder in the backyard of his house near Minneapolis. Daniel, who learned to paint by studying the work of other artists, was named Artist of the Year by the Indiana Chapter of Ducks Unlimited, a waterfowl conservation group, in 1984, and won second place in the Minnesota Duck Stamp art competition the same year. Proceeds from the sale of his prints have helped save the endangered blue heron in Minnesota.

**DEGRAZIA, Ted** (1909–1982) Ted DeGrazia, one of America's most popular and instantly-recognizable artists, was a man of contrasts and paradoxes. Born in Morenci, Arizona, the son of an Italian copper miner, he didn't attend school for the first 11 years of his life but later earned three degrees in art and music from the University of Arizona. He studied with great Mexican muralists Diego Rivera and Jose Clemente Orozco and spent long hours of research and hard work on his paintings, yet he acquired the image of a drunken carouser. A millionaire in the last years of his life, his art was always of the people and for the people, and he strove to keep it affordable. His stylized paintings of Southwestern themes first came to international attention in 1960 when UNICEF sold 100 million Christmas cards bearing the image of his painting "Los Niños." Since then, they have appeared on everything from stained glass to figurines and in collector's plates series for Fairmont/Artists of the World and Gorham, including *DeGrazia Holiday* series and *DeGrazia Children* series.

**DOWN, Jeanne** (1928–    ) Artist Jeanne Down uses her palette and brushes to tell stories—especially of her childhood days in Altoona, Pennsylvania. Though she grew up during the Great Depression, her memories are happy ones. Among other things, she learned to paint at the knee of her grandfather, Pennsylvania realist E.E. Wilt. After graduating high school she temporarily abandoned her avocation to spend 16 years raising a family. But after studying oil painting, watercolor and etching techniques under private teachers she began to offer instruction herself throughout California's San Fernando Valley. In 1975 she opened her own gallery and studio. In her *Friends I Remember* series, Down uses an "impressionistic realist" style to impart feelings as well as images.

**DURAND, Paul** (1925–1977) Paul Durand achieved an international reputation for his illustrations of such children's classics as *The Three Musketeers* and *Treasure Island*. General Charles De Gaulle chose Durand's art to illustrate his 1969 Christmas message to French children. Durand was influenced in Paris by Christian Berard, Jacques DeMachy, René Gruau and André Dignimont. He exhibited at the *Festival Cannes* in 1965, was presented as a candidate for the Hans Christian Andersen Prize in 1970, and did illustrations for numerous French and U.S. publications, including Hachette, Delagrave and Flammarion editions, *Reader's Digest*, *Le Figaro* and *Paris Presse*. He was the artist for the Limoges-Turgot plate series *Durand's Children Collection*.

**DUTHEIL, Jean** (1927–    ) D'Arceau-Limoges artist Jean Dutheil experimented with pigments for more than a year and a half to try to duplicate the rich colors of the medieval French manuscript on which *The Very Rich Hours* plate series is based. Dutheil studied at *L'Ecole de Beaublance* in Limoges, France. His many awards and honors include the *Prix de la Ville de Limoges*, *Prix du Ministre*, *Grand Prix de Porcelaine de Limoges* and the *Meilleur Ouvrier de France*.

**ETÉM, Sue** (1941?–     ) Self-taught painter Sue Etém's first plate, "Renee," which launched the *Playful Memories* series by Fairmont, sold out in two hours at a gallery open house when it was first introduced. It also won NALED's Plate of the Year and Collectible of the Year for 1981. Etém herself was named NALED's Artist of the Year for 1981 and 1982. Like many of Etém's paintings, "*Renee*" began as a snapshot—in this case, of a little neighbor girl who came to the house for chewing gum and ended up playing with a drinking hose. Etém, who now designs for Derby Collection, began drawing at age 3. After a year of formal art training at Arlington State College, she joined an advertising agency as a commercial artist. In the early 1950s she moved to Huntington Beach, California, where she taught art to neighborhood children. She has exhibited throughout the United States and Canada.

**FAURE, Renée** (1939?–     ) Granddaughter of the great American Impressionist Edmund Greacen and daughter of prominent painter Nan Greacon, Renée Faure has demonstrated talent and versatility as an artist in her own right. In the *Once Upon a Rhyme* collector's plate series she created for Heinrich/Villeroy & Boch, Faure captures the charm and appeal of age-old nursery rhymes. Scenes from such favorites as "A Tisket, a Tasket" come alive in Faure's subtle pastels and earth tones. Faure renders the fine detail with superb drafting skill.

a one-man show in Leicester in 1963, and another one in Brunei in 1983. His private commissions had included engraved and sculpted glass works for major corporations, for British nobility and even for her Majesty Queen Elizabeth the Queen Mother, for whom he designed, sculpted and engraved a large crystal presentation bowl. In 1984, he created his first plate series, *Street Sellers of London,* for Wedgwood.

**FISHER, Shell** (1931–     ) Shell Fisher's work, as seen on the plates he has created for Viletta, represents some of the finest examples of contemporary realism. But Fisher is a versatile artist whose credits include interpretive canvasses, portraits commissioned by Queen Elizabeth II and Sammy Davis, Jr., and cartoons for several men's magazines. In his *Nutcracker Ballet Plate Collection,* he depicts the favorite Christmas ballet in vivid colors. Fisher studied at the Art Institute of Chicago, where his work is on display, other places, and has exhibited widely.

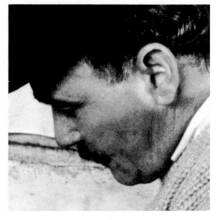

**FINNIE, John** (1934–     ) British artist John Finnie works in a variety of artistic media, from pen, ink and wash to glass engraving and sculpting. Finnie received the National Diploma from the Leicester College of Art in 1956. His work has been exhibited throughout the United Kingdom and has appeared in numerous publications. He had

**FURIESI, Ennio** (1937–     ) Sculptural artist Ennio Furiesi is a native of Tuscany, Italy, which has been a source of fine alabaster marble for hundreds of years. Furiesi is an award-winning portraitist and professor of sculpture at the Art Institute of Volterra. He is known throughout Italy for his sculptural renderings of the Nativ-

ity, which led to his commission to create his first collector's plate series, *Christmas Crèche*, for Studio Dante di Volteradici. It is Sr. Furiesi's interpretation of the classic masterpieces of Neapolitan crèche figures. The series was started in 1986.

**GANEAU, François** (1912–1983) François Ganeau was one of Europe's leading costume and set designers and resident consultant to the *Theatre Comedie Français*. He was widely acclaimed in 1937 for the *Pavillon de l'Elegance*, a mural he created for the Paris World's Fair. As a sculptor and painter he decorated many public buildings and private homes throughout France. He was commissioned by D'Arceau-Limoges to create the *Women of the Century* series bearing the United Nations' emblem for the International Women's Year. The twelve plates in the series picture the progression of 19th and 20th century Paris fashion. Ganeau studied at L'École Boulle, Paris. His works hang in the *Comédie Français*, Paris Opera House and the Louvre.

**GEHM, Charles** (1944–    ) Charles Gehm is a prominent member of the Society of Illustrators and has gained a wide audience through his cover designs for Saul Bellow books. Gehm created the *Grimm's Fairy Tales* collector's plate series for Königszelt Bayern in 1981 to commemorate the two-hundredth anniversary of the Grimm brothers' birth. The plates bear vivid illustrations of such Grimm classics as *Rapunzel* and *Rumplestilzchen*. Gehm is a graduate of the Columbus Art School. He has exhibited at the James Marks Gallery in California and has works hanging in private collections in the United States.

**GIGNILLIAT, Elaine** (1942?–    ) Elaine Gignilliat has been drawing every day since she was three years old. At seventeen she earned a three-year scholarship to the High Museum in Atlanta for her work in a competition of students from all over the southeast United States.

She has painted more than 250 covers for romantic novels, and in 1983 was named Illustrator of the Year by the Romantic Times National Conference. She has considerable experience in portraiture, and loves painting young lovers and the scenes of magic and romance of the great old movies and musicals.

After spending a number of years in New York, Miss Gignilliat has recently returned to Georgia where she was born and raised. Her interests include music, reading, theatre and people. She also likes to paint landscapes; she is currently planning a dream project: to paint scenes from all over the state of Georgia.

**GUIDOU, Jean-Claude** (1946–    ) This young French painter won an international reputation with his sensitive pastel portraits and his studies of ballet dancers and race horses. Important personalities who have commissioned Guidou to execute their portraits include the late General Charles De Gaulle. In "Gigi," the first issue in Guidou's first collector's plate series, he captured his subject's *joie de vivre* on D'Arceau-Limoges porcelain with the pastel soft-focus technique an Impressionist master might have used. Guidou studied at the Louvre and the Royal Museum of Belgium and has exhibited widely.

**HALLETT, Charlotte** (1943–    )
**and William** (1940–    ) In their unique art Charlotte and William Hallett draw upon a rich tradition of myth and ornament to create a world of unicorns, dragons and maidens in love. This husband-and-wife team has collaborated on everything from Greek-inspired sterling flatware to crystal and paintings. Like the *Love For All Seasons* series they designed for Hutschenreuther, all their plates are joint creations. They met as staff designers for a silver company and began to explore the world of color together, having already studied Egyptian, Baroque and Rococo ornamentation, history, fine art and symbolism. Charlotte studied at the University of Connecticut in Bridgeport; William, at Vesper George School of Art in Boston. They have exhibited in local, regional and national shows and their art is in the collections of the Archdiocese of New York and the royal families of Saudi Arabia and Spain, among others.

**HÉTREAU, Remy** (1925–    ) Adept in a variety of styles, French painter Remy Hétreau is the principal artist for Haviland's collector's plates, with two distinctively different series to his credit—from historical chronicle to delightful yuletide fancy in *The Twelve Days of Christmas* series.

**HIBEL, Edna** (1917–    ) Edna Hibel is one of the most respected American painters of her time, and a pioneer in porcelain as a fine-art medium. The plates in her series—which include the *Nobility of Children* and *Oriental Gold* series for Rosenthal, *Hibel's Mother's Day* series for Edwin M. Knowles, and the *Mother and Child* series for Royal Doulton—demonstrate her ability to capture the beauty she sees in life and her love for human beings. Hibel at 22 became the youngest artist to have a painting in a major American museum when the Boston Museum purchased one of her canvasses. She is one of the few living female artists with a U.S. museum—the Hibel Museum of Art in Florida—devoted to her works. She is an elected member of the Royal Society of Arts in London. She has held numerous one-woman shows since 1962 in the United States, England, Monaco, Germany and Argentina and recently became the first American woman to exhibit in Jerusalem. Her works hang in museums across the country. Hibel studied at the Boston Museum of Fine Arts with Carl Zerbe and Jacovleff from 1934 to 1939, and privately with Gregory Michaels in Boston.

**HICKS, Yin-Rei** (1933–    ) Yin-Rei Hicks, a native of mainland China, was born during the Maoist takeover. Her family later fled to Taiwan, where her artistic ability first gained recognition. She won two scholarships from the Univer-

sity of Louisville in Kentucky and graduated with a Master's Degree in Creative Art. She has since become a prominent illustrator and designer of limited-edition collectibles. In 1981 River Shore introduced her *Signs of Love* series, in which Hick's paintings convey the tenderness between wild animals and their young. She has exhibited at the J.B. Speed Museum in Kentucky, the Floyd County Museum, the University of Louisville, and other galleries in Kentucky and southern Indiana. Her works hang in private collections in the United States.

**HOOK, Frances** (1913–1983) Her exquisite understanding of both children and art distinguishes the work of Frances Hook, one of America's premier child portraitists. Her soft pastel style captures dreamy-eyed children in commercial illustrations, prints, lithographs and figurines as well as collector's plates. The public discovered her with her illustrations of the Northern Bath Tissue children—so popular they were sold on 30 million prints. With her late husband Richard, she illustrated *The Children's Living Bible* for Tyndale House Publishers. Her first collector's plate issue was in 1980 for Roman, and her first Bradex-listed series, *A Child's Play*, also for Roman, began in 1982. She also designed the *Frances Hook Legacy*

series for Edwin M. Knowles. Hook studied at the Pennsylvania Museum School of Art.

**HOOK, Richard** (1938– ) Richard Hook is a well-known British illustrator who received his original schooling from the Reigate College of Art in England. In his work, Hook pursues meticulous historical accuracy and does lengthy research to re-create scenes from the past. Throughout his career, he has been in demand for book illustrations from publishers in the United Kingdom, continental Europe, the United States and Japan. In 1986, his first work in the collector's plate medium was introduced by Wedgwood: *The Legend of King Arthur*. It comprises famous incidents from the heroic king's life, and is fired on fine bone china.

**HOOVER, G.A.** (1943– ) In *The Canterbury Tales Collection*, Longton Crown Pottery artist G.A. Hoover carries on a family tradition of artists which began with his grandfather. Hoover holds a Master of Fine Arts degree and is considered a master of the style known as Romantic Realism. He studied at Tulane University in New Orleans and at the John Herron School of Art in Indianapolis. He has executed designs and drawings for Little Brown & Company, McGraw-Hill, Playboy Press, MacMillan and Co., *Reader's Digest*, Harper & Row and Harcourt, Brace and Jovanovich. He has had three one-man shows at Bienville Gallery in New Orleans, participated in an invitational show in Colombia, and has works hanging in several museums and in private collections.

**INGARGIOLA, Franco** (1944– ) Franco Ingargiola studied privately with sculptor Gino Ruggeri, from whom he took over design of the *Grand Opera* series for Studio Dante di Volteradici. Ingargiola worked in onyx and ceramics as well as in the ivory alabaster from which he sculpted the plates in this collection. Ingargiola also studied at Boy's Town in Rome and won first prize at the Craftsmen Arts Show in Cicena, Italy.

**JANSEN, Leo** (1930–1980) Leo Jansen was born in The Hague, The Netherlands. He spent his youth in Indonesia, where he developed his skills as a portrait painter by sketching the bronze-skinned Malay children. He returned to The Netherlands to study at the Academy of Fine Arts and later refined his work in the famous "Pigalle" section of Paris. Jansen designed plates for Kern Collectibles, including the *Leaders of Tomorrow* series, and Royal Bayreuth. In 1970 he won CALED's Plate of the Year award, in Canada. His art has been exhibited at the Avron Brothers Corporation in Los Angeles, California, and hangs in private collections in the United States.

**JERNER, Bart** (1925– ) Bart Jerner received his artistic training at the Chicago Academy of Art, the Art Intitute of Chicago, and the American Academy of Art. He has always combined his career with a great love of the outdoors. For the

past 40 years, he has spent nearly every summer hiking in northern Michigan, the wetlands of central Canada and the mountainous frontier of the Canadian Yukon. Jerner is an active member of the Izaak Walton League of America, one of the first groups to support the conservation of natural resources. His work is exhibited by the National Wildlife Collectors Society, and several of his sculptures are displayed at the Wild Gallery in Dallas and at Taylor's Gallery of Western Art in Santa Fe. In 1986, the Knowles China Company issued Jerner's first collector's plate series, titled *Living with Nature: Jerner's Ducks.*

**JOHNSON, Robert** (1915–    )
Artist Robert Johnson, whose works are in private collections throughout the United States, Europe and the Far East, developed the patented electroplating process used in the creation of the Reed & Barton *Christmas* series. The medium, known as Damascene silver, combines silver, gold, copper and bronze. The process is derived from a hand-crafted method perfected at Damascus in the middle ages. Johnson designed the 1970, 1971 and 1972 plates in the series.

**JULIEN, Michel** (1947–    ) Born in Lille, France, child prodigy Michel Julien quickly gained international renown. Despite his parents poverty, they did everything they could to encourage him, and by the age of eight he had exhibited in Rheims, Munich, and Tokyo. At fifteen, he was awarded the prestigious Medaile de Vermail of the Academy des Beaux Arts. Although he has a BA from the University of Paris, Julien considers himself to be basically self-taught. His work is on display in museums in Belgium, Germany, Canada, Brazil, Argentina, and the United States.

Julien uses the *lavis* technique, which involves working with a combination of black and colored inks to quickly create finely-detailed drawings. His style is a unique blend of Impressionism and Realism.

He lives with his wife and two daughters in a small village near Lille in Northern France; his artwork is exclusively represented by the Gallery Schesmes of Lille. His first plate series, *French Country Landscapes*, is by D'Arceau-Limoges.

**KELLER, Hedi** (1916–    ) Hedi Keller was born in Tuttlingen, West Germany, a village near the Black Forest. She studied for three years at the Kunstakademie in Stuttgart, learning about the great masters—Titian, Rembrandt and Breughel—but later was influenced by Van Gogh and the French Impressionists, who discarded conventional ideas to seek a more personal style. Keller shows her own colorful style in the *Hedi Keller Christmas* series produced by Königszelt Bayern.

Keller's work has been exhibited in galleries in Berlin, Munich and Dusseldorf.

**KRØYER, Peter Severin** (1951–1909) Peter Severin Krøyer grew up in Copenhagen and became interested in art in his teens. After years of painting landscapes and portraits in his native Denmark, Krøyer moved to Paris, where he became part of the Scandinavian artists' colony, and also part of the revolutionary movement that was redefining the criteria for art. It was here that Krøyer met his wife, Marie, in 1889. Although he traveled extensively, Krøyer spent most of his artistic life from 1882 to 1909 at Skagen, a small fishing village on the northern-most tip of Denmark's Jutland peninsula. From 1870 until 1920, Skagen was a unique gathering place for artists and intellectuals from all over the world, and it was there that Krøyer did his finest work. From this work Bing & Grøndahl has created a series titled *A Summer at Skagen*; it was introduced in 1986.

**KRUMEICH, Thaddeus**
(1930–    ) Thaddeus Krumeich is a master of the style known as *trompe l'oeil*, which he calls "magic realism." His magical, clear-eyed cats seem ready to leap off the plates in Anna-Perenna's *Uncle Tad's Cats* series. Krumeich, who studied at New York University and Columbia University, has created illustrations for publications such as *Reader's Digest*, *Time-Life Books* and *Family Circle*. His work was selected for UNICEF greeting cards in 1981 and 1982. Krumeich has had shows throughout the United States and is represented in collections such as those of Mrs. Paul Mellon, "Doc" Severinson and His Excellency Seydou Traori, Mali Ambassador to the United States.

**KUCK, Sandra** (1946–    ) To capture the spontaneous moments in children's lives, Reco artist Sandra Kuck often rounds up a group of neighborhood kids and takes them off to play in the setting she wants to paint. Her "Sunday Best," first issue in Reco's *Days Gone By* series, captured the Plate of the Show award at the 1983 South Bend Convention and was one of the most popular plates that year. Kuck, whose plate career began in 1979, studied art for one year at the University of California at Los Angeles before moving to Manhattan to be close to the great museums. She attended the Art Students' League in Manhattan and studied portraiture and anatomy with established artists. She has shown her work in galleries in New York City, Brooklyn and Long Island. Ms. Kuck has won numerous awards for her work, including *Plate World's* and *NALED's* Artist of the Year award for several years in a row.

**KÜNSTLER, Mort** (1931–    ) Mort Künstler's paintings chronicle American history from the time of the Indians through the space program. He paints with both high realism and imagination. His passion for detail—and respect for history—is showcased in his first collector's plate series, *Oklahoma!*, produced by Edwin M. Knowles, featuring scenes from the classic Rodgers and Hammerstein musical that tells the story of the last frontier land rush. Künstler attended the Pratt Institute in New York City. In his career as an illustrator he has published more than 2,000 illustrations for books, advertisements and magazines, including *Newsweek*, *National Geographic*, *The Saturday Evening Post*, *True*, *Sports Afield* and *Outdoor Life*. His paintings hang in the permanent collections of museums across the country.

**KURSÁR, Raymond** (1944–    ) Until 1978, when "Scarlett," the first plate in Edwin M. Knowles' *Gone With the Wind* series was issued, Raymond Kursár had earned his reputation primarily in the field of commercial illustration. His original paintings for covers for Random House and Ballantine Books have been widely exhibited. He has won awards for his New York theater posters and published illustrations in such magazines as *Ladies Home Journal*, *Better Homes and Gardens* and *Good Housekeeping*. His corporate clients include RCA Records, McDonald's and Coca-Cola. Kursár was educated at the School of Advertising Art, the University of Oregon and the Museum of Modern Art in Portland, Oregon. He came to New York with his portfolio in hand, and, remarkably, has never had to work for a company as an employee.

**LALIQUE, Marie-Claude**
(1921–    ) Chief designer and president of the firm founded by her grandfather René Lalique, Marie-Claude Lalique created the *Annual* series of Lalique crystal collector's plates which began in 1965 and ended in 1976. The third generation in a family of artists, Lalique is know for her versatility. She is an accomplished painter, sculp-

tor, glass-blower and jewelry designer. She is a graduate of the *Grand Chaumiere* and *L'École Normale Superiore des Arts Decoratifs de Paris* where she concentrated on painting until her teacher, Andre Arbus, developed her appreciation of the decorative arts.

**LAMBERT, Georgia** (1948– )
As the child of an Air Force colonel, Georgia Lambert lived for much of her youth in Europe, where she spent countless hours in the great art museums, learning about the techniques of the Old Masters. She most admired the depth of color and sense of glowing light they achieved with numerous layers of paint and varnish. Today she uses the techniques she admired in the medium of china painting, raising a craft to an art form. Instead of simply tracing designs onto china or porcelain and filling them in, she paints originals directly onto porcelain "canvasses." For her first collector's plate series, *The Four Ancient Elements*, produced by Edwin M. Knowles, she applied 20 or more layers of paint to master plates to show the mythological figures of Earth, Air, Fire and Water.

**LAMINCIA, Franco** (1930– )
Born into a family whose artistic heritage spans generations, Franco Lamincia grew up in Deruta, Italy, an ancient village on the Tiber River near Perugia, renowned since the 16th century for its fine majolica, also known as faience. He studied drawing at the local professional school under the great Alpinolo Maguini, who revived the production of true Deruta majolica in the early 1900s. Lamincia reproduced the majolica style when he designed "Noah and the Dove," first issue in Veneto Flair's *St. Mark's of Venice* series. Each plate is a hand-painted recreation of the great mosaics of St. Mark's Cathedral, which chronicle the Old Testament.

**LANGE, Kai** (1905– ) Artist Kai Lange has been with Royal Copenhagen since the age of 17, and after more than half a century with the firm is regarded as one of the most knowledgable artists working in the porcelain medium. The first Lange design selected for the annual *Christmas* plate was for the 1940 issue, and since 1963 every plate except the 1976 issue has been a Lange creation. Lange studied drawing under Carl Schwenn. He is the recipient of several grants and an illustrator for several Danish newspapers. He has created wall hangings for many official institutions. His works hang in the Folkets Hus, Copenhagen.

**LICEA, Eve** (1928– ) Eve Licea's art and life are a study in contrasts. She was born to a poor working-class family in New York's Bronx area, and her family could not afford art lessons. Yet today she lives and works in a fashionable loft in Greenwich Village, and her artworks are exhibited in such prestigious galleries as Lever House, Pindar Gallery and Les Mouches in New York City. A painter, sculptor and lithographer, she is best known for her embossed lithographs and large cast-paper sculptures. Her style is a unique blend of contrasting elements: geometric patterns and rounded natural forms, color and white, matte and gloss surfaces, raised and flat areas. To her two collector's plate series, *Biblical Mothers* and *Licea Christmas*, produced by Edwin M. Knowles, she brings a sculptor's feel for light and shadow along with a painter's feel for line. A creator rather than a recorder, her treatment of subjects the Old Masters painted in a traditional way is very contemporary, and yet realistic. Licea studied at Parson's School of Design in New York. She has done illustrations for numerous publications, including *Good Housekeeping* and *Women's Day*.

**LOCKHART, James** (1912– )
James Lockhart, an ardent naturalist and conservationist, is widely known for his realistic portrayals of wild animals in their natural habitats. His *Lockhart Wildlife* series for Pickard commemorates vanish-

ing forms of American fauna. His paintings and drawings also have appeared in limited edition prints, books, calendars, gift items and magazines, including *Collier's, The Saturday Evening Post* and *Sports Afield.* He is a member of the Board of Governors of Brookfield Zoo and of Chicago's Shedd Aquarium and a trustee of Duck's Unlimited, a waterfowl conservation group.

**LÜCKEL, Christian** (1945–    ) Christian Lückel lives and works in Bavaria, surrounded by the rich beauty of the mountains, forests and the Danube River, all of which are reflected in his work. Lückel has been influenced by the Dutch masters, notably Rembrandt and Vermeer, as well as by such artists of the nineteenth century Munich School as Schleich, Schürer and Hänger, who themselves were followers of the Flemish tradition. Lückel paints mainly in the style known as "genre," preferring subjects such as landscapes, seascapes and farmyard scenes which reflect everyday life in the Germany of the nineteenth century. Recently, Lückel has concentrated on painting miniatures, small paintings of fine detail that are especially suited to the collector's plate medium. In 1986, Christian Seltmann issued the *Lückel's Idyllic Village Life* series, the first series for both artist and maker.

**MALFERTHEINER, Josef** (1931–    ) A master woodcarver from Saint Ulrich, Italy, Josef Malfertheiner studied at the Ortesi Academy of Art and in 1966 became Master Carver for Anri, for whom he designed the *Christmas* series. He is best known for his portrayals of Tyrolean history and three-dimensional replication of Renoir, Van Eyck and Rembrandt. He has works in private collections in Italy, Austria, Germany and Australia.

**MANDRAJJI, Valentin** (1929–    )
**MARSTEN, Barbara** (1935–    ) Barbara Marsten and Valentin Mandrajji are unique as an artistic team in that they work together on the same canvas. They have been working this way and exhibiting together since 1980. Mandrajji was born in Vienna and received his artistic training in Europe. He practiced monumental art, completing 12 frescoes in European churches and non-religious frescoes in Amsterdam and Vienna. Many of his smaller works are now in private collections in Austria, Sweden, Germany, Canada and the United States. Marsten was born in Los Angeles and studied art at U.C.L.A. She has exhibited in California and New York, and has paintings in private collections. Marsten and Mandrajji work together not only as painters, but also as designers for many world-famous companies, including Wedg-

wood and Cartier. In 1986, they created their first plate series for the Knowles China Company, *American Innocents,* which is a tribute to the traditional American folk art of the nineteenth century.

**MASSERIA, Francisco J.J.C.** (1926–    ) Francisco Masseria won his first gold medal at the age of fourteen in the *Salon Annuale de Entre Rios* in his native Argentina. He emigrated to Italy in 1936, made his home in Rome, and studied the works of the Italian and Spanish Renaissance masters. Today he studies the faces of people he sees on the streets. In Royal Doulton's *Portraits of Innocence* series, Masseria mixes two distinct techniques to form his own style, painting classically smooth faces against boldly Impressionistic backgrounds. His numerous awards include NALED's Lithograph of the Year in 1982. He has exhibited in South, Central and North America and in Europe.

**MAYS, Maxwell** (1918–    ) Maxwell Mays, designer of the 1976, 1977 and 1978 plates in Reed & Barton's *Christmas* collector's plate series, specializes in Americana. His art has appeared in such magazines as *Collier's, Yankee, Cosmopolitan* and *New England.*

**McCLELLAND, John** (1919–    )
In 1980, Reco artist John Mc-Clelland's plate "Mary, Mary," first in the *McClelland's Mother Goose* series, out-performed all others on the Bradford Exchange and was named Plate of the Year. It was also named "Best All-Around Collectible" and "Best Plate" by the National Association of Limited Edition Dealers, and McClelland won their "Best Artist" title as well. But he made his mark as a magazine illustrator and portraitist of politicians and artists long before he designed his first collector's plate. McClelland works almost exclusively from live models, whom he may meet by chance, to capture the individuality of children—he saw the model for "Mary, Mary" at a church day-care center. He studied at Auburn University and at Grand Central Art School and Art Career School, in New York, but considers portrait artist Jerry Farnsworth his most valuable teacher. He is the author of books on flower and portrait painting and has had numerous exhibits, primarily on the East Coast. His other plate series include *McClelland Children's Circus Collection* and *Becky's Day*, for Reco.

**MONEY, Rusty** (1939?–    ) In 1981, the Ernst plate series *Seems Like Yesterday* introduced artist Rusty Money to the collector's market. Money was born in Oak Park, Illinois and now lives and paints in Escondido, California. She studied at Arizona State University and the Washington School of Art. Her fa-vorite subjects are children and turn-of-the-century period scenes. Her work is characterized by the use of delicate pastels in a semi-Impressionistic style. She won the International Fine Arts Award competition in 1980. Her works hang in numerous private collections.

**MUELLER, Hans** (1934–    )
Hans Mueller, born in Waldsassen, Bavaria, was the son of a Bareuther artist. He studied engraving and painting at the porcelain academy in Selb and the Porcelain Trade School of Bavaria and in 1952 joined Bareuther as a porcelain painter. He was promoted to chief designer for the firm in 1968. In the *Christmas* and *Father's Day* series Mueller painted castles and country scenes in blue and white.

**MUNINGER, Ludwig**
(1929–    ) Ludwig Muninger has won high praise for his painting—especially his winter scenes—among collectors in many countries. He has been the focus of several one-man shows, and in 1974, the government of Ireland officially honored him for his works. He has also been included in some of Europe's most prestigious collective shows. His work is noted for its mastery of the laws of color and air perspective, as well as the juxtaposition of the grandeur of nature with humbler creations of humankind.

Muninger was born in Augsburg, Bavaria. From there, he relentlessly pursued his dream of painting from childhood on, studying in Germany, France, Italy, Switzerland, and Austria. Although he was surrounded by dizzying changes in the modern art world, he found his inspiration in an earlier era. His mentors were not cubists or abstractionists, but the 17th-century Dutch landscape artists and the Dutch masters. His works evoke a more simple time and place, a world in which man and nature coexist in perfect harmony. His first series for Fursten-berg, titled *Muninger's Romantic Winter Impressions*, exemplifies this viewpoint.

**NEIMAN, LeRoy** (1927–    ) The creator of Royal Doulton's *Commedia Dell' Arte Series* also created the Olympian murals at the 1976 and 1980 Olympics and was named official artist for the 1984 Olympics. He was a gold medalist at the *Salon d'Arte Moderne* in Paris and an illustrator for such magazines as *Vogue, Harper's Bazaar, Glamour, Time, Newsweek* and *The Saturday Evening Post*. His works hang in some of the world's great museums, including the Hermitage Museum in Leningrad, and in private collections. Neiman attended the St. Paul Art Center, the University of Chicago and the Art Institute of Chicago.

**NEUBACHER, Gerda** (1945–    )
The creator of Kaiser's *Classic Fairy Tales Collection* also introduced Austrians to moccasins. Gerda Neubacher was born in the small Austrian mountain village of Pols and intended to make fashion design her career. She studied for four years at the Grace Kelly School of Art in Zurich and has designed shoes, perfume ads and shopping bags. Now she is a realist painter well-known for her scenes of forests, children and wildlife. She moved to Canada with her husband, Fred, also a painter, and has won numerous awards in the many Canadian shows where she has exhibited. Her work, on canvas and on porcelain, is in galleries and private homes all over the world.

**NEWMAN, Colin** (1952–    )
Born in the Fen region of East Anglia, England, Colin Newman so loved the tranquil English countryside that he lives there now with his wife and son. The land inspires his wildlife paintings, which have won him renown in England. His paintings hang in many galleries in Cambridge and London—and are gaining him a respectable reputation in Europe and North America.

Newman received first-class honors at both the Cambridge School of Art and the Hornsey College of Art. He is featured in both the '85–'86 *Illustrator's Annual* and *European Annual of Illustrators.* He has contributed color illustrations to the *Illustrated Animal Encyclopedia* published by MacMillian, as well as to numerous Reader's Digest Field Guides. His ability to bring the creatures he illustrates to life without forsaking critical scientific detail has brought him to the forefront of promising young European illustrators.

A private and retiring man, Newman's interests include angling in local streams, working for neighborhood conservation causes, and sketching the wildlife that can be seen from his doorstep and window. This perspective was his inspiration for the *Colin Newman's Country Panorama* series from Wedgwood.

**NIGHTINGALE, Sandy**
(1953–    ) British artist Sandy Nightingale is known in her native country as a book illustrator for a number of well-established British publishing houses, including Pan, McMillan and Hamlyn, and has exhibited her works in numerous British galleries. In the *Alice in Wonderland* series—Porcelaine Georges Boyer's first collector's series for the United States market—she incorporated scenes from her parents' garden and memories of her childhood. Nightingale studied in England and in the south of France and is a member of the Chelsea Society of Illustrators.

**NITSCHKE, Detlev** (1935–    )
Berlin Design artist Detlev Nitschke is widely known throughout Europe for his historically accurate paintings of turn-of-the-century Berlin. He was born in that city and studied lithography before receiving formal training as a painter and graphic artist. After studying with painter Ehrenfried Viola, Nitschke attended the Masters School for Printing and Graphics in Berlin and the State Institute for Graphics. Creator of the *Holiday Week of the Family Kappelmann* plate series, he has exhibited his work in galleries throughout Germany and the rest of Europe.

**PELTRIAUX, Bernard** (1921–    )
Renowned throughout the international art world for his paintings and lithographs, Bernard Peltriaux also dedicated himself, until his recent retirement, to educating artists from all over the world at the *Lycée Technique d'Etat* in Reims, the cathedral town where he was born

and raised. He attended the *Ecole des Beaux-Arts* in Reims and the *Atelier Rene Jaudon* in Paris. He has numerous prizes and more than fifty solo exhibitions to his credit. *The Children of the Turn of the Century Collection*, produced by Limoges-Turgot, is his first collector's plate series.

**PENTZ, Donald** (1940–    )
Donald Pentz was born in Bridgewater, Nova Scotia, and studied at the Nova Scotia College of Art and Design and at Mt. Allyson University. He earned a Master's Degree in Fine Art from the University of Regina. At the age of 26, Pentz was elected to the Royal Canadian Academy and the Society of Canadian Artists. Pentz also worked as a naturalist for the Nova Scotia Department of Lands and Forests and for Kejimkujik National Park before settling into his artistic career. He has participated in numerous group and solo exhibitons, and his works are in the permanent collections of museums, corporations and academic institutions. Pentz is in demand for private commissions, magazine covers, and book illustrations for such publishers as the Nova Scotia Museum and the National Museum of Natural Science in Ottawa. The Canadian Broadcasting Corporation recently produced a documentary on his life and work. Dominion China initiated his first plate series in 1986 with the *Wings Upon the Wind* series, chronicling the life cycle of the

Canada goose. The first plate in this series, "The Landing," was named Plate of Show at the 1986 Canadian Plate and Collectibles Fair.

**PERILLO, Gregory** (1932–    )
Gregory Perillo has been an artist fascinated by the Old West since his father, an Italian immigrant, told him stories of the Indian Wars and Perillo sketched the details in crayon. Today he is a successful oil painter who paints proud, strong Plains Indians as they used to be. He was born in New York City. He studied at the Pratt Institute, the School of Visual Arts and the Art Student's League. He is also the only living artist to have studied under renowned Western painter William R. Leigh. His collector's plate series for Kern Collectibles and Vague Shadows include *The Professionals*, *The Storybook Collection*, *The Chieftains I* series, a Christmas series and a wildlife series.

**PETER, Nori** (1934–    ) Nori Peter, well-known for her portrayals of life in the Arctic, became entranced with the Innuit people when she saw them and their carvings at an art show. She makes frequent trips to the North from her Ontario, Canada home. Born in Hungary, she fled her country at the age of 21 after the Budapest uprising of 1956. Soon after arriving in Toronto, she began doing children's portraits. Her first collector's plate series was *People of*

*the Midnight Sun* for Kaiser; her second, for Anna-Perenna, was *Arctic Spring*. She also has done *Mother's Day* series plates and twelve figurines for Kaiser. She studied at the Academy of Fine Arts in Budapest.

**QUELLIER, André** (1925–    )
André Quellier, creator of *Quellier's Morals of Perrault* series for Limoges-Turgot, was born in Paris. He received his classical training at *L'Ecole des Beaux Arts* and studied under the direction of Jean Dupas and Edmond Heuze. His work has been shown in the major cities of the world—in the United States, Japan, the Soviet Union, Spain and France, including one of the first exhibits at the Theatre des Champs Elysees in Paris. His portrait of Jean Cocteau is in the home of Jean Marais. His numerous prizes include the *Prix Internationale du Gemmeil d'Art Sacré à Lourdes*, the *Médaille d'Or des Artists Français*, *Pris Casa Vealsquez, a Madrid*, and, in 1945, *Prix de l'Institute*.

**RESTIEAU, André** (1912–1981)
André Restieau was a world authority on the techniques of re-creating medieval stained-glass coloration in porcelain, as seen in his *Stained Glass Christmas (Noel Vitrail)* series for D'Arceau-Limoges. He studied with such masters as Lavelle and Fournier. His commissions also include *The Lafayette Legacy Collection* for D'Arceau-Limoges. In 1966 he exhibited at the *Cercle de la Librairie* in Paris.

**ROBERTS, Luann** (1957– )
Luann Roberts' artistic training began at home in her earliest childhood, where a family of artists helped foster and develop her interests. Born in the Chicago area, she was encouraged in her career by her mother and her aunt and received her professional degree from the American Academy of Art in Chicago. After college, Miss Roberts continued to develop herself professionally in almost every aspect of her field, including design, print production, and commercial illustration. Although she has worked in pen and ink, charcoal, Conte crayon and oil, her favorite mediums are watercolor and pastel.

Miss Roberts is now an accomplished portrait artist and works out of her own studio in Madison, Wisconsin. She likes portraiture because she finds watching people facinating, especially the expressive and uninhibited activities of children. Her other interests include cross-country skiing, biking, and gardening.

**ROCKWELL, Norman** (1894–1978) One of the most widely-known artists of the twentieth century, Norman Rockwell possessed an uncanny—and perhaps unmatched—ability to capture the spirit of American life in its most ordinary and its most festive moments. Rockwell created well over 3,000 works in his long and illustrious career. He drew his first *Saturday Evening Post* cover in 1916, followed by more than 300 more. He also drew numerous illustrations for *Life, Look* and *Boy's Life,* and was well-known for his annual Boy Scouts calendar illustrations. Rockwell studied at Chase School of Fine and Applied Arts, the National Academy of Design and the Art Student's League, all in New York. He had a one-man show in 1941 at the Milwaukee Art Institute and a one-man exhibition at the Dannenberg Galleries in New York City. His works hang in the Smithsonian Institution, the Metropolitan Museum of Art, the Corner House Museum in Stockbridge, Massachusetts, and in other museums throughout the United States. In addition to the well-known and very popular collector's plate series by The Rockwell Society of America, Rockwell's work is also featured on collector's plates by Franklin Mint, Gorham and Royal Devon.

**RODERICK, Merri** (1948– )
Merri Roderick has spent many years in the formal study of art. Her work is included in many private collections, and she recently won a major award at the Invitational Fine Arts Exhibition in the Midwest. She spent several years as an apprentice to sculptor Perrin Gerber, and her *Treasures of the Doré Bible* series in fused bronze relief represents the fulfilment of a long time dream; Ms. Roderick was awed by Doré's biblical etchings even as a child.

Living in the Chicago area, Ms. Roderick hopes to expand into figurine design and is planning a lead crystal Christmas series for plates. She works for a gallery, and last year returned to the University of Illinois. Art is her life she says, it is "What I do."

# BRADEX-LISTED PLATE ARTIST INFORMATION

**ROGERS, Howard** (1932–    )
Howard Rogers says he always knew he wanted to be an artist. At the age of fourteen he worked as a sign painter, using his free time to paint the portraits that eventually helped get him accepted to the Art Center College of Design in Los Angeles. For twenty-five years Rogers worked in New York as a successful illustrator and portrait artist; his work has been exhibited in galleries and museums across the country. He was the only contemporary illustrator to participate in a retrospective of illustrators held at the St. Petersburg Art Museum, alongside such greats as Norman Rockwell.

Rogers and his family live in Montana, where he devotes his time entirely to painting in oils, his favorite medium. His hobbies include horses (especially riding in the mountains), landscaping, woodworking, and creating bronzes.

**ROLLER, Carole** (1953–    ) The first American artist to design plates for Danish company Bing & Grøndahl, Carole Roller has also designed printed fabrics, dinnerware, rugs, towels, Christmas ornaments and stationery. She earned a bachelor's degree in fine arts at the Pratt Institute in New York City. Her plate series include *Children's Day* for Bing & Grøndahl. The company has also produced her figurines and pendants.

**ROMANELLI, Carl** (1913–    )
The sculptor of Incolay's *Great Romances of History Collection* has works on display in memorials, churches, galleries and private collections throughout the world. Romanelli learned his art in a five-year apprenticeship with his father, sculptor Carlo Romanelli. One of his most famous works is a bronze bust of John Henry Cardinal Newman on display in the Vatican. His other commissions include a life-size bronze of Elvis Presley for the Las Vegas Hilton. He has exhibited in galleries across the United States and is a board member of the California Art Club and the American Institute of Fine Arts.

**RUGGERI, Gino** (1918–    )
Gino Ruggeri, a sculptor in the neo-Classical tradition, is best known for his work "The Crucifix," sculpted from the Casa Serena Institute of Cecina Mare, and his two sculptures "Memorials to the Fallen," which pay tribute to World War I victims. He sculpted the 1976-1980 issues in Studio Dante di Volteradici's *Grand Opera Series*. Ruggeri studied at the Academy of Fine Arts in Sienna and the Art Institute in Volterra, Italy. His awards include three first prizes from the Academy of Fine Arts. He has been director of the Cooperative Artien since 1942.

**RUSSELL, Frank** (1921–    )
Frank Russell and his wife, Gertrude Barrer, have blended their talents to become a successful art-producing team. They met at the Art Student's League in New York and five years later were reunited in New York's art center, Greenwich Village. Together they have created lithographs, photographs, frescos, serigraphs, ceramics, sculptures and two plate series for Anna-Perenna, the *Triptych* and *Romantic Love* series. Their work has been exhibited at the Art Institute of Chicago and the Whitney Museum of American Art, and hangs in the private collections of Cyrus Vance, Helmut Schmidt and the U.N. Interfaith Chapel in New York.

**SANTANGELA, Alberto** (1936–    ) When Alberto Santangela was an art student in Florence he was so captivated by the baptistery doors sculpted by 15th-century artist Lorenzo Ghiberti that they inspired him to become a sculptor instead of a painter. Years later he recreated scenes from Ghiberti's doors on collector's plates in the *Ghiberti's Doors* series for Studio Dante di Volteradici. He also sculpted the *Living Madonnas* series. He was born in Italy. Santangela apprenticed to his uncle, Amilcare Santini, at an early age before studying informally in Florence.

**SCHOENER, Toni** (1913–1978) Toni Schoener's first love was porcelain. At the end of elementary school he was appointed chief designer for Altrohlauer Porzellanfabrik, one of the best-known Bavarian porcelain houses of the time. This "non-essential" industry came to a halt in 1939, and after the war Schoener wandered across Europe restoring war-damaged paintings before returning to Bavaria in 1955, when he joined Kaiser as chief designer. His Kaiser creations include *Christmas* and *Mother's Day* plates.

**SCHULZ, Charles** (1922–    )
Cartoonist Charles Schulz' "Peanuts" characters have endeared themselves to millions of Americans through comic strips, television specials, a *Time* magazine cover, and many other media, including collector's plate series produced by Schmid. . Schulz's television creations have won various Peabody and Emmy awards; the "Peanuts" strip won Best Humor Strip of the Year from the National Cartoonists Society in 1962; Yale University voted Schulz Humorist of the Year in 1958; and as governor of California Ronald Reagan proclaimed a Charles Schulz Day in 1967. Schulz studied at Art Instruction, Inc. in Minneapolis and has been awarded honorary degrees by Anderson College in Indiana and St. Mary's College in California. He was Grand Marshal of the Tournament of Roses Parade in 1976. He also won the National Cartoonists' Society "Reuben" Award in 1955 and 1964, the School Bell Award from the National Education Society in 1960 and the Big Brother of the Year Award in California in 1973.

**SHERWOOD, Stewart**
(1941–    ) Because of his love of variety, Stewart Sherwood works in a number of styles and mediums, sometimes combining several techniques in a single piece. A self-taught artist born in Toronto, Canada he commonly works with such mediums as oil, water color, gouache, line, marker, and pastel. He has created illustrations for children's books and greeting cards, but his best works consists of portraits—his portraits of Pope John Paul II, Menachem Begin, John F. Kennedy, Anwar Sadat and Pierre Trudeau are only a few of his pieces that have appeared on the cover of *Maclean's Magazine*. His illustrations have also appeared in *The Toronto Star*, *Reader's Digest*, and *Legion Magazine*.

Still living in Toronto, Sherwood's interests include photography and bike riding. Another hobby is landscape painting; he keeps a rustic cottage "up north" where he finds inspiration.

**SKELTON, Red** (1913–    ) Many people regard film, stage and television comedian and artist Red Skelton as a vital part of America's entertainment heritage. He has made Americans laugh for decades with his portrayals of such characters as Freddie the Freeloader, Clem Kadiddlehopper, Willie Lump-Lump, Sheriff Deadeye, Bolivar Shagnasty, San Fernando Red, George Appleby and Junior the Mean Widdle Kid. Skelton is also a photographer and filmmaker, a recorded composer, a children's fiction writer (with 40 published titles to his credit) and, of course, a painter whose works, reproduced on collector's plates, have endeared him to thousands. His plate series include the *Freddie the Freeloader* and *Freddie's Adventures* series for Crown Parian and the *Famous Clowns* series for Fairmont. Born in Vincennes, Indiana, the son of a clown who died before he was born, Skelton began his career dancing for pennies on the street and joined a traveling medicine show at age ten. Since then he has entertained on vaudeville, stage, screen, radio and television. He is a self-taught artist who paints anytime, anyplace—even on airplanes.

# BRADEX-LISTED PLATE ARTIST INFORMATION

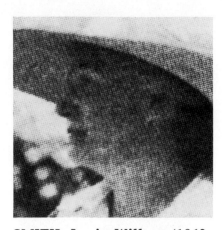

**SMITH, Jessie Willcox** (1863–1935) Born in Philadelphia, Jesse Willcox Smith studied in that city under Thomas Eakins at the Pennsylvania Academy of Fine Arts. She was also influenced by the work of Howard Pyle at the Drexel Institute of Arts and Sciences. Smith became the most highly-paid woman illustrator of her time, and the most admired. She illustrated many classic children's books, including *A Child's Book of Verses, The Water Babies, Heidi* and *Little Women.* Although she was in constant demand to paint portraits of the children of wealthy Philadelphia families, she is best-known for the "ordinary" children she painted for the covers of *Good Housekeeping* magazine from 1918 until 1932. Although she never married, Smith devoted her life to expressing the joys and delights of childhood. This theme is the basis of the *Jessie Willcox Smith Childhood Holiday Memories* series, introduced by the Knowles China Company in 1986.

**SPAULDING, Don** (1926–    ) Edwin M. Knowles artist Don Spaulding is a Norman Rockwell protege and a leading exponent of authentic historical detail in painting. He began study at New York City's Art Student's League on the G.I. Bill when he was fresh out of World War II and in his early 20's. He was among half a dozen students chosen to study and live with Rockwell for a summer, and Rockwell became one of his heroes and an example for his approach to Western art. Each of the props and costumes in his seven-plate *Americana Holidays* series is handpicked and true to the 19th century. He has won several awards at shows of Western painting.

**SPENCER, Irene** (1940?–    ) Irene Spencer received her training at the American Academy of Art and the Art Institute of Chicago, where she developed her distinctive style, reminiscent of the Old Masters. In addition to her accomplishments as a fine artist, she has written and illustrated children's books and worked as a newspaper cartoonist. Her collector's plates include the *Mother's Love* and *Symphony of Roses* series for Pickard and plates for Fairmont and Gorham. In 1979 she won NALED's "Lithograph of the Year" award and in 1980, NALED's "Plate of the Year" award, as well as The Bradford Exchange's award for New Edition of the Year.

**STOBART, John** (1938–    ) John Stobart, artist for Royal Doulton's *The Log of the "Dashing Wave"* series, grew up in the English shipping town of Liverpool. He attended Derby College of Arts and won a scholarship to the Royal Academy of Art in London. He has traveled extensively by sea and some of the most exotic ports in the world have served as settings for his paintings. His works hang in such prestigious collections as the Marine Museum of Upper Canada in Toronto, the National Maritime Museum in Greenwich, England, and the Royal Naval College. His paintings have been featured as cover art for many magazines.

**TELLIER, Liliane** (1924–    ) Noted watercolorist Liliane Tellier, creator of Haviland's *1001 Arabian Nights* series, has an extensive following among connoisseurs of the medium. A native Parisienne, she studied watercolor and gouache at L'École Camondo in Paris and refined her techniques in Sweden. Later she worked for the International Society for Education through Art as a consultant to UNESCO.

**THELANDER, Henry** (1902–    ) Artist Henry Thelander's association with Bing & Grøndahl is unparalleled on the collector's plate market. The 1984 issue marked his twenty-second consecutive design for the *Christmas* series. He also has designed every Bing & Grøndahl *Mother's Day* issue. A self-taught artist, Thelander has spent his five-decade-long career living and working in Copenhagen, London and Stockholm, benefiting from the variety of cultures and artistic influences. Known as the "equivalent of the poet laureate" in the Danish visual arts, he has designed government-sponsored postage stamps and posters.

**TOOTLE, Douglas** (1950–    )
Davenport Pottery artist Douglas Tootle was born and raised in Staffordshire, England, and schooled at one of the region's finest institutions, the Burslen College of Art. He was awarded a number of scholarships and left Staffordshire to study fine art and sculpture in London and Florence. Since returning to his native region he has done extensive modeling for some of its most prestigious potteries, including Coalport, a division of Wedgwood, and Hereford. He modeled "Jack Tar" for the *Toby Plate Collection.*

**TRAUTH, Gero** (1942–    ) Born in Neurode/Selesia, Gero Trauth began studying art there at the age of five. In 1960 he entered the Gutenberg University in Mainz, West Germany, where for five years he studied graphic design, painting, sculpture, the history of book illustration and visual communications, after which he earned his Master of Arts degree summa cum laude.

Since 1966 he has won first place in seven competitions for graphic design at the International Frankfurt Fair, and has participated in numerous prestigious exhibitions throughout Germany and Switzerland. He has designed fabrics, wall coverings, lighting, flatware, and collector's plates, including Villeroy & Boch's *Dreams of Katharina* series.

Gero Trauth lives and works in Siegen, West Germany, with his favorite model (his wife) and their two daughters. In his spare time he actively enjoys ice-dancing, ballet, and adding to his collection of rare and exotic butterflies.

**UOSIKKINEN, Raija** (1925–    )
Born in Hollola, Finland, Raija Uosikkinen is widely regarded as a master ceramicist. She studied at the Institute of Industrial Arts in Helsinki. In 1947 she joined the Arabia design department, and in 1952 she received a grant scholarship from the Arabia-Decora factory to study in Germany. She has taken subsequent study trips to Australia, Turkey, England and Indonesia. A 1954 Helsinki exhibit was devoted exclusively to her creations. Her distinctive contemporary folk art style is exemplified in her plate series *Kalevala.*

**VESTERGAARD, Sven**
(1932–    ) As head artist and chief designer for Royal Copenhagen, Sven Vestergaard is a guardian of the centuries-old tradition of hand-painted ceramics. He enrolled with Royal Copenhagen as an apprentice decorator in 1948 at the age of 16 and four years later had attained the pinnacle of the decorator's art. In 1976, when he was head of the drawing department, his artwork was chosen for the annual Christmas plate, "Danish Watermill." His works of the last decade include the Historical Plates, the Olympic Plates, the *Motherhood* series and the *Hans Christian Andersen* series. Beginning in 1985, Vestergaard has been responsible for the *Christmas* series.

**VICKERS, Mary** (1940–    )
Wedgwood artist Mary Vickers credits a German bomb that fell on London during World War II as her inspiration for becoming an artist. Born in a war-torn suburb of London, she soon set out to create beauty in an often violent, ugly world. Today she is one of the leading contemporary Romantic painters, and is also accomplished in lithographs and etching. She studied at England's St. Martin's School of Art, the New York Art Student's League and the Pratt Institute. Her works are exhibited in major galleries on both sides of the Atlantic and in private collections such as that of the Duke and Duchess of Marlborough. Her collector's plates include *The Blossoming of Suzanne, My Memories* and *Portraits of First Love* series.

**WEBER, Sarah Stilwell** (1878–1939) Sarah Stilwell Weber was born near Philadelphia, Pennsylvania. She studied art at the Drexel Institute in Philadelphia under the tutelage of American illustrator Howard Pyle and was one of the founders of the American Realist movement. Between 1900 and 1930, Weber's work appeared in children's books and on the covers of such magazines as *Collier's* and the *Saturday Evening Post*. Her artwork appears on the plates in Newell Pottery's *Sarah Stilwell Weber Calendar* series.

**WIINBLAD, Bjorn** (1918–   ) Danish artist Bjorn Wiinblad graduated from the Royal Academy of Art in 1944 and worked for *Nymolle Art Fajance Factory* from 1946 to 1956. His creations attracted the attention of Philipp Rosenthal, Jr., head of the Rosenthal company, who, after extensive negotiation, persuaded Wiinblad to design works for the German maker. He was assigned to create products for the Studio-Linie, a high quality, high-priced line of Rosenthal ware. His distinctive collector's plates are world renowned, and the "Lotus" pattern of dinnerware he designed won the 1965 American Interior Design Award. His creations include the *Wiinblad Christmas* series produced by Rosenthal. His works are in the collections of museums throughout Europe.

**WORRALL, Linda** (1951–   ) Linda Worrall graduated with distinction from the Bolton Collage of Art Design in England, the country of her birth. She has completed major private commissions as well as participating in public exhibitions of her work. Worrall is a diploma member of the Society of Industrial Artists and Designers. Her work has been presented at the prestigious Northwest Assoication of Illustrators exhibition in Liverpool. In 1986, Davenport Pottery issued her first work in the medium of collector's plates, *The Poetry Society of London's Treasury of Classic Children's Verse* series.

**WÜLFING, Sulamith** (1901–   ) Sulamith Wülfing was born in 1901 in Elberfeld (now part of Wuppertal), Germany and has lived in that area all of her life. She studied at the Art College in Wuppertal and is known for her art that has been reproduced on numerous cards, books and calendars. Much of her original work was lost during World War II, but this did not discourage her long and distinguished career. Her collector's plates include *Sulamith's Love Song, Sulamith's Christmas* and *A Woman's Love and Life* series for Königszelt Bayern. She has exhibited at the Spring Fair in Frankfurt.

**XARAS, Ted** (1945–   ) Theodore "Ted" Xaras has been enamored of the steam engine since he was a child, when his father told him bedtime tales of building locomotives in Eddystone, Pennsylvania, and took him in borrowed cars to chase their clouds of smoke across the countryside—a pastime

he still enjoys. Xaras' plate "Symphony in Steam: Canadian Pacific Railway," first issue in Christian Bell's *Age of Steam* series, won CALED's 1981 Plate of the Year title and became the first Bradex-listed plate produced in Canada. Xaras holds a B.F.A. in illustration from Philadelphia College of Art and an M.F.A. in painting from the Tyler School of Art in Philadelphia. He is a professor and chairman of the art department at Ursinus College in Pennsylvania. His credits include a cover for *Time* magazine and illustrations for various other books and railroad magazines.

**YATES, Michael** (1927–     ) Michael Yates was born in Pennsylvania. He studied at the Art Institute of Pittsburgh. His works appear in numerous public buildings and churches throughout America as well as in many private collections. His art has been commissioned for the homes of such prominent figures as Gerald Ford, Golda Meir, Johnny Cash and former First Lady Pat Nixon. He designed *Michael Yates' Country Ladies* series, Morgantown Crystal's first limited-edition collector's plate series, in double intaglio-carved crystal.

**ZHAO Huimin** (1919–     ) Zhao Huimin was born into a desperately poor home in China (ED. NOTE: Chinese surnames always precede given names; hence "Zhao" is the artist's surname). He dreamed of becoming an artist, but the family had no money for lessons. Zhao worked during the day and taught himself to paint at night. He became skilled at gouache and traditional watercolor painting, as practiced for centuries by the great Chinese masters. His work became more widely known and in 1958 Zhao was awarded the title of Porcelain Painter in the factory in Ching-te Chen (Jingdezhen). In 1983, he was acclaimed as Master Artisan. Examples of Zhao's work are in porcelain collections all over the world. The *Beauties of the Red Mansion* series, with artwork by Zhao, was initiated in 1986 by Imperial Ching-te Chen Porcelain. It is the first collector's plate series from the People's Republic, and features the beautiful heroines of *The Dream of Red Mansions,* a classic romantic novel and one of China's great literary masterpieces.

**ZOLAN, Donald** (1936–     ) Donald Zolan is consistently rated one of the most popular collector's plate artists living in the United States, for his poignant pictures of special moments in the lives of contemporary children. His first plate, "Erik and Dandelion" in Viletta's *Zolan's Children* series, was released in 1978. In 1979 "Sabina in the Grass" made history when it became the first non-first-issue to receive the Bradford Exchange's "Plate of the Year" award. Zolan's *Wonder of Childhood Collection, Children at Christmas Collection,* and *Children and Pets* series are produced by Pemberton & Oakes. He and his brother, Richard Zolan (who has produced plates for Modern Masters), are the fifth generation of artists in their family. He studied at the Art Institute of Chicago and won a scholarship to the American Academy of Art. His works hang in numerous galleries throughout the United States and in private collections in Mexico, Australia, France, Italy, South Korea and Colombia.

**ZVORYKIN, Boris** (1872–1950) Russian artist Boris Vasilevich Zvorykin was born in Moscow and was one of the last great book illustrators of Tsarist Russia. He was also noted for his murals in the Cathedral at Simferopol. Forced to leave Russia during the 1917 revolution, he settled in Paris in 1920 and became an integral figure in an expatriate movement to retain Imperial Russia's cultural heritage. He elaborately illustrated four books of Russian fairy tales, later published as *The Firebird and Other Russian Fairy Tales* when they caught the eye of book editor Jaqueline Kennedy Onassis. Some of his illustrations appear on collector's plates in Heinrich/Villeroy & Boch's *Russian Fairy Tales* series.

# INDEX OF BRADEX-LISTED
# PLATE MAKERS AND SPONSORS

NOTE: "Maker" is a general term for the name under which a plate is issued and is not necessarily the actual "manufacturer." A Maker can be a distributor, manufacturer or occasionally a "sponsor." See GLOSSARY OF COMMONLY USED TERMS.

# BRADEX-LISTED PLATE MAKERS AND SPONSORS

# OVER-THE-COUNTER ISSUES

---

Over-the-counter plates are issues which are not listed on the *Current Quotations*, or "Bradex," but may still be traded on The Bradford Exchange. Over-the-counter issues are nonetheless true collector's plates, issued in verifiable limited editions. They differ from Bradex-listed plates only in that they are traded far less frequently than Bradex issues.

Over-the-counter issues are arranged alphabetically by country, then alphabetically by maker or maker/sponsor, then chronologically by series. Each entry includes the series name, the year and name of the plate, the edition limit, and the U.S. issue price whenever available.

| | Edition Limit | Issue Price (US) |
|---|---|---|
| **ARGENTINA** | | |
| **Porcelana Granada** | | |
| *Peace on Earth* | | |
| 1971 Annunciation | 9,300 | $ 12.00 |
| 1972 Mary and Elizabeth | 6,000 | 13.00 |
| 1973 Road to Bethlehem | 5,000 | 14.00 |
| 1974 No Room at Inn | 5,000 | 15.00 |
| 1975 Shepherds in Field | 5,000 | 16.50 |
| 1976 Nativity | 5,000 | 17.50 |
| 1977 Three Kings | 5,000 | 18.00 |
| 1978 Young Carpenter | 5,000 | 18.00 |
| 1979 Calling of Disciples | 5,000 | 19.00 |
| 1980 Loaves and Fishes | 5,000 | 20.00 |
| 1981 Suffer Little Children | 5,000 | 21.00 |
| 1982 Triumphal Entry | 5,000 | 22.50 |
| 1983 Gethsemane | 5,000 | 23.50 |
| 1984 Golgotha | 5,000 | 24.00 |
| 1985 Ascension | 5,000 | 24.50 |
| **AUSTRIA** | | |
| **Arta** | | |
| *Mother's Day* | | |
| 1973 Family with Puppy | 1,500 | 50.00 |
| *Christmas* | | |
| 1973 Nativity–In Manger | 1,500 | 50.00 |
| **BELGIUM** | | |
| **Val St. Lambert** | | |
| *American Heritage* | | |
| 1969 Pilgrim Fathers | 500 | 200.00 |
| 1970 Paul Revere's Ride | 500 | 200.00 |
| 1971 Washington on Delaware | 500 | 200.00 |
| *Annual Old Masters* | | |
| 1969 Rubens & Rembrandt (Pair) | 5,000 | 50.00 |
| 1969 Van Gogh & Van Dyck (Pair) | 5,000 | 50.00 |

| | Edition Limit | Issue Price (US) |
|---|---|---|
| 1970 Da Vinci & Michelangelo (Pair) | 5,000 | $ 50.00 |
| 1971 El Greco & Goya (Pair) | 5,000 | 50.00 |
| 1972 Reynolds & Gainsborough (Pair) | 5,000 | 50.00 |
| *(Single issue)* | | |
| 1970 Rembrandt | Year | 25.00 |
| **CANADA** | | |
| **Canadian Collector Plates** | | |
| *Discover Canada* | | |
| 1980 Sawmill-Kings Landing | 10,000 | 98.00 |
| 1981 Quebec Winter | 10,000 | 98.00 |
| 1981 Grist Mill | 10,000 | 125.00 |
| 1982 Grist Mill, Delta | 10,000 | 125.00 |
| 1982 Anglican Church at Magnetawan | 10,000 | 125.00 |
| 1983 Majestic Rockies | 10,000 | 125.00 |
| 1983 Habitants Driving Sleigh | 10,000 | 125.00 |
| 1984 Autumn Memories | 10,000 | 125.00 |
| 1984 After Bath | 10,000 | 125.00 |
| 1985 Postman | 10,000 | 125.00 |
| 1985 Pedlar | 10,000 | 125.00 |
| 1986 Winter Memories | 10,000 | 125.00 |
| *Children of Classics* | | |
| 1982 Anne of Green Gables | 15,000 | 70.00 |
| 1983 Tom Sawyer | 15,000 | 70.00 |
| *Days of Innocence* | | |
| 1982 He Loves Me . . . | 15,000 | 70.00 |
| 1982 Butterflies Are Free | 15,000 | 70.00 |
| *Winter Romance (set of 2)* | | |
| 1986 Male/Female Cardinal (framed and signed) | 3,500 | 160.00 |
| **Christian Bell (Schumann)** | | |
| *Preserving a Way of Life–Chapter I* | | |
| 1980 Making Way for Cars | 5,000 | 60.00 |
| 1980 Atop Hay Wagon | 5,000 | 60.00 |

| | Edition Limit | Issue Price (US) |
|---|---|---|
| 1980 Turning Sod | 5,000 | $ 60.00 |
| 1980 Winter's Morning | 5,000 | 60.00 |
| *Preserving a Way of Life–Chapter II* | | |
| 1981 Sugarbush | 10,000 | 70.00 |
| 1981 Fishing for Redfin | 10,000 | 70.00 |
| 1981 Wheat Harvest | 10,000 | 70.00 |
| 1981 Returning from Village | 10,000 | 70.00 |
| *Preserving a Way of Life–Chapter III* | | |
| 1985 New Horse | 10,000 | 65.00 |
| 1986 To the Sawmill | 10,000 | 65.00 |
| 1987 Day's End | 10,000 | 65.00 |
| *American Steam* | | |
| 1982 Hiawatha | 15,000 | 65.00 |
| 1983 Hittin' Diamond | 15,000 | 65.00 |
| 1983 Morning at Depot | 15,000 | 65.00 |
| 1984 Boston and Maine | 15,000 | 65.00 |
| 1985 On Horseshoe Curve | 15,000 | 65.00 |
| *Men of Rails* | | |
| 1982 Engineer | 30 Days | 39.50 |
| 1983 Conductor | 30 Days | 39.50 |
| 1983 Pullman Porter | 30 Days | 39.50 |
| 1983 Night Operator | 30 Days | 39.50 |
| 1984 Brakeman | 30 Days | 39.50 |
| *Vanishing Africa* | | |
| 1983 Sentinel | 15,000 | 55.00 |
| *Wild North* | | |
| 1983 Emperor of North | 15,000 | 55.00 |
| *Men of Sea* | | |
| 1984 Helmsman | NA | 39.50 |
| 1984 Dorryman | NA | 39.50 |
| *(Single issue)* | | |
| 1984 Royal Hudson "2860" | 25,000 | 75.00 |
| *Last Spike Centennial (Set of two)* | | |
| 1986 Spiral Tunnel | | |
| 1986 Big Hill | 7,500 | 135.00 |
| *Steam on CNR* | | |
| 1986 When I Grow Up | 15,000 | 65.00 |
| 1986 Frosty Morning | 15,000 | 65.00 |

| | Edition Limit | Issue Price (US) |
|---|---|---|
| **Bengough** | | |
| *Christmas* | | |
| 1972 Charles Dickens Christmas Carol | 490 | $125.00 |
| *Northwest Mounted Police* | | |
| 1972 1898 Dress Uniform | 1,000 | 140.00 |
| 1972 First Uniform | 1,000 | 140.00 |
| *Royal Canadian Police* | | |
| 1972 Order Dress | 1,000 | 140.00 |
| **Goldcrown Ceramics** | | |
| *Wild West* | | |
| 1981 Horse and Rider | 5,000 | 49.95 |
| 1982 Bucking Horse | 5,000 | 49.95 |
| 1983 Cowboy | 10,000 | 49.95 |
| 1983 Chuckwagon Race | 10,000 | 49.95 |
| 1984 Bull Rider | 10,000 | 49.95 |
| *Bush Pilot Planes* | | |
| 1983 Fokker Universal | 10,000 | 49.95 |
| 1983 DeHavilland DH80 Puss Moth | 10,000 | 49.95 |
| 1984 Ford 6-AT-AS Tri-Motor | 10,000 | 49.95 |
| 1984 Fairchild 71B | 10,000 | 49.95 |
| *Endangered American Wildlife* | | |
| 1983 Bald Eagle | 15,000 | 59.95 |
| *Famous Fighter Aircraft of World War II* | | |
| 1983 P-51 D Mustang | 10,000 | 49.95 |
| 1983 Chance Vought F4U Corsair | 10,000 | 49.95 |
| 1984 Lockheed P-38 Lightning | 10,000 | 49.95 |
| 1984 Supermarine Spitfire | 10,000 | 49.95 |
| **Keirstead Gallery Ltd.** | | |
| *The Sisters* | | |
| 1987 Brenda's Mill | 4,000 | 55.00 |
| **Prairie Collectibles** | | |
| *Canada, Featuring Saskatchewan* | | |
| 1986 Wascana Park | 5,000 | 50.00 |

| | Edition Limit | Issue Price (US) |
|---|---|---|
| **ld Fashioned Threshing Bee** | | |
| 986 Threshing Scene | 15,000 | $ 50.00 |
| **are Bird** | | |
| *nadian Dream* | | |
| 83 Going to Rink | 7,500 | 70.00 |
| 84 Lacing Up | 7,500 | 70.00 |
| 84 Face Off | 7,500 | 70.00 |
| 85 Winning Goal | 7,500 | 70.00 |
| *rds of Distinction* | | |
| 87 Pause From the Journey | NA | 45.00 |
| *ristmas in Canada* | | |
| 86 The Windmill | 5,000 | 45.00 |
| **oyal Doulton** | | |
| *ed in Wood* | | |
| 84 Sugarbush | 5,000 | 55.00 |
| 84 Peggy's Cove | 5,000 | 55.00 |
| 85 Weathering Storm | 5,000 | 55.00 |
| 85 Thunder in Air | 5,000 | 55.00 |
| *ptured Moments* | | |
| 84 Treasure Seekers | 5,000 | 45.00 |
| 84 Seascape | 5,000 | 45.00 |
| *core* | | |
| 85 Gabriella | 10,000 | 95.00 |
| *efton Meadows* | | |
| 86 All in a Days Work | 5,000 | 45.00 |
| *e Dorothy Francis Annual* | | |
| 87 Happy Days | 7,500 | 45.00 |
| **rrina** | | |
| *ristmas* | | |
| 81 Gingerbread House | 5,000 | 40.00 |
| 82 Christmas Eve at Jesuit House | 5,000 | 42.50 |
| 83 Main Street, Barkerville | 5,000 | 45.00 |
| *untry Friends* | | |
| 83 Meeting at Fence | 10,000 | 65.00 |
| **letta Canada** | | |
| *Brush with Life* | | |
| 87 Racoon Family | 9,800 | 49.50 |
| 87 Fawn at Rest | 9,800 | 49.50 |
| **aldenburg Porcelain** | | |
| *nkinhead Happy Little Bear* | | |
| 83 Punkinhead and His Friends | 5,000 | 39.50 |
| 83 Punkinhead and Santa Claus | 5,000 | 39.50 |
| 84 School's Out | 5,000 | 39.95 |
| **estern Authentics** | | |
| *bute to R.C.M.P.* | | |
| 86 Scarlet and Gold | 19,500 | 49.95 |
| *n Pioneers* | | |
| 86 CPR No. 374 | 15,000 | 49.95 |
| 86 Countess of Dufferin | 15,000 | 49.95 |
| *e Iron Giants* | | |
| 85 The Royal Lady | 15,000 | 40.00 |
| *ns at Sea* | | |
| 86 H.M.C.S. Haida | 5,000 | 39.95 |
| 87 H.M.C.S. Bonaventure | 5,000 | 55.00 |
| *ngle issue)* | | |
| 86 Douglas DC-3 | 7,500 | 39.95 |
| *ngle issue)* | | |
| 86 Pacific Belle | 5,000 | 45.00 |

## HINA (TAIWAN)

**yal Cornwall**

*e Perceptions of Weo Cho*

| | Edition Limit | Issue Price (US) |
|---|---|---|
| 79 Sense of Touch | 19,500 | 55.00 |
| 79 Sense of Sight | 19,500 | 55.00 |
| 79 Sense of Taste | 19,500 | 55.00 |
| 79 Sense of Hearing | 19,500 | 55.00 |
| 79 Sense of Smell | 19,500 | 55.00 |

## ZECHOSLOVAKIA

**hemia**

*ther's Day*

| | Edition Limit | Issue Price (US) |
|---|---|---|
| 74 Mother's Day | 500 | 130.00 |
| 75 Mother's Day | 500 | 140.00 |
| 76 Mother's Day | 500 | 150.00 |


### Koschevak Bros.

| | Edition Limit | Issue Price (US) |
|---|---|---|
| *Mary Gregory Christmas* | | |
| 1973 Christmas | 1,000 | $ 55.00 |
| 1974 Christmas | 1,000 | 60.00 |
| 1975 Christmas | 1,000 | 60.00 |
| 1976 Christmas | 500 | 65.00 |
| *Mary Gregory Mother's Day* | | |
| 1973 Mother's Day | 500 | 55.00 |
| 1974 Mother's Day | 300 | 60.00 |
| 1975 Mother's Day | 300 | 60.00 |
| 1976 Mother's Day | 500 | 65.00 |

### Moser

| | Edition Limit | Issue Price (US) |
|---|---|---|
| *Christmas (Vanoce)* | | |
| 1970 Hradcany Castle | 400 | 75.00 |
| 1971 Karlstein Castle | 1,365 | 75.00 |
| 1972 Old Town Hall | 1,000 | 85.00 |
| 1973 Karlovy Vary Castle | 500 | 90.00 |
| *Mother's Day (Den Matek)* | | |
| 1971 Peacocks | 350 | 75.00 |
| 1972 Butterflies | 750 | 85.00 |
| 1973 Squirrels | 200 | 90.00 |

## DENMARK

### Bing & Grøndahl

| | Edition Limit | Issue Price (US) |
|---|---|---|
| *Olympic Games* | | |
| 1972 Olympiade–Munich | Year | 20.00 |
| 1976 Olympic Montreal | Year | 29.50 |
| 1980 Moscow by Night | Year | 43.00 |
| 1984 Los Angeles | Year | 45.00 |
| *Bicentennial* | | |
| 1976 E. Pluribus Unum | Year | 50.00 |
| *Heritage* | | |
| 1976 Norseman | 5,000 | 30.00 |
| 1977 Navigators | 5,000 | 30.00 |
| 1978 Discovery | 5,000 | 39.50 |
| 1979 Exploration | 5,000 | 39.50 |
| 1980 Helmsman | NA | 45.00 |
| 1981 Swordsman | NA | 49.50 |
| *Carl Larsson (Sets of four)* | | |
| 1977 Flowers on Windowsill | | |
| 1977 Breakfast under Big Birch | | |
| 1977 Yard & Warehouse | | |
| 1977 Kitchen | 7,500 | 150.00 |
| 1978 First Born | | |
| 1978 Room for Mother and Children | | |
| 1978 Portrait of Inga-Maria Thiel | | |
| 1978 Iduna | 7,500 | 170.00 |
| 1979 Forestry | | |
| 1979 Cutting Grass | | |
| 1979 Potato Harvest | | |
| 1979 Fishery | 7,500 | 165.00 |
| *(Single issue)* | | |
| 1977 Madonna | 10,000 | 45.00 |
| *(Single issue)* | | |
| 1978 Seagull | 7,500 | 75.00 |
| *Classical Composers* | | |
| 1979 Beethoven | Year | 37.50 |
| 1980 Bach | Year | 37.50 |
| 1981 Brahms | Year | 37.50 |
| 1982 Chopin | Year | 37.50 |
| 1983 Haydn | Year | 37.50 |
| 1984 Grieg | Year | 37.50 |
| *Windjammers* | | |
| 1980 Danmark | 10,000 | 95.00 |
| 1980 Eagle | 10,000 | 95.00 |
| 1981 Gladan | 10,000 | 95.00 |
| 1981 Gorch/Fock | 10,000 | 95.00 |
| 1982 Amerigo Vespucci | 10,000 | 95.00 |
| 1982 Christian Radich | 10,000 | 95.00 |
| *Year of Viking (Single issue)* | | |
| 1980 Viking | 10,000 | 65.00 |
| *New Generation* | | |
| 1982 Fledglings | 10,000 | 29.50 |
| 1982 Kittens | 10,000 | 29.50 |
| 1982 Bunnies | 10,000 | 29.50 |
| 1982 Fawns | 10,000 | 29.50 |
| *Country Garden Calendar* | | |
| 1984 September | 12,500 | 55.00 |
| 1984 October | 12,500 | 55.00 |
| 1984 November | 12,500 | 55.00 |
| 1984 December | 12,500 | 55.00 |


| | Edition Limit | Issue Price (US) |
|---|---|---|
| 1984 January | 12,500 | $ 55.00 |
| 1984 February | 12,500 | 55.00 |
| 1984 March | 12,500 | 55.00 |
| 1984 April | 12,500 | 55.00 |
| 1984 May | 12,500 | 55.00 |
| 1984 June | 12,500 | 55.00 |
| 1984 July | 12,500 | 55.00 |
| 1984 August | 12,500 | 55.00 |
| *Seasons Remembered* | | |
| 1984 Promise of Spring | 7,500 | 35.00 |
| 1984 Wildflowers of Summer | 7,500 | 35.00 |
| *Gentle Love* | | |
| 1985 Joanna and Jon | 9,500 | 45.00 |
| 1985 Alexandra and Amy | 9,500 | 45.00 |
| 1985 Ingrid and Lise | 9,500 | 45.00 |
| 1986 Elizabeth and David | 9,500 | 45.00 |
| *(Single issue)* | | |
| 1985 Give Me Liberty | 10,000 | 60.00 |
| *Christmas in America* | | |
| 1986 Christmas Eve in Williamsburg | NA | 29.50 |
| *Carl Larsson Miniature* | | |
| 1986 Flower Window | 15,000 | 15.00 |
| 1986 Lunch Under Birch Tree | 15,000 | 15.00 |
| 1986 Winter and the Old Barn | 15,000 | 15.00 |
| 1986 Mama's Room | 15,000 | 15.00 |
| 1986 Iduna's New Dress | 15,000 | 15.00 |
| 1986 Working in the Woods | 15,000 | 15.00 |
| 1986 Harvest | 15,000 | 15.00 |
| 1986 Potato Harvest | 15,000 | 15.00 |
| 1986 Fishing | 15,000 | 15.00 |
| 1986 Opening Day of the Crayfish Season | 15,000 | 15.00 |
| 1986 Azalea | 15,000 | 15.00 |
| 1986 Apple Harvest | 15,000 | 15.00 |

*See also: Ghent Collection (U.S.A.)*

### Grande Copenhagen

| | Edition Limit | Issue Price (US) |
|---|---|---|
| *Bicentennial (Single issue)* | | |
| 1976 Great Seal | Year | 35.00 |

### Grande Danica

| | Edition Limit | Issue Price (US) |
|---|---|---|
| *Mother's Day* | | |
| 1977 Dog with Puppies | 10,000 | 25.00 |
| 1978 Storks | 10,000 | 25.00 |
| 1979 Badgers | 10,000 | 25.00 |

### Georg Jensen

| | Edition Limit | Issue Price (US) |
|---|---|---|
| *Christmas* | | |
| 1972 Doves | Year | 15.00 |
| 1973 Christmas Eve | Year | 15.00 |
| 1974 Christmas Story | Year | 17.50 |
| 1975 Winter Scene | Year | 22.50 |
| 1976 Christmas in Country | Year | 22.50 |
| *Chagall (Single issue)* | | |
| 1972 Lovers | 12,500 | 50.00 |
| *Mother's Day* | | |
| 1973 Mother & Child | Year | 15.00 |
| 1974 Sweet Dreams | Year | 17.50 |
| 1975 Mother's World | Year | 22.50 |

### Svend Jensen

| | Edition Limit | Issue Price (US) |
|---|---|---|
| *Christmas* | | |
| 1970 H.C. Andersen House | Year | 14.50 |
| 1971 Little Match Girl | Year | 15.00 |
| 1972 Mermaid of Copenhagen | Year | 16.50 |
| 1973 Fir Tree | Year | 22.00 |
| 1974 Chimney Sweep | Year | 25.00 |
| 1975 Ugly Duckling | Year | 27.50 |
| 1976 Snow Queen | Year | 27.50 |
| 1977 Snowman | Year | 29.50 |
| 1978 Last Dream of Old Oak | Year | 32.00 |
| 1979 Old Street Lamp | Year | 36.50 |
| 1980 Willie Winky | Year | 42.50 |
| 1981 Uttermost Parts of Sea | Year | 49.50 |
| 1982 Twelve by Mailcoach | Year | 54.50 |
| 1983 Story of Year | Year | 54.50 |
| 1984 Nightingale | Year | 54.50 |
| *Mother's Day* | | |
| 1970 Bouquet for Mother | Year | 14.50 |
| 1971 Mother's Love | Year | 15.00 |
| 1972 Good Night | Year | 16.50 |
| 1973 Flowers for Mother | Year | 20.00 |
| 1974 Daisies for Mother | Year | 25.00 |


| | Edition Limit | Issue Price (US) |
|---|---|---|
| 1975 Surprise for Mother | Year | $ 27.50 |
| 1976 Complete Gardener | Year | 27.50 |
| 1977 Little Friends | Year | 29.50 |
| 1978 Dreams | Year | 32.00 |
| 1979 Promenade | Year | 36.50 |
| 1980 Nursery Scene | Year | 42.50 |
| 1981 Daily Duties | Year | 49.50 |
| 1982 My Best Friend | Year | 54.50 |
| 1983 An Unexpected Meeting | Year | 54.50 |
| 1984 Who Are You? | Year | 54.50 |
| 1985 Mother's Day | Year | 50.00 |
| 1986 Meeting on Meadow | Year | 50.00 |
| *Anniversary* | | |
| 1980 Hans Christian Andersen's Home | NA | 60.00 |

### Kera

| | Edition Limit | Issue Price (US) |
|---|---|---|
| *Christmas* | | |
| 1967 Kobenhavn | Year | 6.00 |
| 1968 Forste | Year | 6.00 |
| 1969 Andersen's House | Year | 6.00 |
| 1970 Langelinie | Year | 6.00 |
| 1971 Lille Peter | Year | 6.00 |
| *Moon* | | |
| 1969 Apollo 11 | Year | 6.00 |
| 1970 Apollo 13 | Year | 6.00 |
| *Mother's Day* | | |
| 1970 Mother's Day | Year | 6.00 |
| 1971 Mother's Day | Year | 6.00 |

### Lund & Clausen

| | Edition Limit | Issue Price (US) |
|---|---|---|
| *Moon* | | |
| 1969 Moon Landing–Apollo 11 | Year | 10.00 |
| 1971 Apollo 13 | Year | 15.00 |
| *Mother's Day* | | |
| 1970 Rose | Year | 10.00 |
| 1971 Forget-Me-Nots | Year | 10.00 |
| 1972 Bluebell | Year | 15.00 |
| 1973 Lily of Valley | Year | 16.00 |
| *Christmas* | | |
| 1971 Animal Garden | Year | 13.50 |
| 1972 Stave Church | Year | 13.50 |
| 1973 Christmas Scene | Year | 13.50 |

### Palisander

| | Edition Limit | Issue Price (US) |
|---|---|---|
| *Christmas* | | |
| 1971 Red Robin on Holly | 1,200 | 50.00 |
| 1972 Flying Geese | 1,200 | 50.00 |
| 1973 Christmas | 1,200 | 50.00 |
| *Presidential* | | |
| 1971 George Washington | 1,000 | 50.00 |
| 1972 Thomas Jefferson | 1,000 | 50.00 |
| 1973 John Adams | 1,000 | 50.00 |
| *(Single issue)* | | |
| 1973 Bicentennial | 250 | 50.00 |

### Royal Copenhagen

| | Edition Limit | Issue Price (US) |
|---|---|---|
| *Mother's Day* | | |
| 1971 American Mother | Year | 12.50 |
| 1972 Oriental Mother | Year | 14.00 |
| 1973 Danish Mother | Year | 16.00 |
| 1974 Greenland Mother | Year | 16.50 |
| 1975 Bird in Nest | Year | 20.00 |
| 1976 Mermaids | Year | 20.00 |
| 1977 Twins | Year | 24.00 |
| 1978 Mother and Child | Year | 26.00 |
| 1979 A Loving Mother | Year | 29.50 |
| 1980 Outing with Mother | Year | 37.50 |
| 1981 Reunion | Year | 39.00 |
| 1982 Children's Hour | Year | 39.50 |
| *Historical* | | |
| 1975 R. C. Bicentennial | Year | 30.00 |
| 1976 U.S. Bicentennial | Year | 35.00 |
| 1977 Electro-Magnetism | Year | 35.00 |
| 1978 Capt. Cook | Year | 37.50 |
| 1979 Adam Oehlenschlager | Year | 42.50 |
| 1980 Amagertorv | Year | 52.50 |
| *National Parks of America* | | |
| 1978 Yellowstone | 5,000 | 75.00 |
| 1979 Shenandoah | 5,000 | 75.00 |
| 1980 Yosemite | 5,000 | 75.00 |
| 1980 Mt. McKinley | 5,000 | 75.00 |
| 1981 Everglades | 5,000 | 75.00 |
| 1981 Grand Canyon | 5,000 | 75.00 |
| *(Single issue)* | | |
| 1980 Year of Viking | 5,000 | 55.00 |

## Hans Christian Andersen

| | Edition Limit | Issue Price (US) |
|---|---|---|
| 1983 Shepherdess and Chimney Sweep | Year | $ 39.50 |
| 1984 Thumbelina | Year | 39.50 |
| 1985 Little Mermaid | Year | 44.50 |
| 1986 The Princess and the Pea | NA | 44.50 |

## FINLAND

### Arabia

*Christmas 100 Years Ago*

| | Edition Limit | Issue Price (US) |
|---|---|---|
| 1978 Inland Village Scene | Year | 49.00 |
| 1979 Forest Village Scene | Year | 72.00 |
| 1980 Seaside Village Scene | Year | 79.00 |
| 1981 Farm Village Scene | Year | 87.00 |
| 1982 Country Village Scene | Year | 95.00 |

*Pictures of Lapland*

| | | |
|---|---|---|
| 1981 Laplander Village | 7,000 | 175.00 |

*Christmas Annual*

| | | |
|---|---|---|
| 1986 Christmas 1986 | NA | 90.00 |

*(Single issue)*

| | | |
|---|---|---|
| 1981 Rose | 2,000 | 360.00 |

## FRANCE

### Bayel of France

*Flowers*

| | Edition Limit | Issue Price (US) |
|---|---|---|
| 1972 Rose | 300 | 50.00 |
| 1973 Lilies | 300 | 50.00 |
| 1973 Orchid | 300 | 50.00 |

*Bicentennial*

| | | |
|---|---|---|
| 1974 Liberty Bell | 500 | 50.00 |
| 1975 Independence Hall | 500 | 60.00 |
| 1976 Spread Eagle | 500 | 60.00 |

*Eagles*

| | | |
|---|---|---|
| 1974 Eagle Head | 300 | 50.00 |
| 1974 Eagle in Flight | 300 | 50.00 |

### Betourne Studios

*Jean-Paul Loup Christmas*

| | | |
|---|---|---|
| 1971 Noel | 300 | 125.00 |
| 1972 Noel | 300 | 150.00 |
| 1973 Noel | 300 | 175.00 |
| 1974 Noel | 400 | 200.00 |
| 1975 Noel | 250 | 250.00 |
| 1976 Noel | 150 | 300.00 |

*Mother's Day (Champleve)*

| | | |
|---|---|---|
| 1974 Mother & Child | 500 | 250.00 |

*Mother's Day (Enamel)*

| | | |
|---|---|---|
| 1975 Mother's Day | 400 | 285.00 |
| 1976 Mother & Child | 250 | 300.00 |

### Cartier

*Cathedral*

| | | |
|---|---|---|
| 1972 Chartres Cathedral | 12,500 | 50.00 |
| 1974 Chartres, Millous | 500 | 130.00 |

### Cristal D'Albret

*Four Seasons*

| | | |
|---|---|---|
| 1972 Summer | 1,000 | 75.00 |
| 1973 Autumn | 648 | 75.00 |
| 1973 Spring | 312 | 75.00 |
| 1974 Winter | 1,000 | 88.00 |

*(Single issue)*

| | | |
|---|---|---|
| 1972 Bird of Peace | 3,700 | 64.00 |

### Daum

*Four Seasons*

| | | |
|---|---|---|
| 1969 Autumn (Amethyst) | 2,000 | 150.00 |
| 1970 Winter (Aquamarine) | 2,000 | 150.00 |
| 1970 Spring (Emerald) | 2,000 | 150.00 |
| 1970 Summer (Topaz) | 2,000 | 150.00 |

*Famous Musicians*

| | | |
|---|---|---|
| 1970 Bach (Emerald) | 2,000 | 60.00 |
| 1970 Beethoven (Amethyst) | 2,000 | 60.00 |
| 1971 Mozart (Tourmaline) | 2,000 | 60.00 |
| 1971 Wagner (Peridot) | 2,000 | 60.00 |
| 1972 Debussy (Topaz) | 2,000 | 60.00 |
| 1972 Gershwin (Sapphire) | 2,000 | 60.00 |

*Dali*

| | | |
|---|---|---|
| 1971 Ceci N'est Pas Une Assiette | 2,000 | 200.00 |
| 1971 Triomphale | 2,000 | 200.00 |

### Art Nouveau

| | Edition Limit | Issue Price (US) |
|---|---|---|
| 1979 Waterlilies | 4,000 | $125.00 |
| 1980 Lily Pond | 4,000 | 150.00 |
| 1981 Swan | 4,000 | 170.00 |

### Gourinat-Dolan

*(Single issue)*

| | | |
|---|---|---|
| 1978 Doves of Peace | 3,000 | 60.00 |

### Haviland

*Historical*

| | | |
|---|---|---|
| 1968 Martha Washington | 2,500 | 35.00 |
| 1969 Lincoln | 2,500 | 100.00 |
| 1970 Grant | 3,000 | 100.00 |
| 1971 Hayes | 2,500 | 110.00 |

*Bicentennial*

| | | |
|---|---|---|
| 1972 Burning of Gaspee | 10,000 | 39.95 |
| 1973 Boston Tea Party | 10,000 | 39.95 |
| 1974 First Continental Congress | 10,000 | 39.95 |
| 1975 Ride of Paul Revere | 10,000 | 40.00 |
| 1976 Declaration of Independence | 10,000 | 48.00 |

*French Collection*

| | | |
|---|---|---|
| 1973 Breakfast | 10,000 | 29.95 |
| 1974 Wash | 10,000 | 29.95 |
| 1975 In Park | 10,000 | 30.00 |
| 1976 To Market | 10,000 | 38.00 |
| 1977 A Wash Before Dinner | 10,000 | 38.00 |
| 1978 An Evening at Home | 10,000 | 40.00 |
| 1979 Happy Mother's Day | 10,000 | 45.00 |

*Theatre Des Saisons*

| | | |
|---|---|---|
| 1978 Spring | 5,000 | 120.00 |
| 1978 Summer | 5,000 | 120.00 |
| 1978 Autumn | 5,000 | 120.00 |
| 1978 Winter | 5,000 | 120.00 |

*Mother's Day*

| | | |
|---|---|---|
| 1980 Child and His Animals | Year | 55.00 |

*Visit from Saint Nicholas*

| | | |
|---|---|---|
| 1980 Twas Night Before Christmas | Year | 55.00 |
| 1981 Children Were Nestled | Year | 60.00 |
| 1982 Tore Open Shutters | Year | 60.00 |
| 1983 What to Wondering Eyes | Year | 60.00 |
| 1984 Up Chimney | Year | 60.00 |
| 1985 Happy Christmas to All | Year | 60.00 |

*Fleurs et Rubens*

| | | |
|---|---|---|
| 1980 Orchidée | 7,500 | 120.00 |
| 1981 Hibiscus | 7,500 | 120.00 |
| 1982 Poppy | 7,500 | 120.00 |

*Traditional Christmas Carols*

| | | |
|---|---|---|
| 1986 Deck the Halls | 2,000 | 75.00 |

### Haviland & Parlon

*Nan Lee (Single issue)*

| | | |
|---|---|---|
| 1973 Peaceable Kingdom | 5,000 | 30.00 |

*Mother's Day*

| | | |
|---|---|---|
| 1975 Laura and Child | 15,000 | 37.50 |
| 1976 Pinky and Baby | 15,000 | 42.50 |
| 1977 Amy and Snoopy | 10,000 | 45.00 |

*King Tut (Single issue)*

| | | |
|---|---|---|
| 1977 Scarab | 2,500 | 80.00 |

*Zodiac (Single issue)*

| | | |
|---|---|---|
| 1977 Astrological Man | 5,000 | 50.00 |

*Enchanted Forest*

| | | |
|---|---|---|
| 1982 Entrance to Forest | 10,000 | 65.00 |
| 1983 Birds of Forest | 10,000 | 65.00 |

See also: Kern Collectibles (U.S.A.)

### HB—Henriot Quimper

*The Chapels of Brittany*

| | | |
|---|---|---|
| 1986 The Chapel of Tronoen | 250 | 75.00 |

### Josair

*Bicentennial*

| | | |
|---|---|---|
| 1972 American Eagle | 400 | 250.00 |
| 1973 American Flag | 400 | 250.00 |
| 1974 Abraham Lincoln | 400 | 250.00 |
| 1975 George Washington | 400 | 250.00 |
| 1976 Declaration of Independence | 400 | 250.00 |

### Poillerat

*Christmas*

| | Edition Limit | Issue Price (US) |
|---|---|---|
| 1972 Three Kings | 500 | 350.00 |
| 1973 Rose | 250 | 350.00 |

### Puiforcat

*Cartes a Jouer*

| | | |
|---|---|---|
| 1972 (Set of five) | 2,000 | 300.00 |

*(Single issue)*

| | | |
|---|---|---|
| 1973 Exodus (Silver) | 2,000 | 200.00 |

### Raynaud-Limoges

*Castles*

| | | |
|---|---|---|
| 1979 Bodiam Castle | 5,000 | 48.00 |
| 1979 Glamis Castle | 5,000 | 48.00 |
| 1979 Tower of London | 5,000 | 48.00 |

*Wildlife Collection*

| | | |
|---|---|---|
| 1978 Tiger Bouquet | Year | 50.00 |

### Royal Limoges

*Christmas*

| | | |
|---|---|---|
| 1972 Nativity | 5,000 | 25.00 |
| 1973 Three Wise Men | 5,000 | 27.50 |

### Sabino

*Annual Crystal*

| | | |
|---|---|---|
| 1970 King Henry IV & Maria De Medici | 1,500 | 65.00 |
| 1971 Milo & Beasts | 1,500 | 65.00 |

## GERMANY

### Anna-Perenna

*Birds of Fancy*

| | Edition Limit | Issue Price (US) |
|---|---|---|
| 1978 Firebird | 5,000 | 110.00 |

*Floral Fantasies*

| | | |
|---|---|---|
| 1978 Empress Gold | 5,000 | 110.00 |

*Enchanted Gardens*

| | | |
|---|---|---|
| 1978 June Dream | 5,000 | 75.00 |
| 1979 Summer Day | 5,000 | 95.00 |

*Oriental Tranquility*

| | | |
|---|---|---|
| 1978 Chun Li at Pond | 5,000 | 100.00 |
| 1979 Ming Tao on Path of Faith | 5,000 | 110.00 |

*Joy of Motherhood*

| | | |
|---|---|---|
| 1979 Gesa and Children | 5,000 | 165.00 |
| 1980 Alexandra and Children | 5,000 | 175.00 |

*American Silhouettes I–Children*

| | | |
|---|---|---|
| 1981 Fiddlers Two | 5,000 | 75.00 |
| 1981 Mary with Lambs | 5,000 | 75.00 |
| 1981 Waiting for Tom | 5,000 | 75.00 |
| 1981 Ring Around Rosie | 5,000 | 75.00 |

*American Silhouettes II–Family*

| | | |
|---|---|---|
| 1982 Family Outing | 5,000 | 75.00 |
| 1982 John and Mary | 5,000 | 75.00 |
| 1982 Homemakers A-Quilting | 5,000 | 75.00 |
| 1982 Leisure Time | 5,000 | 75.00 |

*American Silhouettes III–Valley Life*

| | | |
|---|---|---|
| 1983 Frosty Frolic | 5,000 | 75.00 |
| 1983 Hayride | 5,000 | 75.00 |
| 1983 Sunday Ride | 5,000 | 75.00 |
| 1983 Market Day | 5,000 | 75.00 |

*Bashful Bunnies*

| | | |
|---|---|---|
| 1981 Spring's Surprise | 15,000 | 62.50 |
| 1981 Summer's Sunshine | 15,000 | 62.50 |
| 1982 Fall's Frolic | 15,000 | 62.50 |
| 1982 Winter's Wonder | 15,000 | 62.50 |

*Children of Mother Earth*

| | | |
|---|---|---|
| 1982 Spring | 2,500 | 250.00 |
| 1982 Summer | 2,500 | 250.00 |
| 1982 Autumn | 2,500 | 250.00 |
| 1982 Winter | 2,500 | 250.00 |

*Happy Village*

| | | |
|---|---|---|
| 1982 Spring Picnic | 5,000 | 55.00 |
| 1982 Summer on Pond | 5,000 | 55.00 |
| 1982 Autumn Harvest Dance | 5,000 | 55.00 |
| 1982 Winter Snow Kids | 5,000 | 55.00 |

*Masquerade Fantasy*

| | | |
|---|---|---|
| 1982 Masquerade Party | 9,800 | 95.00 |
| 1982 Clowns and Unicorns | 9,800 | 95.00 |
| 1982 Merry-Go-Round Ballet | 9,800 | 95.00 |

### Uncle Tad's Holiday Cats

| | Edition Limit | Issue Price (US) |
|---|---|---|
| 1982 Jingle Bells | 9,800 | $ 75.0 |
| 1983 Pollyanna | 9,800 | 75.0 |
| 1984 Pumpkins | 9,800 | 75.0 |
| 1985 Perry, Buttercup and Black-Eyed Susan | 9,800 | 75.0 |

*Arctic Spring*

| | | |
|---|---|---|
| 1983 Patience | 9,500 | 75.0 |
| 1984 Proud Mother | 9,500 | 75.0 |
| 1985 We Like It | 9,500 | 75.0 |
| 1986 The Race | 9,500 | 75.0 |

*Flowers of Count Bernadotte*

| | | |
|---|---|---|
| 1983 Iris | 17,800 | 75.0 |
| 1983 Carnation | 17,800 | 75.0 |
| 1984 Freesia | 17,800 | 75. |
| 1984 Lily | 17,800 | 75.0 |
| 1984 Orchid | 17,800 | 75.0 |
| 1984 Rose | 17,800 | 75.0 |
| 1985 Tulip | 17,800 | 75.0 |
| 1985 Chrysanthemum | 17,800 | 75.0 |

*Rhythm and Dance*

| | | |
|---|---|---|
| 1983 Ballroom | 5,000 | 29.5 |
| 1983 Two-Step | 5,000 | 29.5 |
| 1983 Strut | 5,000 | 29.5 |
| 1983 Swing | 5,000 | 29.5 |
| 1983 Aerobics | 5,000 | 29.5 |
| 1983 Jazz | 5,000 | 29.5 |
| 1983 Charleston | 5,000 | 29.5 |
| 1983 Cake-Walk | 5,000 | 29.5 |

*Moss Christmas*

| | | |
|---|---|---|
| 1984 Noel, Noel | 5,000 | 69.0 |
| 1985 Helping Hands | 5,000 | 69.0 |
| 1986 Night Before Christmas | 5,000 | 75.0 |

*Reflections of Youth*

| | | |
|---|---|---|
| 1984 Swimmers | 9,500 | 69.0 |
| 1985 Daydreamer | 9,500 | 69. |
| 1985 Challenging Log | 9,500 | 69. |
| 1985 End of Run | 9,500 | 69.0 |

*Me and My Shadow*

| | | |
|---|---|---|
| 1985 Jason and Ginger | 7,500 | 75.0 |

*Celebration*

| | | |
|---|---|---|
| 1986 Wedding Joy | 5,000 | 100.0 |
| 1987 The Christening | 5,000 | 100.0 |

### Bareuther

*Mother's Day*

| | | |
|---|---|---|
| 1969 Mother & Children | 5,000 | 12.0 |
| 1970 Mother & Children | 5,000 | 12.0 |
| 1971 Mother & Children | 5,000 | 13.5 |
| 1972 Mother & Children | 5,000 | 15.0 |
| 1973 Mother & Children | 5,000 | 15.0 |
| 1974 Musical Children | 5,000 | 19.0 |
| 1975 Spring Outing | 5,000 | 21.5 |
| 1976 Rocking Cradle | 5,000 | 23.0 |
| 1977 Noon Feeding | 5,000 | 24.0 |
| 1978 Blind Man's Bluff | 5,000 | 27.5 |
| 1979 Mother's Love | 5,000 | 35.0 |
| 1980 First Cherries | 5,000 | 37.5 |
| 1981 Playtime | 5,000 | 39.0 |
| 1982 Suppertime | 5,000 | 39.5 |
| 1983 On Farm | 5,000 | 39.5 |
| 1984 Village Children | 5,000 | 42.5 |
| 1985 Sunrise | 5,000 | 42.5 |
| 1986 Playtime | 5,000 | 42.5 |
| 1987 Pets | 5,000 | 46.0 |

*Thanksgiving*

| | | |
|---|---|---|
| 1971 First Thanksgiving | 2,500 | 13.5 |
| 1972 Harvest | 2,500 | 14.5 |
| 1973 Country Road in Autumn | 2,500 | 15.0 |
| 1974 Old Mill | 2,500 | 19.0 |
| 1975 Wild Deer in Forest | 2,500 | 21.5 |
| 1976 Thanksgiving on Farm | 2,500 | 23.0 |
| 1977 Horses | 2,500 | 24.5 |
| 1978 Apple Harvest | 2,500 | 27.0 |
| 1979 Noontime | 2,500 | 35.0 |
| 1980 Longhorns | 2,500 | 37.5 |
| 1981 Gathering Wheat | 2,500 | 39.5 |
| 1982 Autumn | 2,500 | 39.5 |

### Barthmann

*Christmas*

| | | |
|---|---|---|
| 1977 Mary with Child | 300 | 236.0 |
| 1978 Adoration of Child | 500 | 326.0 |
| 1979 Holy Mother of Kasanskaja | 500 | 361.0 |
| 1980 Holy Mother by Kykos | 500 | 385.0 |

| | Edition Limit | Issue Price (US) |
|---|---|---|
| **erlin Design** | | |
| *ather's Day (Historical)* | | |
| 971 Brooklyn Bridge on Opening Day | 12,000 | $ 14.50 |
| 972 Continent Spanned | 3,000 | 15.00 |
| 973 Landing of Columbus | 2,000 | 18.00 |
| 974 Adorn's Balloon | Year | 25.00 |
| 975 Washington Crossing Delaware | Year | 30.00 |
| 976 Tom Thumb | Year | 32.00 |
| 977 Zeppelin | Year | 32.00 |
| 978 Carl Benz | Year | 36.00 |
| 979 Johannes Gutenberg at Mainz | Year | 47.50 |
| *other's Day* | | |
| 971 Grey Poodles | 20,000 | 14.50 |
| 972 Fledglings | 10,000 | 15.00 |
| 973 Duck Family | 6,000 | 16.50 |
| 974 Squirrels | 6,000 | 22.50 |
| 975 Cats | 6,000 | 30.00 |
| 976 Doe and Her Fawn | 6,000 | 32.00 |
| 977 Storks | 6,000 | 32.00 |
| 978 Mare with Foal | 6,000 | 36.00 |
| 979 Swans and Cygnets | 6,000 | 47.50 |
| 980 Goat Family | 6,000 | 55.00 |
| 981 Dachshund Family | 6,000 | 55.00 |
| 982 Partridge Family | 6,000 | 55.00 |
| 983 Swallow Family | 6,000 | 55.00 |
| 984 Care | 6,000 | 55.00 |
| **anish Church** | | |
| *hurch* | | |
| 968 Roskilde Cathedral | Year | 12.00 |
| 969 Ribe Cathedral | Year | 13.00 |
| 970 Marmor Church | Year | 13.00 |
| 971 Ejby Church | Year | 13.00 |
| 972 Kalundborg Church | Year | 13.00 |
| 973 Grundtvig Church | Year | 15.00 |
| 974 Broager Church | Year | 15.00 |
| 975 Sct. Knuds Church | Year | 18.00 |
| 976 Osterlars Church | Year | 22.00 |
| 977 Budolfi Church | Year | 15.95 |
| 978 Haderslev Cathedral | Year | 19.95 |
| 979 Holmens Church | Year | 19.95 |
| 980 Sct. Bendts Church | Year | 24.00 |
| 981 Vor Frue Church | Year | 32.50 |
| 982 Fjennesler Church | Year | 33.00 |
| 983 Udby Church | Year | 39.50 |
| **resden** | | |
| *hristmas* | | |
| 971 Shepherd Scene | 3,500 | 14.50 |
| 972 Niklas Church | 6,000 | 18.00 |
| 973 Schwanstein Church | 6,000 | 18.00 |
| 974 Village Scene | 5,000 | 20.00 |
| 975 Rothenberg Scene | 5,000 | 24.00 |
| 976 Bavarian Village Church | 5,000 | 26.00 |
| 977 Old Mill in Hexenloch | 5,000 | 28.00 |
| *other's Day* | | |
| 972 Doe and Fawns | 8,000 | 15.00 |
| 973 Mare and Colt | 6,000 | 16.00 |
| 974 Tiger and Cub | 5,000 | 20.00 |
| 975 Dachshund Family | 5,000 | 24.00 |
| 976 Mother Owl and Young | 5,000 | 26.00 |
| 977 Chamois | 5,000 | 28.00 |
| **ürstenberg** | | |
| *aster* | | |
| 971 Sheep | 3,500 | 15.00 |
| 972 Chicks | 4,000 | 15.00 |
| 973 Bunnies | 4,000 | 16.00 |
| 974 Pussywillow | 4,000 | 20.00 |
| 975 Village Church | 4,000 | 24.00 |
| 976 Country Watermill | 4,000 | 25.00 |
| *hristmas* | | |
| 971 Rabbits | 7,500 | 14.00 |
| 972 Snowy Village | 6,000 | 15.00 |
| 973 Christmas Eve | 3,000 | 18.00 |
| 974 Sparrows | 4,000 | 20.00 |
| 975 Deer Family | 4,000 | 24.00 |
| 976 Winter Birds | 4,000 | 25.00 |
| *eluxe Christmas* | | |
| 971 Three Wise Men | 1,500 | 45.00 |
| 972 Holy Family and Angel | 2,000 | 45.00 |
| 973 Christmas Eve | 2,000 | 60.00 |
| *other's Day* | | |
| 972 Hummingbird | 5,000 | 15.00 |
| 973 Hedgehogs | 5,000 | 16.00 |

| | Edition Limit | Issue Price (US) |
|---|---|---|
| 1974 Doe with Fawn | 4,000 | $ 20.00 |
| 1975 Swan Family | 4,000 | 24.00 |
| 1976 Koala Bear | 4,000 | 25.00 |
| *Olympic* | | |
| 1972 Olympics–Munich | 5,000 | 20.00 |
| 1976 Olympics–Montreal | 5,000 | 37.50 |
| *New York City Landscape* | | |
| 1981 City Hall | 3,500 | 75.00 |
| 1981 Central Park | 3,500 | 75.00 |
| **Glaskunst/Schott-Zwiesel** | | |
| *Christmas* | | |
| 1977 Three Wise Man | NA | 105.00 |
| 1978 Holy Family | NA | 112.50 |
| 1979 Shepherd of Field | NA | 115.00 |
| 1980 Annunciation of Maria | NA | 118.00 |
| **Goebel** | | |
| *Charlot Byj* | | |
| 1973 Santa at Tree | Year | 16.50 |
| 1974 Santa and Girl | Year | 22.00 |
| 1975 Up and Away | Year | 25.00 |
| 1976 Boy with Teddy Bear | Year | 25.00 |
| 1977 Joy to World | Year | 25.00 |
| *Wildlife* | | |
| 1974 Robin | Year | 45.00 |
| 1975 Blue Titmouse | Year | 50.00 |
| 1976 Barn Owl | Year | 50.00 |
| 1977 Bullfinch | Year | 50.00 |
| 1978 Sea Gull | Year | 55.00 |
| 1979 Mallard | 10,000 | 90.00 |
| 1980 Cardinal | 10,000 | 90.00 |
| 1981 Peregrine Falcon | 10,000 | 90.00 |
| *Mothers* | | |
| 1975 Rabbits | Year | 45.00 |
| 1976 Cats | Year | 45.00 |
| 1977 Panda Bears | Year | 45.00 |
| 1978 Doe and Fawn | Year | 50.00 |
| 1979 Long-Eared Owl | 10,000 | 65.00 |
| 1980 Raccoon and Baby | 10,000 | 75.00 |
| 1981 Ringed Seal | 10,000 | 80.00 |
| 1982 Swan | 10,000 | 80.00 |
| 1983 Walrus | 10,000 | 80.00 |
| *Robson Christmas* | | |
| 1975 Flight to Egypt (Porcelain) | Year | 50.00 |
| 1975 Flight to Egypt (Pewter) | Year | 45.00 |
| *Annual Crystal* | | |
| 1978 Praying Girl | Year | 45.00 |
| 1979 Praying Boy | Year | 50.00 |
| 1980 Praying Angel | 15,000 | 50.00 |
| 1981 Girl with Teddy Bear | 10,000 | 50.00 |
| *Old Testament Themes* | | |
| 1978 Twelve Tribes of Israel | 10,000 | 125.00 |
| 1979 Ten Commandments | 10,000 | 175.00 |
| 1980 Traditions | 10,000 | 225.00 |
| 1981 Prophet | 10,000 | 275.00 |
| *American Heritage* | | |
| 1979 Freedom & Justice Soaring | 15,000 | 100.00 |
| 1980 Wild & Free | 10,000 | 120.00 |
| 1981 Where Buffalo Roam | 5,000 | 125.00 |
| *Crystal Mother's Day* | | |
| 1979 Butterfly | 15,000 | 50.00 |
| 1980 Sparrow | 15,000 | 50.00 |
| 1981 Doves | 5,000 | 50.00 |
| *(Single issue)* | | |
| 1979 Christmas | 200 | 500.00 |
| *Bratsoff* | | |
| 1979 Star Steed | 15,000 | 125.00 |
| *Bavarian Forest* | | |
| 1980 Owls | 7,500 | 150.00 |
| 1981 Deer | 7,500 | 150.00 |
| 1982 Pheasants | 7,500 | 150.00 |
| *North American Wildlife* | | |
| 1980 Beaver | 10,000 | 125.00 |
| 1981 Harp Seal | 10,000 | 125.00 |
| 1982 Polar Bear | 10,000 | 125.00 |
| 1983 Fox and Kits | 10,000 | 125.00 |
| 1984 Lynx | 10,000 | 75.00 |
| *Christmas in Kinderland* | | |
| 1982 A Gift of Joy | 10,000 | 49.50 |
| 1983 A Midnight Clear | 10,000 | 49.50 |
| 1984 Three Wee Kings | 10,000 | 49.50 |
| 1985 Christmas Starglow | 10,000 | 49.50 |

| | Edition Limit | Issue Price (US) |
|---|---|---|
| *Christmas Morning in Dingle Dell* | | |
| 1982 Dolly Dingle | 10,000 | $ 30.00 |
| 1983 Billy Bumps | 10,000 | 30.00 |
| *Dolly Dingle World Traveler* | | |
| 1982 Dolly Visits Germany | 10,000 | 30.00 |
| 1982 Dolly Visits Italy | 10,000 | 30.00 |
| 1982 Dolly Visits Holland | 10,000 | 30.00 |
| 1982 Dolly Visits Spain | 10,000 | 30.00 |
| *Native Companions* | | |
| 1982 Rachel | 10,000 | 49.50 |
| 1983 Hummingbird | 10,000 | 49.50 |
| 1983 Rabbit Dancer | 10,000 | 49.50 |
| 1984 Celebration | 10,000 | 49.50 |
| *Winged Fantasies* | | |
| 1982 Strawberries | 10,000 | 49.50 |
| 1983 Bacchanalia | 10,000 | 49.50 |
| 1983 Cerises | 10,000 | 49.50 |
| 1983 Brambleberries | 10,000 | 49.50 |
| *Blue-Button Twins Christmas* | | |
| 1983 By Fireplace | 10,000 | 30.00 |
| 1983 Down Stairs | 10,000 | 30.00 |
| *English Countryside Cat* | | |
| 1983 James | 10,000 | 35.00 |
| 1983 Henry | 10,000 | 35.00 |
| 1983 Lucy | 10,000 | 35.00 |
| *(Single issue)* | | |
| 1984 Skater's Waltz | 10,000 | 33.00 |
| *Little Hugs* | | |
| 1985 Dolly Dearest | 7,500 | 34.50 |
| 1986 First Puppy | 7,500 | 34.50 |
| **Grafburg** | | |
| *Christmas* | | |
| 1975 Black-Capped Chickadee | 5,000 | 20.00 |
| 1976 Squirrels | 5,000 | 22.00 |
| *Little Music Makers* | | |
| 1987 Band Leader | NA | 90.00 |
| **Heinrich** | | |
| *UNICEF Children in World* | | |
| 1977 Europe | Year | 30.00 |
| 1978 Asia | Year | 30.00 |
| 1979 Africa | Year | 30.00 |
| 1980 America | Year | 30.00 |
| 1981 Malaysia | Year | 30.00 |
| 1982 India | Year | 35.00 |
| 1983 Mexico | Year | 35.00 |
| *(Single issue)* | | |
| 1979 International Year of Child | Year | 35.00 |
| *Flower Fairies Collection* | | |
| 1979 Lavender Fairy | 21 Days | 35.00 |
| 1980 Sweet Pea Fairy | 21 Days | 35.00 |
| 1980 Candytuft Fairy | 21 Days | 35.00 |
| 1980 Heliotrope Fairy | 21 Days | 35.00 |
| 1981 Black Thorne Fairy | 21 Days | 35.00 |
| 1981 Apple Blossom Fairy | 21 Days | 35.00 |
| *Famous Sea Battles* | | |
| 1981 Battle of Trafalgar | Year | 42.00 |
| 1982 Battle/Flamborough Head | Year | 42.00 |
| 1983 Battle of Lepanto | Year | 42.00 |
| *Flower Fairies* | | |
| 1983 Columbine | 21 Days | 39.00 |
| 1983 Cornflower | 21 Days | 39.00 |
| 1984 Mallow | 21 Days | 39.00 |
| 1984 Black Medick | 21 Days | 39.00 |
| 1985 Canterbury Bell | 21 Days | 39.00 |
| 1985 Fuschia | 21 Days | 39.00 |
| **Hibel Studio (Kaiser)** | | |
| *Tribute to Classical Greek Beauty* | | |
| 1980 Diana | 3,000 | 350.00 |
| *World I Love* | | |
| 1981 Leah's Family | 17,500 | 85.00 |
| 1982 Kaylin | 17,500 | 85.00 |
| 1983 Edna's Music | 17,500 | 85.00 |
| 1984 O-Hana | 17,500 | 85.00 |
| *A Tribute to All Children* | | |
| 1984 Giselle | 19,500 | 55.00 |
| 1985 Gerard | 19,500 | 55.00 |
| 1985 Wendy | 19,500 | 55.00 |
| *Flower Girl* | | |
| 1985 Lily | 15,000 | 79.00 |
| 1986 Iris | 15,000 | 79.00 |

| | Edition Limit | Issue Price (US) |
|---|---|---|
| *To Life* | | |
| 1986 Golden's Child | 5,000 | $ 99.00 |
| **Hibel Studio (Rosenthal)** | | |
| *Famous Women and Children* | | |
| 1980 Pharoah's Daughter and Moses | 3,000 | 350.00 |
| 1981 Cornelia and Jewels | 2,500 | 350.00 |
| 1982 Anna and Children | 2,500 | 350.00 |
| 1983 Mozart and Maria | 2,500 | 350.00 |
| **Hutschenreuther** | | |
| *Christmas** | | |
| 1972 On Way to Egypt | 5,000 | NA |
| 1973 Adoration | 5,000 | NA |
| 1974 Annunciation | 5,000 | NA |
| *Series not available in U.S. | | |
| *Gunther Granget Annual* | | |
| 1972 Sparrows | 5,000 | 50.00 |
| 1973 Killdeer | 2,500 | 75.00 |
| 1973 Squirrel | 2,500 | 75.00 |
| 1974 Partridge | 2,500 | 75.00 |
| 1975 Rabbits | 2,500 | 90.00 |
| 1976 Wrens | 2,500 | 100.00 |
| 1976 Freedom in Flight | 5,000 | 100.00 |
| 1977 Bears | 2,500 | 100.00 |
| 1978 Foxes | 1,000 | 125.00 |
| *Songbirds of America* | | |
| 1972 Eastern Bluebird and Goldfinch (Pair) | 5,000 | 100.00 |
| 1973 Mockingbird and Robin (Pair) | 5,000 | 100.00 |
| *Canada Christmas* | | |
| 1973 Parliament Building | Year | 15.00 |
| 1974 Moose | Year | 16.00 |
| 1975 Basilica | Year | 21.00 |
| 1976 Winter on Prairies | Year | 23.00 |
| 1977 Bluenose | Year | 23.00 |
| 1978 Lost Lagoon | Year | 27.00 |
| 1979 Yukon Highway Bridge | Year | 33.00 |
| 1980 Covered Bridge | Year | 38.00 |
| 1981 Saskatchewan Winter | Year | 38.00 |
| 1982 Christmas to Celebrate | Year | 38.00 |
| 1983 Province House | Year | 38.00 |
| 1984 Christmas in Winnipeg | Year | 38.00 |
| *Bicentennial* | | |
| 1976 Freedom in Flight | 5,000 | 100.00 |
| 1976 Freedom in Flight (Gold) | 200 | 200.00 |
| *Plates of Month (Set of 12)* | | |
| 1977 January–December | 5,000 | 780.00 |
| *Mother and Child Annual* | | |
| 1978 Mother and Child | Year | 55.00 |
| 1979 Mother and Child | Year | 65.00 |
| 1980 Mother and Child | Year | 87.50 |
| 1981 Mother and Child | Year | 87.50 |
| *Birthday Annual* | | |
| 1978 Birthday Plate | 10,000 | 165.00 |
| *Winter Christmas* | | |
| 1978 Silent Night | Year | 260.00 |
| 1979 Saint Lucia | Year | 295.00 |
| 1980 Christmas Pavillion | Year | 325.00 |
| 1981 Christmas Sleigh | Year | 400.00 |
| 1982 Joy to World | Year | 400.00 |
| *Friendship Annual* | | |
| 1978 Friendship Plate | Year | 80.00 |
| *Dolores Valenza Enchantment* | | |
| 1979 Princess Snowflake | 5,000 | 50.00 |
| 1979 Blossom Queen | 5,000 | 62.50 |
| 1980 Princess Marina | 5,000 | 87.50 |
| 1980 Princess Starbright | 5,000 | 87.50 |
| 1981 Princess Aura | 5,000 | 87.50 |
| 1981 Harvest Queen | 5,000 | 87.50 |
| *Wedding Annual* | | |
| 1978 Wedding Plate | 10,000 | 210.00 |
| *Zodiac Collection (Set of 12)* | | |
| 1978 Aries–Pisces | 1,500 | 1500.00 |
| *Hans Achtziger Annual* | | |
| 1979 Heading South | 4,000 | 150.00 |
| 1980 Playful Flight | 5,000 | 187.50 |
| 1981 Tropical Skies | 5,000 | 245.00 |
| 1982 Carried by Wind | 2,500 | 250.00 |
| 1983 Toward Sun | 5,000 | 250.00 |
| *Arzberg Christmas* | | |
| 1979 Christmas | 2,500 | 60.00 |

| | Edition Limit | Issue Price (US) |
|---|---|---|
| *(Single issue)* | | |
| 1979 Celebration Plate | Year | $ 67.50 |
| *(Single issue)* | | |
| 1979 Anniversary Plate | Year | 120.00 |
| *(Single issue)* | | |
| 1977 Allegro Ensemble | 7,500 | 120.00 |
| *Hibel Museum (Single issue)* | | |
| 1977 Flower Girl of Provence | 12,750 | 175.00 |
| *Floral Heirlooms* | | |
| 1978 Zinnias in Sugar Bowl | 5,000 | 65.00 |
| 1979 Pansies in Antique Tin | 5,000 | 70.00 |
| 1981 Primroses in Staffordshire Pitcher | 5,000 | 75.00 |
| 1982 Asters | 5,000 | 75.00 |
| *Birds of Paradise* | | |
| 1981 Bluebird of Paradise | 10,000 | 175.00 |
| 1982 Raggis Great Bird of Paradise | 10,000 | 175.00 |
| *Glory of Christmas* | | |
| 1982 Nativity | 25,000 | 80.00 |
| 1983 Angels | 25,000 | 80.00 |
| 1984 Shepherds | 25,000 | 80.00 |
| 1985 Wiseman | 25,000 | 80.00 |
| *Legendary Animals (Set of four)* | | |
| 1982 Unicorn | | |
| 1982 Griffin | | |
| 1982 Dragon | | |
| 1982 Pegasus | 12,500 | 175.00 |
| *Songbirds of North America* | | |
| 1982 Eastern Bluebird | 12,500 | 60.00 |
| 1982 Mockingbird | 12,500 | 60.00 |
| 1982 American Goldfinch | 12,500 | 60.00 |
| 1982 Rosebreasted Grosbeak | 12,500 | 60.00 |
| *Early Memories* | | |
| 1983 Do They Bite? | 7,500 | 75.00 |
| 1983 Tug of War | 7,500 | 75.00 |
| 1984 Explorers | 7,500 | 75.00 |
| 1984 My Turn | 7,500 | 75.00 |
| *Water Babies* | | |
| 1983 Tom and Dragon-Fly | 15 Days | 45.00 |
| 1983 Fairies Take Care of Tom | 15 Days | 45.00 |
| 1983 Tom and Mrs. Do-As-You-Would | 15 Days | 45.00 |
| 1983 Tom and Mrs. Be-Done-By | 15 Days | 45.00 |
| 1984 Tom and Sweet Chest | 15 Days | 45.00 |
| 1984 Ellie Teaches Tom | 15 Days | 45.00 |
| 1984 Tom Takes Care of Baby | 15 Days | 45.00 |
| 1984 Tom and Ellie | 15 Days | 45.00 |
| *Unicorns in Dreamer's Garden (Set of five)* | | |
| 1984 Sound of Melodies | | |
| 1984 Sight of Wonders | | |
| 1984 Smell of Roses | | |
| 1984 Taste of Sweetness | | |
| 1984 Touch of a Dream | 12,500 | 197.50 |
| *Women of Four Seasons* | | |
| 1984 Woman of Spring | 7,500 | 70.00 |
| *Legend of St. George* | | |
| 1985 Knight | 5,000 | 100.00 |
| 1985 Lady | 5,000 | 100.00 |
| 1985 Contest | 5,000 | 100.00 |
| 1985 Wedding | 5,000 | 100.00 |
| *Spring in World of Birds* | | |
| 1985 Pheasants | 2,500 | 325.00 |
| *Concert of Angels* | | |
| 1986 Singing Angel | 7,500 | 80.00 |
| *Wagner Operas* | | |
| 1986 Tristan and Isolde | 5,000 | 125.00 |
| *See also:* | | |
| *Hamilton Collection (U.S.A.)* | | |
| **Kaiser** | | |
| *(Single issue)* | | |
| 1970 Oberammergau Passion Play | Year | 25.00 |
| *(Single issue)* | | |
| 1970 Royal Horse Show–Toronto | 1,000 | 29.00 |
| *Great Yachts* | | |
| 1971 Cetonia | 1,000 | 50.00 |
| 1971 Westward | 1,000 | 50.00 |


| | Edition Limit | Issue Price (US) |
|---|---|---|
| *Anniversary* | | |
| 1972 Love Birds | Year | $ 16.50 |
| 1973 In Park | Year | 18.00 |
| 1974 Canoeing Down River | 7,000 | 22.00 |
| 1975 Tender Moment | 7,000 | 25.00 |
| 1976 Serenade for Lovers | Year | 25.00 |
| 1977 A Simple Gift | Year | 25.00 |
| 1978 Viking Toast | Year | 30.00 |
| 1979 Romantic Interlude | Year | 32.00 |
| 1980 Love at Play | Year | 40.00 |
| 1981 Rendezvous | Year | 40.00 |
| 1982 Betrothal | Year | 40.00 |
| 1983 Sunday Afternoon | Year | 40.00 |
| *Feathered Friends* | | |
| 1978 Blue Jays | 10,000 | 70.00 |
| 1979 Cardinals | 10,000 | 80.00 |
| 1980 Cedar Waxwings | 10,000 | 80.00 |
| 1981 Goldfinches | 10,000 | 80.00 |
| *King Tut* | | |
| 1978 Golden Mask | 15,000 | 65.00 |
| *People of the Midnight Sun* | | |
| 1978 Northern Lullaby | 15,000 | 65.00 |
| 1979 Ilaga, My Friend | 15,000 | 75.00 |
| 1980 Motherhood | 15,000 | 85.00 |
| 1981 Odark and Son Samik | 15,000 | 90.00 |
| 1982 Anana with Little Nutak | 15,000 | 90.00 |
| 1983 Hunter's Reward | 15,000 | 90.00 |
| *Yesterday's World* | | |
| 1978 Time for Dreaming | 5,000 | 70.00 |
| 1979 Summer Is Forever | 5,000 | 75.00 |
| 1980 Sunday Afternoon | 5,000 | 80.00 |
| 1981 Breath of Spring | 5,000 | 80.00 |
| *(Single issue)* | | |
| 1980 Oberammergau Passion Play | Year | 40.00 |
| *Little Men* | | |
| 1980 Magical Moment | 9,500 | 60.00 |
| 1983 A Day to Remember | 9,500 | 60.00 |
| *Four Seasons (Set of four)* | | |
| 1981 Spring | | |
| 1981 Summer | | |
| 1981 Fall | | |
| 1981 Winter | NA | 200.00 |
| *Happy Days* | | |
| 1981 Aeroplane | 5,000 | 75.00 |
| 1982 Julie | 5,000 | 75.00 |
| 1983 Winter Fun | 5,000 | 75.00 |
| 1984 Lookouts | 5,000 | 75.00 |
| *Little Clowns* | | |
| 1981 Red Mask | 9,500 | 35.00 |
| 1982 Pigtails and Puppies | 9,500 | 35.00 |
| 1983 Concertina | 9,500 | 35.00 |
| *Nativity* | | |
| 1981 Old Country Christmas | Year | 20.00 |
| *Romantic Portraits* | | |
| 1981 Lilie | 5,000 | 175.00 |
| 1982 Camelia | 5,000 | 175.00 |
| 1983 Rose | 5,000 | 175.00 |
| 1984 Daisy | 5,000 | 175.00 |
| *Children's Prayers* | | |
| 1982 Now I Lay Me Down to Sleep | 5,000 | 29.50 |
| 1983 Saying Grace | 10,000 | 25.00 |
| *Memories of Christmas* | | |
| 1983 Wonder of Christmas | 19,500 | 42.50 |
| 1984 Christmas Dreams | 19,500 | 42.50 |
| 1985 Christmas Eve | 19,500 | 39.50 |
| 1986 Visit with Santa | 19,500 | 39.50 |
| *Famous Horses* | | |
| 1983 Snow Knight | 3,000 | 95.00 |
| *Traditional Fairy Tales* | | |
| 1983 Cinderella | NA | 39.50 |
| 1983 Jack and Beanstalk | NA | 39.50 |
| 1984 Three Little Pigs | NA | 39.50 |
| 1984 Tom Thumb | NA | 39.50 |
| *Racing for Pride and Profit* | | |
| 1984 Aging Victor | 9,500 | 50.00 |
| 1985 Second Goes Hungry | 9,500 | 50.00 |
| 1986 No Time to Boast | 9,500 | 50.00 |
| 1987 First Fish to Market | 9,500 | 50.00 |
| *Woodland Creatures* | | |
| 1984 Springtime Frolic | 10 Days | 34.95 |
| 1984 Fishing Trip | 10 Days | 34.95 |


| | Edition Limit | Issue Price (US) |
|---|---|---|
| *Bird Dogs* | | |
| 1985 Cocker Spaniel | 15,000 | $ 39.50 |
| 1985 Beagle | 15,000 | 39.50 |
| 1985 English Setter | 15,000 | 39.50 |
| 1985 Black Labrador | 15,000 | 39.50 |
| 1985 German Pointer | 15,000 | 39.50 |
| 1985 Golden Labrador | 15,000 | 39.50 |
| 1985 English Pointer | 15,000 | 39.50 |
| 1985 Irish Setter | 15,000 | 39.50 |
| *Water Fowl* | | |
| 1985 Mallard Ducks | 19,500 | 55.00 |
| 1985 Canvas Back Ducks | 19,500 | 55.00 |
| 1985 Wood Ducks | 19,500 | 55.00 |
| 1986 Pintail Ducks | 19,500 | 55.00 |
| *Harmony in Nature* | | |
| 1985 Spring Encore | NA | 39.50 |
| *Wild Flowers* | | |
| 1985 Trillium | 9,500 | 39.50 |
| 1986 Spring Beauty | 9,500 | 45.00 |
| *See also:* | | |
| *Ghent Collection (U.S.A.)* | | |
| *Hibel Studio (Ger.)* | | |
| **KPM–Royal Berlin** | | |
| *Christmas* | | |
| 1969 Christmas Star | 5,000 | 28.00 |
| 1970 Three Kings | 5,000 | 28.00 |
| 1971 Christmas Tree | 5,000 | 28.00 |
| 1972 Christmas Angel | 5,000 | 31.00 |
| 1973 Christchild on Sled | 5,000 | 33.00 |
| 1974 Angel & Horn | 5,000 | 35.00 |
| 1975 Shepherds | 5,000 | 40.00 |
| 1976 Star of Bethlehem | 5,000 | 43.00 |
| 1977 Mary at Crib | 5,000 | 46.00 |
| 1978 Three Wise Men | 5,000 | 49.00 |
| 1979 At Manger | 5,000 | 55.00 |
| 1980 Shepherd | 5,000 | 59.00 |
| **Lihs-Lindner** | | |
| *Christmas* | | |
| 1972 Little Drummer Boy | 6,000 | 25.00 |
| 1973 Little Carolers | 6,000 | 25.00 |
| 1974 Peace on Earth | 6,000 | 25.00 |
| 1975 Christmas Cheer | 6,000 | 30.00 |
| 1976 Joy of Christmas | 6,000 | 30.00 |
| 1977 Holly-Jolly Christmas | 6,000 | 30.00 |
| *Mother's Day* | | |
| 1972 Mother and Child | 1,000 | 25.00 |
| 1973 Mother and Child | 2,000 | 25.00 |
| 1974 Bouquet for Mother | 2,000 | 25.00 |
| 1975 We Wish You Happiness | 2,000 | 28.00 |
| *Union Pacific Railroad* | | |
| 1972 Union Pacific | 1,500 | 22.00 |
| 1973 Union Pacific Big Boy | 1,500 | 25.00 |
| *History* | | |
| 1973 Tribute to Flag | 3,000 | 60.00 |
| 1974 Golden Spike Centennial | 1,500 | 40.00 |
| *Easter* | | |
| 1973 Happy Easter | 1,500 | 25.00 |
| 1974 Springtime | 1,500 | 25.00 |
| 1975 With Love to You at Easter | 1,500 | 28.00 |
| *America Beautiful* | | |
| 1975 Independence Hall | 1,500 | 42.00 |
| 1975 Statue of Liberty | 1,500 | 42.00 |
| 1975 Niagara Falls | 1,500 | 42.00 |
| 1975 Grand Canyon | 1,500 | 42.00 |
| 1975 Golden State | 1,500 | 42.00 |
| 1975 Capitol | 1,500 | 42.00 |
| *Bicentennial* | | |
| 1976 Freedom Train | 1,500 | 45.00 |
| 1976 Spirit of America | 3,500 | 45.00 |
| *Playmates* | | |
| 1976 Timmy and His Pal | 5,000 | 45.00 |
| 1977 Heidi and Playmate | 5,000 | 45.00 |
| *Golden Spike Centennial* | | |
| 1977 Central Pacific Jupiter | 1,500 | 25.00 |
| 1977 Union Pacific 119 | 1,500 | 25.00 |
| *A Child's Christmas* | | |
| 1978 Holy Night | 5,000 | 40.00 |
| **Marmot** | | |
| *Father's Day* | | |
| 1970 Stag | 3,500 | 12.00 |
| 1971 Horse | 3,500 | 12.50 |


| | Edition Limit | Issue Price (US) |
|---|---|---|
| *Christmas* | | |
| 1970 Polar Bear | 5,000 | $ 13. |
| 1971 Buffalo | 5,000 | 14. |
| 1972 Boy & Grandfather | 5,000 | 20. |
| 1973 Snowman | 3,000 | 20. |
| 1974 Dancing Children | 2,000 | 24. |
| 1975 Covey of Quail | 2,000 | 30. |
| 1976 Windmill | 2,000 | 30. |
| *Presidents* | | |
| 1971 Washington | 1,500 | 25. |
| 1972 Jefferson | 1,500 | 25. |
| 1973 John Adams | 1,500 | 25. |
| *Mother's Day* | | |
| 1972 Seal | 6,000 | 16. |
| 1973 Polar Bear | 2,000 | 20. |
| 1974 Penguins | 2,000 | 24. |
| 1975 Raccoons | 2,000 | 30. |
| 1976 Ducks | 2,000 | 40. |
| **Meissen** | | |
| *Annual* | | |
| 1973 Winter Countryside by Sleigh | 5,000 | 71. |
| 1974 Sleeping Beauty | 5,000 | 75. |
| 1975 Archway to Albrecht's Castle | 5,500 | 92. |
| 1976 Doge's Palace in Venice | 5,000 | 92. |
| 1977 Fra Holle | 5,000 | 114. |
| 1978 Ice Crystal with Children | 7,000 | 123. |
| 1979 Winter Fairy Tale | 7,000 | 151. |
| 1980 Booted Cat | NA | 155. |
| **Mueller** | | |
| *Christmas* | | |
| 1971 Christmas in Tyrol | Year | 20. |
| 1972 Christmas Messenger | Year | 15. |
| 1973 Bringing Home Tree | Year | 20. |
| 1974 Trimming Tree | Year | 25. |
| 1975 Family on Christmas Morning | Year | 27. |
| 1976 Christmas Fire | Year | 28. |
| 1977 Ice Skating | Year | 28. |
| *Father's Day* | | |
| 1973 Three Generations | NA | 17. |
| 1974 Fishing | NA | 20. |
| 1975 Hiking | NA | 27. |
| **Porcelaine Ariel** | | |
| *See: Hamilton Collection (U.S.A.)* | | |
| **Rosenthal** | | |
| *Annual (Porcelain)* | | |
| 1971 Tapio Wirkkala | 3,000 | N |
| 1972 Natale Sapone | 3,000 | N |
| 1973 Otto Piene | 3,000 | N |
| 1974 Gunther Fruhtrunk | 3,000 | N |
| 1975 Srivastava Narendra | 3,000 | N |
| 1976 Salvador Dali | 3,000 | N |
| 1977 Victor Vasarely | 3,000 | N |
| 1978 E. Paolozzi | 3,000 | N |
| 1979 Arnold Leissler | 3,000 | N |
| 1980 O.H. Hajek | 3,000 | N |
| *Artist Plates** | | |
| 1973 NR 1 Gunter Grass | 5,000 | N |
| 1974 NR 2 Jean Cocteau | 5,000 | N |
| 1974 NR 3 Eugen Gomringer | 5,000 | N |
| 1974 NR 4 Otto Piene | 5,000 | N |
| 1975 NR 5 Max Bill | 5,000 | N |
| 1975 NR 6 Hans-Werner Henze | 5,000 | N |
| 1975 NR 7 Bjørn Wiinblad | 5,000 | N |
| 1975 NR 8 Kriwet | 5,000 | N |
| 1976 NR 9 Hildegard Knef | 5,000 | N |
| 1977 NR10 Yehudi Menuhin | 5,000 | N |
| 1977 NR11 Emilio Pucci | 5,000 | N |
| 1978 NR12 Salvador Dali | 5,000 | N |
| 1978 NR13 Victor Vasarely | 5,000 | N |
| 1978 NR14 Almir Mazignier | 5,000 | N |
| 1979 NR15 Ivan Rapuzin | 5,000 | N |
| 1979 NR16 Ottmar Alt | 5,000 | N |
| *Series not available in U.S. | | |
| *Satire Plates** | | |
| NR1 Konrad Adenauer | 5,000 | N |
| NR2 Willy Brandt | 5,000 | N |
| NR3 Theodor Heuss | 5,000 | N |
| NR4 Walter Scheel | 5,000 | N |
| NR5 Helmut Schmidt | 5,000 | N |

| | Edition Limit | Issue Price (US) |
|---|---|---|
| R6 Franz-Josef Strauss | 5,000 | NA |
| R7 Helmut Kohl | 5,000 | NA |
| R8 Heinz Ruhmann | 5,000 | NA |
| R9 Herbert Von Karajan | 5,000 | NA |
| R10 Marlene Dietrich | 5,000 | NA |
| R11 Mao-Tse-Tung | 5,000 | NA |
| R12 Bruno Kreisky | 5,000 | NA |
| eries not available in U.S. | | |
| *nnual (Crystal)* | | |
| 74 Otto Piene (Clear) | 3,000 | $200.00 |
| 74 Otto Piene (Gold Inlaid) | 3,000 | 250.00 |
| 74 Otto Piene (Platinum Inlaid) | 3,000 | 250.00 |
| 75 G. Uecker | 3,000 | 200.00 |
| 76 Bjørn Wiinblad | 3,000 | NA |
| 77 Gunter F. Ris | 3,000 | NA |
| 78 Ivan Rapuzin | 3,000 | 600.00 |
| 79 Salvador Dali | 3,000 | NA |
| 80 Ernst Fuchs | 3,000 | NA |
| *rraine Trester* | | |
| 75 Once Upon a Summertime | 5,000 | 60.00 |
| 76 One Lovely Yesterday | 5,000 | 70.00 |
| *ntasies and Fables* | | |
| 76 Oriental Night Music | NA | 50.00 |
| 77 Mandolin Players | NA | 55.00 |
| *iinblad Studio-Linie* | | |
| 76 Madonna | 2,000 | 150.00 |
| 77 Annunciation | 2,000 | 195.00 |
| 78 Three Kings | 2,000 | 225.00 |
| 79 Holy Family | 2,000 | 230.00 |
| 80 Appearance of Angels | 2,000 | 240.00 |
| 81 Adoration of Shepherds | 2,000 | 295.00 |
| *addin* | | |
| 79 Aladdin and Lamp | NA | 65.00 |
| 79 Aladdin and Street Urchins | NA | 65.00 |
| 80 Aladdin and Magician | NA | 65.00 |
| 80 Aladdin in Garden | NA | 65.00 |
| 81 Aladdin and Spirit | NA | 85.00 |
| 81 Aladdin and Princess | NA | 85.00 |
| 82 Aladdin's Mother and Genie | NA | 85.00 |
| 82 Aladdin's Mother and Sultan | NA | 85.00 |
| 83 Aladdin Rides to Palace | NA | 85.00 |
| 83 Genie Builds Palace | NA | 85.00 |
| *hristmas Carols* | | |
| 83 Silent Night | NA | 195.00 |
| 84 Jingle Bells | NA | 195.00 |
| 85 We Three Kings of Orient Are | NA | 195.00 |
| 86 O Tannenbaum | NA | 225.00 |
| *rables in Glass* | | |
| 86 Rich Man and Beggar | NA | 295.00 |
| *e also:* | | |
| *ibel Studio (Ger.)* | | |
| *rn Collectibles (U.S.A.)* | | |
| **oyal Bayreuth** | | |
| *e: Kern Collectibles (U.S.A.)* | | |
| **oyal Tettau** | | |
| *pal Plates* | | |
| 71 Pope Paul VI | 5,000 | 100.00 |
| 72 Pope John XXIII | 5,000 | 100.00 |
| 73 Pope Pius XII | 5,000 | 100.00 |
| *hristmas (Single issue)* | | |
| 72 Carriage in Village | NA | 12.50 |
| **oyale** | | |
| *hristmas* | | |
| 69 Christmas Fair in Ebeltoft | 6,000 | 12.00 |
| 70 Kalundborg Church | 10,000 | 13.00 |
| 71 Christmas Night | 8,000 | 16.00 |
| 72 Elks | 8,000 | 16.00 |
| 73 Christmas | 6,000 | 20.00 |
| 74 Village at Christmas | 5,000 | 22.00 |
| 75 Feeding Time | 5,000 | 26.00 |
| 76 Christmas at Seaport | 5,000 | 27.50 |
| 77 Sledding | 5,000 | 30.00 |
| *other's Day* | | |
| 70 Swan and Brood | 6,000 | 12.00 |
| 71 Doe and Fawn | 9,000 | 13.00 |

| | Edition Limit | Issue Price (US) |
|---|---|---|
| 1972 Rabbit Family | 9,000 | $ 16.00 |
| 1973 Owl Family | 6,000 | 18.00 |
| 1974 Duck Family | 5,000 | 22.00 |
| 1975 Lynx Family | 5,000 | 26.00 |
| 1976 Woodcock and Young | 5,000 | 27.50 |
| 1977 Koala Bear | 5,000 | 30.00 |
| *Father's Day* | | |
| 1970 U.S. Frigate Constitution | 5,000 | 13.00 |
| 1971 Man Fishing | 5,000 | 13.00 |
| 1972 Mountain Climber | 6,000 | 16.00 |
| 1973 Camping | 4,000 | 18.00 |
| 1974 Eagle | 2,500 | 22.00 |
| 1975 Regatta | 2,500 | 26.00 |
| 1976 Hunting Scene | 2,500 | 27.50 |
| 1977 Fishing | 5,000 | 30.00 |
| *Game* | | |
| 1972 Setters Pointing Quail | 500 | 180.00 |
| 1973 Fox | 500 | 200.00 |
| 1974 Osprey | 250 | 250.00 |
| 1975 California Quail | 250 | 265.00 |
| **Royale Germania** | | |
| *Annual* | | |
| 1970 Orchid (Blue) | 600 | 200.00 |
| 1971 Cyclamen (Red) | 1,000 | 200.00 |
| 1972 Silver Thistle (Green) | 1,000 | 250.00 |
| 1973 Tulips (Lilac) | 600 | 275.00 |
| 1974 Sunflowers (Topaz) | 500 | 300.00 |
| 1975 Snowdrops (Amber) | 350 | 450.00 |
| 1976 Flaming Heart (Red) | 350 | 450.00 |
| *Mother's Day* | | |
| 1971 Roses (Red) | 250 | 135.00 |
| 1972 Elephant (Green) | 750 | 180.00 |
| 1973 Koala Bear (Lilac) | 600 | 200.00 |
| 1974 Squirrels (Topaz) | 500 | 240.00 |
| 1975 Swan Family (Amber) | 350 | 250.00 |
| **Schmid** | | |
| *Bavarian Christmas* | | |
| 1971 Family Portrait | 5,000 | 25.50 |
| 1972 On Horseback | 5,000 | 26.50 |
| 1973 Bringing Home Tree | 5,000 | 26.50 |
| 1974 Decorating Tree | 5,000 | 26.50 |
| 1975 Opening Presents | 5,000 | 26.50 |
| 1976 By Fireside | 5,000 | 26.50 |
| 1977 Skating | 5,000 | 28.50 |
| 1978 Family Picking Tree | 5,000 | 36.00 |
| 1979 Breakfast by Tree | 5,000 | 45.00 |
| 1980 Feeding Animals | 5,000 | 55.00 |
| *Ferrandiz Christmas* | | |
| 1972 Christ in Manger | Year | 30.00 |
| 1973 Christmas | Year | 30.00 |
| *Golden Moments* | | |
| 1978 Tranquility | 15,000 | 250.00 |
| *Christmas (Pewter)* | | |
| 1977 Santa | 5,000 | 30.00 |
| 1978 Beautiful Snow | 5,000 | 45.00 |
| 1979 I Hear America Singing | 6,000 | 50.00 |
| *Ferrandiz Mother and Child* | | |
| 1977 Orchard Mother | 10,000 | 65.00 |
| 1978 Pastoral Mother | 10,000 | 75.00 |
| 1979 Floral Mother | 10,000 | 95.00 |
| 1980 Avian Mother | 10,000 | 100.00 |
| *Beatrix Potter (Pewter)* | | |
| 1978 Peter Rabbit | 5,000 | 50.00 |
| 1979 Jemima-Puddle Duck | 5,000 | 50.00 |
| *Reflections of Life* | | |
| 1980 Quiet Reflections | 10,000 | 85.00 |
| 1981 Tree of Life | 10,000 | 85.00 |
| *Country Pride* | | |
| 1981 Surprise in Cellar | 7,500 | 35.00 |
| 1981 Plum Tuckered Out | 7,500 | 35.00 |
| 1981 Duke's Mixture | 7,500 | 35.00 |
| 1982 Bustin with Pride | 7,500 | 35.00 |
| *Music Makers* | | |
| 1981 Flutist | 10,000 | 25.00 |
| 1982 Entertainer | 10,000 | 25.00 |
| 1982 Magical Medley | 10,000 | 25.00 |
| 1982 Sweet Serenade | 10,000 | 25.00 |
| *My Name Is Star* | | |
| 1981 Star's Spring | 10,000 | 30.00 |
| 1981 Star's Summer | 10,000 | 30.00 |
| 1982 Star's Autumn | 10,000 | 30.00 |
| 1982 Star's Winter | 10,000 | 30.00 |

| | Edition Limit | Issue Price (US) |
|---|---|---|
| *Beautiful Bounty* | | |
| 1982 Summer's Golden Harvest | 10,000 | $ 40.00 |
| 1982 Autumn's Blessing | 10,000 | 40.00 |
| 1983 A Mid-Winter's Dream | 10,000 | 40.00 |
| 1983 Spring Blossoms | 10,000 | 40.00 |
| *Cat Tales* | | |
| 1982 Right Church, Wrong Pew | 12,500 | 37.50 |
| 1982 Company's Coming | 12,500 | 37.50 |
| 1983 Flew Coop | 12,500 | 37.50 |
| 1983 On Move | 12,500 | 37.50 |
| *Prairie Women* | | |
| 1982 Maiden | 12,500 | 35.00 |
| 1982 Courtship Blanket | 12,500 | 35.00 |
| 1983 Mother Now | 12,500 | 35.00 |
| 1983 Passing of Moons | 12,500 | 35.00 |
| *Carousel Fantasies* | | |
| 1983 A Fairy Tale Princess | 7,500 | 50.00 |
| *Lowell Davis Christmas* | | |
| 1983 Country Christmas | 7,500 | 45.00 |
| 1984 Country Christmas | 7,500 | 45.00 |
| 1985 Christmas at Foxfire | 7,500 | 45.00 |
| 1986 Christmas at Red Oak | 7,500 | 45.00 |
| 1987 Blossom's Gift | 7,500 | 47.50 |
| *(Single issue)* | | |
| 1983 Critics | 12,500 | 45.00 |
| *Gift of Happiness* | | |
| 1984 Lilies of Field | 7,500 | 125.00 |
| 1984 Morning Glories | 7,500 | 125.00 |
| *Good Ol' Days (Set of two)* | | |
| 1984 Waiting for Master | | |
| 1984 Minutes Like Hours | 5,000 | 60.00 |
| *Nature's Treasures* | | |
| 1984 Rose Haven/Sparrow | 5,000 | 45.00 |
| 1984 Tulip Nest/Robin | 5,000 | 45.00 |
| 1984 Leafy Bower/Oriole | 5,000 | 45.00 |
| 1984 Nesting/Mockingbird | 5,000 | 45.00 |
| *Prime Time* | | |
| 1984 Love Boat | NA | 30.00 |
| 1984 Dynasty | NA | 30.00 |
| 1984 Dallas | NA | 30.00 |
| *Statuette* | | |
| 1984 Hark Herald | Year | 40.00 |
| *Red Oak Sampler* | | |
| 1986 General Store | 5,000 | 45.00 |
| 1987 Country Wedding | 5,000 | 47.50 |
| *(Single issue)* | | |
| 1986 Home from Market | 7,500 | 55.00 |
| *(Single issue)* | | |
| 1987 Snow White and the Seven Dwarfs | 5,000 | 47.50 |
| *See also: Addams Family (U.S.A.)* | | |
| **Schumann** | | |
| *Composers* | | |
| 1970 Beethoven | NA | 8.00 |
| 1972 Mozart | NA | 13.00 |
| *Christmas* | | |
| 1971 Snow Scene | 10,000 | 12.00 |
| 1972 Deer in Snow | 15,000 | 12.00 |
| 1973 Weihnachten | 5,000 | 12.00 |
| 1974 Church in Snow | 5,000 | 12.00 |
| 1975 Fountain | 5,000 | 12.00 |
| *See also:* | | |
| *Christian Bell (Can.)* | | |
| *Calhoun's Collector's Society (U.S.A.)* | | |
| **Stumar** | | |
| *Christmas* | | |
| 1970 Angel | 10,000 | 8.00 |
| 1971 Old Canal | 10,000 | 8.00 |
| 1972 Countryside | 10,000 | 8.00 |
| 1973 Friendship | 10,000 | 10.00 |
| 1974 Making Fancy | 10,000 | 10.00 |
| 1975 Preparation | 10,000 | 10.00 |
| 1976 Drummer Boy | 10,000 | 10.00 |
| 1977 Joyful Expectations | 10,000 | 15.00 |
| 1978 Christmas | 10,000 | 19.50 |
| *Mother's Day* | | |
| 1971 Amish Mother & Daughter | 10,000 | 8.00 |
| 1972 Children | 10,000 | 8.00 |
| 1973 Mother Sewing | 10,000 | 10.00 |
| 1974 Mother Cradle | 10,000 | 10.00 |

| | Edition Limit | Issue Price (US) |
|---|---|---|
| 1975 Baking | 10,000 | $ 10.00 |
| 1976 Reading to Children | 10,000 | 15.00 |
| 1977 Comforting Child | 10,000 | 15.00 |
| 1978 Tranquility | 10,000 | 19.50 |
| *Egyptian* | | |
| 1977 Ancient Egyptian Trilogy | 5,000 | 45.00 |
| 1978 Charioteer | 5,000 | 54.00 |
| **Tirschenreuth** | | |
| *Christmas* | | |
| 1969 Homestead | 3,500 | 12.00 |
| 1970 Church | 3,500 | 12.00 |
| 1971 Star of Bethlehem | 3,500 | 12.00 |
| 1972 Elk Silhouette | 2,000 | 13.00 |
| 1973 Christmas | Year | 14.00 |
| **Villeroy & Boch** | | |
| *Christmas* | | |
| 1977 Holy Family | 10,000 | 175.00 |
| 1978 Three Holy Kings | 20,000 | 175.00 |
| 1979 Mary with Child | 10,000 | 198.00 |
| 1980 Madonna in Glory | 10,000 | 200.00 |
| 1981 Mary Glorious | 10,000 | 210.00 |
| *World Wildlife* | | |
| 1983 Panda Bear | Year | 38.00 |
| 1983 Tiger | Year | 38.00 |
| 1984 Otter | Year | 38.00 |
| 1984 Orangutan | Year | 38.00 |
| 1985 Seal | Year | 38.00 |
| *Enchanted Fairyland Lovers* | | |
| 1982 Prince | NA | 39.00 |
| 1982 Ivan and Horse | NA | 39.00 |
| 1982 Princess and Stag | NA | 39.00 |
| 1983 Goose Girl | NA | 39.00 |
| 1983 Cinderella | NA | 39.00 |
| 1983 Prince Ahmed and Peri | NA | 39.00 |
| 1984 Ta-Khai and Bird Feng | NA | 39.00 |
| 1984 Fisherman and Dragon King's Daughter | NA | 39.00 |
| *French Fairy Tales* | | |
| 1983 Fortunata and Hen | 19,750 | 70.00 |
| 1983 King of Peacocks | 19,750 | 70.00 |
| 1983 King and Puss in Boots | 19,750 | 70.00 |
| 1984 In Search of Phoenix | 19,750 | 70.00 |
| 1984 Princess Radiant and Phoenix | 19,750 | 70.00 |
| 1985 Monkeys in Garden | 19,750 | 70.00 |
| 1985 Florina and Fairy Pie | 19,750 | 70.00 |
| 1986 Uglinette and Pagodies | 19,750 | 70.00 |
| *Exotic Birds* | | |
| 1984 Fiery Parakeet | 15,000 | 70.00 |
| 1984 Long-Billed Cockatoo | 15,000 | 70.00 |
| 1985 Black-Billed Cockatoo | 15,000 | 70.00 |
| *Dreams of Katharina* | | |
| 1985 Katharina Receives Love | 20,000 | 75.00 |
| 1986 Dream Castle | NA | 75.00 |
| *Famous Sea Battles* | | |
| 1986 Battle of East India | NA | 42.00 |
| *(Single issue)* | | |
| 1985 Golden Lady | 1,000 | 150.00 |
| *(Single issue)* | | |
| 1986 Symbols of Freedom | 21 Days | 38.00 |
| *(Single issue)* | | |
| 1986 Liberty Bas Relief | 21 Days | 32.00 |
| *(Single issue)* | | |
| 1986 Liberty Centennial | 21 Days | 35.00 |
| **WMF Geislingen** | | |
| *Annual* | | |
| 1978 Rose-Motif I | 2,500 | 117.50 |
| 1979 Rose-Motif-II | 2,500 | 120.00 |
| 1980 Rose-Motif III | 2,500 | 120.00 |
| *Christmas* | | |
| 1978 Birth of Christ | 2,500 | 117.50 |
| 1979 Praising King | 2,500 | 120.00 |
| 1980 Praising Shepherd | 2,500 | 120.00 |

## GREAT BRITAIN

| | Edition Limit | Issue Price (US) |
|---|---|---|
| **Aynsley** | | |
| *A Christmas Carol* | | |
| 1979 Mr. Fezziwig's Ball | Year | 30.00 |
| 1980 Marley's Ghost | Year | 36.00 |
| 1981 Cratchit Family | Year | 41.00 |
| 1982 Christmas Day | Year | 41.00 |

# OVER-THE-COUNTER ISSUES

| | Edition Limit | Issue Price (US) |
|---|---|---|
| **Belleek** | | |
| *Irish Countryside Christmas* | | |
| 1984 Irish White Beam | 10,000 | $ 95.00 |
| 1985 Irish Heather | 10,000 | 95.00 |
| 1986 Wild Irish Rose | 10,000 | 95.00 |
| *St. Patrick's Day Annual* | | |
| 1985 Slemish Mountain | 10,000 | 75.00 |
| 1986 Banishing Snakes | 10,000 | 75.00 |
| *(Single issue)* | | |
| 1986 First Sight of Liberty | NA | 55.00 |
| **Boehm Studios** | | |
| *European Bird Plates* | | |
| 1973 Swallow | 5,000 | 48.75 |
| 1973 Chaffinch | 5,000 | 48.75 |
| 1973 Coal Tit | 5,000 | 48.75 |
| 1973 Tree Sparrow | 5,000 | 48.75 |
| 1973 King Fisher | 5,000 | 48.75 |
| 1973 Gold Crest | 5,000 | 48.75 |
| 1973 Blue Tit | 5,000 | 48.75 |
| 1973 Linnet | 5,000 | 48.75 |
| *Honor America* | | |
| 1974 American Bald Eagle | 12,000 | 85.00 |
| *Butterfly* | | |
| 1975 Blue Mountain Swallowtails | 100 | 450.00 |
| 1975 Jezabels | 100 | 450.00 |
| 1976 Comma with Loops | 100 | 450.00 |
| 1976 African Butterflies | 100 | 450.00 |
| 1976 Solandras Maxima | 100 | 450.00 |
| *Hard Fruit* | | |
| 1975 Plums | 100 | 450.00 |
| 1975 Pears | 100 | 450.00 |
| 1976 Peaches | 100 | 450.00 |
| 1976 Apples | 100 | 450.00 |
| *Oriental Birds* | | |
| 1975 Bluebacked Fairy Bluebirds | 100 | 400.00 |
| 1975 Azure-Winged Magpies | 100 | 400.00 |
| 1976 Golden-Fronted Leafbird | 100 | 400.00 |
| 1976 Golden-Throated Barbet | 100 | 400.00 |
| *Seashell* | | |
| 1975 Violet Spider Conch | 100 | 450.00 |
| 1975 Rooster Tail Conch | 100 | 450.00 |
| 1976 Orange Spider Conch | 100 | 450.00 |
| 1976 Cheragra Spider Conch | 100 | 450.00 |
| *Soft Fruit* | | |
| 1975 Loganberries | 100 | 450.00 |
| 1975 Cherries | 100 | 450.00 |
| 1976 Strawberries | 100 | 450.00 |
| 1976 Grapes | 100 | 450.00 |
| *Butterflies of World* | | |
| 1978 Monarch and Daisy | 5,000 | 62.00 |
| 1978 Red Admiral and Thistle | 5,000 | 62.00 |
| *Flower* | | |
| 1975 Lilies | 100 | 450.00 |
| 1975 Passion Flowers | 100 | 450.00 |
| 1976 Double Clematis | 100 | 450.00 |
| *Favorite Floral* | | |
| 1978 Clematis | 2,500 | 58.00 |
| 1978 Rhododendron | 2,500 | 58.00 |
| 1979 Boehm Orchid | 2,500 | 58.00 |
| 1979 Yellow Rose | 2,500 | 58.00 |
| 1980 Spider Orchid | 2,500 | 58.00 |
| 1980 Dahlia | 2,500 | 58.00 |
| *Musical Maidens of Imperial Dynasties* | | |
| 1984 Balloon Guitar | 15,000 | 65.00 |
| 1984 Three-Stringed Guitar | 15,000 | 65.00 |
| 1984 Harp | 15,000 | 65.00 |
| 1984 Gong | 15,000 | 65.00 |
| 1984 Reen Organ | 15,000 | 65.00 |
| 1984 Ceremonial Flute | 15,000 | 65.00 |
| 1984 Lute | 15,000 | 65.00 |
| 1984 Common Flute | 15,000 | 65.00 |
| *See also: Hamilton Collection (U.S.A.)* | | |
| **Caithness Glass** | | |
| *America's Favorite Birds* | | |
| 1979 Crystal Wren | 5,000 | 79.50 |
| **Coalport** | | |
| *Christmas* | | |
| 1976 Christmas Eve | Year | $ 12.00 |
| 1977 Dangerous Skating | Year | 16.00 |
| 1978 Alas! Poor Bruin | Year | 18.00 |
| 1979 Christmas Morning | Year | 22.00 |
| 1980 Blind Man's Bluff | Year | 27.00 |
| 1981 Skating | Year | 32.50 |
| 1982 Snapdragon | Year | 35.00 |
| 1983 Trafalgar Square | Year | 35.00 |
| *Mother's Day* | | |
| 1978 Clematis | Year | 16.00 |
| 1979 Orchid | Year | 21.00 |
| 1980 Peony | Year | 27.00 |
| 1981 Rose | Year | 30.00 |
| *(Single issue)* | | |
| 1972 Indy 500 | 2,000 | 49.95 |
| **Crown Staffordshire** | | |
| *Wildlife in Winter* | | |
| 1982 Tranquility | 10,000 | 55.00 |
| 1983 Winter's Orphan | 10,000 | 55.00 |
| 1983 Early Awakening | 10,000 | 55.00 |
| 1984 Vigilance | 10,000 | 55.00 |
| **Hornsea** | | |
| *Christmas* | | |
| 1979 "C"–Nativity | 10,000 | 21.00 |
| 1980 "H"–Mary and Child | 10,000 | 25.00 |
| 1981 "R"–Three Wise Men | 10,000 | 30.00 |
| 1982 "I" –At Inn | 10,000 | 32.50 |
| 1983 "S"–Shepherds | 10,000 | 35.00 |
| **Mason** | | |
| *Christmas* | | |
| 1975 Windsor Castle | Year | 75.00 |
| 1976 Holyrood House | Year | 75.00 |
| 1977 Buckingham Palace | Year | 75.00 |
| 1978 Balmoral Castle | Year | 75.00 |
| 1979 Hampton Court | Year | 75.00 |
| 1980 Sandringham House | Year | 75.00 |
| **Poole Pottery** | | |
| *Medieval Calendar* | | |
| 1972 Drinking Wine by Fire (January) | 1,000 | 100.00 |
| 1972 Chopping Wood (February) | 1,000 | 100.00 |
| 1973 Digging in Fields and Setting Seeds (March) | 1,000 | 125.00 |
| 1973 Carrying Flowering Branch (April) | 1,000 | 125.00 |
| 1974 Hawking (May) | 1,000 | 125.00 |
| 1974 Mowing Hay (June) | 1,000 | 125.00 |
| 1975 Cutting Corn with Sickle (July) | 1,000 | 125.00 |
| 1975 Threshing with Flail (August) | 1,000 | 125.00 |
| 1976 Picking Grapes (September) | 1,000 | 125.00 |
| 1976 Sowing Winter Corn (October) | 1,000 | 125.00 |
| 1977 Gathering Acorns to Feed Pigs (November) | 1,000 | 125.00 |
| 1977 Pig Killing (December) | 1,000 | 125.00 |
| *Cathedral* | | |
| 1973 Christ on Cross | 11,000 | 125.00 |
| *Christmas* | | |
| 1973 Adoration of Magi | 1,000 | 125.00 |
| 1973 Flight into Egypt | 1,000 | 125.00 |
| *Home at Christmas* | | |
| 1978 Santa's Helpers | 10,000 | 37.50 |
| 1979 Three Wisemen | 10,000 | 37.50 |
| *Birds of North America* | | |
| 1979 Great Horned Owl | 10,000 | 37.50 |
| *Mother's Day* | | |
| 1979 Tenderness | 10,000 | 37.50 |
| **Rhea Silva** | | |
| *Feline Favourites* | | |
| 1982 Long Haired Ladies | 10,000 | 47.00 |
| 1983 Siamese & Apple Blossoms | 10,000 | 47.00 |
| 1984 Abyssinian Playmates | 10,000 | 47.00 |
| *Child's Garden of Verses* | | |
| 1983 Land of Counterpane | 17,500 | 39.00 |
| *Portraits of Countryside* | | |
| 1983 Autumn Wayside | 5,000 | $ 79.00 |
| *Endangered Birds* | | |
| 1984 Whooping Crane | 5,000 | 60.00 |
| **Royal Doulton** | | |
| *Flower Garden* | | |
| 1975 Spring Harmony | 15,000 | 60.00 |
| 1976 Dreaming Lotus | 15,000 | 65.00 |
| 1977 Poet's Garden | 15,000 | 70.00 |
| 1978 Country Bouquet | 15,000 | 70.00 |
| 1980 From My Mother's Garden | 15,000 | 85.00 |
| *Ports of Call* | | |
| 1975 San Francisco | 15,000 | 60.00 |
| 1976 New Orleans | 15,000 | 65.00 |
| 1977 Venice | 15,000 | 70.00 |
| 1978 Montmartre | 15,000 | 70.00 |
| *Reflections on China* | | |
| 1976 Garden of Tranquility | 15,000 | 70.00 |
| 1977 Imperial Palace | 15,000 | 70.00 |
| 1978 Temple of Heaven | 15,000 | 75.00 |
| 1980 Lake of Mists | 15,000 | 85.00 |
| *I Remember America* | | |
| 1977 Pennsylvania Pastorale | 15,000 | 70.00 |
| 1978 Lovejoy Bridge | 15,000 | 70.00 |
| 1979 Four Corners | 15,000 | 75.00 |
| 1980 Marshlands | 15,000 | 95.00 |
| *Victorian Christmas* | | |
| 1977 Skater | Year | 25.00 |
| 1978 Victorian Girl | Year | 27.50 |
| 1979 Sleigh Ride | Year | 29.95 |
| 1980 Victorian Christmas | Year | 32.50 |
| 1981 Carolers | Year | 37.50 |
| 1982 Santa Claus | Year | 37.50 |
| *All God's Children* | | |
| 1978 Brighter Day | 10,000 | 60.00 |
| 1980 Village Children | 10,000 | 65.00 |
| 1981 Noble Heritage | 10,000 | 85.00 |
| 1982 Buddies | 10,000 | 85.00 |
| 1983 Little Brother | 10,000 | 95.00 |
| 1985 Sisterly Love | 10,000 | 95.00 |
| *American Tapestries* | | |
| 1978 Sleigh Bells | 10,000 | 70.00 |
| 1979 Pumpkin Patch | 10,000 | 70.00 |
| 1980 General Store | 10,000 | 95.00 |
| 1981 Fourth of July | 10,000 | 95.00 |
| *Jungle Fantasy* | | |
| 1979 Ark | 10,000 | 75.00 |
| 1980 Compassion | 10,000 | 95.00 |
| 1981 Patience | 10,000 | 95.00 |
| 1982 Refuge | 10,000 | 95.00 |
| *(Single issue)* | | |
| 1980 Winning Colors | 15,000 | 80.00 |
| *Behind Painted Masque* | | |
| 1982 Painted Feelings | 10,000 | 95.00 |
| 1983 Make Me Laugh | 10,000 | 95.00 |
| 1983 Minstrel Serenade | 10,000 | 95.00 |
| 1984 Pleasing Performance | 10,000 | 95.00 |
| *Celebration of Faith* | | |
| 1982 Rosh Hashanah | 7,500 | 250.00 |
| 1982 Passover | 7,500 | 250.00 |
| 1983 Yom Kippur | 7,500 | 250.00 |
| 1983 Chanukah | 7,500 | 250.00 |
| *Children of Pueblo* | | |
| 1983 Apple Flower | 10,000 | 60.00 |
| 1983 Morning Star | 10,000 | 60.00 |
| *Christmas Carol* | | |
| 1983 Silent Night | Year | 39.95 |
| 1984 While Shepherds Watched | Year | 39.95 |
| 1985 Oh, Little Town of Bethlehem | NA | 39.95 |
| 1986 I Saw Three Ships | NA | 39.95 |
| *Festival Children of World* | | |
| 1983 Mariani (Bali) | 15,000 | 65.00 |
| 1983 Magdalena (Mexico) | 15,000 | 65.00 |
| 1984 Michiko (Japan) | 15,000 | 65.00 |
| 1984 Monika (Poland) | 15,000 | 65.00 |
| 1985 Maureen | 15,000 | 65.00 |
| 1985 Marijke | 15,000 | 65.00 |
| *Grandest Gift* | | |
| 1984 Reunion | 10,000 | 75.00 |
| 1985 Storytime | 10,000 | 75.00 |
| **Royal Grafton** | | |
| *Twelve Days of Christmas* | | |
| 1976 Partridge in Pear Tree | 3,000 | $ 17.50 |
| 1977 Two Turtle Doves | 3,000 | 17.50 |
| 1978 Three French Hens | 3,000 | 21.50 |
| 1979 Four Colly Birds | 3,000 | 26.50 |
| 1980 Five Gold Rings | 3,000 | 35.00 |
| 1981 Six Geese A'Laying | 3,000 | 38.50 |
| 1982 Seven Swans A'Swimming | 3,000 | 40.00 |
| 1983 Eight Maids A'Milking | 3,000 | 41.00 |
| **Royal Worcester** | | |
| *Doughty Bird* | | |
| 1972 Redstarts and Beech | 2,750 | 125.00 |
| 1973 Myrtle Warbler/Cherry | 3,000 | 175.00 |
| 1974 Blue-Grey Gnatcatchers | 3,000 | 195.00 |
| 1975 Blackburnian Warbler | 3,000 | 195.00 |
| 1976 Blue-Winged Sivas | 3,000 | 195.00 |
| 1977 Paradise Wydah | 3,000 | 195.00 |
| 1978 Bluetits/Witch Hazel | 3,000 | 195.00 |
| 1979 Mountain Bluebird | 3,000 | 195.00 |
| 1980 Cerulean Warblers | 3,000 | 315.00 |
| 1981 Willow Warbler | 3,000 | 330.00 |
| 1982 Ruby-Crowned Kinglets | 3,000 | 330.00 |
| 1983 Bewick's Wren | 3,000 | 330.00 |
| *Bicentennial* | | |
| 1976 Independence | 10,000 | 150.00 |
| *Fabulous Birds* | | |
| 1976 Peacocks I | 10,000 | 65.00 |
| 1977 Peacocks II | 10,000 | 65.00 |
| *Audubon Birds* | | |
| 1977 Warbler & Jay | 5,000 | 150.00 |
| 1978 Kingbird & Sparrow | 10,000 | 150.00 |
| *Chinoiserie* | | |
| 1977 Bishop Summer | Year | 65.00 |
| *English Christmas* | | |
| 1979 Christmas Eve | Year | 60.00 |
| 1980 Christmas Morning | Year | 65.00 |
| 1981 Christmas Day | Year | 70.00 |
| 1982 Christmas Evening | Year | 70.00 |
| *Kitten Classics* | | |
| 1985 Cat Nap | 14 Days | 29.50 |
| **Spode** | | |
| *Ray Harm Birds (Set of 12)* | | |
| 1970 Rufus-Sided Towhee | | |
| 1970 Winter Wren | | |
| 1971 Eastern Bluebird | | |
| 1971 Stellar's Jay | | |
| 1971 Eastern Mockingbird | | |
| 1971 Barn Swallow | | |
| 1971 Rose-Breasted Grosbeak | | |
| 1971 Cardinal | | |
| 1972 Western Tanager | | |
| 1972 Woodpecker | | |
| 1972 Chickadee | | |
| 1972 American Goldfinch | 5,000 | 300.00 |
| *Maritime Plates (Set of six)* | | |
| 1980 USS United States and HMS Macedonian | | |
| 1980 USS President and HMS Little Belt | | |
| 1980 HMS Shannon and USS Chesapeake | | |
| 1980 USS Constitution and HMS Guerriere | | |
| 1980 USS Constitution and HMN Java | | |
| 1980 HMS Pelican and USS Argus | 2,000 | 300.00 |
| *Christmas Pastimes* | | |
| 1982 Sleigh Ride | Year | 75.00 |
| *World of Charles Dickens* | | |
| 1987 Oliver Twist | NA | 29.50 |
| **Wedgwood** | | |
| *Calendar* | | |
| 1971 Victorian Almanac | Year | 12.00 |
| 1972 Animal Carnival | Year | 12.95 |
| 1973 Bountiful Butterfly | Year | 12.95 |
| 1974 Camelot | Year | 15.00 |
| 1975 Children's Games | Year | 15.00 |
| 1976 Robin | Year | 25.00 |
| 1977 Tonatiuh Warriors | Year | 30.00 |
| 1978 Samurai | Year | 30.00 |

| | Edition Limit | Issue Price (US) |
|---|---|---|
| 79 Sacred Scarab | Year | $ 35.00 |
| 80 Safari | Year | 36.00 |
| 81 Horses | Year | 37.50 |
| 82 Wild West | Year | 40.00 |
| 83 Age of Reptiles | Year | 54.00 |
| 84 Pets | Year | 54.00 |
| 85 Cats | Year | 54.00 |
| 86 British Birds | Year | 54.00 |

**ildren's Story**
| | | |
|---|---|---|
| 71 Sandman | Year | 7.95 |
| 72 Tinder Box | Year | 9.00 |
| 73 Emperor's New Clothes | Year | 9.00 |
| 74 Ugly Duckling | Year | 10.00 |
| 75 Little Mermaid | Year | 12.00 |
| 76 Hansel & Gretel | Year | 12.00 |
| 77 Rumpelstiltskin | Year | 15.00 |
| 78 Frog Prince | Year | 15.00 |
| 79 Golden Goose | Year | 15.00 |
| 80 Rapunzel | Year | 16.00 |
| 81 Tom Thumb | Year | 18.00 |
| 82 Lady and Lion | Year | 20.00 |
| 83 Elves and Shoemaker | Year | 20.00 |
| 84 King Roughbeard | Year | 20.00 |
| 85 Little Tailor | Year | 20.00 |

**centennial**
| | | |
|---|---|---|
| 72 Boston Tea Party | Year | 30.00 |
| 73 Paul Revere's Ride | Year | 35.00 |
| 74 Battle of Concord | Year | 40.00 |
| 75 Across Delaware | Year | 45.00 |
| 75 Victory at Yorktown | Year | 45.00 |
| 76 Declaration Signed | Year | 45.00 |

*ngle issue)*
| | | |
|---|---|---|
| 78 Tri-Color Decade Christmas | 10,000 | 325.00 |

*ngle issue)*
| | | |
|---|---|---|
| 78 Anniversary Christmas | Year | 130.00 |

**ophy**
| | | |
|---|---|---|
| 78 Tutankhamun | 500 | 1000.00 |
| 78 Ankhesenamum | 500 | 1000.00 |

**ild's Christmas**
| | | |
|---|---|---|
| 79 Snowman | Year | 35.00 |
| 80 Bringing Home Tree | Year | 35.00 |
| 81 Tobogganing | Year | 35.00 |
| 82 Skaters | Year | 35.00 |
| 83 Carolers | Year | 35.00 |
| 84 Christmas Baking | Year | 35.00 |

**ueen's Ware Christmas**
| | | |
|---|---|---|
| 80 Windsor Castle | Year | 24.95 |
| 81 Trafalgar Square | Year | 29.95 |
| 82 Piccadilly Circus | Year | 32.50 |
| 83 St. Paul's Cathedral | Year | 32.50 |
| 84 Tower of London | Year | 32.50 |
| 85 Palace of Westminster | Year | 35.00 |

**markable World of Charles Dickens**
| | | |
|---|---|---|
| 80 Oliver Twist and Fagin | 19,500 | 60.00 |
| 80 Scrooge and Marley's Ghost | 19,500 | 60.00 |
| 80 Bob Cratchit | 19,500 | 60.00 |
| 80 David Copperfield | 19,500 | 60.00 |
| 81 Micawber/Uriah Heep | 19,500 | 60.00 |
| 81 Little Nell | 19,500 | 60.00 |
| 81 Madame Defarge | 19,500 | 60.00 |
| 81 Mr. Pickwick | 19,500 | 60.00 |

**lentine's Day**
| | | |
|---|---|---|
| 82 Lilac on White | Year | 55.00 |
| 83 White on Pink | Year | 55.00 |
| 84 White on Teal | Year | 55.00 |

**es of Child**
| | | |
|---|---|---|
| 83 Little Lady Love | 15,000 | 65.00 |
| 84 My Best Friend | 15,000 | 65.00 |
| 85 I Wish Upon a Star | 15,000 | 65.00 |
| 85 In a Child's Thoughts | 15,000 | 65.00 |
| 85 Puppy Love | 15,000 | 65.00 |

*ngle issue)*
| | | |
|---|---|---|
| 83 200 Years of Ballooning | Year | 35.00 |

## NDIA

**arna**

*ristmas*
| | | |
|---|---|---|
| 75 Holy Family | 4,000 | 17.50 |

## ITALY

### Anri

**Mother's Day**
| | Edition Limit | Issue Price (US) |
|---|---|---|
| 1972 Alpine Mother & Children | 5,000 | $ 35.00 |
| 1973 Alpine Mother & Children | 5,000 | 40.00 |
| 1974 Alpine Mother & Children | 5,000 | 50.00 |
| 1975 Alpine Stroll | 5,000 | 60.00 |
| 1976 Knitting | 5,000 | 60.00 |

**Father's Day**
| | | |
|---|---|---|
| 1972 Alpine Father & Children | 5,000 | 35.00 |
| 1973 Alpine Father & Children | 5,000 | 40.00 |
| 1974 Cliff Gazing | 5,000 | 50.00 |
| 1975 Sailing | 5,000 | 60.00 |

**Ferrandiz Birthday**
| | | |
|---|---|---|
| 1972 Birthday Girl | Year | 15.00 |
| 1972 Birthday Boy | Year | 15.00 |
| 1973 Birthday | Year | 20.00 |
| 1974 Birthday Girl | Year | 22.00 |
| 1974 Birthday Boy | Year | 22.00 |
| 1975 Birthday Girl | Year | 35.00 |

**Ferrandiz Mother's Day**
| | | |
|---|---|---|
| 1972 Mother Sewing | 2,500 | 35.00 |
| 1973 Mother and Child | 1,500 | 40.00 |
| 1974 Mother and Child | 1,500 | 50.00 |
| 1975 Mother Holding Dove | 1,500 | 60.00 |
| 1976 Mother and Child | 1,500 | 60.00 |
| 1977 Girl with Flowers | 1,500 | 65.00 |
| 1978 Beginning | 3,000 | 77.50 |
| 1979 All Hearts | 3,000 | 120.00 |
| 1980 Spring Arrivals | 3,000 | 150.00 |
| 1981 Harmony | 3,000 | 150.00 |
| 1982 With Love | 3,000 | 150.00 |

**Ferrandiz Christmas**
| | | |
|---|---|---|
| 1972 Christ in Manger | Year | 30.00 |
| 1973 Boy with Lamb | Year | 30.00 |
| 1974 Nativity | Year | 50.00 |
| 1975 Flight into Egypt | Year | 60.00 |
| 1976 Mary and Joseph Pray | Year | 60.00 |
| 1977 Girl with Tree | 4,000 | 65.00 |
| 1978 Leading Way | 4,000 | 77.50 |
| 1979 Drummer Boy | 4,000 | 120.00 |
| 1980 Rejoice | 4,000 | 150.00 |
| 1981 Spreading Word | 4,000 | 150.00 |
| 1982 Shepherd Family | 4,000 | 150.00 |
| 1983 Peace Attend Thee | 4,000 | 150.00 |

**Ferrandiz Wedding Day**
| | | |
|---|---|---|
| 1972 Wedding | Year | 40.00 |
| 1973 Wedding | Year | 40.00 |
| 1974 Wedding | Year | 48.00 |
| 1975 Wedding | Year | 60.00 |
| 1976 Wedding | Year | 60.00 |

**(Single issue)**
| | | |
|---|---|---|
| 1982 Riding Thru Rain | 2,500 | 550.00 |

**Ferrandiz Annual**
| | | |
|---|---|---|
| 1984 Pastoral Journey | 2,000 | 180.00 |
| 1985 Tender Touch | 2,000 | 170.00 |

**Sarah Kay Annual**
| | | |
|---|---|---|
| 1984 A Time for Secrets | 2,500 | 120.00 |
| 1985 Carousel Magic | 2,500 | 120.00 |

### Capo Di Monte

**Christmas**
| | | |
|---|---|---|
| 1972 Cherubs | 500 | 55.00 |
| 1973 Bells & Holly | 500 | 55.00 |
| 1974 Christmas | 1,000 | 60.00 |
| 1975 Christmas | 1,000 | 60.00 |
| 1976 Christmas | 250 | 65.00 |

**Mother's Day**
| | | |
|---|---|---|
| 1973 Mother's Day | 500 | 55.00 |
| 1974 Mother's Day | 500 | 60.00 |
| 1975 Mother's Day | 500 | 60.00 |
| 1976 Mother's Day | 500 | 65.00 |

### Carlo Monti

**Mother's Day**
| | | |
|---|---|---|
| 1973 Madonna & Child | 2,000 | 35.00 |

### Count Agazzi

**Famous Personalities**
| | | |
|---|---|---|
| 1968 Famous Personalities | 600 | 8.00 |
| 1970 Famous Personalities | 1,000 | 12.50 |
| 1973 Famous Personalities | 600 | 15.00 |

**(Single issue)**
| | Edition Limit | Issue Price (US) |
|---|---|---|
| 1969 Apollo II | 1,000 | $ 17.00 |

**Children's Hour**
| | | |
|---|---|---|
| 1970 Owl | 2,000 | 12.50 |
| 1971 Cat | 2,000 | 12.50 |
| 1972 Pony | 2,000 | 12.50 |
| 1973 Panda | 2,000 | 12.50 |

**Easter**
| | | |
|---|---|---|
| 1971 Playing Violin | 600 | 12.50 |
| 1972 At Prayer | 600 | 12.50 |
| 1973 Winged Cherub | 600 | 12.50 |

**Mother's Day**
| | | |
|---|---|---|
| 1972 Mother's Day | 144 | 35.00 |
| 1973 Mother's Day | 720 | 19.50 |

**Father's Day**
| | | |
|---|---|---|
| 1972 Father's Day | 144 | 35.00 |
| 1973 Father's Day | 288 | 19.50 |

**Christmas**
| | | |
|---|---|---|
| 1973 Christmas | 1,000 | 19.50 |

**(Single issue)**
| | | |
|---|---|---|
| 1973 Peace | 720 | 12.50 |

### Kings

**Mother's Day**
| | | |
|---|---|---|
| 1973 Dancing Girl | 1,500 | 100.00 |
| 1974 Dancing Boy | 1,500 | 115.00 |
| 1975 Motherly Love | 1,500 | 140.00 |
| 1976 Maiden | 1,500 | 180.00 |

**Christmas**
| | | |
|---|---|---|
| 1973 Adoration | 1,500 | 150.00 |
| 1974 Madonna | 1,500 | 150.00 |
| 1975 Heavenly Choir | 1,500 | 160.00 |
| 1976 Girl and Brother | 1,500 | 200.00 |

### Veneto Flair

**Christmas**
| | | |
|---|---|---|
| 1971 Three Kings | 1,500 | 45.00 |
| 1972 Shepherds | 2,000 | 45.00 |
| 1973 Christ Child | 2,000 | 55.00 |
| 1974 Angel | 2,000 | 55.00 |

**Wildlife**
| | | |
|---|---|---|
| 1971 Deer | 500 | 37.50 |
| 1972 Elephant | 1,000 | 37.50 |
| 1973 Puma | 2,000 | 37.50 |
| 1974 Tiger | 2,000 | 40.00 |

**Birds**
| | | |
|---|---|---|
| 1972 Owl | 2,000 | 37.50 |
| 1973 Falcon | 2,000 | 37.50 |
| 1974 Mallard Duck | 2,000 | 45.00 |

**Dogs**
| | | |
|---|---|---|
| 1972 German Shepherd | 2,000 | 37.50 |
| 1973 Poodle | 2,000 | 37.50 |
| 1974 Doberman | 2,000 | 37.50 |
| 1975 Collie | 2,000 | 40.00 |
| 1976 Dachshund | 2,000 | 45.00 |

**Mother's Day**
| | | |
|---|---|---|
| 1972 Madonna and Child | 2,000 | 55.00 |
| 1973 Madonna and Child | 2,000 | 55.00 |
| 1974 Mother and Son | 2,000 | 55.00 |
| 1975 Daughter and Doll | 2,000 | 45.00 |
| 1976 Son and Daughter | 2,000 | 55.00 |
| 1977 Mother and Child | 2,000 | 50.00 |

**Easter**
| | | |
|---|---|---|
| 1973 Rabbits | 2,000 | 50.00 |
| 1974 Chicks | 2,000 | 50.00 |
| 1975 Lamb | 2,000 | 50.00 |
| 1976 Composite | 2,000 | 55.00 |

**Goddess**
| | | |
|---|---|---|
| 1973 Pomona | 1,500 | 75.00 |
| 1974 Diana | 1,500 | 75.00 |

**Mosaic**
| | | |
|---|---|---|
| 1973 Justinian | 500 | 50.00 |
| 1974 Pelican | 1,000 | 50.00 |
| 1977 Theodora | 500 | 50.00 |

**Cats**
| | | |
|---|---|---|
| 1974 Persian | 2,000 | 40.00 |
| 1975 Siamese | 2,000 | 45.00 |
| 1976 Tabby | 2,000 | 45.00 |

**Christmas Card**
| | | |
|---|---|---|
| 1975 Christmas Eve | 5,000 | 45.00 |
| 1976 Old North Church | 5,000 | 50.00 |
| 1977 Log Cabin Christmas | 5,000 | 50.00 |
| 1978 Dutch Christmas | 5,000 | 50.00 |

**Valentine's Day**
| | Edition Limit | Issue Price (US) |
|---|---|---|
| 1977 Valentine Boy | 3,000 | $ 45.00 |
| 1978 Valentine Girl | 3,000 | 45.00 |
| 1979 Hansel | 3,000 | 60.00 |
| 1980 Gretel | 3,000 | 67.50 |

**Flower Children**
| | | |
|---|---|---|
| 1978 Rose | 3,000 | 45.00 |
| 1979 Orchid | 3,000 | 60.00 |
| 1980 Camillia | 3,000 | 65.00 |

**La Belle Femme**
| | | |
|---|---|---|
| 1978 Lily | 9,500 | 70.00 |
| 1978 Gigi | 9,500 | 76.50 |
| 1980 Dominique | 9,500 | 76.50 |
| 1980 Gabrielle | 9,500 | 76.50 |

**American Landscape**
| | | |
|---|---|---|
| 1979 Hudson Valley | 7,500 | 75.00 |
| 1980 Northwest Cascade | 7,500 | 75.00 |

**Children's Christmas**
| | | |
|---|---|---|
| 1979 Carolers | 7,500 | 60.00 |
| 1980 Heading Home | 7,500 | 70.00 |
| 1981 Night Before | 7,500 | 95.00 |
| 1982 A Visit to Santa | 7,500 | 80.00 |

**Mother and Child**
| | | |
|---|---|---|
| 1981 Buffalos | 5,000 | 95.00 |
| 1981 Elephants | 5,000 | 95.00 |
| 1981 Koalas | 5,000 | 95.00 |
| 1981 Lions | 5,000 | 95.00 |
| 1981 Loons | 5,000 | 95.00 |
| 1981 Polar Bears | 5,000 | 95.00 |

**Lamincia Annual**
| | | |
|---|---|---|
| 1981 Young Love | 5,000 | 95.00 |

## JAPAN

### Manjundo

**Chinese Lunar Calendar**
| | | |
|---|---|---|
| 1972 Year of Rat | 5,000 | 15.00 |
| 1973 Year of Ox | 5,000 | 15.00 |

### Noritake

**Christmas**
| | | |
|---|---|---|
| 1975 Madonna with Child | 3,000 | 42.00 |
| 1976 Gratia Hoso Kawa | 3,000 | 54.00 |
| 1977 Julia Otaa | 3,000 | 83.00 |
| 1978 Amakusa Shiro | 3,000 | 109.00 |
| 1979 Munzio Ito | 3,000 | 124.00 |
| 1980 Furst Takayama | 3,000 | 125.00 |

**Annual**
| | | |
|---|---|---|
| 1977 Paradise Birds | 3,000 | 380.00 |
| 1978 Chrysanthemums | 3,000 | 494.00 |
| 1979 Cranes | 3,000 | 556.00 |
| 1980 Water Lilies and Butterflies | 3,000 | 575.00 |

### Sango

**Christmas**
| | | |
|---|---|---|
| 1976 Undesired Slumber | 7,500 | 25.00 |
| 1977 Togetherness | 7,500 | 25.00 |

**Mother's Day**
| | | |
|---|---|---|
| 1976 Spring Delight | 7,500 | 20.00 |
| 1977 Broken Wing | 5,000 | 22.50 |

*See also: Kern Collectibles (U.S.A.)*

### Schmid

**Peanuts Mother's Day**
| | | |
|---|---|---|
| 1972 Linus | Year | 10.00 |
| 1973 Mom? | Year | 10.00 |
| 1974 Snoopy/Wood./Parade | Year | 10.00 |
| 1975 A Kiss for Lucy | Year | 12.50 |
| 1976 Linus and Snoopy | Year | 13.00 |
| 1977 Dear Mom | Year | 13.00 |
| 1978 Thoughts That Count | Year | 15.00 |
| 1979 A Special Letter | 10,000 | 17.50 |
| 1980 A Tribune to Mom | 10,000 | 17.50 |
| 1981 Mission for Mom | 10,000 | 17.50 |
| 1982 Which Way to Mother? | 10,000 | 18.50 |

**Raggedy Ann Christmas**
| | | |
|---|---|---|
| 1975 Gifts of Love | Year | 12.50 |
| 1976 Raggedy Ann Skates | Year | 13.00 |
| 1977 Decorating Tree | Year | 13.00 |
| 1978 Checking List | Year | 15.00 |
| 1979 Little Helper | 15,000 | 17.50 |

**Bicentennial**
| | | |
|---|---|---|
| 1976 Peanuts | NA | 13.00 |
| 1976 Disney | NA | 13.00 |
| 1976 Raggedy Ann | NA | 13.00 |

# OVER-THE-COUNTER ISSUES

| | Edition Limit | Issue Price (US) |
|---|---|---|
| *Raggedy Ann Mother's Day* | | |
| 1976 Motherhood | Year | $ 13.00 |
| 1977 Bouquet of Love | Year | 13.00 |
| 1978 Hello Mom | Year | 15.00 |
| 1979 High Spirits | 10,000 | 17.50 |
| *Peanuts Valentine's Day* | | |
| 1977 Home Where Heart Is | Year | 13.00 |
| 1978 Heavenly Bliss | Year | 13.00 |
| 1979 Love Match | Year | 17.50 |
| 1980 From Snoopy/Love | Year | 17.50 |
| 1981 Hearts-a-Flutter | Year | 17.50 |
| 1982 Love Patch | Year | 17.50 |
| *Raggedy Ann Valentine's Day* | | |
| 1978 As Time Goes By | Year | 13.00 |
| 1979 Daisies Do Tell | Year | 17.50 |
| *Disney Valentine's Day* | | |
| 1979 Hands and Hearts | Year | 17.50 |
| 1980 Mickey's I Love You | Year | 17.50 |
| 1981 Be Mine | Year | 17.50 |
| 1982 Picnic for Two | Year | 17.50 |
| *A Year with Paddington Bear* | | |
| 1979 Pyramid Presents | 25,000 | 12.50 |
| 1980 Springtime | 25,000 | 12.50 |
| 1981 Sandcastles | 25,000 | 12.50 |
| 1981 School Days | 25,000 | 12.50 |
| *Raggedy Ann Annual* | | |
| 1980 Sunshine Wagon | 10,000 | 17.50 |
| 1981 Raggedy Shuffle | 10,000 | 17.50 |
| 1982 Flying High | 10,000 | 18.50 |
| 1983 Winning Streak | 10,000 | 22.50 |
| 1984 Rocking Rodeo | 10,000 | 22.50 |
| *Peanuts 30th Anniversary (Single issue)* | | |
| 1980 Happy Anniversary | 15,000 | 27.50 |
| *Alice in Wonderland Anniversary (Single issue)* | | |
| 1981 Alice in Wonderland | 7,500 | 17.50 |
| *Disney Anniversary (Single issue)* | | |
| 1981 Pluto's 50th Birthday | 7,500 | 17.50 |
| *Four Seasons of Love* | | |
| 1982 Tickets on 50 Yard Line | 10,000 | 17.50 |
| 1982 Let it Snow | 10,000 | 17.50 |
| 1983 Spring Bouquet | 10,000 | 17.50 |
| 1983 Shades of Summer | 10,000 | 17.50 |
| *A Musician's Dream* | | |
| 1982 Beat Goes On | 10,000 | 17.50 |
| 1982 Knowing Score | 10,000 | 17.50 |
| 1983 Perfect Harmony | 10,000 | 17.50 |
| 1983 Tickling Ivory | 10,000 | 17.50 |
| *World's Greatest Athlete* | | |
| 1982 Go Deep | 10,000 | 17.50 |
| 1982 Puck Stops Here | 10,000 | 17.50 |
| 1983 Way You Play Game | 10,000 | 17.50 |
| 1983 Crowd Went Wild | 10,000 | 17.50 |
| *Disney Annual* | | |
| 1983 Sneak Preview | 20,000 | 22.50 |
| 1984 Command Performance | 20,000 | 22.50 |
| 1985 Snow Biz | 20,000 | 22.50 |
| 1986 Tree for Two | 20,000 | 22.50 |
| 1987 Merry Mouse Medley | 20,000 | 25.00 |
| *Paddington Bear Annual* | | |
| 1983 Bear's Noel | 10,000 | 22.50 |
| 1984 How Sweet It Is | 10,000 | 22.50 |
| *Peanuts Annual* | | |
| 1983 Peanuts in Concert | 20,000 | 22.50 |
| 1984 Snoopy/Beaglescouts | 20,000 | 22.50 |
| 1986 Lion Tamer Snoopy | 20,000 | 22.50 |
| *I Love Plate Collecting* | | |
| 1984 A Great Beginning | 20,000 | 22.50 |

*See also: Addams Family (U.S.A.)*

## MEXICO

### Bonita Silver

| | Edition Limit | Issue Price (US) |
|---|---|---|
| *Mother's Day* | | |
| 1972 Mother and Baby | 4,000 | 125.00 |

### Roman Ceramica Excelsis

| | Edition Limit | Issue Price (US) |
|---|---|---|
| *Masterpiece Collection* | | |
| 1979 Adoration | 5,000 | 65.00 |
| 1980 Madonna with Grapes | 5,000 | 87.50 |
| 1981 Holy Family | 5,000 | 95.00 |
| 1982 Madonna of Streets | 5,000 | 85.00 |
| *Ceramica Excelsis Collection* | | |
| 1980 Little Children, Come to Me | 15,000 | $ 45.00 |

## NETHERLANDS

### Blue Delft (Schoonhaven)

| | Edition Limit | Issue Price (US) |
|---|---|---|
| *Christmas* | | |
| 1970 Drawbridge Near Binnehof | Year | 12.00 |
| 1971 St. Lauren's Church | Year | 12.00 |
| 1972 Church at Bierkade | Year | 12.00 |
| 1973 St. Jan's Church | Year | 12.00 |
| 1974 Dongeradeel | Year | 13.00 |
| 1975 Maassluis | Year | 15.00 |
| 1976 Montelbaanstower | Year | 15.00 |
| 1977 Harbour Tower of Hoorn | Year | 19.50 |
| 1978 Binnenpoort Gate | Year | 21.00 |
| *Mother's Day* | | |
| 1971 Mother & Daughter of 1600s | Year | 12.00 |
| 1972 Mother & Daughter of Isle of Urk | Year | 12.00 |
| 1973 Rembrandt's Mother | Year | 12.00 |
| *Father's Day* | | |
| 1971 Francisco Lana's Airship | Year | 12.00 |
| 1972 Dr. Jonathon's Balloon | Year | 12.00 |

### Crown Delft

| | Edition Limit | Issue Price (US) |
|---|---|---|
| *Christmas* | | |
| 1969 Man by Tree | Year | 10.00 |
| 1970 Two Sleigh Riders | Year | 10.00 |
| 1971 Christmas Tree on Market Square | Year | 10.00 |
| 1972 Baking for Christmas | Year | 10.00 |
| *Mother's Day* | | |
| 1970 Sheep | Year | 10.00 |
| 1971 Stork | Year | 10.00 |
| 1972 Ducks | Year | 10.00 |
| 1973 Mother's Day | 1,000 | 10.00 |
| *Father's Day* | | |
| 1970 Father's Day | Year | 10.00 |
| 1971 Father's Day | Year | 10.00 |
| 1972 Father's Day | 1,000 | 10.00 |
| 1973 Father's Day | 1,000 | 10.00 |

### Kurz (Shuler International)

| | Edition Limit | Issue Price (US) |
|---|---|---|
| *Christmas* | | |
| 1972 Christmas | 500 | 60.00 |
| 1973 Christmas | 500 | 70.00 |
| 1974 Christmas | 500 | 65.00 |
| *Mother's Day* | | |
| 1973 Mother's Day | 500 | 65.00 |

### Metawa

| | Edition Limit | Issue Price (US) |
|---|---|---|
| *Christmas* | | |
| 1972 Skaters | 3,000 | 30.00 |
| 1973 One-Horse Sleigh | 1,500 | 30.00 |
| 1974 Sailboat | Year | 35.00 |

### Royal Delft

| | Edition Limit | Issue Price (US) |
|---|---|---|
| *Christmas* | | |
| 1915 Glory to God, Christmas Bells (10″) | Year | NA |
| 1915 Christmas Star (7″) | Year | NA |
| 1916 Star–Floral Design (10″) | Year | NA |
| 1916 Cradle of Child (10″) | Year | NA |
| 1917 Shepherd with Sheep in Stable (10″) | Year | NA |
| 1917 Christmas Star (10″) | Year | NA |
| 1918 Shepherd with Sheep in Stable (10″) | Year | NA |
| 1918 Christmas Star–Peace on Earth (10″) | Year | NA |
| 1919 Church (10″) | Year | NA |
| 1919 Christmas Star (10″) | Year | NA |
| 1920 Holly Wreath (10″) | Year | NA |
| 1920 Church Tower (10″) | Year | NA |
| 1921 Canal Boatman (10″) | Year | NA |
| 1921 Christmas Star (10″) | Year | NA |
| 1922 Landscape (10″) | Year | NA |
| 1922 Christmas Wreath (10″) | Year | NA |
| 1923 Shepherd (10″) | Year | NA |
| 1923 Christmas Star (10″) | Year | NA |
| 1924 Christmas Star (10″) | Year | NA |
| 1924 Town Gate with Shepherd (10″) | Year | NA |
| 1925 Towngate in Delft (10″) | Year | NA |
| 1925 Christmas Star (10″) | Year | NA |
| 1926 Christmas Star (10″) | Year | NA |
| 1926 Bell Tower (7″) | Year | NA |
| 1926 Windmill Landscape (10″) | Year | NA |
| 1927 Christmas Star (10″) | Year | NA |
| 1927 Sailing Boat (10″) | Year | NA |
| 1927 Church Tower (7″) | Year | NA |
| 1928 Christmas Poinsettia (10″) | Year | NA |
| 1928 Mill Christmas (7″) | Year | NA |
| 1928 Lighthouse Christmas (10″) | Year | NA |
| 1929 Christmas Bell (10″) | Year | NA |
| 1929 Church Spire (7″) | Year | NA |
| 1929 Small Dutch Town (10″) | Year | NA |
| 1930 Church Entrance, Delft (10″) | Year | NA |
| 1930 Christmas Rose (10″) | Year | NA |
| 1930 Sailing Boat (7″) | Year | NA |
| 1931 Christmas Star (10″) | Year | NA |
| 1931 Snow Landscape (10″) | Year | NA |
| 1931 Church Tower (7″) | Year | NA |
| 1932 Bell Tower (7″) | Year | NA |
| 1932 Fireplace (10″) | Year | NA |
| 1932 Christmas Star (10″) | Year | NA |
| 1933 Interior Scene with Exterior View (10″) | Year | NA |
| 1934 Interior Scene (10″) | Year | NA |
| 1934 Snowy Stable (10″) | Year | NA |
| 1935 Interior Scene with Exterior View (10″) | Year | NA |
| 1936 Interior Scene with Exterior View (10″) | Year | NA |
| 1937 Interior Scene with Exterior View (10″) | Year | NA |
| 1938 Interior Scene with Exterior View (10″) | Year | NA |
| 1939 Interior Scene with Well-Staircase (10″) | Year | NA |
| 1940 Interior with Christmas Tree (10″) | Year | NA |
| 1941 Interior Scene Fireplace & Tree (10″) | Year | NA |
| 1955 Christmas Star (9″) | Year | NA |
| 1955 Church Tower (10″) | 200 | $ 20.00 |
| 1956 Two Christmas Bells in Floral (9″) | Year | NA |
| 1956 Landscape (10″) | 200 | 20.00 |
| 1956 Flower Design (9″) | Year | NA |
| 1957 Christmas Star (9″) | Year | NA |
| 1957 Landscape (10″) | 225 | 22.00 |
| 1958 Christmas Star (9″) | Year | NA |
| 1958 View of Village at Riverside (10″) | 225 | 25.00 |
| 1959 View of Village at Riverside (10″) | 250 | 25.00 |
| 1959 Landscape with Mill (7″) | 400 | 10.00 |
| 1960 Landscape (7″) | 400 | 10.00 |
| 1960 Street in Delft (10″) | 250 | 25.00 |
| 1961 Snow Landscape (7″) | 500 | 10.00 |
| 1961 Village Scene with Church Town (10″) | 260 | 30.00 |
| 1962 Town View (7″) | 500 | 10.00 |
| 1962 Tower in Leeuwarden (10″) | 275 | 30.00 |
| 1963 Mill in Zeddam (7″) | 500 | 15.00 |
| 1963 Tower in Enkhuisen (10″) | 275 | 35.00 |
| 1964 Tower in Hoorn (10″) | 300 | 35.00 |
| 1964 Mill in Poelenburg (7″) | 600 | 15.00 |
| 1965 Towngate in Kampen (7″) | 600 | 15.00 |
| 1965 Corn-Mill in Rhoon (10″) | 300 | 35.00 |
| 1966 Towngate in Medemblik (7″) | 600 | 20.00 |
| 1966 Snuff Mill in Rotterdam (10″) | 325 | 40.00 |
| 1967 Mill in Hazerswoude (7″) | 700 | 20.00 |
| 1967 Tower in Amsterdam (10″) | 350 | 45.00 |
| 1968 Mill in Schiedam (7″) | 700 | 25.00 |
| 1968 Tower in Amsterdam "Schreierstoren" (10″) | 350 | $ 60.0 |
| 1969 Mill Near Gorkum (7″) | 800 | 35.0 |
| 1969 Church in Utrecht (10″) | 400 | 60.0 |
| 1970 Mill Near Haarlem (7″) | 1,500 | 25.0 |
| 1970 Cathedral in Veere (10″) | 500 | 60.0 |
| 1971 Towngate at Zierikzee (7″) | 3,500 | 25.0 |
| 1971 "Dom" Tower in Utrecht (10″) | 550 | 60.0 |
| 1972 Towngate at Elburg (7″) | 3,500 | 40.0 |
| 1972 Church in Edam (10″) | 1,500 | 70.0 |
| 1973 Towngate at Amersfoort (7″) | 4,500 | 50.0 |
| 1973 DeWaag in Alkmaar (10″) | 1,500 | 75.0 |
| 1974 Watergate at Sneek (7″) | 4,500 | 80.0 |
| 1974 Kitchen in Hindeloopen (10″) | 1,500 | 160.0 |
| 1975 Towngate at Amsterdam (7″) | 1,000 | 140.0 |
| 1975 Farmer in Laren (10″) | 1,500 | 250.0 |
| 1976 Towngate in Gorinehem (7″) | 4,500 | 115.0 |
| 1976 Farmer's Wife in Staphorst (10″) | 1,500 | 220.0 |
| 1977 Dromedaris Tower (7″) | 4,500 | 140.0 |
| 1977 Farm Family in Spakenburg (10″) | 1,500 | 277.0 |
| 1978 Winter Skating Scene (10″) | 1,000 | 277.0 |
| 1978 Christmas Fisherman (7″) | 1,500 | 140.0 |
| 1978 Christmas Angels (7″) | 1,500 | 140.0 |
| 1984 Homecoming (10″) | 500 | 230.0 |
| 1984 Figure Skating (7″) | 1,000 | 120.0 |
| 1985 Church at Woudt (10″) | 500 | 270.0 |
| 1985 The Farmhouse at Woudt (7″) | 1,000 | 140.0 |
| 1986 St. Dionysius in Asselt (10″) | 500 | 324.0 |
| 1986 Farmhouse in Asselt (7″) | 1,000 | 168.0 |
| *Mother's Day* | | |
| 1971 Mother & Daughter (Volendam) | 2,500 | 50.0 |
| 1972 Mother & Daughter (Hindeloopen) | 2,500 | 40.0 |
| 1973 Mother & Daughter (Marken) | 3,000 | 50.0 |
| 1974 Mother & Daughter (Zuid-Beveland) | Year | 80.0 |
| 1975 Mother & Daughter (Spakenburg) | Year | 100.0 |
| 1976 Mother & Daughter (Scheveningen) | Year | 115.0 |
| *Father's Day* | | |
| 1972 Father & Son (Volendam) | 1,500 | 40.0 |
| 1973 Father & Son (Hindeloopen) | 2,000 | 40.0 |
| 1974 Father & Son (Marken) | 1,000 | 80.0 |
| 1975 Father & Son (Zuid-Beveland) | Year | 80.0 |
| 1976 Father & Son (Spakenburg) | Year | 140.0 |
| *Easter* | | |
| 1973 Dutch Easter Palm (7″) | 3,500 | 75.0 |
| 1973 Dutch Easter Palm (10″) | 3,500 | NA |
| 1974 Dutch Easter Palm | 1,000 | 110.0 |
| 1975 Dutch Easter Palm | 1,000 | 125.0 |
| 1976 Dutch Easter Palm | 1,000 | 175.0 |
| *Valentine* | | |
| 1973 Enduring Beauty | 1,500 | 75.0 |
| 1974 Valentine | 1,000 | 125.0 |
| 1975 Valentine | 1,000 | 125.0 |
| 1976 Valentine | 1,000 | 175.0 |
| *Special Bicentenary* | | |
| 1976 George Washington | 2,500 | 350.0 |
| 1976 Eagle Plate | 5,000 | 150.0 |
| *(Single issue)* | | |
| 1986 Halley's Comet | NA | 100.0 |

## Schoonhaven
See: Blue Delft (Neth.)

## Shuler International
See: Kurz (Neth.)

## Zenith Delftware

| | Edition Limit | Issue Price (US) |
|---|---|---|
| *Hans Brinker* | | |
| 1972 Skating | 500 | $ 60.00 |
| 1973 Gretel Tending Geese | 750 | 60.00 |
| *Anniversary* | | |
| 1973 Autumn | 500 | 45.00 |
| 1973 Spring | 500 | 45.00 |
| 1973 Summer | 500 | 45.00 |
| 1973 Winter | 500 | 45.00 |
| *Birthday Boy* | | |
| 1973 Monday's Child | 3,000 | 15.00 |
| 1973 Tuesday's Child | 3,000 | 15.00 |
| 1973 Wednesday's Child | 3,000 | 15.00 |
| 1973 Thursday's Child | 3,000 | 15.00 |
| 1973 Friday's Child | 3,000 | 15.00 |
| 1973 Saturday's Child | 3,000 | 15.00 |
| 1973 Sunday's Child | 3,000 | 15.00 |
| *Birthday Girl* | | |
| 1973 Monday's Child | 3,000 | 15.00 |
| 1973 Tuesday's Child | 3,000 | 15.00 |
| 1973 Wednesday's Child | 3,000 | 15.00 |
| 1973 Thursday's Child | 3,000 | 15.00 |
| 1973 Friday's Child | 3,000 | 15.00 |
| 1973 Saturday's Child | 3,000 | 15.00 |
| 1973 Sunday's Child | 3,000 | 15.00 |

## NORWAY

### Porsgrund

| | Edition Limit | Issue Price (US) |
|---|---|---|
| *(Single issue)* | | |
| 1909 Christmas Flowers | Year | NA |
| *Father's Day* | | |
| 1971 Fishing | Year | 10.00 |
| 1972 Cookout | Year | 10.00 |
| 1973 Sledding | Year | 10.00 |
| 1974 Father and Son | Year | 10.00 |
| 1975 Skating | Year | 12.50 |
| 1976 Skiing | Year | 15.00 |
| 1977 Soccer | Year | 16.50 |
| 1978 Canoeing | Year | 17.50 |
| 1979 Father and Daughter | Year | 19.50 |
| 1980 Sailing | Year | 21.50 |
| 1981 Building a Ship | Year | 24.00 |
| 1982 Father and Daughter | Year | 26.00 |
| 1983 Father's Day | Year | 26.00 |
| 1984 Tree Planting | Year | 25.00 |
| *Easter* | | |
| 1972 Ducks | Year | 7.00 |
| 1973 Birds | Year | 10.00 |
| 1974 Rabbits | Year | 11.00 |
| 1975 Chicks | Year | 16.00 |
| 1976 Sheep in Field | Year | 18.00 |
| 1977 Butterflies | Year | 23.00 |
| *Christmas* | | |
| 1983 Christmas Night | Year | 42.00 |
| 1984 Christmas Sheaf | Year | 40.00 |

## SPAIN

### Lladro

| | Edition Limit | Issue Price (US) |
|---|---|---|
| *Christmas* | | |
| 1971 Caroling | Year | 27.50 |
| 1972 Carolers | Year | 35.00 |
| 1973 Boy and Girl | Year | 45.00 |
| 1974 Carolers | Year | 55.00 |
| 1975 Cherubs | Year | 60.00 |
| 1976 Christ Child | Year | 60.00 |
| 1977 Nativity Scene | Year | 80.00 |
| 1978 Caroling Child | Year | 80.00 |
| 1979 Snow Dance | Year | 90.00 |

### Santa Clara

| | Edition Limit | Issue Price (US) |
|---|---|---|
| *Christmas* | | |
| 1970 Christmas Message | 10,000 | 18.00 |
| 1971 Three Wise Men | 10,000 | 18.00 |
| 1972 Children in Woods | 10,000 | 20.00 |
| 1973 Archangel | 5,000 | 25.00 |
| 1974 Spirit of Christmas | 10,000 | 25.00 |
| 1975 Christmas Eve in Country | 10,000 | 27.50 |
| 1976 Madonna and Child | 10,000 | 25.00 |
| 1977 Mother and Child | 10,000 | 27.50 |

---

| | Edition Limit | Issue Price (US) |
|---|---|---|
| 1978 Angel with Flowers | 10,000 | $ 32.00 |
| 1979 Madonna and Angels | 10,000 | 34.50 |
| *Mother's Day* | | |
| 1971 Mother and Child | 10,000 | 15.00 |
| 1972 Mother and Children | 12,000 | 15.00 |

## SWEDEN

### Kosta

| | Edition Limit | Issue Price (US) |
|---|---|---|
| *Annual* | | |
| 1971 Madonna & Child | Year | 30.00 |
| 1972 St. George & Dragon | Year | 30.00 |
| 1973 Viking Ship | Year | 40.00 |
| 1974 Annual | Year | 40.00 |

### Orrefors

| | Edition Limit | Issue Price (US) |
|---|---|---|
| *Mother's Day* | | |
| 1971 Flowers for Mother | 2,500 | 45.00 |
| 1972 Mother and Children | 2,500 | 45.00 |
| 1973 Mother and Child | 2,500 | 50.00 |
| 1974 Mother and Child | 5,000 | 50.00 |
| 1975 Mother and Child | 2,500 | 60.00 |
| 1976 Children and Puppy | 2,500 | 75.00 |
| 1977 Child and Dove | 1,500 | 85.00 |
| 1978 Mother and Child | 1,500 | 90.00 |

### Rörstrand

| | Edition Limit | Issue Price (US) |
|---|---|---|
| *Christmas* | | |
| 1904 Christmas Night in Stockholm | Year | .27 |
| 1905 Porridge Dish for Tomten | Year | .27 |
| 1906 Star Boys Singing to Lucia | Year | .27 |
| 1907 Christmas Eve in Lapland | Year | .27 |
| 1908 Christmas Eve with Christmas Roses | Year | .27 |
| 1909 Christmas Star over Jerusalem | Year | .27 |
| 1910 Christmas Tree | Year | .27 |
| 1911 Christmas Bells and Angel | Year | .56 |
| 1912 Christmas Service | Year | .56 |
| 1913 Christmas Day Early Service Trip | Year | .56 |
| 1914 Returning Home | Year | .56 |
| 1915 On Way to Church | Year | .56 |
| 1916 Kneeling Shepherd | Year | .56 |
| 1917 Three Kings Following Star | Year | .56 |
| 1918 Sleigh-ride in Dalecarlia | Year | .87 |
| 1919 Christmas on Snow Mountain | Year | .87 |
| 1920 Mary and Child Jesus | Year | .87 |
| 1921 Knight Offering Prayers | Year | .87 |
| 1922 Christmas Bells on Gotland | Year | .87 |
| 1923 Christmas Sheaf | Year | .87 |
| 1924 Tomtefar Bearing Gifts | Year | .87 |
| 1925 Christmas Star and Angels | Year | .87 |
| *Mother's Day* | | |
| 1971 Mother & Child | Year | 15.00 |
| 1972 Shelling Peas | Year | 15.00 |
| 1973 Old Fashioned Picnic | Year | 16.00 |
| 1974 Candle Lighting | Year | 18.00 |
| 1975 Pontius on Floor | Year | 20.00 |
| 1976 Apple Picking | Year | 20.00 |
| 1977 Kitchen | Year | 27.50 |
| 1978 Azalea | Year | 27.50 |
| 1979 Studio Idyll | Year | 31.50 |
| 1980 Lisbeth | Year | 31.50 |
| 1981 Karin with Brita | Year | 42.50 |
| 1982 Mother's Day | Year | 36.00 |
| 1983 Little Girl | Year | 42.50 |
| 1984 Mother and Crafts | Year | 42.50 |
| *Father's Day* | | |
| 1971 Father & Child | Year | 15.00 |
| 1972 Meal at Home | Year | 15.00 |
| 1973 Tilling Fields | Year | 16.00 |
| 1974 Fishing | Year | 18.00 |
| 1975 Painting | Year | 20.00 |
| 1976 Plowing | Year | 20.00 |
| 1977 Sawing | Year | 27.50 |
| 1978 Self Portrait | Year | 27.50 |
| 1979 Bridge | Year | 31.50 |

---

| | Edition Limit | Issue Price (US) |
|---|---|---|
| 1980 My Etch-Nook | Year | $ 31.50 |
| 1981 Esbjorn with Playmate | Year | 42.50 |
| 1982 Father's Day | Year | 36.00 |
| 1983 Man Painting | Year | 42.50 |
| 1984 Farm Life | Year | 42.50 |
| *Christmas Poetry* | | |
| 1979 Silent Night, Holy Night | NA | 173.00 |
| 1980 Three Holy Kings | NA | 180.00 |
| 1981 O Holy Night | NA | 280.00 |
| 1982 Shepherds in Bethlehem | NA | 280.00 |

## UNITED STATES

### Abbey Press (Viletta)

| | Edition Limit | Issue Price (US) |
|---|---|---|
| *Mother's Day* | | |
| 1979 Special Mothers Are God's Creation | 6,000 | 37.50 |
| *Christmas* | | |
| 1979 Christmas Is a Gentle Season | 6,000 | 37.50 |

### Accent on Art

| | Edition Limit | Issue Price (US) |
|---|---|---|
| *Mother Goose* | | |
| 1978 Jack & Jill | 5,000 | 59.50 |
| *Nobility of Plains* | | |
| 1978 Commanche | 12,500 | 80.00 |
| 1979 Moving Day | 3,500 | 80.00 |

### Addams Family (Schmid)

| | Edition Limit | Issue Price (US) |
|---|---|---|
| *Mother's Day* | | |
| 1972 On Tracks | Year | 10.00 |
| *Christmas* | | |
| 1972 Christmas Dinner | Year | 10.00 |

### Allison

| | Edition Limit | Issue Price (US) |
|---|---|---|
| *Nature's Beauty* | | |
| 1981 Winter's Peace | 7,500 | 70.00 |
| 1982 Summer's Joy | 7,500 | 70.00 |
| *Late to Party* | | |
| 1982 Piece of Cake | 12,500 | 35.00 |
| 1983 Cheese Please | 12,500 | 35.00 |
| 1983 Toast to a Mouse | 12,500 | 35.00 |

### American Archives (International Silver)

| | Edition Limit | Issue Price (US) |
|---|---|---|
| *(Single issue)* | | |
| 1972 Christmas Rose | 2,500 | 100.00 |

### American Artists

| | Edition Limit | Issue Price (US) |
|---|---|---|
| *Famous Stallions* | | |
| 1983 Black Stallion | 19,500 | 49.50 |
| 1983 Andalusian | 19,500 | 49.50 |
| *Feathered Friends* | | |
| 1983 Parakeets | 19,500 | 29.50 |
| *Mother and Child Cats* | | |
| 1983 Kitty Love | 19,500 | 29.50 |
| *Noble Tribes* | | |
| 1983 Algonquin | 19,500 | 49.50 |
| 1984 Sioux | 19,500 | 49.50 |
| 1985 Cheyenne | 9,500 | 49.50 |
| *Saturday Evening Post Covers* | | |
| 1983 Santa's Computer | 15 Days | 29.50 |
| *Sport of Kings* | | |
| 1984 Man O' War | 9,500 | 65.00 |
| 1984 Secretariat | 9,500 | 65.00 |
| 1985 John Henry | 9,500 | 65.00 |
| 1985 Seattle Slew | 9,500 | 65.00 |
| *Zoe's Cats* | | |
| 1984 Sniffer | 12,500 | 29.50 |
| 1985 Waiting | 12,500 | 29.50 |
| 1985 Sunshine | 12,500 | 29.50 |
| 1985 Tarzan | 12,500 | 29.50 |
| *Flower Fantasies* | | |
| 1985 Spring Blossoms | 15 Days | 24.50 |
| 1986 Cascade of Flowers | 9,500 | 27.50 |
| *Mare and Foal* | | |
| 1985 Water Trough | 12,500 | 49.50 |
| 1985 Tranquility | 12,500 | 49.50 |
| 1986 Pasture Pest | 12,500 | 49.50 |
| *Feline Fantasies* | | |
| 1986 Summer Breeze | NA | 29.95 |
| 1986 May Queen | NA | 29.95 |
| *Cats for Cat Lovers* | | |
| 1987 Romeo and Juliet | NA | 29.95 |

---

| | Edition Limit | Issue Price (US) |
|---|---|---|
| *(Single issue)* | | |
| 1986 "The Shoe" | 9,500 | $ 75.00 |

### American Arts Services (Viletta)

| | Edition Limit | Issue Price (US) |
|---|---|---|
| *Children* | | |
| 1979 Last of Ninth | 5,000 | 45.00 |

### American Commemorative (Gorham)

| | Edition Limit | Issue Price (US) |
|---|---|---|
| *Southern Landmark* | | |
| 1973 Monticello | 9,800 | 35.00 |
| 1973 Williamsburg | 9,800 | 40.00 |
| 1974 Beauvoir | 9,800 | 40.00 |
| 1974 Cabildo | 9,800 | 40.00 |
| 1975 Hermitage | 9,800 | 40.00 |
| 1975 Oak Hill | 9,800 | 40.00 |
| 1976 Governor Tryon's Palace | 9,800 | 40.00 |
| 1976 Montpelier | 9,800 | 40.00 |
| 1977 Elmscourt | 9,800 | 40.00 |
| 1977 Ashland | 9,800 | 40.00 |
| 1978 Mt. Vernon | 9,800 | 40.00 |
| 1978 White House | 9,800 | 40.00 |
| 1979 Custis Lee | 9,800 | 40.00 |
| 1979 Drayton Hall | 9,800 | 40.00 |
| 1980 Fort Hall | 9,800 | 40.00 |
| 1980 Liberty Hall | 9,800 | 40.00 |

### American Express (Gorham)

| | Edition Limit | Issue Price (US) |
|---|---|---|
| *Four Freedoms* | | |
| 1976 Freedom to Worship | Year | 37.50 |
| 1976 Freedom from Want | Year | 37.50 |
| 1976 Freedom from Fear | Year | 37.50 |
| 1976 Freedom of Speech | Year | 37.50 |
| *Birds of North America* | | |
| 1978 Saw Whet Owls | 9,800 | 38.00 |
| 1978 Bobwhite Quail | 9,800 | 38.00 |
| 1978 October Cardinals | 9,800 | 38.00 |
| 1978 Long-Eared Owl | 9,800 | 38.00 |
| 1978 Eastern Bluebirds | 9,800 | 38.00 |
| 1978 American Woodcock | 9,800 | 38.00 |
| 1978 Ruffed Grouse | 9,800 | 38.00 |
| 1978 House Wren | 9,800 | 38.00 |

### American Express (Lenox)

| | Edition Limit | Issue Price (US) |
|---|---|---|
| *American Trees of Christmas* | | |
| 1976 Douglas Fir | Year | 60.00 |
| 1977 Scotch Pine | Year | 60.00 |

### American Heritage Art (Crown Parian)

| | Edition Limit | Issue Price (US) |
|---|---|---|
| *Battle Wagon* | | |
| 1982 General Quarters | 15,000 | 39.50 |
| 1983 Last Cruise | 11,103 | 39.50 |
| 1984 Delaware | 10,000 | 39.50 |
| 1984 Kentucky | 10,000 | 39.50 |
| *Celebrity Clowns* | | |
| 1982 Emmett | 12,500 | 50.00 |
| 1982 Judy | 12,500 | 50.00 |
| 1982 Jimmy | 12,500 | 50.00 |
| 1982 Shark | 12,500 | 50.00 |
| *Early American Sail* | | |
| 1982 Squall | 5,000 | 39.50 |
| 1983 Young America | 5,000 | 39.50 |
| 1984 Ironsides | 5,000 | 39.50 |
| 1984 Charles W. Morgan | 5,000 | 39.50 |
| *Lil Critters* | | |
| 1982 Inquisitive | 10,000 | 39.50 |
| 1982 Sassy | 10,000 | 39.50 |
| 1983 Vigilance | 10,000 | 39.50 |
| 1983 Chatty | 10,000 | 39.50 |
| *Vanishing West* | | |
| 1982 Hell Bent | 5,000 | 60.00 |
| 1983 Cold Trail | 5,000 | 60.00 |
| 1983 Horse Stick Medicine | 5,000 | 60.00 |
| 1984 Letting 'em Blow | 5,000 | 60.00 |
| 1984 Eyeing Back Trail | 5,000 | 60.00 |
| *Africa's Beauties* | | |
| 1983 Elephant Family | 5,000 | 65.00 |
| 1983 Zebra Family | 5,000 | 65.00 |
| *America's Heritage of Flight* | | |
| 1983 Kitty Hawk | 5,000 | 39.50 |
| 1983 Jenny | 5,000 | 39.50 |
| 1984 Race | 5,000 | 39.50 |
| 1984 Corsair | 5,000 | 39.50 |
| *Craftsman Heritage* | | |
| 1983 Decoy Maker | 5,000 | 39.50 |
| 1983 Sailmaker | 5,000 | 39.50 |
| 1983 Farmer | 5,000 | 39.50 |
| 1984 Platemaker | 5,000 | 39.50 |

| | Edition Limit | Issue Price (US) |
|---|---|---|
| 1984 Blacksmith | 5,000 | $ 39.50 |
| 1984 Spinning Wheel | 5,000 | 39.50 |
| 1985 Gunsmith | 5,000 | 39.50 |
| *Equestrian Love* | | |
| 1983 Arabian Destiny | 5,000 | 39.50 |
| 1983 Quarterhorse Wrangler | 5,000 | 39.50 |
| 1984 Arab Destiny | 5,000 | 39.50 |
| *Sawdust Antics* | | |
| 1983 Emmett's 8 Ball | 5,000 | 50.00 |
| 1983 Emmett with a Bang | 5,000 | 50.00 |
| 1984 Emmett at Races | 5,000 | 50.00 |
| 1984 Emmett at Plate | 5,000 | 50.00 |
| *Clown Antics* | | |
| 1984 Comedy | 10,000 | 19.50 |
| 1984 Tragedy | 10,000 | 19.50 |
| *Endangered* | | |
| 1984 Sidney | 10,000 | 19.50 |
| 1984 Chein | 10,000 | 19.50 |
| *Homer's Antics* | | |
| 1984 Homer at Races | 10,000 | 39.50 |
| 1984 Homer on Wall Street | 10,000 | 39.50 |
| *Indian Greats* | | |
| 1984 Two Moons | 10,000 | 19.50 |
| 1984 Chief Joseph | 10,000 | 19.50 |
| *Kitty Kats* | | |
| 1984 Pansy and Sammy | 10,000 | 19.50 |
| *Whimsical Moments* | | |
| 1984 Three's Company | NA | 29.50 |

### American Historial Plates (Castleton China)

| *Aviation* | Edition Limit | Issue Price (US) |
|---|---|---|
| 1972 Amelia Earhart | 3,500 | 40.00 |
| 1972 Charles Lindberg | 3,500 | 40.00 |

### American Preservation Guild (Gorham)

| *Catesby Collection* | Edition Limit | Issue Price (US) |
|---|---|---|
| 1977 Cardinal | 9,900 | 39.00 |

### American Rose Society (Gorham)

| *All-American Rose* | Edition Limit | Issue Price (US) |
|---|---|---|
| 1975 Oregold | 9,800 | 39.00 |
| 1975 Arizona | 9,800 | 39.00 |
| 1975 Rose Parade | 9,800 | 39.00 |
| 1976 America | 9,800 | 39.00 |
| 1976 Cathedral | 9,800 | 39.00 |
| 1976 Seashell | 9,800 | 39.00 |
| 1977 Yankee Doodle | 9,800 | 39.00 |
| 1977 Double Delight | 9,800 | 39.00 |
| 1977 Prominent | 9,800 | 39.00 |
| 1978 First Edition | 9,800 | 39.00 |
| 1978 Color Magic | 9,800 | 39.00 |
| 1978 Charisma | 9,800 | 39.00 |
| 1979 Paradise | 9,800 | 39.00 |
| 1979 Sundowner | 9,800 | 39.00 |
| 1979 Friendship | 9,800 | 39.00 |
| 1980 Love | 9,800 | 39.00 |
| 1980 Honor | 9,800 | 39.00 |
| 1980 Cherish | 9,800 | 39.00 |
| 1981 Bing Crosby | 9,800 | 49.00 |
| 1981 White Lightnin' | 9,800 | 49.00 |
| 1981 Marina | 9,800 | 49.00 |
| 1982 Shreveport | 9,800 | 49.00 |
| 1982 French Lace | 9,800 | 49.00 |
| 1982 Brandy | 9,800 | 49.00 |
| 1983 Mon Cheri | 9,800 | 49.00 |
| 1983 Sun Flare | 9,800 | 49.00 |
| 1983 Sweet Surrender | 9,800 | 49.00 |
| 1984 Olympiad | 9,800 | 49.00 |
| 1984 Impatient | 9,800 | 49.00 |
| 1984 Intrigue | 9,800 | 49.00 |
| 1985 Showbiz | 9,800 | 49.00 |
| 1985 Peace | 9,800 | 49.00 |
| 1985 Queen Elizabeth | 9,800 | 49.00 |

### Antique Trader

| *Currier & Ives* | Edition Limit | Issue Price (US) |
|---|---|---|
| 1969 Baseball | 2,000 | 9.00 |
| 1969 Franklin Experiment | 2,000 | 9.00 |
| 1969 Haying Time | 2,000 | 9.00 |
| 1969 Winter in Country | 2,000 | 9.00 |
| *Easter* | | |
| 1971 Child and Lamb | 1,500 | 10.95 |
| 1972 Shepherd with Lamb | 1,000 | 10.95 |
| *Mother's Day* | | |
| 1971 Madonna and Child | 1,500 | 10.95 |
| 1972 Mother Cat and Kittens | 1,000 | 10.95 |
| *Father's Day* | | |
| 1971 Pilgrim Father | 1,500 | $ 10.95 |
| 1972 Deer Family | 1,000 | 10.95 |
| *Thanksgiving* | | |
| 1971 Pilgrims | 1,500 | 10.95 |
| 1972 First Thanksgiving | 1,000 | 10.95 |
| *Christmas* | | |
| 1971 Christ Child | 1,500 | 10.95 |
| 1972 Flight into Egypt | 1,000 | 10.95 |
| *C. M. Russell* | | |
| 1971 Bad One | 2,000 | 11.95 |
| 1971 Discovery of Last Chance Gulch | 2,000 | 11.95 |
| 1971 Doubtful Visitor | 2,000 | 11.95 |
| 1971 Innocent Allies | 2,000 | 11.95 |
| 1971 Medicine Man | 2,000 | 11.95 |
| *Bible* | | |
| 1973 David & Goliath | 2,000 | 10.75 |
| 1973 Moses & Golden Idol | 2,000 | 10.75 |
| 1973 Noah's Ark | 2,000 | 10.75 |
| 1973 Samson | 2,000 | 10.75 |

### Arizona Artisan

| *Christmas* | Edition Limit | Issue Price (US) |
|---|---|---|
| 1974 Mexican Christmas | Year | 20.00 |
| 1975 Navajo Christmas | Year | 20.00 |
| *Thanksgiving* | | |
| 1975 Navajo Thanksgiving Feast | Year | 15.00 |

### Arlington Mint

| *Christmas* | Edition Limit | Issue Price (US) |
|---|---|---|
| 1972 Hands in Prayer | Year | 125.00 |

### Armstrong's

| *(Single issue)* | Edition Limit | Issue Price (US) |
|---|---|---|
| 1983 Seventy Years Young | 15,000 | 85.00 |
| *Huggable Puppies* | | |
| 1984 Take Me Home | 10,000 | 29.50 |
| 1985 Oh How Cute | 10,000 | 29.50 |
| *Lovable Kittens* | | |
| 1984 Cat's Meow | 10,000 | 29.50 |
| 1984 Purr-Swayed | 10,000 | 29.50 |
| 1985 Prince of Purrs | 10,000 | 29.50 |
| 1986 Pet and I'll Purr | 10,000 | 29.50 |
| *Three Graces* | | |
| 1984 Thalia | 10,000 | 49.50 |
| 1986 Aglia | 7,500 | 49.50 |
| 1987 Euphrosyne | 10,000 | 49.50 |
| *(Single issue)* | | |
| 1984 Freddie Torchbearer | 15,000 | 62.50 |
| *Companions* | | |
| 1985 All Bark and No Bite | 10,000 | 29.50 |
| *Reflections of Innocence* | | |
| 1985 Me and My Friend | 10,000 | 37.50 |
| 1985 My RainBeau | 10,000 | 37.50 |
| *Statue of Liberty* | | |
| 1985 Dedication Ceremony | 10,000 | 39.50 |
| 1985 Immigrants | 10,000 | 39.50 |
| 1985 Independence | 10,000 | 39.50 |
| 1985 Re-Dedication | 10,000 | 39.50 |
| *(Single issue)* | | |
| 1985 Pete Rose | 10,000 | 45.00 |
| *Signature Collection* | | |
| 1986 Anyone for Tennis? | 10,000 | 62.50 |
| *Infinite Love* | | |
| 1987 Once Upon a Smile | 10,000 | 45.00 |
| *Buckhill Bears* | | |
| 1986 Tiddlywink and Pixie | 10,000 | 29.50 |
| 1986 Rebecca and Friend | 10,000 | 29.50 |
| *Zodiac Collection* | | |
| 1986 Pisces | NA | 35.00 |
| 1986 Capricorn | NA | 35.00 |
| 1986 Cancer | NA | 35.00 |
| 1986 Virgo | NA | 35.00 |

### Art World of Bourgeault

| *Royal Literary Series* | Edition Limit | Issue Price (US) |
|---|---|---|
| 1986 John Bunyan Cottage | 4,500 | 60.00 |
| 1987 Thomas Hardy Cottage | 4,500 | 65.00 |
| *English Countryside Collection* | | |
| 1984 The Country Squire | 1,500 | 150.00 |
| 1985 The Willows | 1,500 | 150.00 |
| *(Single issue)* | | |
| 1986 Lilac Cottage | 500 | 200.00 |

### Artists of the World

| *Ruffin Annual* | Edition Limit | Issue Price (US) |
|---|---|---|
| 1976 Navajo Lullaby | 10,000 | $ 40.00 |
| 1977 Through Years | 5,000 | 45.00 |
| 1978 Child of Pueblo | 5,000 | 50.00 |
| 1979 Colima Madonna | 5,000 | 50.00 |
| 1980 Sun Kachina | 5,000 | 50.00 |
| 1981 Inner Peace | 5,000 | 55.00 |
| 1982 Madonna of Cross | 5,000 | 60.00 |
| 1983 Navajo Princess | 5,000 | 60.00 |
| 1984 Americans All | 7,500 | 60.00 |
| *World of Game Birds* | | |
| 1977 Mallards | 5,000 | 45.00 |
| 1978 Gambel Quail | 5,000 | 45.00 |
| 1979 American Autumn Ring-necked Pheasant | 5,000 | 50.00 |
| 1980 November Journey-Canada Geese | 5,000 | 50.00 |
| *Don Ruffin Self-Portrait* | | |
| 1979 Clown Also Cries | 7,500 | 65.00 |
| *Children of Don Ruffin* | | |
| 1980 Flowers for Mother | 7,500 | 50.00 |
| 1981 Little Eagle | 7,500 | 55.00 |
| 1982 Lost Moccasins | 7,500 | 60.00 |
| 1983 Security | 7,500 | 60.00 |
| 1984 Americans All | 7,500 | 60.00 |
| *Prowlers of Clouds* | | |
| 1981 Great Horned Owl | 5,000 | 55.00 |
| 1981 Screech Owl | 5,000 | 55.00 |
| 1982 Bald Eagle | 5,000 | 60.00 |
| 1982 Golden Eagle | 5,000 | 60.00 |
| *Anthony Sidoni* | | |
| 1982 Little Yankee | 15,000 | 35.00 |
| 1983 Little Satchmo | 15,000 | 40.00 |
| *Vel Miller* | | |
| 1982 Mama's Rose | 15,000 | 35.00 |
| 1983 Papa's Boy | 15,000 | 40.00 |
| *Woodland Friends* | | |
| 1983 Whitetail Deer | 5,000 | 60.00 |
| 1984 Black Bear | 5,000 | 60.00 |
| 1984 No Rest for Night Shift | 5,000 | 60.00 |
| 1985 No Peace in Paradise | 5,000 | 60.00 |
| *(Single issue)* | | |
| 1983 DeGrazia and His Mountain | 15,000 | 65.00 |
| *Sweet-Hearts* | | |
| 1984 We Believe | 10,000 | 40.00 |
| *(Single issue)* | | |
| 1984 Girl Paints DeGrazia | 12,500 | 65.00 |
| *DeGrazia's Children at Play* | | |
| 1985 My First Horse | 15,000 | 65.00 |
| 1986 Girl with Sewing Machine | 15,000 | 65.00 |

### Audubon Crystal

| *Endangered Birds* | Edition Limit | Issue Price (US) |
|---|---|---|
| 1976 Kirtland's Warbler | 5,000 | 195.00 |
| 1976 American Eagle | 5,000 | 195.00 |
| 1977 Peregrine Falcon | 5,000 | 200.00 |

### Avondale

| *Cameos of Childhood* | Edition Limit | Issue Price (US) |
|---|---|---|
| 1978 Melissa | 28,050 | 65.00 |
| 1979 First Born | 12,000 | 70.00 |
| 1980 Melissa's Brother | Year | 70.00 |
| 1981 Daddy and I | Year | 75.00 |
| *Myths of Sea* | | |
| 1979 Poseidon | 15,000 | 70.00 |
| 1980 Maiden of Sea | 15,000 | 70.00 |
| *Tribute to Ageless Art* | | |
| 1979 Court Jesters | 10,000 | 70.00 |
| *World of Dance* | | |
| 1979 Prima Ballerina | 15,000 | 70.00 |
| *Christmas* | | |
| 1981 And Heavens Rejoiced | 6,500 | 90.00 |
| 1982 And There Came Wise Men | 6,500 | 90.00 |
| 1983 Shepherd | 6,500 | 90.00 |
| *Growing Up* | | |
| 1982 Ribbon for Her Hair | 6,500 | 75.00 |
| 1983 Just Like Mother | 6,500 | 75.00 |

*See also: Judaic Heritage Society (U.S.A.)*

### B & J Art Designs

| *Old Fashioned Christmas* | Edition Limit | Issue Price (US) |
|---|---|---|
| 1983 Carol | 15,000 | $ 45.00 |
| 1984 Chris | 15,000 | 45.00 |
| 1985 Noel | 15,000 | 45.00 |
| *Country* | | |
| 1984 Cristina | 20,000 | 39.00 |
| 1985 Laurel | 20,000 | 42.50 |

### Beacon Manufacturing

| *Pacesetters* | Edition Limit | Issue Price (US) |
|---|---|---|
| 1987 Frederick Douglass | 2,500 | 50.00 |
| 1987 Marcus Garvey | 5,000 | 50.00 |
| 1987 Mary McLeod Bethune | NA | 50.00 |

### Blue River Mill Publishing Co.

| *Once Upon a Barn* | Edition Limit | Issue Price (US) |
|---|---|---|
| 1986 Mail Pouch | 5,000 | 45.00 |
| 1987 Rock City | 5,000 | 45.00 |
| 1987 Meramec caverns | 5,000 | 45.00 |
| 1988 Coca-Cola | 5,000 | 45.00 |

### Brantwood Collection

| *Marian Carlsen Mother's Day* | Edition Limit | Issue Price (US) |
|---|---|---|
| 1978 Jennifer and Jenny Fur | Year | 45.00 |
| 1979 Football Brothers | 5,000 | 45.00 |
| *Howe Christmas* | | |
| 1978 Visit from Santa | Year | 45.00 |
| *(Single issue)* | | |
| 1978 Tribute to Rockwell | Year | 35.00 |
| *John Falter Christmas* | | |
| 1979 Christmas Morning | 5,000 | 24.50 |
| *Rockwell Mother's Day* | | |
| 1979 Homecoming | 20,000 | 39.50 |
| *Little Clown* | | |
| 1979 Going to Circus | 5,000 | 29.50 |

### Braymer Hall

| *Childhood Sonatas* | Edition Limit | Issue Price (US) |
|---|---|---|
| 1981 Serenade | 15,000 | 28.50 |
| 1982 Prelude | 15,000 | 28.50 |
| 1982 Caprice | 15,000 | 28.50 |
| *American Folk* | | |
| 1982 Spring Celebration | 10,000 | 24.50 |
| 1982 Summer Bounty | 10,000 | 24.50 |
| *Yesterday's Dreams* | | |
| 1983 Swing Quartet | 5,000 | 50.00 |
| 1983 Sleigh Belles | 5,000 | 50.00 |

### Brentwood Fine Arts (Fairmont)

| *Nostalgic Memories* | Edition Limit | Issue Price (US) |
|---|---|---|
| 1982 Amy | 12,500 | 39.50 |

### Briarcrest

| *Good Ole Summertime* | Edition Limit | Issue Price (US) |
|---|---|---|
| 1982 Watermelon Eater | 10 Days | 42.00 |
| *This Ole Bear* | | |
| 1982 Chauncey James | 5,000 | 45.00 |
| *(Single issue)* | | |
| 1982 Carousel | 10,000 | 35.00 |

### Brimark Ltd.

| *Yetta's Holidays* | Edition Limit | Issue Price (US) |
|---|---|---|
| 1986 Christmas Block | NA | 29.50 |

### John Brindle Fine Arts

| *Fantasy in Motion* | Edition Limit | Issue Price (US) |
|---|---|---|
| 1978 Little Blue Horse | 3,000 | 75.00 |
| 1979 Horse of a Different Color | 3,000 | 75.00 |
| 1980 Horse with Golden Horn | 3,000 | 75.00 |
| *Moods of Orient* | | |
| 1978 Softly, Sun Sets | 4,000 | 75.00 |
| 1980 Tranquil Morn | 4,000 | 75.00 |
| *Expressions* | | |
| 1979 Quiet Eyes | 3,000 | 60.00 |
| *(Single issue)* | | |
| 1980 Homage | 2,500 | 125.00 |
| *Those Precious Years* | | |
| 1980 Little Curt and Friend | 3,000 | 60.00 |

| | Edition Limit | Issue Price (US) |
|---|---|---|
| **Cabochon** | | |
| *Nancy Doyle's Candy Girls* | | |
| 1983 Rebecca | 15,000 | $ 50.00 |
| 1984 Shantelle | 15,000 | 50.00 |
| 1984 Kelly Ann | 15,000 | 50.00 |
| **Calhoun's Collectors Society** | | |
| *Crystal Maidens* | | |
| 1979 Spring–Strawberry Season | 2,500 | 49.50 |
| 1979 Summer–Sunshine Season | 2,500 | 49.50 |
| 1979 Autumn–Scenic Season | 2,500 | 49.50 |
| 1979 Winter–Snowflake Season | 2,500 | 49.50 |
| **Calhoun's Collectors Society (Schumann)** | | |
| *Imperial Christmas* | | |
| 1979 Liebling | 10,000 | 65.00 |
| 1980 Hallelujah | 10,000 | 65.00 |
| 1981 Stille Nacht | 10,000 | 65.00 |
| 1982 Winter Melodie | 10,000 | 75.00 |
| **California Porcelain, Inc.** | | |
| *Best of Sascha* | | |
| 1979 Flower Bouquet | 7,500 | 65.00 |
| *Vanishing Animals* | | |
| 1979 Asian Monarchs | 7,500 | 40.00 |
| 1979 Snow Leopards | 7,500 | 45.00 |
| 1980 Pandas | 7,500 | 45.00 |
| 1981 Polar Bears | 7,500 | 50.00 |
| *(Single issue)* | | |
| 1983 Koala | 5,000 | 29.95 |
| *Now Is Moment* | | |
| 1984 Be Still | 12,500 | 35.00 |
| *Seed of People* | | |
| 1984 Keenah | 10,000 | 29.95 |
| **Carmel Collection** | | |
| *Famous Parades* | | |
| 1983 Thanksgiving Day Parade | Year | 39.50 |
| *First Performances* | | |
| 1983 Darling Diana | 19,500 | 39.50 |
| *Joys of Christmas* | | |
| 1983 Christmas Delight | 19,500 | 39.50 |
| *Memories of Heart* | | |
| 1984 Petals | 15,000 | 28.50 |
| **Carson Mint (Viletta)** | | |
| *Yesterday's Children* | | |
| 1978 Lisa and Jumeau Doll | 5,000 | 60.00 |
| 1979 Adrianne and Bye-Lo Baby | 5,000 | 60.00 |
| 1980 Lydia and Shirley Temple Doll | 5,000 | 60.00 |
| 1981 Melanie and Scarlett O'Hara Doll | 5,000 | 60.00 |
| *Hollywood Squares* | | |
| 1979 Peter Marshall | 100 Days | 28.50 |
| 1980 George Gobel | 100 Days | 28.50 |
| *Moment in Time* | | |
| 1979 Freedom Flight | 5,000 | 55.00 |
| *Old Fashioned Mother's Day* | | |
| 1979 Daisies from Mary-Beth | 20 Days | 37.50 |
| 1980 Daisies from Jimmy | 20 Days | 37.50 |
| 1981 Daisies from Meg | 20 Days | 37.50 |
| 1982 Daisies for Mommie | 20 Days | 37.50 |
| *America Has Heart* | | |
| 1980 My Heart's Desire | Year | 24.50 |
| 1981 Hearts and Flowers | Year | 24.50 |
| 1982 Hearty Sailer | Year | 28.50 |
| 1983 Shannon's Sweetheart | Year | 28.50 |
| *Magic Afternoon* | | |
| 1980 Enchanted Garden | 5,000 | 39.50 |
| 1981 Delightful Tea Party | 5,000 | 39.50 |
| *Big Top* | | |
| 1981 White Face | 60 Days | 28.50 |
| 1982 Tramp | 60 Days | 28.50 |
| *Littlest Christmas* | | |
| 1982 Littlest Stocking | 12,500 | 29.50 |
| 1983 Littlest Santa | 12,500 | 29.50 |

| | Edition Limit | Issue Price (US) |
|---|---|---|
| *Nature's Children* | | |
| 1982 Candice | 12,500 | $ 29.50 |
| 1983 Cory | 12,500 | 29.50 |
| 1984 Ryan's Retreat | 12,500 | 29.50 |
| *Bear Feats* | | |
| 1983 Teddy Bear Picnic | 15,000 | 37.50 |
| 1984 On Beach | 15,000 | 37.50 |
| *To Mom with Love* | | |
| 1983 A Basket of Love | 15,000 | 37.50 |
| **Castleton China** | | |
| *Natural History* | | |
| 1973 Painted Lady | 1,500 | 40.00 |
| 1973 Roseate Spoonbill | 1,500 | 40.00 |
| *(Single issue)* | | |
| 1976 Gen. Douglas MacArthur | 1,000 | 30.00 |
| **Castleton China (Shenango)** | | |
| *Bicentennial* | | |
| 1972 New Dawn | 7,600 | 60.00 |
| 1972 Turning Point | 7,600 | 60.00 |
| 1973 Valley Forge | 7,600 | 60.00 |
| 1973 Declaration | 7,600 | 60.00 |
| 1973 Star Spangled Banner | 7,600 | 60.00 |
| 1973 U.S.S. Constitution | 7,600 | 60.00 |
| 1974 One Nation | 7,600 | 60.00 |
| 1974 Westward Ho | 7,600 | 60.00 |
| *See also: American Historical Plates (U.S.A.)* | | |
| **Caverswall** | | |
| *See: Ghent Collection (U.S.A.)* | | |
| **Ceramic Art Studios** | | |
| *(Single issue)* | | |
| 1986 Chessie | 9,000 | 60.00 |
| **Certified Rarities** | | |
| *Indian Dancer* | | |
| 1978 Eagle Dancer | 2,500 | 300.00 |
| 1979 Hoop Dancer | 2,500 | 300.00 |
| *Postal Artists* | | |
| 1978 Colias Eurydice | 15,000 | 60.00 |
| 1979 Euphydryas Phaeton | 7,500 | 60.00 |
| *Renaissance Masters* | | |
| 1978 Alba Madonna | 15,000 | 55.00 |
| 1979 Pieta | 5,000 | 55.00 |
| **Chilmark** | | |
| *Family Christmas* | | |
| 1978 Trimming Tree | 10,000 | 65.00 |
| *In Appreciation* | | |
| 1979 Flowers of Field | 10,000 | 65.00 |
| *Holy Night* | | |
| 1979 Wisemen | 10,000 | 65.00 |
| *Twelve Days of Christmas* | | |
| 1979 Partridge in Pear Tree | 10,000 | 89.50 |
| **Christian Fantasy Collectibles** | | |
| *Christian Fantasy* | | |
| 1985 Legend/Prayer Bear I | 5,100 | 50.00 |
| 1986 Legend/Prayer Bear II | 5,100 | 50.00 |
| 1987 Legend/Prayer Bear III | 5,100 | 50.00 |
| *Fantasy Cookbook* | | |
| 1986 Picnic in Woods | 7,100 | 50.00 |
| *Realms of Wonder* | | |
| 1986 Wizard's Glade | 9,100 | 50.00 |
| 1987 Mermaid's Grotto | 9,100 | 50.00 |
| *Santa's Night Out* | | |
| 1986 Santa Daydreams | 9,100 | 50.00 |
| **Cleveland Mint** | | |
| *Da Vinci* | | |
| 1972 Last Supper | 5,000 | 125.00 |
| **Collector Creations (Reed & Barton)** | | |
| *Thomas Nast Christmas* | | |
| 1973 Christmas | 750 | 100.00 |
| *(Single issue)* | | |
| 1973 Alice in Wonderland | 750 | 100.00 |
| **Collector's Heirlooms (Fairmont)** | | |
| *Children at Play* | | |
| 1979 Maple Leaf Noses | 7,500 | 60.00 |
| *Passing of Plains Indians* | | |
| 1979 Cheyenne Chieftain | 5,000 | 65.00 |

| | Edition Limit | Issue Price (US) |
|---|---|---|
| **Collector's Heirlooms (Viletta)** | | |
| *Childhood Memories* | | |
| 1978 Jennifer by Candlelight | 5,000 | $ 60.00 |
| 1979 Brian's Birthday | 5,000 | 60.00 |
| *Joys of Motherhood* | | |
| 1978 Crystal's Joy | 7,500 | 60.00 |
| **Collectors Weekly** | | |
| *American* | | |
| 1971 Miss Liberty | 500 | 12.50 |
| 1972 Miss Liberty | 900 | 12.50 |
| 1973 Eagle | 900 | 9.75 |
| **Commemorative Imports** | | |
| *M. Seeley's French Fashion Dolls* | | |
| 1986 Goldonna | 5,000 | 39.00 |
| 1986 Schamare | 5,000 | 39.00 |
| 1986 Jewelette | 5,000 | 39.00 |
| **Concordia Publishing House** | | |
| *Life of Christ* | | |
| 1987 Baptism of Jesus | 7,500 | 34.95 |
| **Continental Mint** | | |
| *Tom Sawyer* | | |
| 1976 Taking His Medicine | 5,000 | 60.00 |
| 1977 Painting Fence | 5,000 | 60.00 |
| 1978 Lost in Cave | 5,000 | 60.00 |
| 1979 Smoking Pipe | 5,000 | 60.00 |
| *(Single issue)* | | |
| 1979 Butter Girl | 7,000 | 60.00 |
| **Creative World** | | |
| *Pearl Buck (Single issue)* | | |
| 1972 Good Earth | 10,000 | NA |
| *Four Seasons* | | |
| 1972 Fall (Silverplate) | 2,000 | 75.00 |
| 1972 Fall (Sterling) | 2,000 | 125.00 |
| 1973 Winter (Silverplate) | 2,000 | 75.00 |
| 1973 Winter (Sterling) | 250 | 125.00 |
| 1973 Spring (Silverplate) | 300 | 75.00 |
| 1973 Spring (Sterling) | 750 | 125.00 |
| 1974 Summer (Silverplate) | 300 | 75.00 |
| 1974 Summer (Sterling) | 750 | 125.00 |
| *Brown's Rockwells* | | |
| 1977 Looking Out to Sea | 15,000 | 50.00 |
| 1978 Yankee Doodle | 15,000 | 50.00 |
| 1979 Girl at Mirror | 15,000 | 55.00 |
| *Immortals of Early American Literature* | | |
| 1978 Village Smithy | 15,000 | 50.00 |
| 1979 Rip Van Winkle | 15,000 | 55.00 |
| *Aesop's Fables* | | |
| 1979 Fox & Grapes | 9,750 | 85.00 |
| *Living Dolls* | | |
| 1982 Eriko and Noriko | 9,500 | 49.50 |
| 1983 Ingrid and Ingemar | 9,500 | 49.50 |
| *Prize* | | |
| 1982 Family Cares | 12,500 | 45.00 |
| 1983 Wind in a Frolic | 12,500 | 45.00 |
| *Wags to Riches* | | |
| 1982 Benji Movie Star | 100 Days | 29.50 |
| 1982 Benji and Tiffany | 100 Days | 29.50 |
| 1983 Merry Christmas Benji | 19,500 | 35.00 |
| 1984 Benji's Barbershop Blues | 19,500 | 35.00 |
| *Help My Friends* | | |
| 1983 Corky's Dream | 100 Days | 35.00 |
| **Crown Parian** | | |
| *Rosemary Calder* | | |
| 1978 Affection | 7,500 | 60.00 |
| *James Daly* | | |
| 1978 Sweet Dreams | 7,500 | 55.00 |
| *Beautiful Cats of World* | | |
| 1979 Sheena | 5,000 | 60.00 |
| 1979 Sheena and Sheena's Cubs | 5,000 | 60.00 |
| 1980 Elisheba | 5,000 | 60.00 |
| 1980 Elisheba's Cubs | 5,000 | 60.00 |
| 1981 Atarah | 5,000 | 60.00 |
| 1981 Atarah's Cubs | 5,000 | 60.00 |
| 1982 Tamar | 5,000 | 60.00 |
| 1982 Tamar's Cubs | 5,000 | 60.00 |
| *Penni Anne Cross* | | |
| 1979 Crow Baby | 7,500 | 55.00 |
| 1981 Paiute Pals | 7,500 | 55.00 |

| | Edition Limit | Issue Price (US) |
|---|---|---|
| 1982 Big Sister's Buckskins | 7,500 | $ 55.00 |
| 1984 Navajo Nanny | 7,500 | 55.00 |
| *Julian Ritter* | | |
| 1979 Reve de Ballet | 7,500 | 55.00 |
| *Western* | | |
| 1979 Under Surveillance | 10,000 | 65.00 |
| 1979 Promised Land | 10,000 | 65.00 |
| 1979 Winter Song | 10,000 | 65.00 |
| 1979 Boomtown and Wildcatters | 10,000 | 65.00 |
| *Sporting Dogs* | | |
| 1980 Decoy | 5,000 | 55.00 |
| 1981 Dusty | 5,000 | 55.00 |
| 1982 Rummy | 5,000 | 55.00 |
| 1983 Scarlet | 5,000 | 55.00 |
| *Happy Art* | | |
| 1981 Woody's Triple Self-Portrait | 10,000 | 39.50 |
| 1982 Gothic Woody | 10,000 | 39.50 |
| 1984 Blue Boy Woody | 10,000 | 39.50 |
| *Portraits of Childhood* | | |
| 1981 Miss Murray | 7,500 | 65.00 |
| 1984 Master Lambton | 10,000 | 65.00 |
| *Children to Love* | | |
| 1982 Wendy | 10,000 | 60.00 |
| 1983 Jake | 10,000 | 60.00 |
| 1984 Katy | 10,000 | 60.00 |
| 1985 Jed | 10,000 | 60.00 |
| *Owl Family* | | |
| 1982 Saw-Whet Owl Family | 5,000 | 55.00 |
| 1982 Great Horned Owl Family | 5,000 | 55.00 |
| 1983 Snowy Owl Family | 5,000 | 55.00 |
| 1983 Barred Owl Family | 5,000 | 55.00 |
| *Reflections of Seasons* | | |
| 1982 Winter's Dream | 7,500 | 39.50 |
| *(Single issue)* | | |
| 1982 Buon Natale | 1,000 | 300.00 |
| *Special Heart* | | |
| 1983 Reaching Together | 40,000 | 35.00 |
| 1983 Love in Your Heart | 40,000 | 35.00 |
| *Holidays Around the World* | | |
| 1984 Elysa's Christmas | 12,500 | 39.50 |
| *Songs of Carolyn* | | |
| 1985 Quiet Moment | 5,000 | 35.00 |
| *See also: American Heritage Art (U.S.A.)* | | |
| **Curator Collection** | | |
| *Masterpieces of Impressionism* | | |
| 1980 Woman with a Parasol | 17,500 | 35.00 |
| 1981 Young Mother Sewing | 17,500 | 35.00 |
| 1982 Sara in Green Bonnet | 17,500 | 35.00 |
| 1983 Margot in Blue | 17,500 | 35.00 |
| *Masterpieces of West* | | |
| 1980 Texas Night Herder | 17,500 | 35.00 |
| 1981 Indian Trapper | 17,500 | 35.00 |
| 1982 Cowboy Style | | |
| 1982 Indian Style (Set of two) | 17,500 | 70.00 |
| *Masterpieces of Rockwell* | | |
| 1980 After Prom | 17,500 | 35.00 |
| 1981 Challenger | 17,500 | 42.50 |
| 1981 Girl at Mirror | 17,500 | 50.00 |
| 1982 Missing Tooth | 17,500 | 50.00 |
| *Jesse's World* | | |
| 1981 This Simple Faith | 17,500 | 39.95 |
| *Magical Moments* | | |
| 1981 Happy Dreams | NA | 29.95 |
| 1981 Harmony | NA | 29.95 |
| 1982 His Majesty | NA | 29.95 |
| 1982 Waiting for Daddy | NA | 29.95 |
| 1983 Thank You, God | NA | 29.95 |
| 1983 Lullaby | NA | 29.95 |
| *Rockwell Americana* | | |
| 1981 Shuffleton's Barbershop | 17,500 | 75.00 |
| 1982 Breaking Home Ties | 17,500 | 75.00 |
| 1983 Walking to Church | 17,500 | 75.00 |
| *Special Occasions* | | |
| 1981 Bubbles | NA | 29.95 |
| 1982 Butterflies | NA | 29.95 |

| | Edition Limit | Issue Price (US) |
|---|---|---|
| ***Stockbridge Trilogy*** | | |
| 1981 Stockbridge in Winter, Part I | NA | $ 45.00 |
| 1982 Stockbridge in Winter, Part II | NA | 45.00 |
| 1983 Stockbridge in Winter, Part III | NA | 45.00 |
| ***Classic Circus*** | | |
| 1982 Favorite Clown | 17,500 | 39.95 |
| ***Playful Pets*** | | |
| 1982 Curiosity | 10,000 | 45.00 |
| 1982 Master's Hat | 10,000 | 45.00 |
| ***Tribute*** | | |
| 1982 I Want You | NA | 29.95 |
| 1982 Gee! I Wish I Were a Man | NA | 29.95 |
| 1983 Soldier's Farewell | NA | 29.95 |
| ***Becker Babies*** | | |
| 1983 Snowpuff | NA | 29.95 |
| 1984 Smiling Through | NA | 29.95 |
| 1984 Pals | NA | 29.95 |
| ***Nursery*** | | |
| 1983 In Slumberland | NA | 35.00 |
| 1983 Awakening | NA | 35.00 |
| ***Mother's Love*** | | |
| 1984 Contentment | 7,500 | 35.00 |
| ***On Road*** | | |
| 1984 Pride of Stockbridge | NA | 35.00 |
| 1985 City Pride | NA | 35.00 |
| 1985 Country Pride | NA | 35.00 |
| ***Simpler Times*** | | |
| 1984 Lazy Daze | 7,500 | 35.00 |
| ***Triple Play*** | | |
| 1984 Chums | NA | 29.95 |
| 1984 Nitey-Nite | NA | 29.95 |
| 1984 Oh, Oh! A Bunny | NA | 29.95 |
| ***Great Trains*** | | |
| 1985 Santa Fe | 7,500 | 35.00 |
| 1985 Twentieth Century Ltd. | 7,500 | 35.00 |
| 1986 Empire Builder | 7,500 | 35.00 |
| ***Portraits of American Brides*** | | |
| 1986 Caroline | 10 Days | 29.50 |
| 1986 Jacqueline | 10 Days | 29.50 |
| 1987 Elizabeth | 10 Days | 29.50 |
| 1987 Emily | 10 Days | 29.50 |
| 1987 Meredith | 10 Days | 29.50 |
| 1987 Laura | 10 Days | 29.50 |
| 1987 Sarah | 10 Days | 29.50 |
| 1987 Rebecca | 10 Days | 29.50 |
| ***Portraits (cats)*** | | |
| 1986 Chantilly | NA | 24.50 |
| 1986 Dynasty | NA | 24.50 |
| 1986 Velvet | NA | 24.50 |
| ***Sailing Through History*** | | |
| 1986 Flying Cloud | 14 Days | 29.50 |
| 1986 Santa Maria | 14 Days | 29.50 |
| 1986 Mayflower | 14 Days | 29.50 |
| *(Single issue)* | | |
| 1986 Motherhood | NA | 37.50 |
| *(Single issue)* | | |
| 1986 The Christening | NA | 37.50 |
| **Danbury Mint** | | |
| ***Currier & Ives (Silver)*** | | |
| 1972 Road Winter | 7,500 | 125.00 |
| 1973 Central Park Winter | 7,500 | 125.00 |
| 1974 Winter in Country | 7,500 | 125.00 |
| 1975 American Homestead | 7,500 | 125.00 |
| 1976 American Winter-Evening | 7,500 | 135.00 |
| 1977 Winter Morning | 7,500 | 135.00 |
| ***Christmas*** | | |
| 1975 Silent Night | NA | 24.50 |
| 1976 Joy to World | NA | 27.50 |
| 1977 Away in Manger | NA | 27.50 |
| 1978 First Noel | NA | 29.50 |
| ***Bicentennial (Silver)*** | | |
| 1973 Boston Tea Party | 7,500 | 125.00 |
| 1974 First Continental Congress | 7,500 | 125.00 |
| 1975 Paul Revere's Ride | 7,500 | 125.00 |
| 1976 Declaration of Independence | 7,500 | 125.00 |
| 1977 Washington at Valley Forge | 7,500 | 125.00 |
| 1978 Molly Pitcher | 7,500 | $125.00 |
| 1979 Bon Homme Richard | 7,500 | 125.00 |
| ***Michelangelo (Silver)*** | | |
| 1973 Creation of Adam | 7,500 | 125.00 |
| 1973 Pieta | 7,500 | 125.00 |
| 1973 Moses | 7,500 | 125.00 |
| 1973 Holy Family | 7,500 | 125.00 |
| ***Great Art Masterpieces (Silver)*** | | |
| 1975 Mona Lisa | 7,500 | 125.00 |
| 1975 Last Supper | 7,500 | 125.00 |
| 1976 Sunflower | 7,500 | 125.00 |
| 1976 Blue Boy | 7,500 | 125.00 |
| **Derby Collection** | | |
| ***Mischief Makers*** | | |
| 1985 Puddles | 10,000 | 39.95 |
| 1985 Buckles | 10,000 | 39.95 |
| ***Wild Innocence*** | | |
| 1985 My Buddy | 5,000 | 29.95 |
| **Designers Collection** | | |
| ***Faerie Seasons*** | | |
| 1984 Meadow Nymph | 10,000 | 29.00 |
| 1984 Flower Nymph | 10,000 | 29.00 |
| 1984 Arbor Nymph | 10,000 | 29.00 |
| 1984 Woodland Nymph | 10,000 | 29.00 |
| **Stuart Devlin Silver** | | |
| ***Americana*** | | |
| 1972 Gaspee Incident | 1,000 | 130.00 |
| **Walt Disney Productions** | | |
| ***Enchantment of Snow White*** | | |
| 1984 At Wishing Well | 15,000 | 26.50 |
| 1984 Dance | 15,000 | 26.50 |
| 1984 Witch and Apple | 15,000 | 26.50 |
| 1984 Happily Ever After | 15,000 | 26.50 |
| 1984 Enchantment of Snow White | 15,000 | 26.50 |
| ***Disney's Magic Memories*** | | |
| 1986 Snow White/Dwarfs | 24,500 | 37.50 |
| 1986 Pinocchio | 24,500 | 37.50 |
| 1986 Fantasia | 24,500 | 37.50 |
| 1986 Dumbo | 24,500 | 37.50 |
| 1986 Bambi | 24,500 | 37.50 |
| 1986 Cinderella | 24,500 | 37.50 |
| 1986 Alice in Wonderland | 24,500 | 37.50 |
| 1986 Peter Pan | 24,500 | 37.50 |
| 1986 Lady and Tramp | 24,500 | 37.50 |
| 1986 Sleeping Beauty | 24,500 | 37.50 |
| 1986 101 Dalmatians | 24,500 | 37.50 |
| 1986 Sword in Stone | 24,500 | 37.50 |
| 1986 Jungle Book | 24,500 | 37.50 |
| 1986 Aristocats | 24,500 | 37.50 |
| 1986 Robin Hood | 24,500 | 37.50 |
| 1986 Rescuers | 24,500 | 37.50 |
| 1986 Fox and Hound | 24,500 | 37.50 |
| **Duncan Royale** | | |
| ***History of Santa Claus II*** | | |
| 1986 Lord of Misrule | 10,000 | 80.00 |
| 1986 The Alsace Angel | 10,000 | 80.00 |
| ***Portraits of Santa*** | | |
| 1986 Dedt Moroz | 10,000 | 40.00 |
| 1986 Medieval | 10,000 | 40.00 |
| 1986 Pioneer | 10,000 | 40.00 |
| 1986 Kris Kringle | 10,000 | 40.00 |
| 1986 Soda Pop | 10,000 | 40.00 |
| 1986 Nast | 10,000 | 40.00 |
| 1986 Civil War | 10,000 | 40.00 |
| 1986 Wassail | 10,000 | 40.00 |
| 1986 St. Nick | 10,000 | 40.00 |
| 1986 Russian | 10,000 | 40.00 |
| 1986 Black Peter | 10,000 | 40.00 |
| 1986 Victorian | 10,000 | 40.00 |
| **Ebeling & Reuss** | | |
| ***Christmas*** | | |
| 1981 Waiting for Christmas | 7,000 | 15.00 |
| 1982 Time of Song and Caroling | 7,500 | 15.00 |
| *(Single issue)* | | |
| 1983 Love One Another | 12,500 | 17.50 |
| **Enesco** | | |
| ***Christmas*** | | |
| 1981 Come Let Us Adore Him | 15,000 | $ 40.00 |
| 1982 Heaven and Nature Sing | 15,000 | 40.00 |
| 1983 Wee Three Kings | 15,000 | 40.00 |
| 1984 Unto Us a Child Is Born | 15,000 | 40.00 |
| ***Inspired Thoughts*** | | |
| 1981 Love One Another | 15,000 | 40.00 |
| 1981 Make a Joyful Noise | 15,000 | 40.00 |
| 1982 I Believe in Miracles | 15,000 | 40.00 |
| 1983 Love Is Kind | 15,000 | 40.00 |
| ***Mother's Love*** | | |
| 1981 Mother Sew Dear | 15,000 | 40.00 |
| 1982 Purr-fect Grandma | 15,000 | 40.00 |
| 1983 Hand That Rocks Future | 15,000 | 40.00 |
| 1984 Loving Thy Neighbor | 15,000 | 40.00 |
| ***Little Bible Friends*** | | |
| 1981 Nativity | 25,000 | 40.00 |
| 1982 Flight into Egypt | 25,000 | 40.00 |
| 1982 Last Supper | 25,000 | 40.00 |
| ***Joy of Christmas*** | | |
| 1982 Play My Drum for Him | Year | 40.00 |
| 1983 Christmas Time | Year | 40.00 |
| 1984 Wonder of Christmas | Year | 40.00 |
| 1985 Tell Me Story of Jesus | Year | 40.00 |
| ***Four Seasons*** | | |
| 1985 Voice of Spring | Year | 40.00 |
| 1985 Summer's Joy | Year | 40.00 |
| 1986 Autumn's Praise | Year | 40.00 |
| 1986 Winter's Song | Year | 40.00 |
| ***Christmas Love*** | | |
| 1986 Sending You a White Christmas | NA | 45.00 |
| 1987 My Peace I Give Unto Thee | Year | 45.00 |
| ***Birds of North America*** | | |
| 1987 Owl | 2,500 | 40.00 |
| ***Water Birds*** | | |
| 1987 Swan | 2,500 | 40.00 |
| ***Hummingbird*** | | |
| 1987 Hummingbird with Blue Flower | 2,500 | 40.00 |
| **Ernst, Inc.** | | |
| ***Performance*** | | |
| 1979 Act I | 5,000 | 65.00 |
| ***Women of West*** | | |
| 1979 Expectation | 10,000 | 39.50 |
| 1979 Silver Dollar Sal | 10,000 | 39.50 |
| 1980 School Marm | 10,000 | 39.50 |
| 1980 Dolly | 10,000 | 39.50 |
| ***Love Is*** | | |
| 1980 Rufus and Roxanne | 19,000 | 14.95 |
| ***A Beautiful World*** | | |
| 1981 Tahitian Dreamer | 27,500 | 27.50 |
| 1982 Flirtation | 27,500 | 27.50 |
| 1983 Elke of Oslo | 27,500 | 27.50 |
| ***Hollywood Greats*** | | |
| 1980 John Wayne | 27,500 | 29.95 |
| 1981 Gary Cooper | 27,500 | 29.95 |
| 1982 Clark Gable | 27,500 | 29.95 |
| 1983 Alan Ladd | 27,500 | 29.95 |
| ***Classy Cars*** | | |
| 1981 '26 T | 20 Days | 24.50 |
| 1982 Model A | 20 Days | 24.50 |
| 1982 Model A Pickup | 20 Days | 24.50 |
| 1983 Panel Van | 20 Days | 24.50 |
| ***Commemoratives*** | | |
| 1981 John Lennon | 30 Days | 39.50 |
| 1981 Elvis Presley | 30 Days | 39.50 |
| 1982 Marilyn Monroe | 30 Days | 39.50 |
| 1983 Judy Garland | 30 Days | 39.50 |
| ***A Love Story*** | | |
| 1981 Chapter One | 20 Days | 24.50 |
| ***Pinups*** | | |
| 1981 Stars and Stripes Forever | 20 Days | 24.50 |
| ***So Young, So Sweet*** | | |
| 1981 Girl with Straw Hat | 10 Days | 39.50 |
| 1982 My Favorite Necklace | 10 Days | 39.50 |
| 1983 Breakfast Time | 10 Days | 39.50 |
| ***Turn of Century*** | | |
| 1981 Riverboat Honeymoon | 10 Days | $ 35.00 |
| 1982 Children's Carousel | 10 Days | 35.00 |
| 1982 Flower Market | 10 Days | 35.00 |
| 1983 Ballroom Race | 10 Days | 35.00 |
| ***Little Misses Young and Fair*** | | |
| 1982 Heart of a Child | 29,000 | 60.00 |
| 1983 Where Wild Flowers Grow | 29,000 | 60.00 |
| 1984 Whispered Memories | 29,000 | 60.00 |
| 1985 Final Touch | 29,000 | 60.00 |
| ***Mommie and Me*** | | |
| 1982 First Tea | 10 Days | 35.00 |
| 1983 Baby's Sleeping | 10 Days | 35.00 |
| ***My Fair Ladies*** | | |
| 1982 Lady Sabrina | 29,000 | 50.00 |
| 1983 Lady Victoria | 29,000 | 50.00 |
| *(Single issue)* | | |
| 1982 Henry Fonda | 100 Days | 45.00 |
| ***Fondest Memories*** | | |
| 1983 A Touching Moment | NA | 60.00 |
| 1984 Mother's Pearls | NA | 60.00 |
| ***Liebchen*** | | |
| 1983 Winter Liebchen | 30 Days | 19.50 |
| 1983 Spring Liebchen | 30 Days | 19.50 |
| 1984 Summer Liebchen | 30 Days | 19.50 |
| 1984 Autumn Liebchen | 30 Days | 19.50 |
| ***Narrow Gauge*** | | |
| 1983 Halfway to Alamosa | 10 Days | 29.50 |
| 1984 Down from Rico | 10 Days | 29.50 |
| ***Star Trek*** | | |
| 1983 Mr. Spock | 90 Days | 29.50 |
| 1983 Dr. McCoy | 90 Days | 29.50 |
| 1984 Sulu | 90 Days | 29.50 |
| 1984 Scotty | 90 Days | 29.50 |
| 1984 Uhura | 90 Days | 29.50 |
| 1984 Chekov | 90 Days | 29.50 |
| 1985 Captain Kirk | 90 Days | 29.50 |
| 1985 Beam Us Down Scotty | 90 Days | 29.50 |
| 1985 Enterprise | 90 Days | 29.50 |
| ***Yesterdays*** | | |
| 1983 Amber | 10 Days | 24.50 |
| 1983 Elmer | 10 Days | 24.50 |
| 1986 Katie | 10 Days | 24.50 |
| ***Americana*** | | |
| 1984 Somewhere in Autumn | 20 Days | 29.50 |
| 1985 Crystal Winds | 20 Days | 29.50 |
| ***Childhood Memories*** | | |
| 1984 Sometimes an Angel | 20 Days | 24.50 |
| 1985 First Performance | 20 Days | 24.50 |
| ***Children of Past*** | | |
| 1984 Buttercup Test | NA | 29.50 |
| 1984 Minuet | NA | 29.50 |
| 1986 Boy with Hoop | NA | 29.50 |
| ***Days Ago*** | | |
| 1984 Blue Belle | 20 Days | 24.50 |
| ***Fishing Boats*** | | |
| 1984 Sunset at Monterey | 10 Days | 24.50 |
| 1984 Blue Sea | 10 Days | 24.50 |
| ***Friends*** | | |
| 1984 I Love You Orville | 20 Days | 24.50 |
| 1985 Cookies for Corky | 20 Days | 24.50 |
| ***Romantic Memories*** | | |
| 1984 Sunday Afternoon | 14,400 | 60.00 |
| 1985 Freedom | 5,000 | 29.50 |
| 1985 Lily | 5,000 | 29.50 |
| ***Bare Innocence*** | | |
| 1985 Singing in Rain | 10 Days | 24.50 |
| 1985 Free at Last | 10 Days | 24.50 |
| ***Go for Gold*** | | |
| 1985 Valerie | 5,000 | 29.50 |
| ***Me and Mom*** | | |
| 1985 Beach Baby | 5,000 | 29.50 |
| ***Shades of Time*** | | |
| 1985 Morning Glo | 5,000 | 45.00 |
| 1986 Scent and Satin | 5,000 | 45.00 |
| 1987 Golden Flame | 5,000 | 45.00 |
| ***This Land Is Our Land*** | | |
| 1985 Oak Creek Canyon | 5,000 | 29.50 |
| 1986 Dunes | 5,000 | 29.50 |
| 1986 Emerald Bay | 5,000 | 29.50 |
| 1986 Mohave | 5,000 | 29.50 |

| | Edition Limit | Issue Price (US) |
|---|---|---|
| *Fogg and Steam* | | |
| 1986 Pride of Northwest | 7,500 | $ 39.50 |
| 1986 Autumn in New England | 7,500 | 39.50 |
| *Our Country Cousins* | | |
| 1986 She's All Yours | NA | 24.50 |
| 1987 Yep, That's It | NA | 24.50 |
| *Americana* | | |
| 1984 Somewhere in Autumn | 5,000 | 29.50 |
| 1986 Spring Magic | 5,000 | 29.50 |
| *Vintage Classics* | | |
| 1986 Duesenberg | NA | 29.50 |
| *Elvira* | | |
| 1986 Night Rose | NA | 29.50 |
| *Daddy's Little Girl* | | |
| 1986 Look at Me Daddy | 90 Days | 29.95 |
| *Little Farmers* | | |
| 1986 You Been Farming Long? | NA | 24.50 |
| 1987 Are You Pushing, or Pulling? | NA | 24.50 |
| *The Commemorative Collection* | | |
| 1987 Trouble with Tribbles | NA | 29.50 |
| **Evergreen Press** | | |
| *Catalina Island Series* | | |
| 1986 Pleasure Pier | 5,000 | 39.95 |
| **Fairmont** | | |
| *Carousel Horses* | | |
| 1977 (Set of two) | 3,000 | 80.00 |
| *Spencer Annual* | | |
| 1977 Patient Ones | 10,000 | 42.50 |
| 1978 Yesterday, Today and Tomorrow | 10,000 | 47.50 |
| *Irene Spencer's Special Requests* | | |
| 1978 Hug Me | 10,000 | 55.00 |
| 1978 Sleep Little Baby | 10,000 | 65.00 |
| *Olaf Wieghorst* | | |
| 1978 Sioux Warrior | 5,000 | 65.00 |
| 1979 Indian Scout | 5,000 | 65.00 |
| *Rural America* | | |
| 1978 Fence | 5,000 | 45.00 |
| *Timeless Moments* | | |
| 1978 Tenderness | 5,000 | 45.00 |
| 1979 Renaissance | 5,000 | 50.00 |
| 1980 Coming in Glory | 5,000 | 39.95 |
| *Children of America* | | |
| 1979 Eskimo Girl | 3,000 | 48.00 |
| *Lords of Plains* | | |
| 1979 Sitting Bull | 5,000 | 60.00 |
| *Rockwell Early Works* | | |
| 1979 Old Man Winter | 15,000 | 19.95 |
| 1980 Inventor | 15,000 | 19.95 |
| 1980 Ready for School | 15,000 | 19.95 |
| 1980 Music Master | 15,000 | 19.95 |
| 1981 Tinkerer | 15,000 | 19.95 |
| *Gnome Holiday* | | |
| 1980 Gnome Bliss | 5,000 | 24.50 |
| 1981 Gift of Love | 5,000 | 29.95 |
| *Gnomes Four Seasons* | | |
| 1980 Little Swinger (Spring) | 15,000 | 29.50 |
| 1980 Gnome de Bloom (Summer) | 15,000 | 29.50 |
| 1980 Lookouts (Fall) | 15,000 | 29.50 |
| 1980 First Skater (Winter) | 15,000 | 29.50 |
| 1981 Spring Sharing (Spring) | 15,000 | 29.95 |
| 1981 Fun and Games (Summer) | 15,000 | 29.95 |
| 1981 Up Up and Away (Fall) | 15,000 | 29.95 |
| 1981 First Skier (Winter) | 15,000 | 29.95 |
| 1982 Gnome Knowledge (Spring) | 15,000 | 29.95 |
| 1982 Summer Harvest (Summer) | 15,000 | 29.95 |
| 1982 Gnome Family Tailors (Fall) | 15,000 | 29.95 |
| 1982 Keep Gnome Fires Burning (Winter) | 15,000 | 29.95 |
| *American's Most Beloved (Single issue)* | | |
| 1980 John Wayne | 5,000 | 13.95 |
| *Long Road West* | | |
| 1981 Trailblazers | 20,000 | 40.00 |
| 1981 Prairie Schooner | 20,000 | 40.00 |


| | Edition Limit | Issue Price (US) |
|---|---|---|
| 1981 Pony Express | 20,000 | $ 40.00 |
| 1981 Peacemakers | 20,000 | 40.00 |
| 1981 Cowboys of West | 20,000 | 40.00 |
| 1981 Lawmen of West | 20,000 | 40.00 |
| *When I Grow Up* | | |
| 1981 I'll Be Loved | 7,500 | 29.95 |
| 1981 I'll Be Like Mommy | 7,500 | 29.95 |
| 1982 I'll Be First Lady | 7,500 | 29.95 |
| 1982 I'll Be a Star | 7,500 | 29.95 |
| *Jansen's International Beauties* | | |
| 1982 Lisa | 7,500 | 55.00 |
| 1983 Ingrid | 7,500 | 55.00 |
| *Vanishing Americana* | | |
| 1983 American Eagle | 15,000 | 13.50 |
| 1984 Country Doctor | 15,000 | 13.50 |
| *(Single issue)* | | |
| 1983 I Love Teddy Bears | NA | 39.50 |
| *(Single issue)* | | |
| 1983 My Little Sheltie | 5,000 | 39.95 |
| *(Single issue)* | | |
| 1983 Organ Grinder | 5,000 | 19.95 |
| *Legends of Gnomes* | | |
| 1984 Gnome Home | 15,000 | 29.95 |
| *Dreams Do Come True* | | |
| 1985 Little Ballerina | 5,000 | 29.95 |
| *Secrets of the Gnomes* | | |
| 1986 Search for the Stradivarius | 15,000 | 29.95 |
| 1986 Rommelpots and Air Compressors | 15,000 | 29.95 |
| 1986 Noah's Ark and the Gnomes | 15,000 | 29.95 |
| 1986 Which Way the Wind Blows | 15,000 | 29.95 |
| *Gnomes* | | |
| 1987 Gnomatic Fitness | 10,000 | 29.95 |
| 1987 Origin of The Newborn | 10,000 | 29.95 |
| 1987 Origin of Santa Claus | 10,000 | 29.95 |
| 1987 Supreme Justice | 10,000 | 29.95 |

*See also:*
*Brentwood Fine Arts (U.S.A.)*
*Collector's Heirlooms (U.S.A.)*
*Ghent Collection (U.S.A.)*
*Mistwood Designs (U.S.A.)*

**Fenton Glass**

| | Edition Limit | Issue Price (US) |
|---|---|---|
| *American Craftsman* | | |
| 1970 Glassmaker | Year | 10.00 |
| 1971 Printer | Year | 10.00 |
| 1972 Blacksmith | Year | 10.00 |
| 1973 Shoemaker | Year | 10.00 |
| 1974 Cooper | Year | 11.00 |
| 1975 Silversmith | Year | 13.50 |
| 1976 Gunsmith | Year | 13.50 |
| 1977 Potter | Year | 15.00 |
| 1978 Wheelwright | Year | 15.00 |
| 1979 Cabinetmaker | Year | 15.00 |
| 1980 Tanner | Year | 16.50 |
| 1981 Housewright | Year | 17.50 |
| *Christmas in America* | | |
| 1970 Little Brown Church (Blue Satin) | Year | 12.50 |
| 1970 Little Brown Church (Carnival) | Year | 12.50 |
| 1970 Little Brown Church (Brown) | Year | 17.50 |
| 1971 Old Brick Church (Blue Satin) | Year | 12.50 |
| 1971 Old Brick Church (Brown) | Year | 17.50 |
| 1971 Old Brick Church (Carnival) | Year | 12.50 |
| 1971 Old Brick Church (White Satin) | Year | 12.50 |
| 1972 Two Horned Church (Blue Satin) | Year | 12.50 |
| 1972 Two Horned Church (Brown) | Year | 17.50 |
| 1972 Two Horned Church (Carnival) | Year | 12.50 |
| 1972 Two Horned Church (White Satin) | Year | 12.50 |
| 1973 St. Mary's (Blue Satin) | Year | 12.50 |
| 1973 St. Mary's (Carnival) | Year | 12.50 |
| 1973 St. Mary's (White Satin) | Year | 12.50 |


| | Edition Limit | Issue Price (US) |
|---|---|---|
| 1973 St. Mary's (Brown) | Year | $ 17.50 |
| 1974 Nation's Church (Blue Satin) | Year | 13.50 |
| 1974 Nation's Church (Carnival) | Year | 13.50 |
| 1974 Nation's Church (White Satin) | Year | 13.50 |
| 1974 Nation's Church (Brown) | Year | 18.50 |
| 1975 Birthplace of Liberty (Blue Satin) | Year | 13.50 |
| 1975 Birthplace of Liberty (Carnival) | Year | 13.50 |
| 1975 Birthplace of Liberty (White Satin) | Year | 13.50 |
| 1975 Birthplace of Liberty (Brown) | Year | 20.00 |
| 1976 Old North Church (Blue Satin) | Year | 15.00 |
| 1976 Old North Church (Carnival) | Year | 15.00 |
| 1976 Old North Church (White Satin) | Year | 15.00 |
| 1976 Old North Church (Brown) | Year | 25.00 |
| 1977 San Carlos (Blue Satin) | Year | 15.00 |
| 1977 San Carlos (Carnival) | Year | 15.00 |
| 1977 San Carlos (White Satin) | Year | 15.00 |
| 1978 Church of Holy Trinity (Blue Satin) | Year | 15.00 |
| 1978 Church of Holy Trinity (Carnival) | Year | 15.00 |
| 1978 Church of Holy Trinity (White Satin) | Year | 15.00 |
| 1979 San Jose y Miguel de Aguayo (Blue Satin) | Year | 15.00 |
| 1979 San Jose y Miguel de Aguayo (Carnival) | Year | 15.00 |
| 1979 San Jose y Miguel de Aguayo (White Satin) | Year | 15.00 |
| 1980 Christ Church (Blue Satin) | Year | 16.50 |
| 1980 Christ Church (Carnival) | Year | 16.50 |
| 1980 Christ Church (White Satin) | Year | 16.50 |
| 1981 Mission of San Xavier del Bac (Blue Satin) | Year | 18.50 |
| 1981 Mission of San Xavier del Bac (Carnival) | Year | 18.50 |
| 1981 Mission of San Xavier del Bac (White Satin) | Year | 18.50 |
| *Mother's Day* | | |
| 1971 Madonna, Sleeping Child (Blue Satin) | Year | 12.50 |
| 1971 Madonna, Sleeping Child (Carnival) | Year | 12.50 |
| 1972 Madonna of Goldfinch (Blue Satin) | Year | 12.50 |
| 1972 Madonna of Goldfinch (Carnival) | Year | 12.50 |
| 1972 Madonna of Goldfinch (White Satin) | Year | 12.50 |
| 1973 Cowper Madonna (Blue Satin) | Year | 12.50 |
| 1973 Cowper Madonna (Carnival) | Year | 12.50 |
| 1973 Cowper Madonna (White Satin) | Year | 12.50 |
| 1974 Madonna of Grotto (Blue Satin) | Year | 12.50 |
| 1974 Madonna of Grotto (Carnival) | Year | 12.50 |
| 1974 Madonna of Grotto (White Satin) | Year | 12.50 |
| 1975 Taddei Madonna (Blue Satin) | Year | 13.50 |
| 1975 Taddei Madonna (Carnival) | Year | 13.50 |
| 1975 Taddei Madonna (White Satin) | Year | 13.50 |
| 1976 Holy Night (Blue Satin) | Year | 13.50 |
| 1976 Holy Night (Carnival) | Year | 13.50 |
| 1976 Holy Night (White Satin) | Year | 13.50 |
| 1977 Madonna & Child (Blue Satin) | Year | 15.00 |


| | Edition Limit | Issue Price (US) |
|---|---|---|
| 1977 Madonna & Child (Carnival) | Year | $ 15.00 |
| 1977 Madonna & Child (White Satin) | Year | 15.00 |
| 1978 Madonnina (Blue Satin) | Year | 15.00 |
| 1978 Madonnina (Carnival) | Year | 15.00 |
| 1978 Madonnina (White Satin) | Year | 15.00 |
| 1979 Madonna of Rose Hedge (Blue Satin) | Year | 15.00 |
| 1979 Madonna of Rose Hedge (Carnival) | Year | 15.00 |
| 1979 Madonna of Rose Hedge (White Satin) | Year | 15.00 |
| *Valentine's Day* | | |
| 1972 Romeo and Juliet (Blue Satin) | Year | 15.00 |
| 1972 Romeo and Juliet (Carnival) | Year | 15.00 |
| *Bicentennial* | | |
| 1974 Eagle (Blue Satin) | Year | 15.00 |
| 1975 Eagle (Red Satin) | Year | 15.00 |
| 1976 Eagle (Chocolate) | Year | 17.50 |
| 1976 Eagle (White Satin) | Year | 15.00 |
| *Alliance* | | |
| 1975 Lafayette and Washington (Blue Satin) | Year | 15.00 |
| 1975 Lafayette and Washington (Red Satin) | Year | 17.50 |
| 1975 Lafayette and Washington (White Satin) | Year | 15.00 |
| 1976 Lafayette and Washington (Blue Satin) | Year | 15.00 |
| 1976 Lafayette and Washington (Chocolate) | Year | 17.50 |
| 1976 Lafayette and Washington (White Satin) | Year | 15.00 |
| *Christmas Classics* | | |
| 1979 Nature's Christmas | Year | 30.00 |
| 1980 Going Home | Year | 38.50 |
| 1981 All Is Calm | Year | 42.50 |
| 1982 Country Christmas | Year | 42.50 |
| *Currier & Ives* | | |
| 1980 Old Grist Mill | Year | 25.00 |
| 1981 Harvest | Year | 25.00 |
| 1982 Old Homestead in Winter | Year | 25.00 |
| 1983 Winter Pastime | Year | 25.00 |
| *Mother's Day Classics* | | |
| 1980 New Born | Year | 28.50 |
| 1981 Gentle Fawn | Year | 32.50 |
| 1982 Nature's Awakening | Year | 35.00 |
| 1983 Where's Mom? | Year | 35.00 |
| 1984 Precious Panda | Year | 35.00 |
| *Artists* | | |
| 1982 After Snow | 15,000 | 14.50 |
| 1983 Winter Chapel | 15,000 | 15.00 |
| *Childhood Treasures* | | |
| 1983 Teddy Bear | 15,000 | 15.00 |
| 1984 Hobby Horse | 15,000 | 15.00 |
| *Christmas Fantasy* | | |
| 1983 Anticipation | 7,500 | 45.00 |
| 1984 Expectation | 7,500 | 50.00 |
| *Designer* | | |
| 1983 Down Home | 1,000 | 65.00 |
| 1983 Lighthouse Point | 1,000 | 65.00 |
| *(Single issue)* | | |
| 1986 Statue of Liberty | 1,250 | 75.00 |
| *American Classic* | | |
| 1987 The Central Pacific Jupiter | 5,000 | 75.00 |
| **Fine Arts Marketing Enterprise** | | |
| *Turn . . . Turn . . . Turn . . .* | | |
| 1986 Autumn Back Home | 5,000 | 50.00 |
| 1986 Winter Memories | 5,000 | 50.00 |
| *Autumn Flights* | | |
| 1987 Canadians | 5,000 | 55.00 |
| 1987 Mallards | 5,000 | 55.00 |

# OVER-THE-COUNTER ISSUES

| | Edition Limit | Issue Price (US) |
|---|---|---|
| **Firehouse** | | |
| *This Ole Bear* | | |
| 1982 Emma Louise | 5,000 | $ 39.50 |
| 1983 Buster and Sam | 5,000 | 39.50 |
| 1984 Matilda Jane | 5,000 | 39.50 |
| **Fleetwood Collection (Gorham)** | | |
| *Birds and Flowers of Meadow and Garden* | | |
| 1980 Robin and Crab Apple Blossom | * | 39.00 |
| 1980 Goldfinch and Bull Thistle | * | 39.00 |
| 1980 Cardinal and Wild Lupine | * | 39.00 |
| 1980 Chickadee and New England Aster | * | 39.00 |
| 1980 Baltimore Oriole and Morning Glory | * | 39.00 |
| 1980 Blue Bird and Black-Eyed Susan | * | 39.00 |
| 1980 Painted Bunting and Blackberry | * | 39.00 |
| 1980 Golden-Crowned Kinglet and Downey Phlox | * | 39.00 |
| 1980 Red-Breasted Nuthatch and Japanese Honeysuckle | * | 39.00 |
| 1980 Magnolia Warbler and Day Lily | * | 39.00 |
| 1980 Ruby-Throated Hummingbird and Fire Pink | * | 39.00 |
| 1980 Scarlet Tanager and Blue Columbine | * | 39.00 |
| *Subscription period | | |
| *Christmas* | | |
| 1980 Magi | 7,500 | 49.50 |
| 1981 Holy Child | 7,500 | 49.50 |
| 1982 Shepherds | 7,500 | 49.50 |
| *Mother's Day* | | |
| 1980 Cottontails | 5,000 | 45.00 |
| 1981 Raccoons | 5,000 | 45.00 |
| 1982 Whitetail Deer | 5,000 | 50.00 |
| 1983 Canada Geese | 5,000 | 50.00 |
| *Blossoms of China* | | |
| 1981 Azalea | 7,500 | 49.50 |
| 1981 Camelia | 7,500 | 49.50 |
| 1981 Herbaceous Peony | 7,500 | 49.50 |
| 1981 Chrysanthemum | 7,500 | 49.50 |
| 1981 Lotus | 7,500 | 49.50 |
| 1981 Magnolia | 7,500 | 49.50 |
| 1981 Narcissus | 7,500 | 49.50 |
| 1981 Orchid | 7,500 | 49.50 |
| 1981 Peony | 7,500 | 49.50 |
| 1981 Plum Blossom | 7,500 | 49.50 |
| 1981 Rose | 7,500 | 49.50 |
| 1981 Winter Jasmine | 7,500 | 49.50 |
| *Tsarevich's Bride* | | |
| 1981 Arrow in Air | 7,500 | 50.00 |
| 1982 Boyar's Courtyard | 7,500 | 50.00 |
| 1982 Rich Merchant's Yard | 7,500 | 50.00 |
| 1983 Mouth of Frog | 7,500 | 50.00 |
| *Golden Age of Sail* | | |
| 1982 Flying Cloud | 5,000 | 39.00 |
| 1982 New World | 5,000 | 39.00 |
| 1982 Young America | 5,000 | 39.00 |
| 1982 Courier | 5,000 | 39.00 |
| 1982 Sea Witch | 5,000 | 39.00 |
| 1982 Great Republic | 5,000 | 39.00 |
| *(Single issue)* | | |
| 1983 Mom's Apple Pie | NA | 29.00 |
| *(Single issue)* | | |
| 1985 Presidential Inaugural | 9,500 | 50.00 |
| **Fostoria** | | |
| *American Milestones* | | |
| 1971 Betsy Ross Flag | 5,000 | 12.50 |
| 1972 National Anthem | 8,000 | 12.50 |
| 1973 Washington Crossing Delaware | Year | 12.50 |
| 1974 Spirit of '76 | Year | 13.00 |
| 1975 Mount Rushmore | Year | 16.00 |
| *State Plates* | | |
| 1971 California | 6,000 | 12.50 |
| 1971 New York | 12,000 | 12.50 |
| 1971 Ohio | 3,000 | 12.50 |
| 1972 Florida | Year | 12.50 |

| | Edition Limit | Issue Price (US) |
|---|---|---|
| 1972 Hawaii | Year | $ 12.50 |
| 1972 Pennsylvania | Year | 12.50 |
| 1972 Massachusetts | Year | 13.00 |
| 1972 Texas | Year | 13.00 |
| 1973 Michigan | Year | 13.50 |
| **Fountainhead** | | |
| *Wings of Freedom* | | |
| 1985 Courtship Flight | 2,500 | 250.00 |
| 1986 Wings of Freedom | 2,500 | 250.00 |
| *The Seasons* | | |
| 1987 Spring Robins | 5,000 | 85.00 |
| 1987 Summer Goldfinches | 5,000 | 85.00 |
| 1987 Fall Cardinals | 5,000 | 85.00 |
| 1987 Winter Chickadees | 5,000 | 85.00 |
| *Americana Cats* | | |
| 1987 The Mantle | 7,500 | 39.50 |
| 1987 The Pantry | 7,500 | 39.50 |
| **Franklin Crystal** | | |
| *Historical* | | |
| 1976 Liberty Tree | 10,927 | 120.00 |
| *Seven Seas* | | |
| 1976 Atlantic Ocean | 2,799 | 120.00 |
| 1976 Caribbean | 2,799 | 120.00 |
| 1976 Indian Ocean | 2,799 | 120.00 |
| 1976 Mediterranean | 2,799 | 120.00 |
| 1976 Pacific | 2,799 | 120.00 |
| 1976 South China Sea | 2,799 | 120.00 |
| 1976 Arctic | 2,799 | 120.00 |
| *Annual* | | |
| 1977 Snowflake | 3,428 | 185.00 |
| 1978 Snowbird | 798 | 185.00 |
| *Rockwell's American Sweethearts* | | |
| 1977 Youngsters at Play | 1,004 | 120.00 |
| 1977 Teenagers Together | 1,004 | 120.00 |
| 1978 Bride and Groom | 1,004 | 120.00 |
| 1978 Proud Parents | 1,004 | 120.00 |
| 1978 Graduation Day | 1,004 | 120.00 |
| 1978 Retirement Kiss | 1,004 | 120.00 |
| **Franklin Mint** | | |
| *American West* | | |
| 1972 Horizon's West (Silver) | 5,860 | 150.00 |
| 1972 Horizon's West (Gold) | 67 | 2200.00 |
| 1973 Mountain Man (Silver) | 5,860 | 150.00 |
| 1973 Mountain Man (Gold) | 67 | 2200.00 |
| 1973 Prospector (Silver) | 5,860 | 150.00 |
| 1973 Prospector (Gold) | 67 | 2200.00 |
| 1973 Plains Hunter (Silver) | 5,860 | 150.00 |
| 1973 Plains Hunter (Gold) | 67 | 2200.00 |
| *Audubon Society* | | |
| 1972 Goldfinch | 10,193 | 125.00 |
| 1972 Wood Duck | 10,193 | 125.00 |
| 1973 Cardinal | 10,193 | 125.00 |
| 1973 Ruffed Grouse | 10,193 | 125.00 |
| *Mother's Day* | | |
| 1972 Mother and Child | 21,987 | 125.00 |
| 1973 Mother and Child | 6,154 | 125.00 |
| 1974 Mother and Child | 5,116 | 150.00 |
| 1975 Mother and Child | 2,704 | 175.00 |
| 1976 Mother and Child | 1,858 | 180.00 |
| *Presidential* | | |
| 1972 George Washington | 10,304 | 150.00 |
| 1972 John Adams | 4,859 | 150.00 |
| 1972 Thomas Jefferson | 4,933 | 150.00 |
| 1972 James Madison | 3,058 | 150.00 |
| 1972 James Monroe | 2,722 | 150.00 |
| 1972 John Quincy Adams | 2,501 | 150.00 |
| 1972 Andrew Jackson | 2,408 | 150.00 |
| 1973 Martin Van Buren | 2,291 | 150.00 |
| 1973 William H. Harrison | 2,182 | 150.00 |
| 1973 John Tyler | 2,144 | 150.00 |
| 1973 James Polk | 2,083 | 150.00 |
| 1973 Zachary Taylor | 2,023 | 150.00 |
| 1973 Millard Fillmore | 1,967 | 150.00 |
| 1974 Franklin Pierce | 1,907 | 150.00 |
| 1974 James Buchanan | 1,841 | 150.00 |
| 1974 Abraham Lincoln | 2,955 | 150.00 |
| 1974 Andrew Johnson | 1,777 | 150.00 |
| 1974 Ulysses S. Grant | 1,754 | 150.00 |
| 1975 Rutherford B. Hayes | 1,705 | 150.00 |
| 1975 James A. Garfield | 1,675 | 150.00 |
| 1975 Chester A. Arthur | 1,604 | 150.00 |
| 1975 Grover Cleveland | 1,644 | 150.00 |
| 1976 Benjamin Harrison | 1,619 | 150.00 |
| 1976 William McKinley | 1,571 | 150.00 |
| 1976 Theodore Roosevelt | 1,555 | 150.00 |

| | Edition Limit | Issue Price (US) |
|---|---|---|
| 1976 William H. Taft | 1,592 | $150.00 |
| 1976 Woodrow Wilson | 1,563 | 150.00 |
| 1977 Warren G. Harding | 1,544 | 150.00 |
| 1977 Calvin Coolidge | 1,527 | 150.00 |
| 1977 Herbert Hoover | 1,520 | 150.00 |
| 1977 Franklin D. Roosevelt | 1,770 | 150.00 |
| 1977 Harry S. Truman | 1,493 | 150.00 |
| 1978 Dwight D. Eisenhower | 1,494 | 150.00 |
| 1978 John F. Kennedy | 1,494 | 150.00 |
| 1978 Lyndon B. Johnson | 1,483 | 150.00 |
| 1978 Richard M. Nixon | 1,475 | 150.00 |
| 1978 Gerald R. Ford | NA | 150.00 |
| 1978 Jimmy Carter | NA | 150.00 |
| *Thanksgiving—by Dohanos* | | |
| 1972 First Thanksgiving | 10,142 | 125.00 |
| 1973 American Wild Turkey | 3,547 | 125.00 |
| 1974 Thanksgiving Prayer | 5,150 | 150.00 |
| 1975 Family Thanksgiving | 3,025 | 175.00 |
| 1976 Home from Hunt | 3,474 | 175.00 |
| *James Wyeth* | | |
| 1972 Along Brandywine | 19,670 | 125.00 |
| 1973 Winter Fox | 10,394 | 125.00 |
| 1974 Riding to Hunt | 10,751 | 150.00 |
| 1975 Skating on Brandywine | 8,058 | 175.00 |
| 1976 Brandywine Battlefield | 6,968 | 180.00 |
| *Younger's Bird* | | |
| 1972 Cardinal | 13,939 | 125.00 |
| 1972 Bobwhite | 13,939 | 125.00 |
| 1972 Mallards | 13,939 | 125.00 |
| 1972 American Bald Eagle | 13,939 | 125.00 |
| *John James Audubon* | | |
| 1973 Wood Thrush | 5,273 | 150.00 |
| 1973 Bald Eagle | 3,040 | 150.00 |
| 1974 Night Heron | 3,005 | 150.00 |
| 1974 Audubon's Warbler | 3,034 | 150.00 |
| *Bernard Buffet* | | |
| 1973 Gazelle | 570 | 150.00 |
| 1974 Panda | 408 | 150.00 |
| 1975 Giraffe | 333 | 150.00 |
| 1976 Lion | 263 | 150.00 |
| 1977 Rhinoceros | 200 | 150.00 |
| *Bicentennial* | | |
| 1973 Jefferson Drafting Declaration of Independence | 8,556 | 175.00 |
| 1974 John Adams Champions Cause of Independence | 8,442 | 175.00 |
| 1975 Caesar Rodney Decides Vote on Independence | 8,319 | 175.00 |
| 1976 John Hancock Signs Declaration of Independence | 10,166 | 175.00 |
| *Easter* | | |
| 1973 Resurrection | 7,116 | 175.00 |
| 1974 He Is Risen | 3,719 | 185.00 |
| 1975 Last Supper | 2,004 | 200.00 |
| 1976 Crucifixion | 3,904 | 250.00 |
| 1977 Resurrection | 1,206 | 250.00 |
| *Presidential Inaugural* | | |
| 1973 Nixon/Agnew | 10,483 | 150.00 |
| 1974 Ford (Silver) | 1,141 | 200.00 |
| 1974 Ford (Gold) | 11 | 3500.00 |
| 1977 Carter | 928 | 225.00 |
| *Roberts' Zodiac* | | |
| 1973 Aries | NA | 150.00 |
| 1973 Taurus | NA | 150.00 |
| 1973 Gemini | NA | 150.00 |
| 1973 Cancer | NA | 150.00 |
| 1973 Leo | NA | 150.00 |
| 1973 Virgo | NA | 150.00 |
| 1973 Libra | NA | 150.00 |
| 1973 Scorpio | NA | 150.00 |
| 1973 Sagittarius | NA | 150.00 |
| 1973 Capricorn | NA | 150.00 |
| 1973 Aquarius | NA | 150.00 |
| 1973 Pisces | NA | 150.00 |
| *Four Seasons* | | |
| 1975 Spring Blossoms | 2,648 | 240.00 |
| 1975 Summer Bouquet | 2,648 | 240.00 |
| 1976 Autumn Garland | 2,648 | 240.00 |
| 1976 Winter Spray | 2,648 | 240.00 |
| *American Revolution Bicentennial* | | |
| 1976 Boston Tea Party | 3,596 | 75.00 |
| 1976 Patrick Henry Urges Armed Resistance | 3,596 | 75.00 |

| | Edition Limit | Issue Price (US) |
|---|---|---|
| 1976 Paul Revere's Ride | 3,596 | $ 75.00 |
| 1976 Battle of Concord Bridge | 3,596 | 75.00 |
| 1976 Capture of Fort Ticonderoga | 3,596 | 75.00 |
| 1976 Battle of Bunker Hill | 3,596 | 75.00 |
| 1977 Signing of Declaration | 3,596 | 75.00 |
| 1977 Washington Crosses Delaware | 3,596 | 75.00 |
| 1977 Burgoyne Defeated at Saratoga | 3,596 | 75.00 |
| 1977 Winter at Valley Forge | 3,596 | 75.00 |
| 1977 Alliance with France | 3,596 | 75.00 |
| 1977 Bonhomme Richard Defeats Serapis | 3,596 | 75.00 |
| 1977 Victory at Yorktown | 3,596 | 75.00 |
| *Annual* | | |
| 1977 Tribute to Arts | 1,901 | 280.00 |
| 1978 Tribute to Nature | 435 | 280.00 |
| *Belskie* | | |
| 1977 Mother's Day | 290 | 210.00 |
| *Currier & Ives* | | |
| 1977 Winter Pastime | 1,836 | 39.50 |
| 1977 Preparing for Market | 1,836 | 39.50 |
| 1977 Winter in Country | 1,836 | 39.50 |
| 1977 American Homestead—Winter | 1,836 | 39.50 |
| 1977 American Forest Scene | 1,836 | 39.50 |
| 1977 American Homestead—Summer | 1,836 | 39.50 |
| 1977 American Homestead—Autumn | 1,836 | 39.50 |
| 1977 Haying Time—Last Load | 1,836 | 39.50 |
| 1977 American Express Train | 1,836 | 39.50 |
| 1977 Haying Time—First Load | 1,836 | 39.50 |
| 1977 Catching a Trout | 1,836 | 39.50 |
| 1977 Yosemite Valley | 1,836 | 39.50 |
| *Freedom* | | |
| 1977 Lafayette Joins Washington | 546 | 275.00 |
| *Rockwell Thanksgiving* | | |
| 1977 Old Fashioned Thanksgiving | 2,361 | 85.00 |
| *Christmas* | | |
| 1977 Skating Party | 908 | 55.00 |
| **Franklin Porcelain** | | |
| *Hans Christian Andersen* | | |
| 1976 Princess and Pea | 16,875 | 38.00 |
| 1976 Ugly Duckling | 16,875 | 38.00 |
| 1976 Little Mermaid | 16,875 | 38.00 |
| 1976 Emperor's New Clothes | 16,875 | 38.00 |
| 1976 Steadfast Tin Soldier | 16,875 | 38.00 |
| 1976 Little Match Girl | 16,875 | 38.00 |
| 1977 Snow Queen | 16,875 | 38.00 |
| 1977 Red Shoes | 16,875 | 38.00 |
| 1977 Tinder Box | 16,875 | 38.00 |
| 1977 Nightingale | 16,875 | 38.00 |
| 1977 Thumbelina | 16,875 | 38.00 |
| 1977 Shepherdess & Chimney Sweep | 16,875 | 38.00 |
| *Christmas Annual* | | |
| 1976 Silent Night | 19,286 | 65.00 |
| 1977 Deck Halls | 9,185 | 65.00 |
| 1978 We Three Kings | Year | 75.00 |
| 1979 Hark, Herald Angels Sing | Year | 75.00 |
| 1980 Joy to World | Year | 125.00 |
| 1981 O, Holy Night | Year | 125.00 |
| *Flowers of Year* | | |
| 1976 January | 27,394 | 50.00 |
| 1976 February | 27,394 | 50.00 |
| 1977 March | 27,394 | 50.00 |
| 1977 April | 27,394 | 50.00 |
| 1977 May | 27,394 | 50.00 |
| 1978 June | 27,394 | 50.00 |
| 1978 July | 27,394 | 50.00 |
| 1978 August | 27,394 | 50.00 |
| 1978 September | 27,394 | 50.00 |
| 1979 October | 27,394 | 50.00 |
| 1979 November | 27,394 | 50.00 |
| 1979 December | 27,394 | 50.00 |

| | Edition Limit | Issue Price (US) |
|---|---|---|
| *Mother's Day* | | |
| 1977 A Mother's Love | Year | $ 65.00 |
| 1978 A Mother's Joy | Year | 65.00 |
| 1979 A Mother's Gift | Year | 75.00 |
| *Songbirds of World* | | |
| 1977 Baltimore Oriole | 20,225 | 55.00 |
| 1977 Bohemian Waxwing | 20,225 | 55.00 |
| 1977 Magnolia Warbler | 20,225 | 55.00 |
| 1977 Bobolink | 20,225 | 55.00 |
| 1977 Western Bluebird | 20,225 | 55.00 |
| 1977 Cardinal | 20,225 | 55.00 |
| 1977 European Goldfinch | 20,225 | 55.00 |
| 1977 Wood Thrush | 20,225 | 55.00 |
| 1977 Scarlet Tanager | 20,225 | 55.00 |
| 1977 Barn Swallow | 20,225 | 55.00 |
| 1977 Bluethroat | 20,225 | 55.00 |
| 1977 Turquoise Wren | 20,225 | 55.00 |
| *Mark Twain* | | |
| 1977 Whitewashing Fence | 2,645 | 38.00 |
| 1977 Stealing a Kiss | 2,645 | 38.00 |
| 1977 Traveling River | 2,645 | 38.00 |
| 1977 Trading Lives | 2,645 | 38.00 |
| 1977 Rafting Down River | 2,645 | 38.00 |
| 1978 Riding Bronc | 2,645 | 38.00 |
| 1978 Jumping Frog Race | 2,645 | 38.00 |
| 1978 Facing Charging Knight | 2,645 | 38.00 |
| 1978 Disguising Huck | 2,645 | 38.00 |
| 1978 Living Along River | 2,645 | 38.00 |
| 1978 Learning to Smoke | 2,645 | 38.00 |
| 1978 Finger Printing Pays Off | 2,645 | 38.00 |
| *Flowers of American Wilderness* | | |
| 1978 New England | 8,759 | 39.00 |
| 1978 Alaska | 8,759 | 39.00 |
| 1978 Everglades of Florida | 8,759 | 39.00 |
| 1978 Mississippi Delta | 8,759 | 39.00 |
| 1978 California | 8,759 | 39.00 |
| 1978 Rocky Mountains | 8,759 | 39.00 |
| 1978 Cape Cod | 8,759 | 39.00 |
| 1978 Northwest | 8,759 | 39.00 |
| 1978 Southwest | 8,759 | 39.00 |
| 1978 Appalachian Mountains | 8,759 | 39.00 |
| 1978 Prairies | 8,759 | 39.00 |
| 1978 Great Lakes | 8,759 | 39.00 |
| *Game Birds of World* | | |
| 1978 Chinese Pheasant | 76,294 | 55.00 |
| 1978 Red-Legged Partridge | 76,294 | 55.00 |
| 1978 Common Snipe | 76,294 | 55.00 |
| 1978 Common Partridge | 76,294 | 55.00 |
| 1978 Rock Ptarmigan | 76,294 | 55.00 |
| 1978 Woodcock | 76,294 | 55.00 |
| 1978 Common Pheasant | 76,294 | 55.00 |
| 1978 Hazel Grouse | 76,294 | 55.00 |
| 1978 Red Grouse | 76,294 | 55.00 |
| 1978 Black Grouse | 76,294 | 55.00 |
| 1978 Capercaillie | 76,294 | 55.00 |
| 1978 Common Quail | 76,294 | 55.00 |
| *Grimm's Fairy Tales* | | |
| 1978 Sleeping Beauty | 27,006 | 42.00 |
| 1978 Twelve Dancing Princesses | 27,006 | 42.00 |
| 1978 Brementown Musicians | 27,006 | 42.00 |
| 1979 Golden Goose | 27,006 | 42.00 |
| 1979 Hansel and Gretel | 27,006 | 42.00 |
| 1979 Rapunzel | 27,006 | 42.00 |
| 1980 Snow White/Seven Dwarfs | 27,006 | 42.00 |
| 1980 Frog Prince | 27,006 | 42.00 |
| 1980 Red Riding Hood | 27,006 | 42.00 |
| 1981 Rumpelstilskin | 27,006 | 42.00 |
| 1981 Cinderella | 27,006 | 42.00 |
| 1981 Shoemaker and Elves | 27,006 | 42.00 |
| *Days of Week* | | |
| 1979 Monday's Child | 1,890 | 39.00 |
| 1979 Tuesday's Child | 1,890 | 39.00 |
| 1979 Wednesday's Child | 1,890 | 39.00 |
| 1979 Thursday's Child | 1,890 | 39.00 |
| 1979 Friday's Child | 1,890 | 39.00 |
| 1979 Saturday's Child | 1,890 | 39.00 |
| 1979 Sunday's Child | 1,890 | 39.00 |
| *Hometown Memories* | | |
| 1979 Country Fair | Year | 29.00 |
| 1980 Little Red School House | Year | 29.00 |
| 1981 Sunday Picnic | Year | 29.00 |
| 1982 Skating Party | Year | 29.00 |


| | Edition Limit | Issue Price (US) |
|---|---|---|
| *Country Year* | | |
| 1980 Woodlands in April | 89,173 | $ 55.00 |
| 1980 Country Path in May | 89,173 | 55.00 |
| 1980 June in Country Garden | 89,173 | 55.00 |
| 1980 July Beside River | 89,173 | 55.00 |
| 1980 Wheatfields in August | 89,173 | 55.00 |
| 1980 September on Moors | 89,173 | 55.00 |
| 1980 Colors of Autumn in October | 89,173 | 55.00 |
| 1980 Country Lane in December | 89,173 | 55.00 |
| 1980 January—Lambing Season | 89,173 | 55.00 |
| 1980 Country Church in March | 89,173 | 55.00 |
| 1980 Secluded Stream in November | 89,173 | 55.00 |
| *International Gallery of Flowers* | | |
| 1980 Wheat | 4,294 | 55.00 |
| 1980 Orchid | 4,294 | 55.00 |
| 1980 Irises | 4,294 | 55.00 |
| 1980 Camelias | 4,294 | 55.00 |
| 1980 Cherry Blossoms | 4,294 | 55.00 |
| 1980 English Wild Flowers | 4,294 | 55.00 |
| *Woodland Birds of World* | | |
| 1980 Blue Jay | 5,507 | 65.00 |
| 1980 White-Winged Crossbill | 5,507 | 65.00 |
| 1980 Painted Redstart | 5,507 | 65.00 |
| 1980 Rivoli's Hummingbird | 5,507 | 65.00 |
| 1980 Chaffinch | 5,507 | 65.00 |
| 1980 Collared Trogon | 5,507 | 65.00 |
| *Calendar* | | |
| 1981 Turn-of-Century Scenes | Year | 55.00 |
| 1982 Turn-of-Century Children | Year | 58.00 |
| *Clipper Ships* | | |
| 1982 Red Jacket | NA | 55.00 |
| 1982 Sea Witch | NA | 55.00 |
| 1982 Cutty Sark | NA | 55.00 |
| 1982 Thermoplyae | NA | 55.00 |
| 1982 Ariel | NA | 55.00 |
| 1982 Patriarch | NA | 55.00 |
| 1982 Nightingale | NA | 55.00 |
| 1982 Flying Cloud | NA | 55.00 |
| 1982 Marco Polo | NA | 55.00 |
| *Cobblestone Kids* | | |
| 1982 Making Friends | NA | 65.00 |
| 1982 Extra, Extra | NA | 65.00 |
| 1982 Just Ducky | NA | 65.00 |
| 1982 Feeding Raccoon | NA | 65.00 |
| 1982 A Stitch in Time | NA | 65.00 |
| 1982 Testing Wind | NA | 65.00 |
| *Golden Age of Sail* | | |
| *(Royal Society of Marine Artists)* | | |
| 1987 Sovereign of Seas | NA | 55.00 |
| **Frankoma** | | |
| *Christmas* | | |
| 1965 Goodwill Toward Man | Year | 5.00 |
| 1966 Bethlehem Shepherds | Year | 5.00 |
| 1967 Gifts for Christ Child | Year | 5.00 |
| 1968 Flight into Egypt | Year | 5.00 |
| 1969 Laid in a Manger | Year | 5.00 |
| 1970 King of Kings | Year | 5.00 |
| 1971 No Room in Inn | Year | 5.00 |
| 1972 Seeking Christ Child | Year | 5.00 |
| 1973 Annunciation | Year | 5.00 |
| 1974 She Loved & Cared | Year | 5.00 |
| 1975 Peace on Earth | Year | 5.00 |
| 1976 Gift of Love | Year | 6.00 |
| 1977 Birth of Eternal Life | Year | 6.00 |
| 1978 All Nature Rejoiced | Year | 6.00 |
| 1979 Stay of Hope | Year | 6.00 |
| 1980 Unto Us a Child Is Born | Year | 10.00 |
| 1981 O Come Let Us Adore Him | Year | 12.00 |
| 1982 Wise Men Rejoice | Year | 12.00 |
| 1983 Wise Men Bring Gifts | Year | 12.00 |
| *Bicentennial* | | |
| 1972 Provocations | Year | 6.00 |
| 1973 Patriots & Leaders | Year | 6.00 |
| 1974 Battles, Independence | Year | 5.00 |


| | Edition Limit | Issue Price (US) |
|---|---|---|
| 1975 Victories for Independence | Year | $ 6.00 |
| 1976 Symbols of Freedom | Year | 6.00 |
| *Teenagers of Bible* | | |
| 1973 Jesus, Carpenter | Year | 5.00 |
| 1974 David, Musician | Year | 5.00 |
| 1975 Jonathan, Archer | Year | 5.00 |
| 1976 Dorcas, Seamstress | Year | 5.00 |
| 1977 Peter, Fisherman | Year | 5.00 |
| 1978 Martha, Homemaker | Year | 7.50 |
| 1979 Daniel, Courageous | Year | 7.50 |
| 1980 Ruth, Devoted | Year | 8.00 |
| 1981 Joseph, Dreamer | Year | 8.00 |
| 1982 Mary, Mother | Year | 8.00 |
| *Madonnas* | | |
| 1977 Grace Madonna | Year | 12.50 |
| 1978 Madonna of Love | Year | 12.50 |
| **Gallery Classics** | | |
| *Wild Duck Collection* | | |
| 1986 Green Winged Teal | 15,000 | 49.50 |
| 1986 Mallards | 15,000 | 49.50 |
| 1986 Wood Ducks | 15,000 | 49.50 |
| 1986 Pintails | 15,000 | 49.50 |
| **Gartlan Associates** | | |
| *(Single issue)* | | |
| 1986 George Brett | 2,000 | 100.00 |
| *(Single issue)* | | |
| 1987 Roger Staubach (signed) | 1,979 | 100.00 |
| **Ghent Collection** | | |
| *Christmas Wildlife* | | |
| 1974 Cardinals in Snow | 10,135 | 20.00 |
| 1975 We Three Kings | 12,750 | 29.00 |
| 1976 Partridge and Pear Tree | 12,750 | 32.00 |
| 1977 Foxes and Evergreen | 12,750 | 32.00 |
| 1978 Snowy Owls | 12,750 | 32.00 |
| *Mother's Day* | | |
| 1975 Cotton Tail | 12,750 | 22.00 |
| 1976 Mallard Family | 12,750 | 29.00 |
| 1977 Chipmunks & Trillium | 12,750 | 32.00 |
| 1978 Raccoon Family | 12,750 | 32.00 |
| 1979 Maytime | 12,750 | 32.00 |
| *American Bicentennial Wildlife* | | |
| 1976 American Bald Eagle | 2,500 | 95.00 |
| 1976 American White-Tailed Deer | 2,500 | 95.00 |
| 1976 American Bison | 2,500 | 95.00 |
| 1976 American Wild Turkey | 2,500 | 95.00 |
| *Fausett Mural (Single issue)* | | |
| 1976 From Sea to Shining Sea | 1,976 | 76.00 |
| *(Single issue)* | | |
| 1978 Pilgrim of Peace | 15 Days | 29.50 |
| *Lands of Fable* | | |
| 1981 Xanadu | 17,500 | 55.00 |
| 1982 Atlantis | 17,500 | 55.00 |
| *Man's Dream of Flight* | | |
| 1981 Flight of Icarus | 19,500 | 37.50 |
| 1981 Vision of Leonardo | 19,500 | 37.50 |
| 1981 First Lighter-than-Air Flight | 19,500 | 37.50 |
| 1981 Wright Brothers | 19,500 | 37.50 |
| 1981 Lindbergh Flies Atlantic | 19,500 | 37.50 |
| 1981 Barnstormers | 19,500 | 37.50 |
| 1981 Jet Age | 19,500 | 37.50 |
| 1981 Giant Leap for Mankind | 19,500 | 37.50 |
| *Hans Brinker Delft* | | |
| 1982 Hero of Haarlem | 17,500 | 29.50 |
| 1982 Race | 17,500 | 29.50 |
| 1982 Thousand Guilders | 17,500 | 29.50 |
| 1982 On Canal | 17,500 | 29.50 |
| 1982 Shadows in Home | 17,500 | 29.50 |
| 1982 Mysterious Watch | 17,500 | 29.50 |
| **Ghent Collection (Bing & Grøndahl)** | | |
| *Hans Christian Andersen* | | |
| 1979 Thumbelina | 7,500 | 42.50 |
| 1979 Princess and Pea | 7,500 | 42.50 |
| 1979 Wild Swans | 7,500 | 42.50 |
| 1979 Emperor's New Clothes | 7,500 | 42.50 |
| 1980 Little Mermaid | 7,500 | 42.50 |
| 1980 Nightingale | 7,500 | 42.50 |


| | Edition Limit | Issue Price (US) |
|---|---|---|
| **Ghent Collection (Caverswall)** | | |
| *Christmas Annual* | | |
| 1979 Good King Wenceslaus | 2,500 | $350.00 |
| *Country Diary of an Edwardian Lady* | | |
| 1979 April | 10,000 | 80.00 |
| 1979 June | 10,000 | 80.00 |
| 1980 September | 10,000 | 80.00 |
| 1980 December | 10,000 | 80.00 |
| 1981 July | 10,000 | 80.00 |
| 1981 October | 10,000 | 80.00 |
| 1982 January | 10,000 | 80.00 |
| 1982 May | 10,000 | 80.00 |
| 1983 February | 10,000 | 80.00 |
| 1983 March | 10,000 | 80.00 |
| 1984 August | 10,000 | 80.00 |
| 1984 November | 10,000 | 80.00 |
| **Ghent Collection (Fairmont)** | | |
| *Legends of Christmas* | | |
| 1979 Bringing in Tree | 5,000 | 65.00 |
| *Memory Annual* | | |
| 1978 1977 Memory Plate | 1,977 | 77.00 |
| 1979 1978 Memory Plate | 1,978 | 78.00 |
| 1980 1979 Memory Plate | 1,979 | 79.00 |
| *Israeli Commemorative (Single issue)* | | |
| 1978 Promised Land | 5,738 | 79.00 |
| *Spirit of America* | | |
| 1978 Making of a Nation | 1,978 | 78.00 |
| 1979 Growing Years | 1,978 | 78.00 |
| **Ghent Collection (Gorham)** | | |
| *April Fool Annual* | | |
| 1978 April Fool's Day | 10,000 | 35.00 |
| 1979 April Fool's Day | 10,000 | 35.00 |
| 1980 April Fool's Day | 10,000 | 37.50 |
| **Ghent Collection (Kaiser)** | | |
| *Treasures of Tutankhamun* | | |
| 1978 Golden Mask | 3,247 | 90.00 |
| 1978 Golden Throne | 3,247 | 90.00 |
| 1978 Horus Falcon | 3,247 | 90.00 |
| 1978 Ivory Chest | 3,247 | 90.00 |
| **Ghent Collection (Viletta)** | | |
| *Olympics* | | |
| 1980 1980 Winter Olympics | 13 Days | 24.50 |
| 1980 1980 Summer Olympics | 13 Days | 29.50 |
| **Gnomes United** | | |
| *Gnomes* | | |
| 1979 Gnome on Range | 10,000 | 23.00 |
| *Gnome Patrol* | | |
| 1979 Dr. Kwik | 5,000 | 45.00 |
| **Golf Digest** | | |
| *Second Hole (Single issue)* | | |
| 1973 Dorado Beach Club | 2,000 | 45.00 |
| *Twelfth Hole (Single issue)* | | |
| 1973 Spyglass Hill | 2,000 | 45.00 |
| **Gorham** | | |
| *(Single issue)* | | |
| 1970 American Family Tree | 5,000 | 17.00 |
| *Lionel Barrymore* | | |
| 1971 Quiet Waters | 15,000 | 25.00 |
| 1972 San Pedro Harbor | 15,000 | 25.00 |
| 1972 Little Boatyard (Silver) | 1,000 | 100.00 |
| 1972 Nantucket (Silver) | 1,000 | 100.00 |
| *Bicentennial* | | |
| 1971 Burning of Gaspee (Pewter) | 5,000 | 35.00 |
| 1972 Burning of Gaspee (Silver) | 750 | 550.00 |
| 1972 1776 (China) | 18,500 | 17.50 |
| 1972 1776 (Vermeil) | 500 | 500.00 |
| 1972 1776 (Silver) | 750 | 250.00 |
| 1972 Boston Tea Party (Pewter) | 5,000 | 35.00 |
| 1973 Boston Tea Party (Silver) | 750 | 550.00 |
| *Gallery of Masters* | | |
| 1971 Man in Gilt Helmet | 10,000 | 50.00 |
| 1972 Self-Portrait Rembrandt, with Saskia | 10,000 | 50.00 |
| 1973 Honorable Mrs. Graham | 7,500 | 50.00 |

| | Edition Limit | Issue Price (US) |
|---|---|---|
| *Moppets Mother's Day* | | |
| 1973 Flowers for Mother | 20,000 | $ 10.00 |
| 1974 Mother's Hat | 20,000 | 12.00 |
| 1975 In Mother's Clothes | 20,000 | 13.00 |
| 1976 Flowers | 20,000 | 13.00 |
| 1977 Gift for Mother | 18,500 | 13.00 |
| 1978 Moppet's Mother's Day | 18,500 | 10.00 |
| *Moppets Christmas* | | |
| 1973 Christmas March | 20,000 | 10.00 |
| 1974 Trimming Tree | 20,000 | 12.00 |
| 1975 Carrying Tree | 20,000 | 13.00 |
| 1976 Asleep under Tree | 18,500 | 13.00 |
| 1977 Star for Treetop | 18,500 | 13.00 |
| 1978 Presents | 18,500 | 10.00 |
| 1979 Moppet's Christmas | 18,500 | 12.00 |
| 1980 Happy Merry Christmas Tree | Year | 12.00 |
| 1981 Happy Merry Christmas Tree | Year | 12.00 |
| 1982 Happy Merry Christmas Tree | Year | 12.00 |
| *Remington Western* | | |
| 1973 Aiding a Comrade | Year | 25.00 |
| 1973 New Year on Cimarron | Year | 25.00 |
| 1973 Fight for Waterhole | Year | 25.00 |
| 1973 Flight | Year | 25.00 |
| 1974 Old Ramond | Year | 20.00 |
| 1974 Breed | Year | 20.00 |
| 1975 Cavalry Officer | 5,000 | 37.50 |
| 1975 Trapper | 5,000 | 37.50 |
| *Irene Spencer Annual* | | |
| 1974 Dear Child | 10,000 | 37.50 |
| 1975 Promises to Keep | 10,000 | 40.00 |
| *(Single issue)* | | |
| 1974 Streakers | Year | 19.50 |
| *(Single issue)* | | |
| 1974 Golden Rule | Year | 19.50 |
| *(Single issue)* | | |
| 1974 Big Three | 10,000 | 17.50 |
| *(Single issue)* | | |
| 1974 Weigh-In | 10,000 | 17.50 |
| *(Single issue)* | | |
| 1975 Benjamin Franklin | 18,500 | 19.50 |
| *Boy Scouts of America* | | |
| 1975 Our Heritage | 18,500 | 19.50 |
| 1976 Scout Is Loyal | 18,500 | 19.50 |
| 1977 Scoutmaster | 18,500 | 19.50 |
| 1977 Good Sign | 18,500 | 19.50 |
| 1978 Pointing Way | 18,500 | 19.50 |
| 1978 Campfire Story | 18,500 | 19.50 |
| *American Artists* | | |
| 1976 Apache Mother & Child | 9,800 | 25.00 |
| 1976 Black Regiment | 7,500 | 25.00 |
| *America's Cup Plates (Set of five)* | | |
| 1976 America, 1861 | | |
| 1976 Puritan | | |
| 1976 Reliance | | |
| 1976 Ranger | | |
| 1976 Courageous | 1,000 | 200.00 |
| *Omnibus Muralis* | | |
| 1976 200 Years with Old Glory | 5,000 | 60.00 |
| 1977 Life of Christ | 5,000 | 65.00 |
| *First Lady* | | |
| 1977 Amy and Rosalynn | Year | 24.95 |
| *Presidential* | | |
| 1977 John F. Kennedy | 9,800 | 30.00 |
| 1977 Eisenhower | 9,800 | 30.00 |
| *Prince Tatters* | | |
| 1977 Johnny and Duke | 7,500 | 40.00 |
| 1978 Randy and Rex | 7,500 | 42.50 |
| 1979 Furry Friends | 7,500 | 47.50 |
| 1980 Benji's Burro | 7,500 | 50.00 |
| *Julian Ritter Christmas* | | |
| 1977 Christmas Visit | 9,800 | 24.50 |
| *Ritter's Four Seasons Clowns* | | |
| 1977 Falling in Love (Set of four) | 5,000 | 100.00 |
| 1978 To Love a Clown (Set of four) | 5,000 | 120.00 |
| *Santa Fe Railway* | | |
| 1977 Navajo Silversmith | 7,500 | 37.50 |
| 1978 Turquoise Bead Maker | 7,500 | 37.50 |

| | Edition Limit | Issue Price (US) |
|---|---|---|
| 1979 Basketweaver | 7,500 | $ 42.50 |
| 1980 Arrow Maker | 7,500 | 45.00 |
| *Borsato Masterpiece* | | |
| 1977 Serenity | 5,000 | 75.00 |
| 1978 Titian Madonna | 5,000 | 75.00 |
| 1979 Ballerina | 5,000 | 75.00 |
| *Little Men* | | |
| 1977 Come Ride with Me | 9,500 | 50.00 |
| 1978 Julian Ritter Valentine | 7,500 | 45.00 |
| *Moppets Anniversary* | | |
| 1979 Moppet Couple | 20,000 | 13.00 |
| *(Single issue)* | | |
| 1978 Triple Self-Portrait | Year | 37.50 |
| *Wild West* | | |
| 1980 Bronc to Breakfast | 9,800 | 38.00 |
| 1981 In Without Knocking | 9,800 | 38.00 |
| 1982 Cowboy Life | 9,800 | 45.00 |
| 1983 Ignorance Is Bliss | 9,800 | 45.00 |
| *Four Seasons Landscape* | | |
| 1980 Summer Respite | 15,000 | 45.00 |
| 1980 Autumn Reflections | 15,000 | 45.00 |
| 1981 Winter Delights | 15,000 | 45.00 |
| 1981 Spring Recess | 15,000 | 45.00 |
| *Rockwell Four Seasons* | | |
| 1981 Old Timers (Set of four) | Year | 100.00 |
| 1982 Life with Father (Set of four) | Year | 100.00 |
| 1983 Old Buddies (Set of four) | Year | 115.00 |
| 1984 Traveling Salesman (Set of four) | Year | 115.00 |
| *(Single issue—Set of two)* | | |
| 1981 Day in Life of Boy | | |
| 1981 Day in Life of Girl | Year | 50.00 |
| *Four Ages of Love* | | |
| 1981 Sweet Song So Young | 10,000 | 100.00 |
| 1982 Flowers in Tender Bloom | 10,000 | 100.00 |
| *Masterpieces of Rockwell* | | |
| 1981 Girl at Mirror | 17,500 | 50.00 |
| *Young Love* | | |
| 1981 Beguiling Buttercup | 17,500 | 62.50 |
| 1982 Flying High | 17,500 | 62.50 |
| *Encounters, Survival and Celebrations* | | |
| 1982 A Fine Welcome | 7,500 | 50.00 |
| 1983 Winter Trails | 7,500 | 50.00 |
| 1984 Alouette | 7,500 | 62.50 |
| 1984 Trader | 7,500 | 62.50 |
| 1985 Winter Camp | 7,500 | 62.50 |
| 1985 Trapper Takes a Wife | 7,500 | 62.50 |
| *Pastoral Symphony* | | |
| 1982 When I Was a Child | 7,500 | 42.50 |
| 1983 Gather Children | 7,500 | 42.50 |
| 1984 Sugar and Spice | 7,500 | 42.50 |
| 1985 He Loves Me | 7,500 | 42.50 |
| *A Merry Mouse* | | |
| 1983 A Merry Mouse Christmas | 5,000 | 15.00 |
| *Museum Doll* | | |
| 1983 Lydia | 5,000 | 29.00 |
| 1984 Belton Bebe | 5,000 | 29.00 |
| 1984 Lucille | 5,000 | 29.00 |
| 1985 Bebe Jumeau | 5,000 | 29.00 |
| *Heaven Mother's Day* | | |
| 1984 Mother Is Love | 5,000 | 24.95 |
| *Museum Doll Christmas* | | |
| 1985 Christmas Lady | 7,500 | 32.50 |
| *Beverly Port Plate Series* | | |
| 1986 Miss Emily "Bearing Up" | 5,000 | 32.50 |
| 1987 Big Bear, The Toy Collector | 5,000 | 32.50 |

See also:
*American Commemorative (U.S.A.)*
*American Express (U.S.A.)*
*American Preservation Guild (U.S.A.)*
*American Rose Society (U.S.A.)*
*Fleetwood Collection (U.S.A.)*
*Ghent Collection (U.S.A.)*
*Lincoln Mint (U.S.A.)*
*Volair (U.S.A.)*

| | Edition Limit | Issue Price (US) |
|---|---|---|
| **Greentree Potteries** | | |
| *Grant Wood* | | |
| 1971 Studio | 2,000 | $ 10.00 |
| 1972 Antioch School | 2,000 | 10.00 |
| 1973 At Stone City | 2,000 | 10.00 |
| 1974 Adolescence | 2,000 | 10.00 |
| 1975 Birthplace | 2,000 | 10.00 |
| 1976 American Gothic | 2,000 | 10.00 |
| *Kennedy* | | |
| 1972 Center for Performing Arts | 2,000 | 20.00 |
| 1973 Birthplace, Brookline, Mass. | 2,000 | 12.00 |
| *Motorcar* | | |
| 1972 1929 Packard Dietrich Convertible | 2,000 | 20.00 |
| 1973 Model "A" Ford | 2,000 | 20.00 |
| *Mississippi River* | | |
| 1973 Delta Queen | 2,000 | 10.00 |
| 1973 Tri-Centennial | 2,000 | 10.00 |
| **Dave Grossman Designs** | | |
| *Margaret Keane* | | |
| 1976 Balloon Girl | 5,000 | 25.00 |
| 1977 My Kitty | 5,000 | 25.00 |
| 1978 Bedtime | 5,000 | 25.00 |
| *Tom Sawyer* | | |
| 1975 Whitewashing Fence | 10,000 | 24.00 |
| 1976 First Smoke | 10,000 | 24.00 |
| 1977 Take Your Medicine | 10,000 | 24.00 |
| 1978 Lost in Cave | 10,000 | 25.00 |
| *Looney Tunes Mother's Day* | | |
| 1976 Bugs Bunny | 10,000 | 13.00 |
| *Looney Tunes Christmas* | | |
| 1977 Christmas | 10,000 | 13.00 |
| 1978 Christmas | 5,000 | 14.00 |
| *Children of Week* | | |
| 1978 Monday's Child | 5,000 | 30.00 |
| 1979 Tuesday's Child | 5,000 | 30.00 |
| 1979 Wednesday's Child | 5,000 | 30.00 |
| 1980 Thursday's Child | 5,000 | 30.00 |
| 1980 Friday's Child | 5,000 | 30.00 |
| 1981 Saturday's Child | 5,000 | 30.00 |
| 1981 Sunday's Child | 5,000 | 30.00 |
| *Annual Fall* | | |
| 1978 Peace | 5,000 | 55.00 |
| 1979 Santa | 5,000 | 55.00 |
| *Annual* | | |
| 1979 Leapfrog | Year | 50.00 |
| 1980 Lovers | Year | 60.00 |
| 1981 Dreams of Long Ago | Year | 60.00 |
| *Rockwell* | | |
| 1979 Butter Boy | 5,000 | 40.00 |
| *Huckleberry Finn* | | |
| 1979 Secret | 10,000 | 40.00 |
| 1980 Listening | 10,000 | 40.00 |
| 1981 No Kings Nor Dukes | 10,000 | 40.00 |
| 1982 Snake Escapes | 10,000 | 40.00 |
| *(Single issue)* | | |
| 1980 Norman Rockwell Back to School | 10,000 | 24.00 |
| *Rockwell Christmas* | | |
| 1980 Christmas Trio | Year | 75.00 |
| 1981 Santa's Good Boys | Year | 75.00 |
| 1982 Faces of Christmas | Year | 75.00 |
| *Rockwell Boy Scout Annual* | | |
| 1981 Can't Wait | 10,000 | 30.00 |
| 1982 A Guiding Hand | 10,000 | 30.00 |
| 1983 Tomorrow's Leader | 10,000 | 30.00 |
| *Magic People* | | |
| 1982 Music for a Queen | 9,500 | 65.00 |
| 1982 Fantasy Festival | 10,000 | 65.00 |
| 1983 Bubble Chariot | 10,000 | 65.00 |
| 1983 Kite Carriage | 10,000 | 65.00 |
| *Milk Glass* | | |
| 1983 Dreamboats | 15,000 | 24.00 |
| *(Single issue)* | | |
| 1984 Secret | 10,000 | 39.50 |
| *Emmett Kelly Christmas* | | |
| 1986 Christmas Carol | NA | 20.00 |
| **Hackett American Collectors** | | |
| *Corita Kent Annual* | | |
| 1979 I Love You Very | 30,000 | 21.95 |
| 1980 You Bring Spring | 10,000 | 21.95 |

| | Edition Limit | Issue Price (US) |
|---|---|---|
| 1981 Love | 10,000 | $ 30.00 |
| 1982 Cheers | 10,000 | 32.50 |
| *Endangered Species* | | |
| 1980 California Sea Otters | 7,500 | 35.00 |
| 1981 Asian Pandas | 7,500 | 37.50 |
| 1982 Australian Koala Bears | 7,500 | 39.50 |
| 1982 River Otters | 7,500 | 39.50 |
| *Ocean Moods* | | |
| 1980 Sunset Tide | 5,000 | 50.00 |
| 1981 Moonlight Flight | 5,000 | 50.00 |
| 1982 Morning Surf | 5,000 | 50.00 |
| 1983 Afternoon Surf | 5,000 | 50.00 |
| *Save Whales* | | |
| 1980 Trust and Love | 10,000 | 30.00 |
| *Snow Babies* | | |
| 1980 Canadian Harp Seals | 7,500 | 39.50 |
| 1981 Polar Bear Cubs | 7,500 | 39.50 |
| 1982 Snow Leopards | 7,500 | 42.50 |
| *Friends of Forest* | | |
| 1981 Forest Alert | 7,500 | 50.00 |
| 1982 Brookside Protection | 7,500 | 50.00 |
| 1982 Mountain Guardian | 7,500 | 50.00 |
| 1983 Lookouts | 7,500 | 50.00 |
| *Horses in Action* | | |
| 1981 Challenge | 10,000 | 39.50 |
| 1982 Country Days | 10,000 | 50.00 |
| 1983 Family Portrait | 10,000 | 50.00 |
| 1983 All Grown Up | 10,000 | 50.00 |
| *Parkhurst Christmas* | | |
| 1981 Christmas Tear | 7,500 | 39.50 |
| 1982 Christmas Morning | 7,500 | 39.50 |
| 1983 Night Before Christmas | 7,500 | 39.50 |
| *Wonderful World of Clowns* | | |
| 1981 Kiss for a Clown | 7,500 | 39.50 |
| 1981 Rainbow's End | 7,500 | 39.50 |
| 1982 Happy Days | 7,500 | 42.50 |
| 1982 Filling Pop's Shoes | 7,500 | 42.50 |
| *Wonderous Years* | | |
| 1981 After Rains | 5,000 | 39.50 |
| 1982 I Got One | 5,000 | 42.50 |
| 1982 Fascination | 5,000 | 42.50 |
| *(Single issue)* | | |
| 1981 John Lennon | 90 Days | 25.00 |
| *Crazy Cats* | | |
| 1982 Primping Time | 10,000 | 42.50 |
| *Daisy Cats* | | |
| 1982 Daisy Kitten | 10,000 | 42.50 |
| 1982 Daisy Cat | 10,000 | 42.50 |
| *Days Remembered* | | |
| 1982 First Birthday | 19,500 | 29.50 |
| 1983 First Haircut | 19,5000 | 35.00 |
| *Early Discoveries* | | |
| 1982 Let's Play | 10,000 | 42.50 |
| *Escalera Christmas* | | |
| 1982 Special Delivery | 19,500 | 32.50 |
| 1983 Especially for You | 19,500 | 35.00 |
| *Everyone's Friends* | | |
| 1982 Springtime | 10,000 | 42.50 |
| 1982 Autumn Bandit | 10,000 | 42.50 |
| 1983 Snowtime Bunnies | 10,000 | 42.50 |
| 1983 Summer Bandits | 10,000 | 42.50 |
| *Family Portraits* | | |
| 1982 Mother's Joy | 7,500 | 85.00 |
| *Fashions by Irene* | | |
| 1982 Elegant Lady | 15,000 | 45.00 |
| *Escalera Father's Day* | | |
| 1982 Daddy's Rose | 10,000 | 42.50 |
| 1983 Daddy's Wish | 10,000 | 42.50 |
| *Impressions by Joanne Mix* | | |
| 1982 Windy Day | 10,000 | 42.50 |
| 1982 Sunny Day | 10,000 | 42.50 |
| 1983 Summer's Day | 10,000 | 42.50 |
| *Joanne Mix Christmas* | | |
| 1982 Christmas Love | 10,000 | 39.50 |
| *Kelly's Stable* | | |
| 1982 My Champion | 15,000 | 42.50 |
| 1983 Glory Bound | 15,000 | 42.50 |
| 1983 Arabian Spring | 15,000 | 42.50 |
| 1984 Summer Days | 15,000 | 42.50 |
| *Landfalls* | | |
| 1982 San Francisco Bay | 7,500 | 39.50 |
| 1983 Newport Harbor | 7,500 | 39.50 |
| 1983 Miami Beach | 7,500 | 39.50 |

| | Edition Limit | Issue Price (US) |
|---|---|---|
| *tle Orphans* | | |
| 82 Surprise Package | 19,500 | $ 29.50 |
| 83 Castaway | 19,500 | 32.50 |
| 84 Furry Surprise | 19,500 | 35.00 |
| *other and Child* | | |
| 82 Mother's Love | 10,000 | 42.50 |
| 82 Tenderness | 10,000 | 42.50 |
| 83 Serenity | 10,000 | 42.50 |
| 84 Navajo Madonna | 10,000 | 42.50 |
| *rkhurst Mother's Day* | | |
| 82 Daisies for Mother | 10,000 | 42.50 |
| *ean Stars* | | |
| 82 Sea Horses | 10,000 | 42.50 |
| 82 Dolphins | 10,000 | 42.50 |
| 83 Whales | 10,000 | 42.50 |
| *rkhurst Diamond* | | |
| 82 Chance Encounter | 1,500 | 300.00 |
| *aceful Retreat* | | |
| 82 Refuge | 19,500 | 29.50 |
| 83 Solitude | 19,500 | 32.50 |
| 83 Tranquility | 19,500 | 35.00 |
| 84 Seclusion | 19,500 | 35.00 |
| *airie Children* | | |
| 82 Young Pioneers | 19,500 | 32.50 |
| 83 Adam | 19,500 | 35.00 |
| *de by Side* | | |
| 82 My Hero | 19,500 | 32.50 |
| 83 Sippin' Soda | 19,500 | 35.00 |
| *ecial Moments* | | |
| 82 April | 10,000 | 42.50 |
| 82 Rachel | 10,000 | 42.50 |
| *nday Best* | | |
| 82 Stacey | 10,000 | 42.50 |
| 82 Laurie | 10,000 | 42.50 |
| *aterbird Families* | | |
| 82 Marsh Venture | 10,000 | 42.50 |
| 82 Afternoon Swim | 10,000 | 42.50 |
| 83 Nesting Wood Ducks | 10,000 | 42.50 |
| 83 Returning Home | 10,000 | 42.50 |
| *orld of Ozz Franca* | | |
| 82 Images | 10,000 | 42.50 |
| 82 Lost and Found | 10,000 | 42.50 |
| 83 Best Friends | 10,000 | 42.50 |
| *ingle issue)* | | |
| 82 Hog Heaven | 15,000 | 42.50 |
| *ingle issue)* | | |
| 82 Henry Fonda | 10,000 | 39.50 |
| *ingle issue)* | | |
| 82 Reggie Jackson | 10,000 | 60.00 |
| *ingle issue)* | | |
| 82 John Wayne | 10,000 | 39.50 |
| *assic Cars* | | |
| 83 '57 Chevy | 5,000 | 39.50 |
| 84 '57 Thunderbird | 5,000 | 39.50 |
| *ostume Party* | | |
| 83 Belinda | 7,500 | 39.50 |
| *amous Planes of Yesterday* | | |
| 83 Spirit of St. Louis | 5,000 | 39.50 |
| 84 Byrd Antarctic | 5,000 | 39.50 |
| *avorite Dreams* | | |
| 83 Daddy's Sailor | 7,500 | 39.50 |
| 84 Daddy's Engineer | 7,500 | 39.50 |
| *olfing Greats* | | |
| 83 Arnold Palmer | 100 Days | 45.00 |
| 84 Gary Player | 100 Days | 45.00 |
| *uggable Moments* | | |
| 83 Naptime | 10,000 | 39.50 |
| 83 Playtime | 10,000 | 39.50 |
| *an Horton Christmas* | | |
| 83 Moonlight Sleighride | 5,000 | 39.50 |
| *ys of Christmas* | | |
| 83 Toy Shop | 5,000 | 39.50 |
| *ngle Babies* | | |
| 83 Baby Bengals | 5,000 | 39.50 |
| *emorable Impressions* | | |
| 83 Beachcomber | 7,500 | 39.50 |
| 83 Beach Girl | 7,500 | 39.50 |
| *uzzling Moments* | | |
| 83 Problem Solver | 7,500 | 39.50 |
| 83 Practice Makes Perfect | 7,500 | 39.50 |

| | Edition Limit | Issue Price (US) |
|---|---|---|
| *Reflections of Sea* | | |
| 1983 Golden Shores | 5,000 | $ 42.50 |
| 1984 Summer Sands | 5,000 | 39.50 |
| *Sadako's Helpers* | | |
| 1983 Artist's Pal | 7,500 | 39.50 |
| 1984 Artist's Helper | 7,500 | 39.50 |
| *Sensitive Moments* | | |
| 1983 Sharing Beauty | 5,000 | 39.50 |
| *Snow Babies* | | |
| 1982 Arctic Foxes | 7,500 | 42.50 |
| 1982 Canadian Harp Seal | 7,500 | 42.50 |
| 1982 Polar Bear Cubs | 7,500 | 42.50 |
| 1982 Snow Leopards | 7,500 | 42.50 |
| *Summer Fun* | | |
| 1983 Fishing Together | 7,500 | 39.50 |
| 1983 Swinging Together | 7,500 | 39.50 |
| *Yesterday's Expressions* | | |
| 1983 Gloria | 5,000 | 39.50 |
| *(Single issue-Set of two)* | | |
| 1983 Bjorn Borg | | |
| 1983 Martina Navratilova | 15,000 | 39.50 |
| *(Single issue)* | | |
| 1983 Frog Heaven | 5,000 | 39.50 |
| *(Single issue)* | | |
| 1983 Hopalong Cassidy | 7,500 | 42.50 |
| *(Single issue)* | | |
| 1983 Laurel and Hardy | 15,000 | 42.50 |
| *(Single issue)* | | |
| 1983 Otter Heaven | 5,000 | 39.50 |
| *(Single issue)* | | |
| 1983 Steve Garvey | 10,000 | 60.00 |
| *Billowing Sails* | | |
| 1984 Flying Cloud | 7,500 | 60.00 |
| *Childhood Memories* | | |
| 1984 Cookie Thief | 7,500 | 29.50 |
| *Grandparents* | | |
| 1984 Grandpa's Delight | 10,000 | 27.50 |
| *Little Friends* | | |
| 1984 Tiny Creatures | 5,000 | 35.00 |
| *Moments to Cherish* | | |
| 1984 Kerry | 5,000 | 29.50 |
| *(Single issue)* | | |
| 1984 Steve Carlton | 4,400 | 45.00 |
| *(Single issue)* | | |
| 1984 Bill Rogers | 7,991 | 42.50 |
| *(Single issue)* | | |
| 1984 Babe | 10,000 | 29.50 |
| *(Single issue)* | | |
| 1984 Owl Heaven | 10,000 | 39.50 |
| *(Single issue)* | | |
| 1984 Forever Yours | 15,000 | 42.50 |
| *(Single issue)* | | |
| 1984 King Remembered | 10,000 | 50.00 |
| *(Single issue)* | | |
| 1984 Nolan Ryan | 8,402 | 42.50 |
| *(Single issue)* | | |
| 1984 Tom Seaver | 6,728 | 42.50 |
| *Big Chiefs* | | |
| 1985 Chief Joseph | 5,000 | 32.50 |
| *Joyful Memories* | | |
| 1985 Chrissy | 15,000 | 39.50 |
| *Reggie Jackson's Famous Collector Cars* | | |
| 1985 Jackson '65 Corvette | 10,000 | 45.00 |
| *(Single issue)* | | |
| 1985 Hank Aaron | 5,000 | 45.00 |
| *(Single issue)* | | |
| 1985 Sadako's Scotties | 5,000 | 35.00 |
| *(Single issue)* | | |
| 1985 Whitey Ford | 4,528 | 45.00 |
| *(Single issue)* | | |
| 1986 Ty Cobb | 4,191 | 39.50 |

## Hadley House

| | Edition Limit | Issue Price (US) |
|---|---|---|
| *Glow Series* | | |
| 1986 Evening Glow | 5,000 | 55.00 |
| 1986 Morning Glow | 5,000 | 55.00 |
| *Redlin's Retreat* | | |
| 1986 Morning Retreat | 9,500 | 65.00 |
| 1987 Evening Retreat | 9,500 | 65.00 |
| 1987 Golden Retreat | 9,500 | 65.00 |

| | Edition Limit | Issue Price (US) |
|---|---|---|
| *(Single issue)* | | |
| 1986 Quiet Water | 9,500 | $ 44.95 |

## Hamilton Collection

| | Edition Limit | Issue Price (US) |
|---|---|---|
| *Japanese Floral Calendar* | | |
| 1981 New Year's Day | 10 Days | 32.50 |
| 1982 Early Spring | 10 Days | 32.50 |
| 1982 Spring | 10 Days | 32.50 |
| 1982 Girl's Day | 10 Days | 32.50 |
| 1982 Buddah's Birthday | 10 Days | 32.50 |
| 1983 Heralds of Spring | 10 Days | 32.50 |
| 1983 Boy's Doll Day | 10 Days | 32.50 |
| 1983 Summer | 10 Days | 32.50 |
| 1983 Autumn | 10 Days | 32.50 |
| 1983 Festival of Full Moon | 10 Days | 32.50 |
| 1983 Late Autumn | 10 Days | 32.50 |
| 1983 Winter | 10 Days | 32.50 |
| *Legends of Camelot* | | |
| 1981 Secret Romance | 12,500 | 62.50 |
| 1982 Merlin Magician | 12,500 | 62.50 |
| 1982 Sir Lancelot | 12,500 | 62.50 |
| 1982 King Arthur | 12,500 | 62.50 |
| 1982 Jousting Tournament | 12,500 | 62.50 |
| 1982 Sword and Stone | 12,500 | 62.50 |
| 1982 Rescued | 12,500 | 62.50 |
| 1982 Knights of Round Table | 12,500 | 62.50 |
| *Story of Heidi* | | |
| 1981 Heidi | 14,750 | 45.00 |
| 1981 Grandfather | 14,750 | 45.00 |
| 1981 Heidi and Peter | 14,750 | 45.00 |
| 1981 Grandmother | 14,750 | 45.00 |
| 1982 Kittens | 14,750 | 45.00 |
| 1982 Mountain Cure | 14,750 | 45.00 |
| *Story of Noah's Ark* | | |
| 1981 Two by Two . . . | 12,500 | 45.00 |
| 1982 In Divine Harmony | 12,500 | 45.00 |
| 1982 Rainbow | 12,500 | 45.00 |
| 1982 Ark Beckons | 12,500 | 45.00 |
| 1982 Be Fruitful | 12,500 | 45.00 |
| 1982 Journey's End | 12,500 | 45.00 |
| *Treasures of Chinese Mandarins* | | |
| 1981 Bird of Paradise | 2,500 | 75.00 |
| 1982 Guardians of Heaven | 2,500 | 75.00 |
| 1982 Tree of Immortality | 2,500 | 75.00 |
| 1982 Dragon of Eternity | 2,500 | 75.00 |
| *Tribute to Ballet* | | |
| 1981 Nutcracker | 15,000 | 62.50 |
| *Fairies of Fields and Flowers* | | |
| 1982 Willow Fairy | NA | 45.00 |
| *Lewis & Clark Expedition* | | |
| 1982 In Bitteroots | NA | 55.00 |
| 1982 Sacajawea at Big Water | NA | 55.00 |
| 1982 Lewis Crossing | NA | 55.00 |
| 1982 Buffalo Gangue | NA | 55.00 |
| 1982 Salt Makers | NA | 55.00 |
| 1982 Up Jefferson | NA | 55.00 |
| 1982 Arrival of Sgt. Pryor | NA | 55.00 |
| 1982 Visitors at Fort Clatsop | NA | 55.00 |
| *Eternal Wishes of Good Fortune* | | |
| 1983 Friendship | 10 Days | 34.95 |
| 1983 Love | 10 Days | 34.95 |
| 1983 Fertility | 10 Days | 34.95 |
| 1983 Purity and Perfection | 10 Days | 34.95 |
| 1983 Illustrious Offspring | 10 Days | 34.95 |
| 1983 Peace | 10 Days | 34.95 |
| 1983 Longevity | 10 Days | 34.95 |
| 1983 Immortality | 10 Days | 34.95 |
| 1983 Marital Bliss | 10 Days | 34.95 |
| 1983 Beauty | 10 Days | 34.95 |
| 1983 Fortitude | 10 Days | 34.95 |
| 1983 Youth | 10 Days | 34.95 |
| *Gardens of Orient* | | |
| 1983 Flowering of Spring | 10 Days | 19.50 |
| 1983 Festival of May | 10 Days | 19.50 |
| 1983 Cherry Blossom Brocade | 10 Days | 19.50 |
| 1983 A Winter's Repose | 10 Days | 19.50 |
| 1983 Garden Sanctuary | 10 Days | 19.50 |
| 1983 Summer's Glory | 10 Days | 19.50 |
| 1983 June's Creation | 10 Days | 19.50 |
| *Majestic Birds of Prey* | | |
| 1983 Golden Eagle | 12,500 | 55.00 |
| 1983 Cooper's Hawk | 12,500 | 55.00 |
| 1983 Great Horned Owl | 12,500 | 55.00 |
| 1983 Bald Eagle | 12,500 | 55.00 |
| 1983 Barred Owl | 12,500 | 55.00 |
| 1983 Sparrow Hawk | 12,500 | 55.00 |

| | Edition Limit | Issue Price (US) |
|---|---|---|
| 1983 Peregrine Falcon | 12,500 | $ 55.00 |
| 1983 Osprey | 12,500 | 55.00 |
| *Utz Mother's Day* | | |
| 1983 A Gift of Love | Year | 27.50 |
| 1984 A Helping Hand | Year | 27.50 |
| 1985 Mother's Angel | Year | 27.50 |
| *(Single issue)* | | |
| 1983 Princess Grace | NA | 40.00 |
| *America at Work* | | |
| 1984 School Teacher | 10 Days | 29.50 |
| 1984 Piano Workman | 10 Days | 29.50 |
| 1984 Zoo Keeper | 10 Days | 29.50 |
| 1984 Cleaning Women | 10 Days | 29.50 |
| 1984 Hatcheck Girl | 10 Days | 29.50 |
| 1984 Census Taker | 10 Days | 29.50 |
| 1984 Shop Owner | 10 Days | 29.50 |
| 1984 Artist | 10 Days | 29.50 |
| *A Child's Garden of Verses* | | |
| 1984 Picture Books in Winter | 10 Days | 24.50 |
| 1984 Drops in Water | 10 Days | 24.50 |
| 1984 A Child's Question | 10 Days | 24.50 |
| 1984 Glass River | 10 Days | 24.50 |
| 1984 Busy Bee | 10 Days | 24.50 |
| 1984 At Seaside | 10 Days | 24.50 |
| 1984 Tea Party | 10 Days | 24.50 |
| 1984 Foreign Land | 10 Days | 24.50 |
| 1984 In Hayloft | 10 Days | 24.50 |
| 1984 Among Poppies | 10 Days | 24.50 |
| 1984 5:00 Tea | 10 Days | 24.50 |
| 1984 Love for Kittens | 10 Days | 24.50 |
| *Gamebirds of North America* | | |
| 1985 Ring-necked Pheasant | 15,000 | 62.50 |
| 1985 Bobwhite | 15,000 | 62.50 |
| 1985 American Woodcock | 15,000 | 62.50 |
| 1985 Wild Turkey | 15,000 | 62.50 |
| 1985 California Quail | 15,000 | 62.50 |
| 1985 Ruffed Grouse | 15,000 | 62.50 |
| 1985 Willow Partridge | 15,000 | 62.50 |
| 1985 Prairie Grouse | 15,000 | 62.50 |
| *Tale of Genji* | | |
| 1985 Serene Autumn Moon | NA | 45.00 |
| 1985 Dragon and Phoenix Boats | NA | 45.00 |
| 1985 Romantic Quest | NA | 45.00 |
| 1985 Blue Ocean Dance | NA | 45.00 |
| 1985 Evening Faces | NA | 45.00 |
| 1985 Archery Meet | NA | 45.00 |
| 1985 Moon Viewing | NA | 45.00 |
| 1985 Table Game | NA | 45.00 |
| *A Child's Best Friend* | | |
| 1986 In Disgrace | 14 Days | 24.50 |
| *Poetic Gardens of Japan* | | |
| 1986 Golden Tranquility | 15,000 | 55.00 |
| *Butterfly Garden Collection* | | |
| 1987 Spicebush Swallowtail | NA | 29.50 |
| *Star Wars Collection* | | |
| 1987 Han Solo | NA | 29.50 |
| *Noble Owls of North America* | | |
| 1987 Morning Mist | 15,000 | 55.00 |
| *Treasure Days* | | |
| 1987 Ashley | NA | 24.50 |

## Hamilton Collection (Boehm Studios)

| | Edition Limit | Issue Price (US) |
|---|---|---|
| *Rose* | | |
| 1979 Peace Rose | 15,000 | 45.00 |
| 1979 Queen Elizabeth Rose | 15,000 | 45.00 |
| 1979 White Masterpiece Rose | 15,000 | 45.00 |
| 1979 Angel Face Rose | 15,000 | 45.00 |
| 1979 Tropicana Rose | 15,000 | 45.00 |
| 1979 Elegance Rose | 15,000 | 45.00 |
| 1979 Royal Highness Rose | 15,000 | 45.00 |
| 1979 Mister Lincoln Rose | 15,000 | 45.00 |
| *Boehm Owl* | | |
| 1980 Snowy Owl | 15,000 | 45.00 |
| 1980 Boreal Owl | 15,000 | 45.00 |
| 1980 Barn Owl | 15,000 | 45.00 |
| 1980 Saw Whet Owl | 15,000 | 45.00 |
| 1980 Great Horned Owl | 15,000 | 45.00 |
| 1980 Screech Owl | 15,000 | 45.00 |
| 1980 Short Eared Owl | 15,000 | 45.00 |
| 1980 Barred Owl | 15,000 | 45.00 |

# OVER-THE-COUNTER ISSUES

| | Edition Limit | Issue Price (US) |
|---|---|---|
| *Hummingbird* | | |
| 1980 Calliope Hummingbird | 15,000 | $ 62.50 |
| 1980 Broadtail Hummingbird | 15,000 | 62.50 |
| 1980 Rufous Flame-Bearer Hummingbird | 15,000 | 62.50 |
| 1980 Broad-Billed Hummingbird | 15,000 | 62.50 |
| 1980 Streamer-Tail Hummingbird | 15,000 | 62.50 |
| 1980 Blue-Throated Hummingbird | 15,000 | 62.50 |
| 1980 Crimson-Topaz Hummingbirds | 15,000 | 62.50 |
| 1980 Brazilian Ruby | 15,000 | 62.50 |
| *Roses of Excellence* | | |
| 1981 Love Rose | Year | 62.50 |
| 1982 White Lightnin' | Year | 62.50 |
| 1983 Brandy | Year | 62.50 |
| *Water Bird Collection* | | |
| 1981 Canadian Geese | 15,000 | 55.00 |
| 1981 Wood Ducks | 15,000 | 55.00 |
| 1981 Common Mallards | 15,000 | 55.00 |
| 1981 Green-Winged Teals | 15,000 | 55.00 |
| 1981 Ross' Geese | 15,000 | 55.00 |
| 1981 Canvas-Backs | 15,000 | 55.00 |
| 1981 Hooded Mergansers | 15,000 | 55.00 |
| 1981 American Pintails | 15,000 | 55.00 |
| *Blossoms and Berries* | | |
| 1982 Winter Holiday Bouquet | 15,000 | 62.50 |
| 1982 Thanksgiving | 15,000 | 62.50 |
| 1982 School Days | 15,000 | 62.50 |
| 1982 Indian Summer | 15,000 | 62.50 |
| 1982 Mid-Summer | 15,000 | 62.50 |
| 1982 Autumn | 15,000 | 62.50 |
| 1982 Warm Days | 15,000 | 62.50 |
| 1982 Summer Majesty | 15,000 | 62.50 |
| 1982 Harvest Time | 15,000 | 62.50 |
| 1982 Spring Images | 15,000 | 62.50 |
| 1982 Mid-Winter | 15,000 | 62.50 |
| 1982 Late-Summer | 15,000 | 62.50 |
| *Life's Best Wishes* | | |
| 1982 Longevity | 15,000 | 75.00 |
| 1982 Happiness | 15,000 | 75.00 |
| 1982 Fertility | 15,000 | 75.00 |
| 1982 Prosperity | 15,000 | 75.00 |
| *Miniature Roses* | | |
| 1982 Toy Clown | 28 Days | 39.50 |
| 1982 Rise 'n Shine | 28 Days | 39.50 |
| 1982 Cuddles | 28 Days | 39.50 |
| 1982 Puppy Love | 28 Days | 39.50 |
| 1982 Magic Carousel | 28 Days | 39.50 |
| 1982 Pacesetter | 28 Days | 39.50 |
| 1982 Gloriglo | 28 Days | 39.50 |
| 1982 Beauty Secret | 28 Days | 39.50 |
| *Tribute to Award-Winning Roses* | | |
| 1983 Irish Gold | 15,000 | 62.50 |
| 1983 Handel | 15,000 | 62.50 |
| 1983 Queen Elizabeth | 15,000 | 62.50 |
| 1983 Elizabeth of Glamis | 15,000 | 62.50 |
| 1983 Iceberg | 15,000 | 62.50 |
| 1983 Mountbatten | 15,000 | 62.50 |
| 1983 Silver Jubilee | 15,000 | 62.50 |
| 1983 Peace | 15,000 | 62.50 |
| *A Country Summer* | | |
| 1986 Butterfly Beauty | 10 Days | 29.50 |
| 1986 Golden Puppy | 10 Days | 29.50 |
| 1987 The Rocking Chair | 10 Days | 29.50 |
| 1987 My Bunny | 10 Days | 29.50 |
| **Hamilton Collection (Caverswall)** | | |
| *Woodland Serenade* | | |
| 1986 American Redstart | 15,000 | 45.00 |
| **Hamilton Collection (Hutschenreuther)** | | |
| *Roses of Redouté* | | |
| 1983 China Rose | 17,500 | 32.50 |
| **Hamilton Collection (Kaiser)** | | |
| *Summer Days of Childhood* | | |
| 1983 Mountain Friends | 10 Days | 29.50 |
| 1983 Garden Magic | 10 Days | 29.50 |
| **Hamilton Collection (Porcelaine Ariel)** | | |
| *A Tribute to Love* | | |
| 1980 Shaft of Light | 17,500 | 45.00 |
| 1980 Jug of Wine | 17,500 | 45.00 |
| 1981 Sultan After Sultan | 17,500 | 45.00 |

| | Edition Limit | Issue Price (US) |
|---|---|---|
| 1981 Bird Is on Wing | 17,500 | $ 45.00 |
| 1982 If Today Be Sweet | 17,500 | 45.00 |
| 1982 Flower Once Has Blown | 17,500 | 45.00 |
| *Greatest Show on Earth* | | |
| 1981 Clowns-Heart of Circus | 10 Days | 30.00 |
| 1981 Elephants | 10 Days | 30.00 |
| 1981 Aerialists | 10 Days | 30.00 |
| 1981 Great Parade | 10 Days | 30.00 |
| 1982 Midway | 10 Days | 30.00 |
| 1982 Equestrians | 10 Days | 30.00 |
| 1982 Lion Tamer | 10 Days | 30.00 |
| 1982 Grande Finale | 10 Days | 30.00 |
| **Hamilton Collection (River Shore)** | | |
| *Favorite American Songbirds* | | |
| 1985 Western Tanager | 14 Days | 24.50 |
| *Lovable Teddies* | | |
| 1986 Bedtime Blues | 10 Days | 21.50 |
| 1986 Bearly Frightful | 10 Days | 21.50 |
| 1986 Caught in the Act | 10 Days | 21.50 |
| 1987 Fireside Friends | 10 Days | 21.50 |
| *Passage to China* | | |
| 1986 Alliance | 15,000 | 55.00 |
| 1986 Grand Turk | 15,000 | 55.00 |
| 1987 Seawitch | 15,000 | 55.00 |
| 1987 Flying Cloud | 15,000 | 55.00 |
| **Hamilton Collection (Roman)** | | |
| *Lord's Prayer* | | |
| 1986 Our Father | 10 Days | 24.50 |
| **Hamilton Collection (Royal Devon)** | | |
| *Rockwell Home of Brave* | | |
| 1981 Reminiscing | 18,000 | 35.00 |
| 1981 Hero's Welcome | 18,000 | 35.00 |
| 1981 Back to His Old Job | 18,000 | 35.00 |
| 1981 War Hero | 18,000 | 35.00 |
| 1982 Willie Gillis in Church | 18,000 | 35.00 |
| 1982 War Bond | 18,000 | 35.00 |
| 1982 Uncle Sam Takes Wings | 18,000 | 35.00 |
| 1982 Mother over Top | 18,000 | 35.00 |
| *Woodland Serenade* | | |
| 1986 American Redstart | 15,000 | 45.00 |
| *Japanese Blossoms of Autumn* | | |
| 1986 Bellflower | NA | 45.00 |
| *Little Rascals* | | |
| 1986 Three for the Show | NA | 24.50 |
| 1987 Butch's Challenge | NA | 24.50 |
| **Hamilton Collection (Viletta)** | | |
| *Coppelia Ballet* | | |
| 1980 Franz's Fantasy Love | 28 Days | 25.00 |
| 1980 Creation of a Doll | 28 Days | 25.00 |
| 1981 Secret Is Unlocked | 28 Days | 25.00 |
| 1981 Swanhilda's Deception | 28 Days | 25.00 |
| 1981 An Uneasy Sleep | 28 Days | 25.00 |
| 1981 Coppelia Awakens | 28 Days | 25.00 |
| 1982 A Shattered Dream | 28 Days | 25.00 |
| 1982 Wedding | 28 Days | 25.00 |
| *Portraits of Childhood* | | |
| 1981 Butterfly Magic | 28 Days | 24.95 |
| 1982 Sweet Dreams | 28 Days | 24.95 |
| 1983 Turtle Talk | 28 Days | 24.95 |
| *Waltzes of Johann Strauss* | | |
| 1981 Emperor's Waltz | 28 Days | 25.00 |
| 1981 Blue Danube | 28 Days | 25.00 |
| 1981 Voices of Spring | 28 Days | 25.00 |
| 1981 Vienna Life | 28 Days | 25.00 |
| 1982 Roses of South | 28 Days | 25.00 |
| 1982 Wine, Women and Song | 28 Days | 25.00 |
| 1982 Artist's Life | 28 Days | 25.00 |
| 1982 Tales of Vienna Woods | 28 Days | 25.00 |
| *Carefree Days* | | |
| 1982 Autumn Wanderer | 10 Days | 24.50 |
| 1982 Best Friends | 10 Days | 24.50 |
| 1982 Feeding Time | 10 Days | 24.50 |
| 1983 Bathtime Visitor | 10 Days | 24.50 |
| 1983 First Catch | 10 Days | 24.50 |
| 1983 Monkey Business | 10 Days | 24.50 |
| 1984 Touchdown | 10 Days | 24.50 |
| 1984 Nature Hunt | 10 Days | 24.50 |

| | Edition Limit | Issue Price (US) |
|---|---|---|
| **Hamilton Mint** | | |
| *Picasso* | | |
| 1972 Le Gourmet | 5,000 | $125.00 |
| 1972 Tragedy | 5,000 | 125.00 |
| 1973 Lovers | 5,000 | 125.00 |
| *Kennedy* | | |
| 1974 (Gold on Pewter) | Year | 40.00 |
| 1974 (Pewter) | Year | 25.00 |
| *Man's Best Friend* | | |
| 1978 Hobo | 9,500 | 40.00 |
| 1978 Doctor | 9,500 | 40.00 |
| 1979 Making Friends | 9,500 | 40.00 |
| 1979 Gone Fishing | 9,500 | 40.00 |
| 1980 Thief | 9,500 | 40.00 |
| 1980 Puppy Love | 9,500 | 40.00 |
| **Hartman House** | | |
| *Sounds of Innocence* | | |
| 1987 Fleishhacker Carousel | 5,000 | 45.00 |
| **Heirloom Tradition** | | |
| *Christmas* | | |
| 1985 It's a Wonderful Life | 10,000 | 35.00 |
| 1986 Dickens' Christmas Carol | 10,000 | 35.00 |
| *Cinema Classics* | | |
| 1985 High Noon | 10,000 | 35.00 |
| 1985 Indiscreet | 10,000 | 35.00 |
| *(Single issue)* | | |
| 1985 Barry Manilow | 20,000 | 35.00 |
| *(Single issue)* | | |
| 1986 Varga | 10,000 | 45.00 |
| **Historic Providence Mint** | | |
| *(Single issue)* | | |
| 1979 Children's Year | 3,000 | 95.00 |
| *Children of Seasons* | | |
| 1980 Children of Spring | 3,000 | 107.50 |
| *America Beautiful* | | |
| 1981 Spacious Skies | 17,500 | 37.50 |
| 1981 Amber Waves of Grain | 17,500 | 37.50 |
| 1981 Purple Mountain Majesties | 17,500 | 37.50 |
| 1981 God Shed His Grace | 17,500 | 37.50 |
| 1981 Crown Good with Brotherhood | 17,500 | 37.50 |
| 1981 From Sea to Shining Sea | 17,500 | 37.50 |
| *Vanishing American Barn* | | |
| 1983 Bucks County Barn | 14,500 | 39.50 |
| 1983 Victorian Barn | 14,500 | 39.50 |
| 1983 New England Barn | 14,500 | 39.50 |
| 1983 Southern Tobacco Barn | 14,500 | 39.50 |
| 1983 Forebay Barn | 14,500 | 39.50 |
| 1983 Appalachian Barn | 14,500 | 39.50 |
| 1983 Connected Barn | 14,500 | 39.50 |
| 1983 Hudson River Barn | 14,500 | 39.50 |
| 1983 Log Barn | 14,500 | 39.50 |
| 1983 Thatched Barn | 14,500 | 39.50 |
| 1983 Lancaster Barn | 14,500 | 39.50 |
| 1983 Round Barn | 14,500 | 39.50 |
| *Alice in Wonderland* | | |
| 1986 Tea Party | 45 Days | 29.50 |
| 1986 Caterpillar | 45 Days | 29.50 |
| 1986 Duchess and Cook | 45 Days | 29.50 |
| 1986 White Knight | 45 Days | 29.50 |
| 1986 Off With Their Heads! | 45 Days | 29.50 |
| 1987 The Red & White Queens | 45 Days | 29.50 |
| 1987 The White Rabbit | 45 Days | 29.50 |
| *Lil' Peddlers* | | |
| 1986 Forget Me Nots | NA | 29.50 |
| 1986 Extra, Extra | NA | 29.50 |
| 1987 Coolin' Off | NA | 29.50 |
| 1987 Poppin' Corn | NA | 29.50 |
| 1987 Oven Fresh | NA | 29.50 |
| **Ralph Homan Studios (Viletta)** | | |
| *Seasons of Oak* | | |
| 1979 Lazy Days | 5,000 | 55.00 |
| 1980 Come Fly with Me | 5,000 | 55.00 |
| **Home Plates (Mingolla)** | | |
| *Christmas (Enamel on Copper)* | | |
| 1973 Christmas | 1,000 | 95.00 |
| 1974 Christmas | 1,000 | 110.00 |
| 1975 Christmas | 1,000 | 125.00 |

| | Edition Limit | Iss Pri (U |
|---|---|---|
| 1976 Christmas | 1,000 | $125. |
| 1977 Scene from Childhood | 2,000 | 200. |
| *Christmas (Porcelain)* | | |
| 1974 Christmas | 5,000 | 35. |
| 1975 Christmas | 5,000 | 35. |
| 1976 Christmas | 5,000 | 35. |
| 1977 Winter Wonderland | 7,000 | 45. |
| *Four Seasons (Enamel on Copper)* | | |
| 1978 Dashing Thru Snow | 2,000 | 150. |
| 1979 Spring Flowers | 2,000 | 150. |
| 1980 Beach Fun | 2,000 | 150. |
| 1981 Balloon Breeze | 2,000 | 150. |
| *Christmas in Country (Enamel on Copper)* | | |
| 1979 Dear Santa | 1,000 | 70. |
| 1980 Country Cousin | 1,000 | 90. |
| **Hoyle Products** | | |
| *Clown* | | |
| 1977 Runaway | 7,500 | 45. |
| 1978 It's Your Move | 7,500 | 45. |
| 1979 Understudy | 7,500 | 45. |
| 1980 Idol | 7,500 | 45. |
| *Traveling Salesman* | | |
| 1977 Traveling Salesman | 7,500 | 35. |
| 1978 Country Pedlar | 7,500 | 40. |
| 1979 Horse Trader | 7,500 | 40. |
| 1980 Expert Salesman | 7,500 | 45. |
| *Wilderness Wings* | | |
| 1978 Gliding In | 5,000 | 35. |
| 1979 Taking Off | 5,000 | 40. |
| 1980 Joining Up | 5,000 | 45. |
| 1981 Canvasbacks | 5,000 | 47. |
| *Four Seasons* | | |
| 1978 Gay Blades | Year | 55. |
| 1979 Boy Meets Dog | Year | 55. |
| 1980 Chilly Reception | Year | 65. |
| *Rockwell Four Seasons (Bronze)* | | |
| 1979 Adventurers Between Adventures | 9,500 | 55. |
| *Cowboy* | | |
| 1977 Sharing an Apple | 5,000 | 35. |
| 1978 Split Decision | 5,000 | 35. |
| 1979 Hiding Out | 5,000 | 35. |
| 1980 In Trouble | 5,000 | 35. |
| *Family Circus Christmas* | | |
| 1980 Christmas | 5,000 | 25. |
| 1981 Christmas | 5,000 | 30. |
| *Mother's Day* | | |
| 1980 Mother's Day | 5,000 | 25. |
| *Rare Rockwells* | | |
| 1980 Mrs. O'Leary's Cow | 7,500 | 30. |
| 1981 Come and Get It | 7,500 | 30. |
| *Hilda* | | |
| 1981 Toasting Marshmallows | 5,000 | 25. |
| *Nostalgia* | | |
| 1981 Pepsi Cola Girl | 5,000 | 25. |
| 1982 Olympia Girl | 5,000 | 30. |
| 1982 Savannah Beer Girl | 5,000 | 30. |
| 1983 Dr. Pepper Girl | 5,000 | 30. |
| *Remember When* | | |
| 1982 A Surprise for Kitty | 10,000 | 30. |
| 1982 Washday | 10,000 | 30. |
| 1983 Playing Grandmother | 10,000 | 30. |
| 1983 Physician | 10,000 | 30. |
| *Wings of Wild* | | |
| 1982 Cinnamon Teal | 5,000 | 30. |
| 1982 Moment of Rest | 5,000 | 30. |
| 1983 Mourning Doves | 5,000 | 30. |
| *Gothic Romance* | | |
| 1982 Moonlight Romance | 5,000 | 30. |
| *By-Gone Days* | | |
| 1983 Breakfast with Teddy | 12,500 | 35. |
| 1984 Flower Basket | 12,500 | 35. |
| *Nostalgia–Children* | | |
| 1983 Pear's Soap Ad | 12,500 | 35. |
| 1984 Morton Salt Ad | 12,500 | 35. |
| *Nostalgia–Magazine Covers* | | |
| 1983 Ladies Home Journal | 12,500 | 35. |
| 1984 Saturday Evening Post | 12,500 | 35. |
| **Hudson Pewter** | | |
| *Bicentennial* | | |
| 1975 Spirit of '76 | 10,000 | 45. |

| | Edition Limit | Issue Price (US) |
|---|---|---|
| **other's Day** | | |
| '79 Cherished | 10,000 | $ 35.00 |
| **ngbirds of Four Seasons** | | |
| '79 Hummingbird | 7,500 | 35.00 |
| **merica's Sailing Ships** | | |
| '79 U.S.S. Constitution | 5,000 | 35.00 |
| **Child's Christmas** | | |
| '79 Littlest Angels | 10,000 | 35.00 |
| '80 Heaven's Christmas Tree | 10,000 | 42.50 |
| **vas Night Before Christmas** | | |
| '82 Not a Creature Was Stirring | 10,000 | 47.50 |
| '83 Visions of Sugar Plums | 10,000 | 47.50 |
| **nperial** | | |
| **merica Beautiful** | | |
| '69 U.S. Capitol | 500 | 17.50 |
| '70 Mount Rushmore | 500 | 17.50 |
| '71 Statue of Liberty | 500 | 17.50 |
| '72 Monument Valley, Arizona | 500 | 17.50 |
| '73 Liberty Bell | 500 | 17.50 |
| '74 Golden Gate | 500 | 19.95 |
| '75 Mt. Vernon | 500 | 19.95 |
| **hristmas** | | |
| '70 Partridge (Carnival) | Year | 12.00 |
| '70 Partridge (Crystal) | Year | 15.00 |
| '71 Two Turtle Doves (Carnival) | Year | 12.00 |
| '71 Two Turtle Doves (Crystal) | Year | 16.50 |
| '72 Three French Hens (Carnival) | Year | 12.00 |
| '72 Three French Hens (Crystal) | Year | 16.50 |
| '73 Four Colly Birds (Carnival) | Year | 12.00 |
| '73 Four Colly Birds (Crystal) | Year | 16.50 |
| '74 Five Golden Rings (Carnival) | Year | 12.00 |
| '74 Five Golden Rings (Crystal) | Year | 16.50 |
| '75 Six Geese A-Laying (Carnival) | Year | 14.00 |
| '75 Six Geese A-Laying (Crystal) | Year | 19.00 |
| '76 Seven Swans (Carnival) | Year | 16.00 |
| '76 Seven Swans (Crystal) | Year | 21.00 |
| '77 Eight Maids A-Milking (Carnival) | Year | 18.00 |
| '77 Eight Maids A-Milking (Crystal) | Year | 23.00 |
| '78 Nine Ladies Dancing (Carnival) | Year | 20.00 |
| '78 Nine Ladies Dancing (Crystal) | Year | 25.00 |
| '79 Ten Lords A-Leaping (Carnival) | Year | 22.00 |
| '79 Ten Lords A-Leaping (Crystal) | Year | 27.00 |
| '80 Eleven Pipers Piping (Carnival) | Year | 24.00 |
| '80 Eleven Pipers Piping (Crystal) | Year | 29.00 |
| '81 Twelve Drummers Drumming (Carnival) | Year | 28.00 |
| '81 Twelve Drummers Drumming (Crystal) | Year | 34.00 |
| **oin Crystal** | | |
| '71 1964 Kennedy Half Dollar | Year | 15.00 |
| '72 Eisenhower Dollar | Year | 15.00 |
| **single issue** | | |
| '76 Bicentennial | Year | 20.00 |
| **ncolay Studios** | | |
| **ife's Interludes** | | |
| '79 Uncertain Beginning | Year | 95.00 |
| '80 Finally Friends | 12,000 | 95.00 |
| **our Elements** | | |
| '83 Air | 9,170 | 25.00 |
| **nchanted Moments** | | |
| '84 Tiffany's World | 7,500 | 95.00 |
| '85 Jennifer's World | 7,500 | 95.00 |


| | Edition Limit | Issue Price (US) |
|---|---|---|
| **International Museum** | | |
| *Christmas Stamp Art* | | |
| 1979 Gingerbread Santa | 9,900 | $ 29.00 |
| 1980 Madonna and Child | 9,900 | 37.50 |
| 1981 Botticelli's Madonna and Child | 9,900 | 45.00 |
| 1982 Madonna of Goldfinch | 9,900 | 45.00 |
| *Dance, Ballerina, Dance* | | |
| 1982 First Slippers | 14,500 | 47.50 |
| 1982 At Barre | 14,500 | 47.50 |
| 1982 Recital | 14,500 | 47.50 |
| 1982 Pirouette | 14,500 | 47.50 |
| 1982 Swan Lake | 14,500 | 47.50 |
| 1982 Opening Night | 14,500 | 47.50 |
| *Letter Writers* | | |
| 1982 Portrait of Michelangelo | 15,000 | 45.00 |
| 1982 Mrs. John Douglas | 15,000 | 45.00 |
| 1983 Don Antonio de Noriega | 15,000 | 45.00 |
| 1983 Lovely Reader | 15,000 | 45.00 |
| 1984 Lady Writing Letter | 15,000 | 45.00 |
| 1984 Five Feminine Virtues | 15,000 | 45.00 |
| *Super Heroes* | | |
| 1983 Superman | NA | 29.50 |
| 1983 Wonder Woman | NA | 39.50 |
| 1983 Batman and Robin | NA | 39.50 |
| 1984 Shazam | NA | 39.50 |
| 1984 Aquaman | NA | 39.50 |
| 1984 Justice League | NA | 39.50 |
| **International Silver** | | |
| *We Are One* | | |
| 1972 Declaration of Independence | 7,500 | 40.00 |
| 1973 Midnight Ride of Paul Revere | 7,500 | 40.00 |
| 1973 Stand at Concord Bridge | 7,500 | 40.00 |
| 1974 Crossing Delaware | 7,500 | 50.00 |
| 1974 Battle of Valley Forge | 7,500 | 50.00 |
| 1975 Surrender at Yorktown | 7,500 | 50.00 |
| *Christmas* | | |
| 1974 Tiny Tim | 7,500 | 75.00 |
| 1975 Caught | 7,500 | 75.00 |
| 1976 Bringing Home Tree | 7,500 | 75.00 |
| 1977 Fezziwig's Christmas Ball | 7,500 | 75.00 |
| 1978 Alleluia | 7,500 | 75.00 |
| 1979 Rejoice | 7,500 | 100.00 |
| 1980 Adoration | 7,500 | 125.00 |
| *Presidential* | | |
| 1975 Washington | 7,500 | 75.00 |
| 1976 Jefferson | 7,500 | 75.00 |
| 1976 Lincoln | 7,500 | 75.00 |
| 1976 F. Roosevelt | 7,500 | 75.00 |
| 1977 Eisenhower | 7,500 | 75.00 |
| 1977 Kennedy | 7,500 | 75.00 |
| *Seasons American Past* | | |
| 1976 Autumn | 7,500 | 60.00 |
| 1976 Spring | 7,500 | 60.00 |
| 1976 Summer | 7,500 | 60.00 |
| 1976 Winter | 7,500 | 60.00 |
| *See also: American Archives (U.S.A.)* | | |
| **Interpace** | | |
| *Modigliani (Single issue)* | | |
| 1972 Caryatid | 10,000 | 60.00 |
| *Architects of Democracy (Set of four)* | | |
| 1974 George Washington | | |
| 1974 John Adams | | |
| 1974 Thomas Jefferson | | |
| 1974 Alexander Hamilton | 1,776 | 225.00 |
| **JM Company** | | |
| *Competitive Sports* | | |
| 1979 Downhill Racing Slalom | 10,000 | 25.00 |
| *Oriental Birds* | | |
| 1979 Window at Tiger Spring Temple | 10,000 | 39.00 |
| *Love* | | |
| 1980 Love's Serenade | 5,000 | 50.00 |


| | Edition Limit | Issue Price (US) |
|---|---|---|
| **Joys (Viletta)** | | |
| *Precious Moments* | | |
| 1979 Friend in Sky | 28 Days | $ 21.50 |
| 1980 Sand in Her Shoe | 28 Days | 21.50 |
| 1980 Snow Bunny | 28 Days | 21.50 |
| 1980 Seashells | 28 Days | 21.50 |
| 1981 Dawn | 28 Days | 21.50 |
| 1981 My Kitty | 28 Days | 21.50 |
| **Judaic Heritage Society** | | |
| *Jewish Holidays* | | |
| 1972 Chanukah (Silver) | 2,000 | 150.00 |
| 1972 Chanukah (Gold) | 25 | 1900.00 |
| 1972 Pesach (Silver) | 2,000 | 150.00 |
| 1972 Pesach (Gold) | 25 | 1900.00 |
| 1972 Purim (Silver) | 2,000 | 150.00 |
| *(Single issue)* | | |
| 1974 Purim (Silver) | 1,000 | 150.00 |
| *Great Jewish Women* | | |
| 1976 Golda Meir | 4,000 | 35.00 |
| 1976 Henrietta Szold | 4,000 | 35.00 |
| 1976 Emma Lazarus | 4,000 | 35.00 |
| *Heritage Plates* | | |
| 1976 Rabbi | 4,000 | 35.00 |
| 1976 Hasidim | 4,000 | 35.00 |
| 1976 Shtetl | 4,000 | 35.00 |
| *(Single issue)* | | |
| 1977 Jacob and Angel | 5,000 | 45.00 |
| *(Single issue)* | | |
| 1977 Hatikvah (Copper) | 5,000 | 55.00 |
| *(Single issue)* | | |
| 1977 Hatikvah (Gold Plated) | 1,000 | 75.00 |
| *(Single issue)* | | |
| 1977 Hatikvah (Sterling Silver) | 500 | 180.00 |
| *Jewish Holidays* | | |
| 1979 Chanukah | 2,500 | 50.00 |
| 1979 Purim | 2,500 | 50.00 |
| 1979 Shavout | 2,500 | 50.00 |
| 1979 Rosh Hashanah | 2,500 | 50.00 |
| 1979 Simchat Torah | 2,500 | 50.00 |
| 1979 Pesach | 2,500 | 50.00 |
| *Jerusalem Wedding* | | |
| 1979 Bride of Jerusalem | 6,000 | 65.00 |
| 1979 Hasidic Dancers | 6,000 | 65.00 |
| **Judaic Heritage Society (Avondale)** | | |
| *(Single issue)* | | |
| 1980 Shalom–Peace | 6,000 | 95.00 |
| **Judaic Heritage Society (Viletta)** | | |
| *Israel's 30th Anniversary (Single issue)* | | |
| 1979 L'Chayim to Israel | 10,000 | 59.50 |
| *Israel's 30th Anniversary (Single issue)* | | |
| 1979 Prophecy of Isaiah | 4,000 | 59.50 |
| **David Kaplan Studio** | | |
| *Fiddler's People* | | |
| 1978 Fiddler on Roof | 7,500 | 60.00 |
| 1979 Tevya | 7,500 | 60.00 |
| 1980 Miracle of Love | 7,500 | 60.00 |
| 1981 Wedding | 7,500 | 60.00 |
| *Loveables* | | |
| 1982 Little Angel | 12,500 | 40.00 |
| **Keller & George (Reed & Barton)** | | |
| *Bicentennial* | | |
| 1972 Monticello (Damascene) | 1,000 | 75.00 |
| 1972 Monticello (Silver Plate) | 200 | 200.00 |
| 1973 Mt. Vernon (Damascene) | Year | 75.00 |
| **Kensington** | | |
| *Children of Week* | | |
| 1980 Wednesday's Child | 27,500 | 28.50 |
| **Kern Collectibles** | | |
| *Linda's Little Loveables* | | |
| 1977 Blessing | 7,500 | 30.00 |
| 1978 Appreciation | 7,500 | 37.50 |
| 1979 Adopted Burro | 7,500 | 42.50 |
| *Runci Mother's Day* | | |
| 1977 Darcy | 5,000 | 50.00 |
| 1978 A Moment to Reflect | 5,000 | 55.00 |


| | Edition Limit | Issue Price (US) |
|---|---|---|
| 1979 Fulfillment | 5,000 | $ 45.00 |
| 1980 A Renewal of Faith | 5,000 | 45.00 |
| *Christmas of Yesterday* | | |
| 1978 Christmas Call | 5,000 | 45.00 |
| 1979 Woodcutter's Christmas | 5,000 | 50.00 |
| 1980 Making Christmas Goodies | 5,000 | 55.00 |
| 1981 Singing Christmas Carols | 5,000 | 55.00 |
| *Adventures of Old West* | | |
| 1981 Grizzly Ambush | 7,500 | 65.00 |
| 1982 Train Robbers | 7,500 | 65.00 |
| 1983 Bank Holdup | 7,500 | 65.00 |
| 1984 Nature Strikes | 7,500 | 65.00 |
| *My Favorite Pets* | | |
| 1981 Schnauzers | 7,500 | 39.95 |
| 1982 Cocker Spaniels | 7,500 | 39.95 |
| 1983 Pointers | 7,500 | 42.50 |
| *Horses of Harland Young* | | |
| 1982 Quarterhorses | 10,000 | 55.00 |
| 1983 Arabians | 10,000 | 55.00 |
| 1984 Mustangs | 10,000 | 55.00 |
| 1985 Thoroughbreds | 10,000 | 55.00 |
| *School Days* | | |
| 1982 Apple for My Teacher | 7,500 | 65.00 |
| 1983 Arithmetic Lesson | 7,500 | 65.00 |
| *This Little Pig* | | |
| 1982 Pig Went to Market | 9,800 | 39.95 |
| 1983 Pig Stayed Home | 9,800 | 42.50 |
| 1984 Pig Had Roast Beef | 9,800 | 45.00 |
| 1985 Pig Had None | 9,800 | 45.00 |
| *Childhood Innocence* | | |
| 1983 Sarah | 7,500 | 55.00 |
| 1984 Kelly | 7,500 | 55.00 |
| *A Child's World* | | |
| 1983 Kathie | 9,800 | 45.00 |
| 1983 Meredith | 9,800 | 45.00 |
| 1984 Freddie | 9,800 | 45.00 |
| 1984 Jamie | 9,800 | 45.00 |
| 1985 Robbie | 9,800 | 45.00 |
| *Kitty Cats* | | |
| 1983 Morrie | 7,500 | 39.00 |
| 1984 Tattoo | 7,500 | 39.00 |
| 1985 Topsie | 7,500 | 39.00 |
| 1987 Zorba | 7,500 | 39.00 |
| *North American Game Birds* | | |
| 1983 Canadian Geese | 7,500 | 60.00 |
| 1984 Mallards | 7,500 | 60.00 |
| 1984 Pheasants | 7,500 | 60.00 |
| 1987 Ruffed Grouse | 7,500 | 60.00 |
| *Zoological Garden* | | |
| 1983 Elephants | 5,000 | 55.00 |
| 1984 Tigers | 5,000 | 55.00 |
| *Children of Southwest* | | |
| 1984 Navaho Pixie | 7,500 | 36.00 |
| 1984 Morning Sun | 7,500 | 36.00 |
| 1987 Dark Eyes | 7,500 | 36.00 |
| *Country Friends* | | |
| 1984 Elizabeth | 7,500 | 35.00 |
| *Memories of Yesterday* | | |
| 1984 Patricia | 7,500 | 35.00 |
| *Tribal Companions* | | |
| 1984 My Best Friend | 6,000 | 35.00 |
| *(Single issue)* | | |
| 1984 Champ | 7,500 | 39.50 |
| *Birds of Distinction* | | |
| 1985 New Light, New Life | NA | 29.50 |
| *Women of Timeless Beauty* | | |
| 1985 Melinda | 5,000 | 35.00 |
| **Kern Collectibles (Haviland & Parlon)** | | |
| *Patti Canaris Songbird* | | |
| 1980 Cardinals | 5,000 | 65.00 |
| 1981 Blue Birds | 5,000 | 70.00 |
| 1982 Orioles | 5,000 | 70.00 |
| 1983 Goldfinches | 5,000 | 70.00 |
| *Patti Canaris Butterfly* | | |
| 1984 Monarchs | 7,500 | 75.00 |
| 1985 Sonora Blue | 7,500 | 80.00 |
| **Kern Collectibles (Pickard)** | | |
| *Cowboy Artists (Sets of two)* | | |
| 1976 Out There | | |
| 1976 Cutting Out a Stray | 3,000 | 130.00 |

| | | Edition Limit | Issue Price (US) |
|---|---|---|---|
| 1977 | Broken Cinch | | $130.00 |
| 1977 | No Place to Cross | 1,000 | $130.00 |

*Companions*

| 1977 | Cubs | 5,000 | 40.00 |
| 1978 | Mighty Sioux | 5,000 | 40.00 |
| 1979 | Nature Girl | 5,000 | 50.00 |
| 1980 | Buffalo Boy | 5,000 | 50.00 |
| 1981 | Shepherds | 5,000 | 55.00 |

### Kern Collectibles (Rosenthal)

*John Falter Harvest Time*

| 1976 | Gathering Pumpkins | 5,000 | 70.00 |
| 1977 | Honest Day's Work | 4,000 | 70.00 |

*Runci Classic*

| 1977 | Summertime | 5,000 | 95.00 |
| 1978 | Springtime | 5,000 | 95.00 |

### Kern Collectibles (Royal Bayreuth)

*Christmas*

| 1972 | Carriage in Village | 4,000 | 15.00 |
| 1973 | Snow Scene | 5,000 | 16.50 |
| 1974 | Old Mill | 4,000 | 24.00 |
| 1975 | Forest Chalet "Serenity" | 4,000 | 27.50 |
| 1976 | Christmas in Country | 5,000 | 40.00 |
| 1977 | Peace on Earth | 5,000 | 40.00 |
| 1978 | Peaceful Interlude | 5,000 | 45.00 |
| 1979 | Homeward Bound | 5,000 | 50.00 |

*Sun Bonnet Babies (Set of seven)*

| 1974 | Monday (Washing Day) | | |
| 1974 | Tuesday (Ironing Day) | | |
| 1974 | Wednesday (Mending Day) | | |
| 1974 | Thursday (Scrubbing Day) | | |
| 1974 | Friday (Sweeping Day) | | |
| 1974 | Saturday (Baking Day) | | |
| 1974 | Sunday (Fishing Day) | 15,000 | 120.00 |

*Antique American Art*

| 1976 | Farmyard Tranquility | 3,000 | 50.00 |
| 1977 | Half Dome | 3,000 | 55.00 |
| 1978 | Down Memory Lane | 3,000 | 65.00 |

*(Single issue)*

| 1976 | Sun Bonnet Babies Composite | 15,000 | 75.00 |

*L. Henry*

| 1976 | Just Friends | 5,000 | 50.00 |
| 1977 | Interruption | 4,000 | 55.00 |

*Anniversary*

| 1980 | Young Americans | 5,000 | 125.00 |

*Sun Bonnet Babies Playtime*

| 1981 | Swinging | 5,000 | 60.00 |
| 1981 | Round Dance | 5,000 | 60.00 |
| 1982 | Marbles | 5,000 | 60.00 |
| 1982 | Playing Catch | 5,000 | 60.00 |

### Kern Collectibles (Sango)

*Living American Artist*

| 1976 | Sweethearts (Rockwell) | 10,000 | 30.00 |
| 1977 | Apache Girl (Perillo) | 5,000 | 35.00 |
| 1978 | Natural Habitat | 5,000 | 40.00 |

*Great Achievements in Art*

| 1980 | Arabian | 3,000 | 65.00 |
| 1981 | Texas Longhorns | 3,000 | 70.00 |

### Kilkelly

*St. Patrick's Day*

| 1975 | Pipe and Shamrock | Year | 16.50 |
| 1976 | Third Look in Logan | Year | 20.00 |

### Killman Art Gallery

*Native Wildcat Kittens of North America*

| 1985 | The Adorable Oselot | 7,500 | 39.00 |
| 1986 | Bashful Babies | 7,500 | 39.00 |
| 1987 | Bouncy Bobcat | 7,500 | 45.00 |

### Kirk

*DeGrazia*

| 1972 | Heavenly Blessing | 200 | 75.00 |

*Mother's Day*

| 1972 | Mother and Child | 3,500 | 75.00 |
| 1973 | Mother and Child | 2,500 | 80.00 |

*Bicentennial*

| 1972 | U.S.S. Constellation | 825 | 75.00 |
| 1972 | Washington | 5,000 | 75.00 |


| | | Edition Limit | Issue Price (US) |
|---|---|---|---|

*Thanksgiving*

| 1972 | Thanksgiving Ways and Means | 3,500 | $150.00 |

*Christmas*

| 1972 | Flight into Egypt | 3,500 | 150.00 |

### Lake Shore Prints

*Rockwell*

| 1973 | Butter Girl | 9,433 | 14.95 |
| 1974 | Truth about Santa | 15,141 | 19.50 |
| 1975 | Home from Fields | 8,500 | 24.50 |
| 1976 | A President's Wife | 2,500 | 70.00 |

### Lapsys

*Crystal Christmas*

| 1977 | Snowflake | 5,000 | 47.50 |
| 1978 | Peace on Earth | 5,000 | 47.50 |

### Legacy, Ltd.

*Christmas*

| 1986 | Whitetail Buck | 5,000 | 39.50 |

### Lenox

*Boehm Birds, Young America*

| 1972 | Bird of Peace (Mute Swan) | 5,000 | 150.00 |
| 1973 | 1776 | 6,000 | 175.00 |

*Boehm Woodland Wildlife*

| 1973 | Raccoons | Year | 50.00 |
| 1974 | Red Foxes | Year | 52.50 |
| 1975 | Cottontail Rabbits | Year | 58.50 |
| 1976 | Eastern Chipmunks | Year | 62.50 |
| 1977 | Beaver | Year | 67.50 |
| 1978 | Whitetail Deer | Year | 70.00 |
| 1979 | Squirrels | Year | 76.00 |
| 1980 | Bobcats | Year | 92.50 |
| 1981 | Martens | Year | 100.00 |
| 1982 | Otters | Year | 100.00 |

*Christmas Tree*

| 1976 | Douglas Fir | Year | 50.00 |
| 1977 | Scotch Pine | Year | 55.00 |
| 1978 | Blue Spruce | Year | 65.00 |
| 1979 | Balsam Fir | Year | 65.00 |
| 1980 | Brewer's Spruce | Year | 75.00 |
| 1981 | China Fir | Year | 75.00 |
| 1982 | Aleppo Pine | Year | 80.00 |

*Colonial Christmas Wreath*

| 1981 | Virginia | Year | 65.00 |
| 1982 | Massachusetts | Year | 65.00 |
| 1983 | Maryland | Year | 70.00 |
| 1984 | Rhode Island | Year | 70.00 |
| 1985 | Connecticut | Year | 70.00 |
| 1986 | New Hampshire | Year | 39.50 |

*Butterflies and Flowers*

| 1982 | Question Mark and New England Aster | 25,000 | 65.00 |
| 1983 | Sonoran Blue and Mariposa Lily | 25,000 | 65.00 |
| 1983 | Malachite and Orchid | 25,000 | 65.00 |
| 1984 | Ruddy Daggerwing and Lantana | 25,000 | 70.00 |
| 1984 | American Lady and Virginia Rose | 25,000 | 70.00 |
| 1985 | Buckeye and Bluebells | 25,000 | 75.00 |

*American Wildlife*

| 1983 | Red Foxes | 9,500 | 65.00 |
| 1983 | Ocelots | 9,500 | 65.00 |
| 1983 | Sea Lions | 9,500 | 65.00 |
| 1983 | Raccoons | 9,500 | 65.00 |
| 1983 | Dall Sheep | 9,500 | 65.00 |

*Nature's Nursery*

| 1983 | Snow Leopards | 15,000 | 65.00 |
| 1983 | Koalas | 15,000 | 65.00 |
| 1984 | Llamas | 15,000 | 70.00 |
| 1984 | Bengal Tigers | 15,000 | 70.00 |
| 1985 | Emperor Penguins | 15,000 | 75.00 |
| 1985 | Polar Bears | 15,000 | 75.00 |
| 1986 | Harp Seals | 15,000 | 80.00 |
| 1986 | Zebras | 15,000 | 80.00 |

*See also: American Express (U.S.A.)*

### Lincoln Mint

*Great Artists (Dali)*

| 1971 | Unicorn Dyonisiaque (Gold) | 100 | 1500.00 |
| 1971 | Unicorn Dyonisiaque (Silver) | 5,000 | 100.00 |


| | | Edition Limit | Issue Price (US) |
|---|---|---|---|
| 1972 | Dyonisiaque et Pallas Athens (Gold) | 300 | $2000.00 |
| 1972 | Dyonisiaque et Pallas Athens (Gold Plate) | 2,500 | 150.00 |
| 1972 | Dyonisiaque et Pallas Athens (Silver) | 7,500 | 125.00 |

*Easter*

| 1972 | Christ (Silver) | 20,000 | 150.00 |
| 1972 | Christ (Gold Plate) | 10,000 | 200.00 |
| 1974 | Christ (Pewter) | Year | 45.00 |

*Mother's Day*

| 1972 | Collies (Silver) | 3,000 | 125.00 |

*Christmas*

| 1972 | Madonna Della Seggiola (Gold Plate) | 125 | 150.00 |
| 1972 | Madonna Della Seggiola (Silver) | 3,000 | 125.00 |

*Dali Cross Plate*

| 1977 | Gold Cross | 5,000 | 225.00 |
| 1977 | Silver Cross | 10,000 | 175.00 |

### Lincoln Mint (Gorham)

*Christmas*

| 1978 | Santa Belongs to All Children | 7,500 | 29.50 |

### Litt

*Christmas*

| 1978 | Madonna & Child | 1,000 | 200.00 |
| 1979 | O Holy Night | 1,000 | 200.00 |

*Annual*

| 1979 | Apache Sunset | 1,250 | 275.00 |

### Lynell Studios

*Little Traveler*

| 1978 | On His Way | 4,000 | 45.00 |
| 1979 | On Her Way | 4,000 | 45.00 |

*American Adventure*

| 1979 | Whaler | 7,500 | 50.00 |
| 1979 | Trapper | 7,500 | 50.00 |
| 1980 | Forty-Niner | 7,500 | 50.00 |
| 1981 | Pioneer Woman | 7,500 | 50.00 |
| 1981 | Wagon Master | 7,500 | 50.00 |
| 1982 | Wagon Ho! | 7,500 | 50.00 |

*All-American Soap Box Derby*

| 1979 | Last Minute Changes | Year | 24.50 |
| 1980 | At Gate | Year | 24.50 |
| 1981 | In Stretch | Year | 29.50 |

*Rockwell Legendary Art Christmas*

| 1979 | Snow Queen | 60 Days | 29.50 |
| 1980 | Surprises for All | 60 Days | 29.50 |
| 1981 | Grandpop and Me | 60 Days | 29.50 |
| 1982 | Santa's Secret | 10,000 | 35.00 |
| 1983 | Looking for Santa | 10,000 | 35.00 |

*John Wayne*

| 1979 | Man of Golden West | Year | 45.00 |

*RCA Victor Nipper Plate*

| 1980 | His Master's Voice | NA | 24.50 |

*Rockwell Legendary Art Annual*

| 1980 | Artist's Daughter | Year | 65.00 |

*Rockwell Legendary Art Mother's Day*

| 1980 | Cradle of Love | 60 Days | 29.50 |
| 1981 | A Mother's Blessing | 60 Days | 29.50 |
| 1982 | Memories | 60 Days | 29.50 |
| 1983 | Dear Mother | 60 Days | 29.50 |
| 1984 | First Mother's Day | 60 Days | 29.50 |

*Rockwell Legendary Art Rare Rockwell Paintings*

| 1980 | Poor Richard | 17,500 | 45.00 |

*Popeye's 50th Anniversary (Single issue)*

| 1980 | Happy Birthday Popeye | Year | 22.50 |

*Great Chiefs of Canada*

| 1980 | Chief Joseph Brant | 7,500 | 65.00 |
| 1981 | Crowfoot | 7,500 | 65.00 |
| 1982 | Tecumseh | 7,500 | 65.00 |

*Betsey Bates Christmas*

| 1979 | Olde Country Inn | 7,500 | 38.50 |
| 1980 | Village School House | 7,500 | 38.50 |
| 1981 | Village Blacksmith | 7,500 | 38.50 |
| 1982 | Christmas Village | 7,500 | 38.50 |

*Children's World*

| 1981 | Official Babysitter | 15,000 | 24.50 |
| 1981 | Cowboy Capers | 15,000 | 29.50 |
| 1982 | Nurse Nancy | 15,000 | 29.50 |
| 1982 | Pet Shop | 15,000 | 29.50 |


| | | Edition Limit | Issue Price (US) |
|---|---|---|---|

*Eyes of Seasons*

| 1981 | Winter | 19,500 | $38. |
| 1981 | Spring | 19,500 | 38. |
| 1981 | Summer | 19,500 | 38. |
| 1981 | Autumn | 19,500 | 38. |

*Hagel Christmas*

| 1981 | Shhh! | 17,500 | 29. |
| 1982 | Kiss for Santa | 10,000 | 35. |

*How West Was Won*

| 1981 | Pony Express | 19,500 | 38. |
| 1982 | Oregon Trail | 19,500 | 38. |
| 1982 | California Gold Rush | 19,500 | 38. |
| 1982 | Cattle Drive | 19,500 | 38. |
| 1983 | Peace Pipe | 19,500 | 38. |
| 1983 | Driving Golden Spike | 19,500 | 38. |

*North American Wildlife*

| 1981 | Snuggling Cougars | 7,500 | 65. |

*Oriental Dreams*

| 1981 | Tranquility | 15,000 | 55. |

*Rockwell's Scotty*

| 1981 | Scotty Stowaway | 17,500 | 45. |
| 1982 | Scotty Strikes Bargain | 17,500 | 35. |

*(Single issue)*

| 1981 | Reagan-Bush Inaugural | 17,500 | 45. |

*Best of Times*

| 1982 | Candy Shop | 15,000 | 38. |

*Circus Dreams*

| 1982 | Two for Show | 19,500 | 24. |

*Greatest Clowns of Circus*

| 1982 | Emmett Kelly | NA | 38. |
| 1982 | Lou Jacobs | NA | 38. |
| 1982 | Felix Adler | NA | 38. |
| 1982 | Otto Griebling | NA | 38. |

*Hagel Mother's Day*

| 1982 | Once Upon a Time | 60 Days | 29. |

*Hobo Joe*

| 1982 | Hold Onions | 10,000 | 50. |
| 1982 | Do Not Disturb | 10,000 | 50. |
| 1983 | No Camping or Fishing | 10,000 | 50. |
| 1983 | Traveling in Style | 10,000 | 50. |

*Little House on Prairie*

| 1982 | Welcome to Walnut Creek | 19,500 | 45. |
| 1982 | Country Girls | 19,500 | 45. |
| 1982 | Women at Harvestime | 19,500 | 45. |
| 1982 | Sweethearts Tree | 19,500 | 45. |
| 1983 | School Marm | 19,500 | 45. |
| 1983 | Bell for Grove | 19,500 | 45. |
| 1983 | Mary's Gift | 19,500 | 45. |
| 1983 | Caroline's Eggs | 19,500 | 45. |
| 1983 | Medicine Show | 19,500 | 45. |
| 1983 | Brotherhood on the Prairie | 19,500 | 45. |
| 1983 | The Founders' Day Picnic | 19,500 | 45. |
| 1983 | The Ingalls Family | 19,500 | 45. |

*(Single issue)*

| 1982 | Betty Boop | 15,000 | 24. |

*(Single issue)*

| 1982 | I Love Lucy | 100 Days | 45. |

*(Single issue)*

| 1982 | Norman Rockwell Tribute | 5,000 | 55. |

*(Single issue)*

| 1982 | Thanks for Memories | 100 Days | 45. |

*(Single issue)*

| 1982 | Young at Heart | 100 Days | 45. |

*Lionel Barrymore*

| 1983 | Nantucket | 7,500 | 45. |

*(Single issue)*

| 1984 | Wayne Gretzky | Year | 39.9 |

### Mallek Studios

*Navajo Christmas*

| 1971 | Indian Wise Men | 1,000 | 15. |
| 1972 | On Reservation | 2,000 | 17. |
| 1973 | Hoke Denetsosie | 2,000 | 17. |
| 1974 | Monument Valley | 2,000 | 18. |
| 1975 | Coming Home for Christmas | 2,000 | 18. |
| 1976 | Deer with Rainbow | 2,000 | 20. |
| 1977 | Goat Herders | 2,000 | 20. |
| 1978 | Hogan Christmas | 2,000 | 20. |
| 1979 | Navajo Madonna | 3,000 | 25. |
| 1980 | Children's Playmates | 3,500 | 25. |

| | Edition Limit | Issue Price (US) |
|---|---|---|
| **inese Lunar Calendar** | | |
| 72 Year of Rat | 1,000 | $ 15.00 |
| 73 Year of Ox | 1,000 | 15.00 |
| 74 Year of Rabbit | 1,000 | 15.00 |
| **ristmas Game Birds** | | |
| 72 Gambel Quail | 1,000 | 15.00 |
| 73 Partridge | 1,000 | 15.00 |
| 74 Owl and Cactus | 1,000 | 15.00 |
| 75 Chinese Wood Duck | 1,000 | 15.00 |
| 76 Wild Turkey | 1,000 | 15.00 |
| 77 Mallard | 1,000 | 15.00 |
| 78 Canadian Geese | 1,000 | 15.00 |
| 79 American Woodcock | 1,000 | 15.00 |
| **exican Christmas** | | |
| 72 Manger | 1,000 | 15.00 |
| 73 Madonna | 1,000 | 15.00 |
| 74 Corona | 1,000 | 18.00 |
| 75 Pinata | 1,000 | 18.00 |
| 76 Procession | 1,000 | 20.00 |
| 77 Wisemen | 1,000 | 20.00 |
| **avidad (Single issue)** | | |
| 72 Navidad en Mexico | 500 | 15.00 |
| **ingle issue)** | | |
| 72 Amish Harvest | 1,000 | 17.00 |
| **B.C.'s** | | |
| 74 A.B.C. Rabbit | 1,000 | 15.00 |
| 75 A.B.C. Mice | 1,000 | 15.00 |
| 76 A.B.C. Ducklings | 1,000 | 15.00 |
| 77 A.B.C. Elephant | 1,000 | 15.00 |
| 78 A.B.C. Owls | 1,000 | 15.00 |
| **ingle issue)** | | |
| 76 Kewpie Doll | 1,000 | 15.00 |
| **ingle issue)** | | |
| 82 Barnyard Serenade | 5,000 | 25.00 |
| **ingle issue)** | | |
| 82 Beep, Beep | 2,000 | 25.00 |
| **Marigold** | | |
| **uper Stars** | | |
| 83 Mickey Mantle | 10,000 | 60.00 |
| 84 Joe DiMaggio | 10,000 | 60.00 |
| 84 Willie Mays | 10,000 | 60.00 |
| **Mary Engelbreit Society** | | |
| **elieve** | | |
| 986 Santa's Treasure | 10,000 | 29.95 |
| **Master Engravers of America** | | |
| **dian Dancers** | | |
| 979 Eagle Dancer | 2,500 | 300.00 |
| 980 Hoop Dancer | 2,500 | 300.00 |
| **McCalla Enterprises (Viletta)** | | |
| **aking Friends** | | |
| 978 Feeding Neighbor's Pony | 5,000 | 45.00 |
| 979 Cowboys 'n' Indians | 5,000 | 47.50 |
| 980 Surprise for Christy | 5,000 | 47.50 |
| **ove Letters** | | |
| 980 Mail Order Bride | 5,000 | 60.00 |
| **Metal Arts** | | |
| **merica's First Family (Single issue)** | | |
| 977 Carters | 9,500 | 40.00 |
| **reedom (Single issue)** | | |
| 977 Washington at Valley Forge (Sterling) | 500 | 225.00 |
| **reedom (Single issue)** | | |
| 977 Washington at Valley Forge (Pewter) | 1,000 | 95.00 |
| **inslow Homer's Sea** | | |
| 977 Breezing Up | 9,500 | 29.95 |
| **ockwell Copper Christmas** | | |
| 978 Christmas Gift | Year | 48.00 |
| 979 Big Moment | Year | 48.00 |
| **Metlox Potteries** | | |
| ee: Vernonware (U.S.A.) | | |
| **Metropolitan Museum of Art** | | |
| **reasures of Tutankhamun** | | |
| 977 King Tut | 2,500 | 150.00 |


| | Edition Limit | Issue Price (US) |
|---|---|---|
| **Mingolla** | | |
| *See: Home Plates (U.S.A.)* | | |
| **Mistwood Designs (Fairmont)** | | |
| *American Wildlife* | | |
| 1981 Desperado at Waterhole | 5,000 | $ 45.00 |
| 1981 Bayou Bunnies | 5,000 | 50.00 |
| *Woodland Game Birds* | | |
| 1981 After Flight | 5,000 | 60.00 |
| **Modern Concepts** | | |
| *Special Moments* | | |
| 1982 David's Dilemma | 12,500 | 35.00 |
| 1983 Secrets | 12,500 | 35.00 |
| 1983 Enough for Two | 12,500 | 38.50 |
| 1984 Chatterbox | 12,500 | 38.50 |
| *Magic of Sea* | | |
| 1983 Future Miss | NA | 25.00 |
| 1984 One, Two, Three! | NA | 26.50 |
| *Signs of Love* | | |
| 1983 When Hearts Touch | 17,500 | 39.00 |
| 1984 My Very Own | 17,500 | 39.00 |
| *Nursery Rhyme Favorites* | | |
| 1984 Sugar & Spice | 7,500 | 35.00 |
| 1985 Snips & Snails | 7,500 | 35.00 |
| **Modern Masters** | | |
| *Through Eyes of Love* | | |
| 1981 Enchanted Eyes | 9,500 | 55.00 |
| 1982 Summer Secrets | 9,500 | 55.00 |
| 1983 Garden Gathering | 9,500 | 55.00 |
| *Babes in Woods* | | |
| 1982 Newborn Fawn | 9,500 | 45.00 |
| 1983 First Outing | 9,500 | 45.00 |
| 1983 Baby Bandit | 9,500 | 50.00 |
| 1984 Moment's Rest | 9,500 | 50.00 |
| *Floral Felines* | | |
| 1982 Baron | 9,500 | 55.00 |
| 1983 Her Majesty | 9,500 | 55.00 |
| 1984 Duchess | 9,500 | 55.00 |
| 1984 His Lordship | 9,500 | 55.00 |
| *Will Moses America* | | |
| 1982 September Fair | 7,500 | 45.00 |
| 1983 Spring Recess | 7,500 | 45.00 |
| *Litter Basket* | | |
| 1983 Last of Litter | 15 Days | 35.00 |
| 1984 Double Delight | 15 Days | 35.00 |
| 1984 Tender Trio | 15 Days | 35.00 |
| 1985 Litter Bug | 15 Days | 35.00 |
| 1985 Hide and Seek | 15 Days | 35.00 |
| 1985 Poodle Picnic | 15 Days | 35.00 |
| *Little Ladies* | | |
| 1983 When Mommy's Away | 15 Days | 29.50 |
| 1984 Before Show Begins | 15 Days | 29.50 |
| *(Single issue)* | | |
| 1983 Twelve Days of Christmas | 12 Days | 45.00 |
| *Childhood Revisited* | | |
| 1984 Young Virtuoso | 9,500 | 39.50 |
| 1985 Fantasy and Fairy Tales | 9,500 | 39.50 |
| 1985 Petit Fleur | 9,500 | 39.50 |
| *Wings of Nobility* | | |
| 1984 American Bald Eagle | 7,500 | 49.50 |
| 1984 Peregrine Falcon | 7,500 | 49.50 |
| 1984 Red-Shouldered Hawk | 7,500 | 49.50 |
| *Sally Miller Christmas* | | |
| 1985 They Came to Adore Him | 5,000 | 39.50 |
| *(Single issue)* | | |
| 1985 They Came to Adore Him | 5,000 | 39.50 |
| **Modern Masters/GBS** | | |
| *Family Treasures* | | |
| 1981 Cora's Recital | 18,500 | 39.50 |
| 1982 Cora's Tea Party | 18,500 | 39.50 |
| 1983 Cora's Garden Party | 18,500 | 39.50 |
| *Horses of Fred Stone* | | |
| 1981 Patience | 9,500 | 55.00 |
| 1982 Arabian Mare and Foal | 9,500 | 55.00 |
| 1982 Safe and Sound | 9,500 | 55.00 |
| 1983 Contentment | 9,500 | 55.00 |
| *A Child's Best Friend* | | |
| 1982 Christi's Kitty | 15 Days | 29.50 |
| 1982 Patrick's Puppy | 15 Days | 29.50 |


| | Edition Limit | Issue Price (US) |
|---|---|---|
| **Moussalli** | | |
| *Birds of Four Seasons* | | |
| 1978 Cardinal (Winter) | 1,000 | $375.00 |
| 1979 Indigo Bunting (Fall) | 1,000 | 375.00 |
| 1979 Hummingbird (Summer) | 1,000 | 375.00 |
| 1980 Wren (Spring) | 1,000 | 375.00 |
| *Mother's Day* | | |
| 1979 Chickadee | 500 | 450.00 |
| **Museum Collections** | | |
| *Coca Cola Collection* | | |
| 1987 Barefoot Boy | 10,000 | 35.00 |
| **Museum Editions (Ridgewood)** | | |
| *Colonial Heritage* | | |
| 1974 Tidewater, Virginia | 9,900 | 40.00 |
| 1975 Pennsbury Manor | 9,900 | 40.00 |
| 1975 Old New York | 9,900 | 40.00 |
| 1976 Hammond-Harwood House | 9,900 | 40.00 |
| 1976 Joseph Webb House | 9,900 | 40.00 |
| 1977 Old Court House | 9,900 | 40.00 |
| 1977 Mulberry Plantation | 9,900 | 40.00 |
| **Museum Editions (Viletta)** | | |
| *Christmas Annual* | | |
| 1978 Expression of Faith | 7,400 | 49.95 |
| 1979 Skating Lesson | 7,400 | 49.95 |
| *Colonial Heritage* | | |
| 1978 Moffatt-Ladd House | 9,900 | 40.00 |
| 1978 Trent House | 9,900 | 40.00 |
| 1979 Cupola House | 9,900 | 40.00 |
| 1979 Nicholas House | 9,900 | 40.00 |
| 1980 Derby House | 9,900 | 40.00 |
| 1980 Davenport House | 9,900 | 40.00 |
| **Northwest Highland Supply Ltd** | | |
| *The Argyll & Sutherland Highlander* | | |
| 1987 The Scottish Soldier | 5,000 | 34.50 |
| **Nostalgia Collectibles** | | |
| *Shirley Temple* | | |
| 1982 Baby Take a Bow | 25,000 | 75.00 |
| 1983 Curly Top | 25,000 | 75.00 |
| 1983 Stand Up and Cheer | 25,000 | 75.00 |
| *Shirley Temple Classics* | | |
| 1983 Captain January | 25,000 | 35.00 |
| 1984 Heidi | 25,000 | 35.00 |
| 1984 Little Miss Marker | 25,000 | 35.00 |
| 1984 Bright Eyes | 25,000 | 35.00 |
| 1985 Little Colonel | 25,000 | 35.00 |
| 1985 Rebecca of Sunnybrook Farm | 25,000 | 35.00 |
| 1986 Poor Little Rich Girl | 25,000 | 35.00 |
| 1986 Wee Willie Winkie | 25,000 | 35.00 |
| *(Single issue)* | | |
| 1985 Elvis—Once and Forever King | 25,000 | 40.00 |
| *(Single issue)* | | |
| 1985 James Dean—America's Rebel | 25,000 | 45.00 |
| *(Single issue)* | | |
| 1986 Mircle on 34th Street | 15,000 | 35.00 |
| **Ohio Arts** | | |
| *Norman Rockwell* | | |
| 1979 Looking Out to Sea | 20,000 | 19.50 |
| **OK Collectibles** | | |
| *Fantasy Farm* | | |
| 1984 Lowena | 3,000 | 39.95 |
| *Meadow* | | |
| 1984 Chester | 5,000 | 55.00 |
| **Pacific Art** | | |
| *Just Like Daddy's Hats* | | |
| 1983 Jessica | 10,000 | 29.00 |
| *(Single issue)* | | |
| 1983 Guardian Angel | 7,500 | 29.50 |
| **Paramount Classics (Pickard)** | | |
| *(Single issue)* | | |
| 1977 Coronation Plate | 5,000 | 95.00 |
| *(Single issue)* | | |
| 1977 Queen Victoria | 5,000 | 95.00 |
| *(Single issue)* | | |
| 1977 King George III | 5,000 | 95.00 |


| | Edition Limit | Issue Price (US) |
|---|---|---|
| **Pemberton & Oakes (Viletta)** | | |
| *Moments Alone* | | |
| 1980 Dreamer | 15 Days | $ 28.80 |
| 1981 Reverie | 15 Days | 28.80 |
| 1982 Gentle Thoughts | 15 Days | 28.80 |
| 1983 Wheat Field | 4,800 | 28.80 |
| *Nutcracker II* | | |
| 1981 Nutcracker Grand Finale | 28 Days | 24.40 |
| 1982 Arabian Dancers | 28 Days | 24.40 |
| 1983 Dewdrop Fairy | 28 Days | 24.40 |
| 1984 Clara's Delight | 28 Days | 24.40 |
| *Swan Lake* | | |
| 1983 Swan Queen | 15,000 | 35.00 |
| *Robert Anderson's Little Girls* | | |
| 1985 Curious Kitten | 15,000 | 29.00 |
| 1986 Making Magic | 15,000 | 29.00 |
| 1987 Sunny Umbrellas | 15,000 | 29.00 |
| *Zolan Father's Day* | | |
| 1986 Daddy's Home | 19 Days | 19.00 |
| *Childhood Friendship* | | |
| 1987 Beach Break | NA | 19.00 |
| **Pickard** | | |
| *Presidential* | | |
| 1971 Truman | 3,000 | 35.00 |
| 1973 Lincoln | 5,000 | 35.00 |
| *Children of Mexico* | | |
| 1981 Maria | 5,000 | 85.00 |
| 1981 Miguel | 5,000 | 85.00 |
| 1982 Regina | 5,000 | 90.00 |
| 1983 Raphael | 5,000 | 90.00 |
| *(Single issue)* | | |
| 1982 Great Seal of United States | 10,000 | 95.00 |
| *Children of Christmas Past* | | |
| 1983 Sledding on Christmas Day | 7,500 | 60.00 |
| *Children of Mary Cassatt* | | |
| 1983 Simone in a White Bonnet | 7,500 | 60.00 |
| 1983 Children Playing on Beach | 7,500 | 60.00 |
| 1984 Child in a Straw Hat | 7,500 | 60.00 |
| *Let's Pretend* | | |
| 1984 Cleopatra | 5,000 | 80.00 |
| 1984 Mark Antony | 5,000 | 80.00 |
| 1985 Robin Hood | 5,000 | 80.00 |
| 1985 Maid Marian | 5,000 | 80.00 |
| *(Single Issue)* | | |
| 1984 Statue of Liberty | 10,000 | 150.00 |
| *Wings of Freedom* | | |
| 1985 Courtship Flight | 2,500 | 250.00 |
| 1986 Wings of Freedom | 2,500 | 250.00 |
| *Gardens of Monet* | | |
| 1986 Summer Splendor | 3,500 | 85.00 |
| 1987 Time Gone By | 3,500 | 85.00 |
| *The Nativity Triptych* | | |
| 1986 Unto Us a Child is Born | 3,500 | 95.00 |
| *See also:* | | |
| *Kern Collectibles (U.S.A.)* | | |
| *Paramount Classics (U.S.A.)* | | |
| **Porcelain Limited** | | |
| *Children of Seasons* | | |
| 1982 Spring Joy | 9,800 | 49.95 |
| 1982 Summer Love | 9,800 | 49.95 |
| 1982 Fall's Adventure | 9,800 | 49.95 |
| 1982 Winter's Dreamer | 9,800 | 49.95 |
| **Ram** | | |
| *Boston 500* | | |
| 1973 Easter | 500 | 30.00 |
| 1973 Mother's Day | 500 | 30.00 |
| 1973 Father's Day | 500 | 30.00 |
| 1973 Christmas | 500 | 30.00 |
| *Great Bird Heroes* | | |
| 1973 Cher Ami | 1,000 | 7.95 |
| 1973 Mocker | 1,000 | 7.95 |
| **Reco International** | | |
| *Americana (Single issue)* | | |
| 1972 Gaspee | 1,000 | 130.00 |

# OVER-THE-COUNTER ISSUES

| | Edition Limit | Issue Price (US) |
|---|---|---|
| *Four Seasons (Set of four)* | | |
| 1973 Fall | | |
| 1973 Spring | | |
| 1973 Summer | | |
| 1973 Winter | 2,500 | $200.00 |
| *Western (Single issue)* | | |
| 1974 Mountain Man | 1,000 | 165.00 |
| *Christmas (Single issue)* | | |
| 1977 Old Mill in Valley | 5,000 | 28.00 |
| *Games Children Play* | | |
| 1979 Me First | 10,000 | 45.00 |
| 1980 Forever Bubbles | 10,000 | 45.00 |
| 1981 Skating Pals | 10,000 | 45.00 |
| 1982 Join Me | 10,000 | 45.00 |
| *Grandparents* | | |
| 1981 Grandma's Cookie Jar | Year | 37.50 |
| 1981 Grandpa and Doll House | Year | 37.50 |
| *Arabelle and Friends* | | |
| 1982 Ice Delight | 15,000 | 35.00 |
| 1983 First Love | 15,000 | 35.00 |
| *Little Professionals* | | |
| 1982 All Is Well | 10,000 | 39.50 |
| 1983 T.L.C. | 10,000 | 39.50 |
| 1984 Lost and Found | 10,000 | 39.50 |
| 1985 Reading, Writing and ... | 10,000 | 39.50 |
| *A Childhood Almanac* | | |
| 1984 School Days | 14 Days | 29.50 |
| 1984 Fireside Dreams | 14 Days | 29.50 |
| 1984 Be Mine | 14 Days | 29.50 |
| 1985 Easter Morning | 14 Days | 29.50 |
| 1985 For Mom | 14 Days | 29.50 |
| 1985 Summer Secrets | 14 Days | 29.50 |
| 1985 Just Dreaming | 14 Days | 29.50 |
| 1985 Star-Spangled Sky | 14 Days | 29.50 |
| 1985 Christmas Magic | 14 Days | 29.50 |
| 1986 Indian Summer | 14 Days | 29.50 |
| 1986 Giving Thanks | 14 Days | 29.50 |
| 1986 Winds of March | 14 Days | 29.50 |
| *Mother's Day* | | |
| 1985 Once Upon a Time | Year | 29.50 |
| 1986 Times Remembered | Year | 29.50 |
| 1987 A Cherished Time | Year | 29.50 |
| *Sophisticated Ladies* | | |
| 1985 Felicia | 21 Days | 29.50 |
| 1985 Samantha | 21 Days | 29.50 |
| 1985 Phoebe | 21 Days | 29.50 |
| 1985 Cleo | 21 Days | 29.50 |
| 1986 Cerissa | 21 Days | 29.50 |
| 1986 Natasha | 21 Days | 29.50 |
| 1986 Bianka | 21 Days | 29.50 |
| 1986 Chelsea | 21 Days | 29.50 |
| *Springtime of Life* | | |
| 1985 Teddy's Bathtime | 14 Days | 29.50 |
| *Children's Christmas Pageant* | | |
| 1986 Silent Night | Year | 32.50 |
| *Vanishing Animal Kingdom* | | |
| 1986 Rami the Tiger | 21,000 | 35.00 |
| 1987 Olepi the Buffalo | 21,500 | 35.00 |
| *Great Stories From the Bible* | | |
| 1987 Moses in the Bulrushes | 14 Days | 29.50 |
| *Barefoot Children* | | |
| 1987 Night Time Story | NA | 29.50 |
| **Reed & Barton** | | |
| *Audubon* | | |
| 1970 Pine Siskin | 5,000 | 60.00 |
| 1971 Red-Shouldered Hawk | 5,000 | 60.00 |
| 1972 Stilt Sandpiper | 5,000 | 60.00 |
| 1973 Red Cardinal | 5,000 | 60.00 |
| 1974 Boreal Chickadee | 5,000 | 60.00 |
| 1975 Yellow-Breasted Chat | 5,000 | 65.00 |
| 1976 Bay-Breasted Warbler | 5,000 | 65.00 |
| 1977 Purple Finch | 5,000 | 65.00 |
| *(Single issue)* | | |
| 1970 Zodiac | 1,500 | 75.00 |
| *California Missions* | | |
| 1971 San Diego | 1,500 | 75.00 |
| 1972 Carmel | 1,500 | 75.00 |
| 1973 Santa Barbara | 1,500 | 60.00 |
| 1974 Santa Clara | 1,500 | 60.00 |
| 1976 San Gabriel | 1,500 | 65.00 |
| *Annual* | | |
| 1972 Free Trapper | 2,500 | 65.00 |
| 1973 Outpost | 2,500 | 65.00 |

| | Edition Limit | Issue Price (US) |
|---|---|---|
| 1974 Toll Collector | 2,500 | $ 65.00 |
| 1975 Indians Discovering Lewis & Clark | 2,500 | 65.00 |
| *Currier & Ives* | | |
| 1972 Village Blacksmith | 1,500 | 85.00 |
| 1972 Western Migration | 1,500 | 85.00 |
| 1973 Oaken Bucket | 1,500 | 85.00 |
| 1973 Winter in Country | 1,500 | 85.00 |
| 1974 Preparing for Market | 1,500 | 85.00 |
| *Kentucky Derby* | | |
| 1972 Nearing Finish | 1,000 | 75.00 |
| 1973 Riva Ridge | 1,500 | 75.00 |
| 1974 100th Running | 1,500 | 75.00 |
| *(Single issue)* | | |
| 1972 Delta Queen | 2,500 | 75.00 |
| *(Single issue)* | | |
| 1972 Road Runner | 1,500 | 65.00 |
| *Founding Father* | | |
| 1973 Ben Franklin | 2,500 | 65.00 |
| 1974 George Washington | 2,500 | 65.00 |
| 1975 Thomas Jefferson | 2,500 | 65.00 |
| 1976 Patrick Henry | 2,500 | 65.00 |
| 1976 John Hancock | 2,500 | 65.00 |
| 1976 John Adams | 2,500 | 65.00 |
| *(Single issue)* | | |
| 1975 Chicago Fire | Year | 60.00 |
| *(Single issue)* | | |
| 1975 Mississippi Queen | 2,500 | 75.00 |
| *See also: Collector Creations (U.S.A.) Keller & George (U.S.A.)* | | |
| **Ridgewood** | | |
| *Bicentennial* | | |
| 1974 First in War | 12,500 | 40.00 |
| *Tom Sawyer (Set of four)* | | |
| 1974 Trying a Pipe | | |
| 1974 Lost in Cave | | |
| 1974 Painting Fence | | |
| 1974 Taking Medicine | 3,000 | 39.95 |
| *Wild West (Set of four)* | | |
| 1975 Discovery of Last Chance Gulch | | |
| 1975 Doubtful Visitor | | |
| 1975 Bad One | | |
| 1975 Cattleman | 15,000 | 65.00 |
| *Leyendecker Christmas* | | |
| 1975 Christmas Morning | 10,000 | 24.50 |
| 1976 Christmas Surprise | 10,000 | 24.50 |
| *Leyendecker Mother's Day* | | |
| 1976 Grandma's Apple Pie | 5,000 | 24.50 |
| 1977 Tenderness | 10,000 | 35.00 |
| *Little Women* | | |
| 1976 Sweet Long Ago | 5,000 | 45.00 |
| 1976 Song of Spring | 5,000 | 45.00 |
| 1977 Joy in Morning | 5,000 | 45.00 |
| *See also: Museum Editions (U.S.A.)* | | |
| **River Shore** | | |
| *Baby Animals* | | |
| 1979 Akiku | 20,000 | 65.00 |
| 1980 Roosevelt | 20,000 | 65.00 |
| 1981 Clover | 20,000 | 65.00 |
| 1982 Zuela | 20,000 | 65.00 |
| *Della Robbia Annual* | | |
| 1979 Adoration | 5,000 | 550.00 |
| 1980 Virgin and Child | 5,000 | 450.00 |
| *Remington Bronze* | | |
| 1977 Bronco Buster | 15,000 | 55.00 |
| 1978 Coming Thru Rye | 15,000 | 60.00 |
| 1979 Cheyenne | 15,000 | 60.00 |
| 1980 Mountain Man | 15,000 | 60.00 |
| *(Single issue)* | | |
| 1979 Spring Flowers | 17,000 | 75.00 |
| *(Single issue)* | | |
| 1980 Looking Out to Sea | 17,000 | 75.00 |
| *Grant Wood* | | |
| 1981 American Gothic | 17,000 | 80.00 |
| *Rockwell's Four Freedoms* | | |
| 1981 Freedom of Speech | 17,000 | 65.00 |
| *Vignette* | | |
| 1981 Broken Window | 22,500 | 19.50 |
| 1982 Sunday Best | 22,500 | 19.50 |

| | Edition Limit | Issue Price (US) |
|---|---|---|
| *(Single issue)* | | |
| 1981 Grandpa's Guardian | 17,000 | $ 80.00 |
| *Christmas After Christmas* | | |
| 1982 Kay's Doll | 9,500 | 75.00 |
| **River Shore—Woodmere** | | |
| *Children of American Frontier* | | |
| 1986 In Trouble Again | NA | 24.50 |
| 1986 Desperados | NA | 24.50 |
| 1986 Riders Wanted | NA | 24.50 |
| **Rockford Editions** | | |
| *Little Mothers* | | |
| 1985 Love is Blind | NA | 29.95 |
| 1986 Little Bit Independent | NA | 29.95 |
| 1987 First Step | NA | 29.95 |
| 1987 May We Come In? | NA | 29.95 |
| *A Child's Best Friend* | | |
| 1986 On The Up and Up | NA | 24.50 |
| 1987 Mine | NA | 24.50 |
| 1987 Going to Town | NA | 24.50 |
| *Precious Portraits* | | |
| 1987 Sunbeam | NA | 24.50 |
| **Rockwell Collectors Club** | | |
| *Christmas* | | |
| 1978 Christmas Story | 15,000 | 24.50 |
| **Rockwell Museum** | | |
| *American Family* | | |
| 1978 Baby's First Step | 9,900 | 28.50 |
| 1978 Happy Birthday Dear Mother | 9,900 | 28.50 |
| 1978 Sweet Sixteen | 9,900 | 28.50 |
| 1978 First Haircut | 9,900 | 28.50 |
| 1979 First Prom | 9,900 | 28.50 |
| 1979 Student | 9,900 | 28.50 |
| 1979 Wrapping Christmas Presents | 9,900 | 28.50 |
| 1979 Birthday Party | 9,900 | 28.50 |
| 1979 Little Mother | 9,900 | 28.50 |
| 1980 Washing Our Dog | 9,900 | 28.50 |
| 1980 Mother's Little Helper | 9,900 | 28.50 |
| 1980 Bride & Groom | 9,900 | 28.50 |
| *Christmas* | | |
| 1979 Day After Christmas | 25,000 | 75.00 |
| 1980 Checking His List | Year | 75.00 |
| 1981 Ringing in Good Cheer | Year | 75.00 |
| 1982 Waiting for Santa | Year | 75.00 |
| 1983 High Hopes | Year | 75.00 |
| 1984 Space Age Santa | Year | 55.00 |
| 1985 Christmas Prayers | Year | 35.00 |
| *(Single issue)* | | |
| 1979 Norman Rockwell Remembered | Year | 45.00 |
| *American Family II* | | |
| 1980 New Arrival | 22,500 | 35.00 |
| 1980 Sweet Dreams | 22,500 | 35.00 |
| 1980 Little Shaver | 22,500 | 35.00 |
| 1980 We Missed You Daddy | 22,500 | 35.00 |
| 1980 Home Run Slugger | 22,500 | 35.00 |
| 1980 Giving Thanks | 22,500 | 35.00 |
| 1980 Space Pioneers | 22,500 | 35.00 |
| 1980 Little Salesman | 22,500 | 35.00 |
| 1980 Almost Grown Up | 22,500 | 35.00 |
| 1980 Courageous Hero | 22,500 | 35.00 |
| 1980 At Circus | 22,500 | 35.00 |
| 1980 Good Food, Good Friends | 22,500 | 35.00 |
| *Classic* | | |
| 1981 Puppy Love | 60 Days | 24.50 |
| 1981 While Audience Waits | 60 Days | 24.50 |
| 1981 Off to School | 60 Days | 24.50 |
| 1982 Country Doctor | 60 Days | 24.50 |
| 1982 Spring Fever | 60 Days | 24.50 |
| 1982 Dollhouse for Sis | 60 Days | 24.50 |
| *Mother's Day* | | |
| 1982 A Tender Moment | 5,000 | 70.00 |
| *World of Children* | | |
| 1982 Downhill Racer | 15,000 | 45.00 |
| 1982 Vacation's Over | 15,000 | 45.00 |
| 1982 Little Patient | 15,000 | 45.00 |
| 1982 Bicycle Boys | 15,000 | 45.00 |
| *(Single issue)* | | |
| 1983 A Tribute to J.F.K. | NA | 39.50 |
| *(Single issue)* | | |
| 1983 With This Ring | NA | 45.00 |

| | Edition Limit | Issue Price (US) |
|---|---|---|
| *A Touch of Rockwell* | | |
| 1984 Songs of Praise | NA | $ 14.9 |
| 1984 Bedtime Prayers | NA | 14.9 |
| 1984 First Day of School | NA | 14.9 |
| 1984 Surprise Treat | NA | 14.9 |
| 1984 Runaway | NA | 14.9 |
| **Roman** | | |
| *Child's World* | | |
| 1982 Baby Blossoms | 15,000 | 24.9 |
| 1982 I Wish, I Wish | 15,000 | 24.9 |
| 1982 Trees So Tall | 15,000 | 24.9 |
| 1982 Daisy Dreamer | 15,000 | 24.9 |
| 1983 Caught it Myself | 15,000 | 24.9 |
| 1983 Winter Wrappings | 15,000 | 24.9 |
| 1983 So Cuddley | 15,000 | 24.9 |
| 1983 Can I Keep Him? | 15,000 | 24.9 |
| *Ice Capades Clown* | | |
| 1983 Presenting Freddie Trenkler | 30 Days | 24.5 |
| *Petty Girls of Ice Capades* | | |
| 1983 Ice Princess | 30 Days | 24.5 |
| *Cats* | | |
| 1984 Grizabella | 30 Days | 29.5 |
| 1984 Mr. Mistoffelees | 30 Days | 29.5 |
| 1984 Rum Tum Tugger | 30 Days | 29.5 |
| 1985 Growltiger | 30 Days | 29.5 |
| 1985 Skimbleshanks | 30 Days | 29.5 |
| 1985 Mungojerrie and Rumpelteazer | 30 Days | 29.5 |
| *Magic of Childhood* | | |
| 1984 Special Friends | 10 Days | 24.5 |
| 1985 Feeding Time | 10 Days | 24.5 |
| *(Single issue)* | | |
| 1984 Carpenter | NA | 100.0 |
| *Lord's Prayer* | | |
| 1986 Our Father | NA | 24.5 |
| 1986 Thy Kingdom Come | NA | 24.5 |
| 1987 Forgive Our Trespasses | NA | 24.5 |
| 1987 As We Forgive | NA | 24.5 |
| 1987 Give Us This Day | NA | 24.5 |
| *Sweetest Songs* | | |
| 1986 A Baby's Prayer | NA | 39.5 |
| 1987 This Little Piggy | NA | 39.5 |
| *Fontanini Christmas Story* | | |
| 1986 A King is Born | NA | 60.0 |
| 1987 O Come, Let Us Adore Him | NA | 50.0 |
| *(Single issue)* | | |
| 1987 The Christening | NA | 24.5 |
| **Royal Cornwall** | | |
| *Bethlehem Christmas* | | |
| 1977 First Christmas Eve | 10,000 | 29.9 |
| 1978 Glad Tidings | 10,000 | 34.5 |
| 1979 Gift Bearers | 10,000 | 34.5 |
| 1980 Great Joy | 10,000 | 39.9 |
| *Creation* | | |
| 1977 In Beginning | 19,500 | 45.0 |
| 1977 In His Image | 19,500 | 45.0 |
| 1977 Adam's Rib | 19,500 | 45.0 |
| 1977 Banished from Eden | 19,500 | 45.0 |
| 1977 Noah and Ark | 19,500 | 45.0 |
| 1977 Tower of Babel | 19,500 | 45.0 |
| 1978 Sodom & Gomorrah | 19,500 | 45.0 |
| 1978 Jacob's Wedding | 19,500 | 45.0 |
| 1978 Rebekah at Well | 19,500 | 45.0 |
| 1978 Jacob's Ladder | 19,500 | 45.0 |
| 1978 Joseph's Coat of Many Colors | 19,500 | 45.0 |
| 1978 Joseph Interprets Pharaoh's Dream | 19,500 | 45.0 |
| *Classic Christmas* | | |
| 1978 Child of Peace | 17,500 | 55.0 |
| 1978 Silent Night | 17,500 | 55.0 |
| 1978 Most Precious Gift | 17,500 | 55.0 |
| 1978 We Three Kings | 17,500 | 55.0 |
| *Four Seasons* | | |
| 1978 Warmth | 17,500 | 60.00 |
| 1978 Voices of Spring | 17,500 | 60.00 |
| 1978 Fledgling | 17,500 | 60.00 |
| 1978 We Survive | 17,500 | 60.00 |
| *Golden Age of Cinema* | | |
| 1978 King & His Ladies | 22,500 | 45.00 |
| 1978 Fred & Ginger | 22,500 | 45.00 |
| 1978 Judy & Mickey | 22,500 | 45.00 |
| 1979 Philadelphia Story | 22,500 | 45.00 |

| | Edition Limit | Issue Price (US) |
|---|---|---|
| 79 Thin Man | 22,500 | $ 45.00 |
| 79 Gigi | 22,500 | 45.00 |
| *ther's Day* | | |
| 78 God Bless Mommy | 10,000 | 35.00 |
| *ice in Wonderland* | | |
| 79 Alice and White Rabbit | 27,500 | 45.00 |
| 79 Advice from a Caterpillar | 27,500 | 45.00 |
| 79 Cheshire Cat's Grin | 27,500 | 45.00 |
| 79 Mad Hatter's Tea Party | | |
| 79 Queen's Croquet Match | 27,500 | 45.00 |
| 79 Who Stole Tarts? | 27,500 | 45.00 |
| *tten's World* | | |
| 79 Just Curious | 27,500 | 45.00 |
| 79 Hello, World | 27,500 | 45.00 |
| 79 Are You a Flower? | 27,500 | 45.00 |
| 79 Talk to Me | 27,500 | 45.00 |
| 79 My Favorite Toy | 27,500 | 45.00 |
| 79 Purr-Fect Pleasure | 27,500 | 45.00 |
| *omised Land* | | |
| 79 Pharaoh's Daughter Finds Moses | 24,500 | 45.00 |
| 79 Burning Bush | 24,500 | 45.00 |
| 79 Let My People Go | 24,500 | 45.00 |
| 79 Parting of Red Sea | 24,500 | 45.00 |
| 79 Miriam's Song of Thanksgiving | 24,500 | 45.00 |
| 79 Manna from Heaven | 24,500 | 45.00 |
| 79 Water from Rock | 24,500 | 45.00 |
| 79 Battle of Amalek | 24,500 | 45.00 |
| 79 Ten Commandments | 24,500 | 45.00 |
| 79 Golden Calf | 24,500 | 45.00 |
| 79 Moses Smashes Tablets | 24,500 | 45.00 |
| 79 Glorious Tabernacle | 24,500 | 45.00 |
| *easures of Childhood* | | |
| 79 My Cuddlies Collection | 19,500 | 45.00 |
| 79 My Coin Collection | 19,500 | 45.00 |
| 79 My Shell Collection | 19,500 | 45.00 |
| 79 My Stamp Collection | 19,500 | 45.00 |
| 79 My Doll Collection | 19,500 | 45.00 |
| 79 My Rock Collection | 19,500 | 45.00 |
| *auty of Bouguereau* | | |
| 80 Lucie | 19,500 | 35.00 |
| 80 Madelaine | 19,500 | 35.00 |
| 80 Frere et Soeur | 19,500 | 35.00 |
| 80 Solange et Enfant | 19,500 | 35.00 |
| 80 Colette | 19,500 | 35.00 |
| 80 Jean et Jeanette | 19,500 | 35.00 |
| *ur Faces of Love* | | |
| 80 Romeo & Juliet | 17,500 | 55.00 |
| 80 Young Galahad | 17,500 | 55.00 |
| 80 At Locksley Hall | 17,500 | 55.00 |
| 80 St. Agnes Eve | 17,500 | 55.00 |
| *orothy's Day* | | |
| 80 Brand New Day | 15,000 | 55.00 |
| 80 All by Myself | 15,000 | 55.00 |
| 81 Off to School | 15,000 | 55.00 |
| 81 Best Friends | 15,000 | 55.00 |
| 81 Helping Mommy | 15,000 | 55.00 |
| 81 Bless Me Too | 15,000 | 55.00 |
| *gendary Ships of Seas* | | |
| 80 Flying Dutchman | 19,500 | 49.50 |
| 81 Refanu | 19,500 | 49.50 |
| 81 Gaspé Bay | 19,500 | 49.50 |
| 81 Rescue | 19,500 | 49.50 |
| 80 Copenhagen | 19,500 | 49.50 |
| 82 Palatine | 19,500 | 49.50 |
| 82 Pride | 19,500 | 49.50 |
| 82 Foochow Sea Junk | 19,500 | 49.50 |
| 82 Roth Ramhach | 19,500 | 49.50 |
| 82 Frigorifique | 19,500 | 49.50 |
| *ittle People* | | |
| 80 Off to Picnic | 19,500 | 34.50 |
| 81 Decorating Tree | 19,500 | 34.50 |
| 81 Cruising Down River | 19,500 | 34.50 |
| 81 Sweetest Harvest | 19,500 | 34.50 |
| 81 Happy Chorus | 19,500 | 34.50 |
| 81 Painting Leaves | 19,500 | 34.50 |
| *lemories of America* | | |
| 80 Bringing in Maple Sugar | 5,000 | 120.00 |
| 80 Old Automobile | 5,000 | 120.00 |
| 81 Halloween | 5,000 | 120.00 |
| 81 Rainbow | 5,000 | 120.00 |

| | Edition Limit | Issue Price (US) |
|---|---|---|
| *Windows on World* | | |
| 1980 Golden Gate of San Francisco | 19,500 | $ 45.00 |
| 1981 Snow Village/Madulain | 19,500 | 45.00 |
| 1981 Rainy Day in London | 19,500 | 45.00 |
| 1981 Water Festival/Venice | 19,500 | 45.00 |
| 1981 Harvesting in Ukraine | 19,500 | 45.00 |
| 1981 Serengeti Plain | 19,500 | 45.00 |
| 1982 Springtime in Paris | 19,500 | 45.00 |
| 1982 Lunch in Michelstadt | 19,500 | 45.00 |
| 1982 Flamenca of Madrid | 19,500 | 45.00 |
| 1982 Tokyo at Cherry Time | 19,500 | 45.00 |
| 1982 Palace of Winds, Jaipur | 19,500 | 45.00 |
| 1982 Carnival Time in Rio | 19,500 | 45.00 |
| *Exotic Birds of Tropique* | | |
| 1981 Scarlet Macaws | 19,500 | 49.50 |
| 1981 Toco Toucan | 19,500 | 49.50 |
| 1981 Rosy Flamingos | 19,500 | 49.50 |
| 1982 Greater Cockatoo | 19,500 | 49.50 |
| 1982 Ultramarine King | 19,500 | 49.50 |
| 1982 Red Fan Parrot | 19,500 | 49.50 |
| 1982 Bird of Paradise | 19,500 | 49.50 |
| 1982 Mariqua Sunbird | 19,500 | 49.50 |
| 1982 Andean Cock-of-Rock | 19,500 | 49.50 |
| 1983 Rufous Hornbill | 19,500 | 49.50 |
| 1983 Seven-colored Tanager | 19,500 | 49.50 |
| 1983 Ivory-billed Aracari | 19,500 | 49.50 |
| *Love's Precious Moments* | | |
| 1981 Love's Sweet Vow | 17,500 | 55.00 |
| 1981 Love's Sweet Verse | 17,500 | 55.00 |
| 1981 Love's Sweet Offering | 17,500 | 55.00 |
| 1981 Love's Sweet Embrace | 17,500 | 55.00 |
| 1981 Love's Sweet Melody | 17,500 | 55.00 |
| 1981 Love's Sweet Kiss | 17,500 | 55.00 |
| *Most Precious Gifts of Shen-Lung* | | |
| 1981 Fire | 19,500 | 49.50 |
| 1981 Water | 19,500 | 49.50 |
| 1981 Sun | 19,500 | 49.50 |
| 1982 Moon | 19,500 | 49.50 |
| 1982 Earth | 19,500 | 49.50 |
| 1982 Sky | 19,500 | 49.50 |
| *Puppy's World* | | |
| 1981 1st Birthday | 19,500 | 49.50 |
| 1981 Beware of Dog | 19,500 | 49.50 |
| 1981 Top Dog | 19,500 | 49.50 |
| 1981 Need a Friend? | 19,500 | 49.50 |
| 1981 Double Trouble | 19,500 | 49.50 |
| 1981 Just Clowning | 19,500 | 49.50 |
| 1981 Guest for Dinner | 19,500 | 49.50 |
| 1981 Gift Wrapped | 19,500 | 49.50 |
| *Courageous Few* | | |
| 1982 Fall of Jericho | 24,500 | 59.50 |
| 1982 Gideon's Three Hundred | 24,500 | 59.50 |
| 1982 Strength of Samson | 24,500 | 59.50 |
| 1982 Ruth | 24,500 | 59.50 |
| 1982 David and Goliath | 24,500 | 59.50 |
| 1982 Solomon's Wisdom | 24,500 | 59.50 |
| 1983 Building of Temple | 24,500 | 59.50 |
| 1983 Elijah | 24,500 | 59.50 |
| 1983 Job | 24,500 | 59.50 |
| 1983 A Psalm of David | 24,500 | 59.50 |
| 1983 Daniel and Lions | 24,500 | 59.50 |
| 1983 Jonah and Whale | 24,500 | 59.50 |
| *Impressions of Yesteryear* | | |
| 1982 Moon Mist | 19,500 | 59.50 |
| 1982 Fall Flowers | 19,500 | 59.50 |
| 1982 Wishing Well | 19,500 | 59.50 |
| 1982 Letter | 19,500 | 59.50 |
| 1982 Sledding | 19,500 | 59.50 |
| 1982 Swans | 19,500 | 59.50 |
| 1983 Winter Park | 19,500 | 59.50 |
| 1983 Seashore | 19,500 | 59.50 |
| 1983 Red Tree | 19,500 | 59.50 |
| 1983 Sailboat | 19,500 | 59.50 |
| 1983 Red Balloon | 19,500 | 59.50 |
| 1983 Snowman | 19,500 | 59.50 |
| *Legend of Peacock Maidens* | | |
| 1982 Dance of Peacock Maiden | 19,500 | 69.50 |
| 1982 Promise of Love | 19,500 | 69.50 |
| 1982 Betrayal | 19,500 | 69.50 |
| 1982 Prince and Python | 19,500 | 69.50 |
| *Noble Flower Maidens* | | |
| 1982 Iris Maiden | 19,500 | 65.00 |
| 1982 Plum Blossom Maiden | 19,500 | 65.00 |
| 1982 Quince Maiden | 19,500 | 65.00 |

| | Edition Limit | Issue Price (US) |
|---|---|---|
| 1982 Cherry Blossom Maiden | 19,500 | $ 65.00 |
| 1982 Crysanthemum Maiden | 19,500 | 65.00 |
| 1982 August Lily Maiden | 19,500 | 65.00 |
| *2000 Years of Sailing Ships* | | |
| 1982 USS Constitution | NA | 39.50 |
| 1982 Santa Maria | NA | 39.50 |
| 1983 Mayflower | NA | 39.50 |
| 1983 Drakar | NA | 39.50 |
| 1983 Cutty Sark Thermopylae | NA | 39.50 |
| 1983 HMS Royal Sovereign | NA | 39.50 |
| 1983 Vasa | NA | 39.50 |
| 1983 Bounty | NA | 39.50 |
| 1983 HMS Victory | NA | 39.50 |
| 1983 Royal Barge | NA | 39.50 |
| 1984 America | NA | 39.50 |
| 1984 Golden Hind | NA | 39.50 |
| *America's Golden Years* | | |
| 1983 County Fair | 19,000 | 49.50 |
| 1983 Sunday Picnic | 19,500 | 49.50 |
| 1983 Barnstorming | 19,500 | 49.50 |
| 1983 Amusement Park | 19,500 | 49.50 |
| 1983 Fourth of July | 19,500 | 49.50 |
| 1983 County Fair | 19,500 | 49.50 |
| 1983 Big Top | 19,500 | 49.50 |
| 1983 Old Boardwalk | 19,500 | 49.50 |
| 1983 On Bay | 19,500 | 49.50 |
| 1983 Harvest Dance | 19,500 | 49.50 |
| 1983 Whistle Stop | 19,500 | 49.50 |
| 1983 Halloween | 19,500 | 49.50 |
| 1983 Christmas Eve | 19,500 | 49.50 |
| *Memories of Western Prairies* | | |
| 1983 Picking Daisies | Year | 49.50 |
| 1984 Feeding Colt | Year | 49.50 |
| *Joyful World of Children* | | |
| 1984 China Doll | NA | 29.50 |
| **Royal Devon** | | |
| See: Hamilton Collection (U.S.A.) | | |
| **Royal Oaks Limited** | | |
| *Love's Labor* | | |
| 1982 Intruder | 15,000 | 50.00 |
| 1982 It's My Turn! | 15,000 | 50.00 |
| 1983 Look! I Can Fly! | 15,000 | 50.00 |
| 1983 Just Like Your Own! | 15,000 | 50.00 |
| **Royal Orleans** | | |
| *Pink Panther Christmas* | | |
| 1982 Sleigh Ride | 13,000 | 25.00 |
| 1983 Happy Landings | 13,000 | 18.50 |
| 1984 Down Chimney | 13,000 | 18.50 |
| *(Single issue)* | | |
| 1982 M*A*S*H | Year | 25.00 |
| *In Trompe L'Oeil* | | |
| 1984 Up to Mischief | 10,000 | 25.00 |
| *Yorkshire Brontës* | | |
| 1984 Wuthering Heights | 30 Days | 35.00 |
| 1985 Jane Eyre | 30 Days | 35.00 |
| *Coca-Cola Classic Santa* | | |
| 1983 Good Boys and Girls | 15,000 | 55.00 |
| 1983 Gift to Santa | 15,000 | 65.00 |
| 1985 Santa, Pause Here | 15,000 | 65.00 |
| 1986 Santa's Favorite Gift | 15,000 | 65.00 |
| *Marilyn—An American Classic* | | |
| 1983 Seven Year Itch | 20,000 | 35.00 |
| 1984 Gentlemen Prefer Blondes | 20,000 | 35.00 |
| 1985 Niagara | 20,000 | 35.00 |
| 1987 Monkey Business | 15,000 | 35.00 |
| *Elvis in Concert* | | |
| 1984 Aloha in Hawaii | 20,000 | 35.00 |
| 1985 Las Vegas | 20,000 | 35.00 |
| 1986 Detroit New Year's Eve | 15,000 | 35.00 |
| *(Single issue)* | | |
| 1984 Buddy Holly | Year | 25.00 |
| *Famous Movies* | | |
| 1985 Cat on Hot Tin Roof | 20,000 | 35.00 |
| *Dynasty* | | |
| 1985 Dynasty | 20,000 | 35.00 |
| 1986 Krystal and Baby | NA | 35.00 |
| *N.F.L. Hall of Fame* | | |
| 1986 Class of 1986 | 10,000 | 35.00 |

| | Edition Limit | Issue Price (US) |
|---|---|---|
| **Royal Worcester** | | |
| *Birth of a Nation* | | |
| 1972 Boston Tea Party | 10,000 | $ 45.00 |
| 1973 Ride of Paul Revere | 10,000 | 45.00 |
| 1974 Incident at Concord Bridge | 10,000 | 50.00 |
| 1975 Declaration of Independence | 10,000 | 65.00 |
| 1976 Washington Crossing Delaware | 10,000 | 65.00 |
| *Currier & Ives* | | |
| 1974 Road-Winter | 10,000 | 59.50 |
| 1975 Old Grist Mill | 10,000 | 59.50 |
| 1976 Winter Pastime | 10,000 | 59.50 |
| *American History* | | |
| 1977 Washington's Inauguration | 1,250 | 65.00 |
| *Annual* | | |
| 1977 Home to Thanksgiving | 500 | 59.50 |
| **Royalwood** | | |
| *(Single issue)* | | |
| 1977 Doctor and Doll | Year | 21.50 |
| *Leyendecker* | | |
| 1978 Cornflake Boy | 10,000 | 25.00 |
| 1978 Cornflake Girl | 10,000 | 25.00 |
| **John A. Ruthven** | | |
| *Moments of Nature* | | |
| 1977 Screech Owls | 5,000 | 37.50 |
| 1979 Chickadees | 5,000 | 39.50 |
| 1980 California Quail | 5,000 | 39.50 |
| **Schofield Gallery** | | |
| *Clowns, Klowns, Klownz* | | |
| 1986 Painting on a Smile | 7,500 | 47.50 |
| 1987 Keystone Kop | 7,500 | 47.50 |
| **Sebastian** | | |
| *America's Favorite Scenes* | | |
| 1978 Motif #1 | 10,000 | 75.00 |
| 1979 Grand Canyon | 10,000 | 75.00 |
| **Seeley's Doll Plates** | | |
| *Antique French Dolls* | | |
| 1979 Bru | 5,000 | 39.00 |
| 1979 E.J. | 5,000 | 39.00 |
| 1979 A.T. | 5,000 | 39.00 |
| 1980 Alexandre | 5,000 | 39.00 |
| 1980 Schmitt | 5,000 | 39.00 |
| 1980 Marque | 5,000 | 39.00 |
| *Old German Dolls* | | |
| 1981 Lucy | 7,500 | 39.00 |
| 1981 Whistler | 7,500 | 39.00 |
| 1982 April | 7,500 | 39.00 |
| 1982 Elise | 7,500 | 39.00 |
| *(Single issue)* | | |
| 1981 Dear Googly | 7,500 | 39.00 |
| *Old Baby Dolls* | | |
| 1982 Hilda | 9,500 | 43.00 |
| 1982 Goldie | 9,500 | 43.00 |
| 1982 Lori | 9,500 | 43.00 |
| 1982 Bye-Lo | 9,500 | 43.00 |
| 1982 Laughing Baby | 9,500 | 43.00 |
| *French Dolls II* | | |
| 1983 Snow Angel | 5,000 | 39.00 |
| 1983 "H's" Bébé Halo | 5,000 | 39.00 |
| 1983 Bru's Faith | 5,000 | 39.00 |
| 1984 Steiner's Easter | 5,000 | 39.00 |
| 1984 Marque's Alyce | 5,000 | 39.00 |
| 1984 Jumeau's Gaynell | 5,000 | 39.00 |
| **Seven Seas** | | |
| *Historical Event* | | |
| 1969 Moon Landing, No Flag | 2,000 | 13.50 |
| 1969 Moon Landing, with Flag | 25,000 | 13.50 |
| 1970 Year of Crisis | 4,000 | 15.00 |
| 1971 First Vehicular Travel | 3,000 | 15.00 |
| 1972 Last Moon Journey | 2,000 | 15.00 |
| 1973 Peace | 3,000 | 15.00 |
| *Mother's Day* | | |
| 1970 Girl of All Nations | 5,000 | 15.00 |
| 1971 Sharing Confidence | 1,400 | 15.00 |
| 1972 Scandinavian Girl | 1,600 | 15.00 |
| 1973 All-American Girl | 1,500 | 15.00 |

# OVER-THE-COUNTER ISSUES

| | Edition Limit | Issue Price (US) |
|---|---|---|
| *Christmas Carols* | | |
| 1970 I Heard Bells | 4,000 | $ 15.00 |
| 1971 Oh Tannenbaum | 4,000 | 15.00 |
| 1972 Deck Halls | 1,500 | 18.00 |
| 1973 O Holy Night | 2,000 | 18.00 |
| 1974 Jingle Bells | 1,200 | 25.00 |
| 1975 Winter Wonderland | 1,500 | 25.00 |
| 1976 Twelve Days of Christmas | 1,200 | 25.00 |
| 1977 Up on Housetop | 1,500 | 25.00 |
| 1978 Little Town of Bethlehem | 1,500 | 25.00 |
| 1979 Santa Claus Is Coming to Town | 1,500 | 25.00 |
| 1980 Frosty Snowman | 1,500 | 25.00 |
| *New World* | | |
| 1970 Holy Family | 3,500 | 15.00 |
| 1971 Three Wise Men | 1,500 | 15.00 |
| 1972 Shepherds Watched | 1,500 | 18.00 |
| *Passion Play (Single issue)* | | |
| 1970 Oberammergau | 2,500 | 18.00 |
| **Shenango** | | |
| *See: Castleton China (U.S.A.)* | | |
| **Sierra Productions** | | |
| *My Favorite Puppy* | | |
| 1984 Caught | 7,500 | 30.00 |
| *War Parties* | | |
| 1984 Sioux | 5,000 | 30.00 |
| **Signature Collection** | | |
| *Carnival* | | |
| 1982 Knock 'em Down | 19,500 | 39.95 |
| 1982 Carousel | 19,500 | 39.95 |
| 1983 Fortune Teller | 19,500 | 39.95 |
| 1983 Ring Bell | 19,500 | 39.95 |
| *How Do I Love Thee . . .* | | |
| 1982 Alaina | 24,000 | 39.95 |
| 1982 Taylor | 24,000 | 39.95 |
| 1983 Rendezvous | 24,000 | 39.95 |
| 1983 Embrace | 24,000 | 39.95 |
| *Legends* | | |
| 1982 Paul Bunyan | 10,000 | 45.00 |
| 1983 Rip Van Winkle | 10,000 | 45.00 |
| *Melodies of Childhood* | | |
| 1982 Twinkle, Twinkle | 25,000 | 35.00 |
| 1983 Row Your Boat | 25,000 | 39.95 |
| 1984 Mary Had a Lamb | 19,500 | 35.00 |
| *Angler's Dream* | | |
| 1983 Brook Trout | 9,800 | 55.00 |
| 1983 Striped Bass | 9,800 | 55.00 |
| 1984 Largemouth Bass | 9,800 | 55.00 |
| 1984 Chinook Salmon | 9,800 | 55.00 |
| *Baker Street Duo* | | |
| 1983 Sherlock Holmes | 9,800 | 55.00 |
| 1983 Watson | 9,800 | 55.00 |
| *Childhood Delights* | | |
| 1983 Amanda | 10,000 | 45.00 |
| *Grandma's Scrapbook* | | |
| 1983 Courting | 12,500 | 45.00 |
| 1983 Sunday Drive | 12,500 | 45.00 |
| *Unicorn Magic* | | |
| 1983 Morning Encounter | 10,000 | 50.00 |
| 1983 Afternoon Outing | 10,000 | 50.00 |
| *Songs of Stephen Foster* | | |
| 1984 Oh! Susannah | 3,500 | 60.00 |
| 1984 Jeanie/Light Brown Hair | 3,500 | 60.00 |
| **Silver Creations** | | |
| *Churchillian Heritage* | | |
| 1972 Hour of Decision | NA | 150.00 |
| 1973 Yalta Conference | NA | 150.00 |
| 1973 Clydesdales | NA | 150.00 |
| **Smith Glass** | | |
| *Americana* | | |
| 1971 Morgan Silver Dollar | 5,000 | 10.00 |
| *Christmas* | | |
| 1971 Family at Christmas | NA | 10.00 |
| 1972 Flying Angel | NA | 10.00 |
| 1973 St. Mary's in Mountains | NA | 10.00 |
| *Famous Americans* | | |
| 1971 Kennedy | 2,500 | 10.00 |
| 1971 Lincoln | 2,500 | 10.00 |
| 1972 Jefferson Davis | 5,000 | $ 11.00 |
| 1972 Robert E. Lee | 5,000 | 11.00 |
| **Southern Living Gallery** | | |
| *Wildflowers of South* | | |
| 1981 Wild Honeysuckle | 19,500 | 49.50 |
| 1981 Flowering Dogwood | 19,500 | 49.50 |
| 1981 Buttercup | 19,500 | 49.50 |
| 1981 Regal Lily | 19,500 | 49.50 |
| 1981 Queen Anne's Lace | 19,500 | 49.50 |
| 1981 Bluebonnet | 19,500 | 49.50 |
| 1981 Southern Magnolia | 19,500 | 49.50 |
| 1981 Bee Balm | 19,500 | 49.50 |
| 1981 Lady Slipper Orchid | 19,500 | 49.50 |
| 1981 Birdsfoot Violet | 19,500 | 49.50 |
| 1981 Frost Aster | 19,500 | 49.50 |
| 1981 Black-Eyed Susan | 19,500 | 49.50 |
| *Game Birds of South* | | |
| 1982 Bobwhite Quail | 19,500 | 39.95 |
| 1982 Wild Turkey | 19,500 | 39.95 |
| 1982 Mourning Dove | 19,500 | 39.95 |
| 1982 Mallard Duck | 19,500 | 39.95 |
| 1982 Wood Duck | 19,500 | 39.95 |
| 1982 Ruffed Grouse | 19,500 | 39.95 |
| 1982 Pintail Duck | 19,500 | 39.95 |
| 1982 Ring-necked Pheasant | 19,500 | 39.95 |
| 1982 American Woodcock | 19,500 | 39.95 |
| 1982 American Coot | 19,500 | 39.95 |
| 1982 Canada Goose | 19,500 | 39.95 |
| 1982 Green-winged Teal | 19,500 | 39.95 |
| *Southern Forest Families* | | |
| 1984 Eastern Cottontail | 19,500 | 39.50 |
| 1984 Raccoon | 19,500 | 39.50 |
| 1984 Whitetail Deer | 19,500 | 39.50 |
| 1984 Oppossum | 19,500 | 39.50 |
| 1984 Striped Skunk | 19,500 | 39.50 |
| 1984 Bobcat | 19,500 | 39.50 |
| 1984 Fox Squirrel | 19,500 | 39.50 |
| 1984 Chipmunk | 19,500 | 39.50 |
| 1984 Flying Squirrel | 19,500 | 39.50 |
| 1984 Beaver | 19,500 | 39.50 |
| 1984 Muskrat | 19,500 | 39.50 |
| *Songbirds of South* | | |
| 1985 American Goldfinch | 19,500 | 39.90 |
| 1985 Cardinal | 19,500 | 39.95 |
| 1985 Tufted Titmouse | 19,500 | 39.95 |
| 1985 Blue Jay | 19,500 | 39.95 |
| **Sports Impression** | | |
| *(Single issue)* | | |
| 1986 Mickey Mantle (signed) | 1,000 | 95.00 |
| 1986 Mickey Mantle (unsigned) | 2,000 | 60.00 |
| *(Single issue)* | | |
| 1986 Darryl Strawberry (signed) | 1,000 | 95.00 |
| 1986 Darryl Strawberry (unsigned) | 2,000 | 60.00 |
| *(Single issue)* | | |
| 1986 Al Kaline (signed) | 1,000 | 95.00 |
| 1986 Al Kaline (unsigned) | 2,000 | 60.00 |
| *(Single issue)* | | |
| 1987 Mickey, Willie, & The Duke (signed) | 1,500 | 150.00 |
| 1987 Mickey, Willie, & The Duke (unsigned) | 3,500 | 75.00 |
| *(Single issue)* | | |
| 1987 Mickey at Night (signed) | 1,500 | 100.00 |
| 1987 Mickey at Night (unsigned) | 3,500 | 60.00 |
| *(Single issue)* | | |
| 1987 Larry Bird (signed) | 2,000 | 100.00 |
| 1987 Larry Bird (unsigned) | 5,000 | 60.00 |
| *(Single issue)* | | |
| 1987 Don Mattingly (signed) | 2,500 | 125.00 |
| 1987 Don Mattingly (unsigned) | 5,000 | 60.00 |
| **Sterling America** | | |
| *Christmas Customs* | | |
| 1970 England | 2,500 | 18.00 |
| 1971 Holland | 2,500 | 18.00 |
| 1972 Norway | 2,500 | 18.00 |
| 1973 Germany | 2,500 | 20.00 |
| 1974 Mexico | 2,500 | 24.00 |
| *Twelve Days of Christmas* | | |
| 1970 Partridge | 2,500 | $ 18.00 |
| 1971 Turtle Doves | 2,500 | 18.00 |
| 1972 French Hens | 2,500 | 18.00 |
| 1973 Colly Birds | 2,500 | 18.00 |
| 1974 Five Rings | 2,500 | 24.00 |
| 1975 Six Geese | 2,500 | 24.00 |
| 1976 Seven Swans | 2,500 | 24.00 |
| 1977 Eight Maids | 2,500 | 28.00 |
| *Mother's Day* | | |
| 1971 Mare & Foal | 2,500 | 18.00 |
| 1972 Horned Owl | 2,500 | 18.00 |
| 1973 Raccoons | 2,500 | 20.00 |
| 1974 Deer | 2,500 | 24.00 |
| 1975 Quail | 2,500 | 24.00 |
| **Stieff** | | |
| *Bicentennial* | | |
| 1972 Declaration of Independence | 10,000 | 50.00 |
| 1974 Betsy Ross | 10,000 | 50.00 |
| 1975 Crossing Delaware | 10,000 | 50.00 |
| 1976 Serapio & Bon Homme | 10,000 | 50.00 |
| **Stratford Collection** | | |
| *Famous Clowns* | | |
| 1982 Emmett Looking Out | 10,000 | 35.00 |
| 1982 Jack Thum and Child | 10,000 | 35.00 |
| *Real Children* | | |
| 1982 Michael's Miracle | 24,500 | 45.00 |
| 1983 Susan's World | 24,500 | 45.00 |
| *Young Wildlife* | | |
| 1982 Siberian Cub at Play | 15,000 | 35.00 |
| 1982 Curious Raccoon | 15,000 | 35.00 |
| **Stuart International** | | |
| *Childhood Secrets* | | |
| 1983 Billy's Treasure | 19,500 | 39.50 |
| *American Road* | | |
| 1984 Farmer Takes a Ride | 9,800 | 22.50 |
| 1984 Henry's First Ride | 9,800 | 22.50 |
| *Spring Flowers* | | |
| 1984 Megan | 5,500 | 55.00 |
| 1985 Danielle | 5,500 | 55.00 |
| **Syracuse China** | | |
| *Grandma Moses (Sets of four)* | | |
| 1972 Old Checkered House in Winter | | |
| 1972 Mary and Little Lamb | | |
| 1972 In Harvest Time | | |
| 1972 Sugaring Off | NA | 80.00 |
| 1972 Hoosick Valley from Window | | |
| 1972 Taking in Laundry | | |
| 1972 It Snows, Oh it Snows | | |
| 1972 Joy Ride | NA | 80.00 |
| **Towle Silversmiths** | | |
| *Valentines* | | |
| 1972 Single Heart | Year | 10.00 |
| 1973 Entwined Hearts | Year | 10.00 |
| *Christmas* | | |
| 1972 Three Wise Men | 2,500 | 250.00 |
| **Transparent Images** | | |
| *(Single issue)* | | |
| 1986 Our Great Lady | 500 | 75.00 |
| **U.S. Historical Society** | | |
| *Annual Historical* | | |
| 1974 Thomas Jefferson | 2,500 | 75.00 |
| 1974 Abigail Adams | 2,500 | 75.00 |
| 1975 Patrick Henry | 2,500 | 75.00 |
| 1975 John Paul Jones | 2,500 | 75.00 |
| 1976 Benjamin Franklin | 2,500 | 75.00 |
| 1976 Alexander Hamilton | 2,500 | 75.00 |
| 1977 Great Events | 5,000 | 60.00 |
| 1978 Great Events | 10,000 | 75.00 |
| *Stained Glass Cathedral Christmas* | | |
| 1978 Nativity | 10,000 | 87.00 |
| 1979 Flight into Egypt | 10,000 | 97.00 |
| 1980 Madonna and Child | 10,000 | 125.00 |
| 1981 Magi | 10,000 | 150.00 |
| 1982 Flight into Egypt | 10,000 | 150.00 |
| 1983 Shepherds at Bethlehem | 10,000 | 150.00 |
| 1984 O Come Let Us Adore Him | 10,000 | $150. |
| 1985 Tidings of Great Joy | 10,000 | 160. |
| *American Christmas Carols* | | |
| 1982 Deck Halls | 10,000 | 55. |
| 1983 O Christmas Tree | 10,000 | 55. |
| 1984 Winter Wonderland | 10,000 | 55.( |
| 1985 Here We Come A' Caroling | 10,000 | 65. |
| 1986 Chestnuts Roasting on an Open Fire | 10,000 | 55.( |
| *Great American Sailing Ships* | | |
| 1983 Old Ironsides–U.S.S. Constitution | 10,000 | 135.( |
| 1984 Charles W. Morgan | 10,000 | 135. |
| 1985 Flying Cloud | 10,000 | 150.C |
| *Stained Glass Flowers* | | |
| 1983 Spring Flowers | 10,000 | 135.C |
| *200 Years of Flight* | | |
| 1983 Man's First Flight | 5,000 | 85.C |
| 1983 Miracle at Kitty Hawk | 5,000 | 85.C |
| 1984 China Clipper | 5,000 | 85.C |
| 1984 Man in Space | 5,000 | 85.C |
| *Buffalo Bill's Wild West* | | |
| 1984 Pony Express | 5,000 | 55.0 |
| 1984 Annie Oakley | 5,000 | 55.0 |
| 1984 Sitting Bull | 5,000 | 55.0 |
| 1984 Buffalo Hunter | 5,000 | 55.0 |
| 1984 Farewell Appearance | 5,000 | 55.0 |
| 1984 Deadwood Stage | 5,000 | 55.0 |
| 1984 Rough Riders | 5,000 | 55.0 |
| 1984 Royal Visit | 5,000 | 55.C |
| *Stained Glass with Pewter—Easter* | | |
| 1987 The Good Shepard | 5,000 | 160.0 |
| *Stained Glass Mother's Day* | | |
| 1987 A Mother's Love | 5,000 | 160.0 |
| *(Single issue)* | | |
| 1984 Robert E. Lee | 10,000 | 150.0 |
| **Vague Shadows** | | |
| *Plainsmen* | | |
| 1979 Buffalo Hunt | 2,500 | 300.0 |
| 1979 Proud One | 2,500 | 300.0 |
| *Professionals* | | |
| 1979 Big Leaguer | 15,000 | 29.9 |
| 1980 Ballerina's Dilemma | 15,000 | 32.5 |
| 1981 Quarterback | 15,000 | 32.5 |
| 1982 Rodeo Joe | 15,000 | 35.0 |
| 1983 Major Leaguer | 15,000 | 35.0 |
| 1983 Hockey Player | 15,000 | 35.0 |
| *Santa* | | |
| 1980 Santa's Joy | Year | 29.9 |
| 1981 Santa's Bundle | Year | 29.9 |
| *Storybook Collection* | | |
| 1980 Little Red Riding Hood | 18 Days | 29.9 |
| 1981 Cinderella | 18 Days | 29.9 |
| 1981 Hansel and Gretel | 18 Days | 29.9 |
| 1982 Goldilocks and Three Bears | 18 Days | 29.9 |
| *Arctic Friends (Set of two)* | | |
| 1981 Siberian Love | | |
| 1981 Snow Pals | 7,500 | 100.0( |
| *Four Princesses* | | |
| 1981 Lily of Mohawks | 7,500 | 50.0( |
| 1981 Pocahontas | 7,500 | 50.0( |
| 1982 Minnehaha | 7,500 | 50.0( |
| 1982 Sacajawea | 7,500 | 50.0( |
| *(Single issue)* | | |
| 1981 Apache Boy | 5,000 | 95.0( |
| *Child Life* | | |
| 1982 Siesta | 12,500 | 45.0C |
| 1983 Sweet Dreams | 3,500 | 45.00 |
| *Legends of West* | | |
| 1982 Daniel Boone | 10,000 | 65.00 |
| 1982 Davy Crockett | 10,000 | 65.00 |
| 1983 Kit Carson | 10,000 | 65.00 |
| 1983 Buffalo Bill | 10,000 | 65.00 |
| *Nature's Harmony* | | |
| 1982 Peaceable Kingdom | 12,500 | 100.00 |
| 1982 Zebra | 12,500 | 50.00 |
| 1982 Tiger | 12,500 | 50.00 |
| 1983 Black Panther | 12,500 | 50.00 |
| 1983 Elephant | 12,500 | 50.00 |

| | Edition Limit | Issue Price (US) |
|---|---|---|
| **War Ponies** | | |
| 1982 Sioux War Pony | 7,500 | $ 60.00 |
| 1983 Nez Perce War Pony | 7,500 | 60.00 |
| 1983 Apache War Pony | 7,500 | 60.00 |
| **Chieftains II** | | |
| 1983 Chief Pontiac | 7,500 | 70.00 |
| 1984 Chief Victorio | 7,500 | 70.00 |
| 1984 Chief Tecumseh | 7,500 | 70.00 |
| 1984 Chief Cochise | 7,500 | 70.00 |
| 1985 Chief Black Kettle | 7,500 | 70.00 |
| **Indian Nations** | | |
| 1983 Blackfoot | 7,500 | 35.00 |
| 1983 Cheyenne | 7,500 | 35.00 |
| 1983 Apache | 7,500 | 35.00 |
| 1983 Sioux | 7,500 | 35.00 |
| **Motherhood** | | |
| 1983 Madre | 12,500 | 50.00 |
| 1984 Madonna of Plains | 3,500 | 50.00 |
| 1985 Abuela | 3,500 | 50.00 |
| 1986 Naptime | 3,500 | 50.00 |
| **Perillo Masterpiece** | | |
| 1983 Papoose | 3,000 | 100.00 |
| **Thoroughbreds** | | |
| 1984 Whirlaway | 9,500 | 50.00 |
| 1984 Secretariat | 9,500 | 50.00 |
| 1984 Seabiscuit | 9,500 | 50.00 |
| 1984 Man O'War | 9,500 | 50.00 |
| **Tribal Ponies** | | |
| 1984 Arapaho | 3,500 | 65.00 |
| 1984 Comanche | 3,500 | 65.00 |
| 1984 Crow | 3,500 | 65.00 |
| **(Single issue)** | | |
| 1984 Lovers | NA | 50.00 |
| **(Single issue)** | | |
| 1984 Navajo Girl | 3,000 | 95.00 |
| **Indian Horses** | | |
| 1985 Pinto | 5,000 | 40.00 |
| **Pride of America's Indians** | | |
| 1986 Brave and Free | 10 Days | 24.50 |
| 1986 Dark-Eyed Friends | 10 Days | 24.50 |
| 1986 Noble Companions | 10 Days | 24.50 |
| 1987 Kindred Spirits | 10 Days | 24.50 |
| 1987 Loyal Alliance | 10 Days | 24.50 |
| 1987 Small and Wise | 10 Days | 24.50 |
| 1987 Winter Scouts | 10 Days | 24.50 |
| 1987 Peaceful Comrades | 10 Days | 24.50 |
| **(Single issue)** | | |
| 1986 Navajo Boy | 3,500 | 95.00 |
| **The Arabians** | | |
| 1986 Silver Streak | 3,500 | 95.00 |
| **Young Emotions (Set of Two)** | | |
| 1986 Tears | | |
| 1986 Smiles | 5,000 | 75.00 |
| **Vette Vues Magazine** | | |
| **Corvette Collection** | | |
| 1986 '86 Pace Care Convertible | 2,000 | 29.95 |
| 1987 '63 Split Window Coupe | 2,000 | 29.95 |
| 1987 1953–1954–1955 Corvettes | 2,000 | 29.95 |
| **Vernonware (Metlox Potteries)** | | |
| **Songs of Christmas** | | |
| 1971 Twelve Days | 9,000 | 15.00 |
| 1972 Jingle Bells | 9,000 | 17.50 |
| 1973 First Noel | 9,000 | 20.00 |
| 1974 Upon a Midnight Clear | 9,000 | 20.00 |
| 1975 O Holy Night | 10,000 | 20.00 |
| 1976 Hark! Herald Angels | 10,000 | 20.00 |
| 1977 Away in Manger | 10,000 | 30.00 |
| 1978 White Christmas | 10,000 | 30.00 |
| 1979 Little Drummer Boy | 10,000 | 30.00 |


| | Edition Limit | Issue Price (US) |
|---|---|---|
| **Viletta** | | |
| **Disneyland** | | |
| 1976 Betsy Ross | 3,000 | $ 15.00 |
| 1976 Crossing Delaware | 3,000 | 15.00 |
| 1976 Signing Declaration | 3,000 | 15.00 |
| 1976 Spirit of '76 | 3,000 | 15.00 |
| **Bicentennial** | | |
| 1977 Patriots | 15,000 | 37.00 |
| **In Tribute to America's Great Artists** | | |
| 1978 DeGrazia by Don Marco | 5,000 | 65.00 |
| **Days of West** | | |
| 1978 Cowboy Christmas | 5,000 | 55.00 |
| **Alice in Wonderland** | | |
| 1980 Alice and White Rabbit | 28 Days | 25.00 |
| 1981 Mad Hatter's Tea Party | 28 Days | 25.00 |
| 1981 Alice and Cheshire Cat | 28 Days | 25.00 |
| 1981 Alice and Croquet Match | 28 Days | 25.00 |
| 1982 Advice to Caterpillar | 28 Days | 25.00 |
| 1982 End of a Dream | 28 Days | 25.00 |
| **Down Home Memories** | | |
| 1984 Watermelon Party | 19,500 | 39.95 |
| 1984 Cleaning off Cemetery | 19,500 | 39.95 |
| 1984 Waiting for Bedtime | 19,500 | 39.95 |
| 1984 Hunting Blackberries | 19,500 | 39.95 |
| 1984 Opossum Hunt | 19,500 | 39.95 |
| 1984 Weighing up Cotton | 19,500 | 39.95 |
| 1984 Hilly Town | 19,500 | 39.95 |
| 1984 April Plowing | 19,500 | 39.95 |
| 1984 Churning on Front Porch | 19,500 | 39.95 |
| 1984 Summer Rain | 19,500 | 39.95 |
| 1984 Sunning Quilts | 19,500 | 39.95 |
| 1984 Summer Baptism | 19,500 | 39.95 |

See also:
Abbey Press (U.S.A.)
American Arts Services (U.S.A.)
Carson Mint (U.S.A.)
Collector's Heirlooms (U.S.A.)
R. J. Ernst Enterprises (U.S.A.)
Ghent Collection (U.S.A.)
Hamilton Collection (U.S.A.)
Ralph Homan Studios (U.S.A.)
Joys (U.S.A.)
Judaic Heritage Society (U.S.A.)
McCalla Enterprises (U.S.A.)
Museum Editions (U.S.A.)
Pemberton & Oakes (U.S.A.)
Warwick (U.S.A.)
Westbury (U.S.A.)
Edward Weston Editions (U.S.A.)

| | Edition Limit | Issue Price (US) |
|---|---|---|
| **Volair (Gorham)** | | |
| **Audubon American Wildlife Heritage** | | |
| 1977 House Mouse | 2,500 | 90.00 |
| 1977 Royal Louisiana Heron | 2,500 | 90.00 |
| 1977 Virginia Deer | 2,500 | 90.00 |
| 1977 Snowy Owl | 2,500 | 90.00 |
| **Warwick (Viletta)** | | |
| **Great Comedians** | | |
| 1978 Little Tramp | 7,500 | 35.00 |
| 1978 Outrageous Groucho | 7,500 | 35.00 |
| **George Washington Mint** | | |
| **American Indian** | | |
| 1972 Curley (Gold) | 100 | 2000.00 |
| 1972 Curley (Proof) | 100 | 1000.00 |
| 1972 Curley (Sterling) | 7,300 | 150.00 |
| 1973 Two Moons (Gold) | 100 | 2000.00 |
| 1973 Two Moons (Proof) | 100 | 1000.00 |
| 1973 Two Moons (Sterling) | 7,300 | 150.00 |
| **Mother's Day** | | |
| 1972 Whistler's Mother (Gold) | 100 | 2000.00 |
| 1972 Whistler's Mother (Proof) | 100 | 1000.00 |
| 1972 Whistler's Mother (Sterling) | 9,800 | 150.00 |


| | Edition Limit | Issue Price (US) |
|---|---|---|
| 1974 Motherhood (Gold) | 100 | $2000.00 |
| 1974 Motherhood (Proof) | 100 | 1000.00 |
| 1974 Motherhood (Sterling) | 2,300 | 175.00 |
| **Picasso** | | |
| 1972 Don Quixote (Gold) | 100 | 2000.00 |
| 1972 Don Quixote (Proof) | 100 | 1000.00 |
| 1972 Don Quixote (Sterling) | 9,800 | 125.00 |
| **Remington** | | |
| 1972 Rattlesnake (Gold) | 100 | 2000.00 |
| 1972 Rattlesnake (Proof) | 100 | 1000.00 |
| 1972 Rattlesnake (Sterling) | 800 | 250.00 |
| **Da Vinci** | | |
| 1972 Last Supper | NA | 125.00 |
| **N. C. Wyeth** | | |
| 1972 Uncle Sam's America (Gold) | 100 | 2000.00 |
| 1972 Uncle Sam's America (Proof) | 100 | 1000.00 |
| 1972 Uncle Sam's America (Sterling) | 9,800 | 150.00 |
| 1973 Massed Flags (Gold) | 100 | 2000.00 |
| 1973 Massed Flags (Proof) | 100 | 1000.00 |
| 1973 Massed Flags (Sterling) | 2,300 | 150.00 |
| **Israel Anniversary (Single issue)** | | |
| 1973 Struggle | 10,000 | 300.00 |
| **Picasso (Single issue)** | | |
| 1974 Rites of Spring (Sterling) | 9,800 | 125.00 |
| **Remington (Single issue)** | | |
| 1974 Coming Through Rye (Sterling) | 2,500 | 300.00 |
| **Wendell August Forge** | | |
| **Great Americans** | | |
| 1971 J.F.K. (Pewter) | 5,000 | 40.00 |
| 1971 J.F.K. (Silver) | 500 | 200.00 |
| 1972 Lincoln (Pewter) | 5,000 | 40.00 |
| 1972 Lincoln (Silver) | 500 | 200.00 |
| **Great Moments** | | |
| 1971 Columbus (Pewter) | 5,000 | 40.00 |
| 1971 Columbus (Silver) | 500 | 200.00 |
| 1972 Landing of Pilgrims (Pewter) | 5,000 | 40.00 |
| 1972 Landing of Pilgrims (Silver) | 500 | 200.00 |
| 1973 First Thanksgiving (Pewter) | 5,000 | 40.00 |
| 1973 First Thanksgiving (Silver) | 500 | 200.00 |
| 1974 Patrick Henry (Pewter) | 5,000 | 40.00 |
| 1974 Patrick Henry (Silver) | 500 | 200.00 |
| 1975 Paul Revere (Pewter) | 5,000 | 45.00 |
| 1975 Paul Revere (Silver) | 500 | 200.00 |
| 1976 Signing of Declaration (Pewter) | 5,000 | 50.00 |
| 1976 Signing of Declaration (Silver) | 500 | 200.00 |
| **Wings of Man** | | |
| 1971 Columbus' Ships (Pewter) | 5,000 | 40.00 |
| 1971 Columbus' Ships (Silver) | 500 | 200.00 |
| 1972 Conestoga Wagon (Pewter) | 5,000 | 40.00 |
| 1972 Conestoga Wagon (Silver) | 500 | 200.00 |
| **Peace (Single issue)** | | |
| 1973 Facing Doves (Silver) | 2,500 | 250.00 |
| **Christmas** | | |
| 1974 Caroler (Bronze) | 2,500 | 25.00 |
| 1974 Caroler (Pewter) | 2,500 | 30.00 |
| 1975 Christmas in Country (Bronze) | 2,500 | 30.00 |
| 1975 Christmas in Country (Pewter) | 2,500 | 35.00 |
| 1976 Lamplighter (Bronze) | 2,500 | 35.00 |
| 1976 Lamplighter (Pewter) | 2,500 | 40.00 |


| | Edition Limit | Issue Price (US) |
|---|---|---|
| 1977 Covered Bridge (Bronze) | 2,500 | $ 40.00 |
| 1977 Covered Bridge (Pewter) | 2,500 | 45.00 |
| **Wildlife** | | |
| 1977 On Guard (Aluminum) | 1,900 | 35.00 |
| 1977 On Guard (Bronze) | 1,500 | 45.00 |
| 1977 On Guard (Pewter) | 1,500 | 55.00 |
| 1977 On Guard (Silver) | 100 | 250.00 |
| 1978 Thunderbird (Aluminum) | 1,900 | 40.00 |
| 1978 Thunderbird (Bronze) | 1,500 | 50.00 |
| 1978 Thunderbird (Pewter) | 1,500 | 60.00 |
| 1978 Thunderbird (Silver) | 100 | 250.00 |
| **Westbury (Viletta)** | | |
| **Tender Moments** | | |
| 1978 Old Fashioned Persuasion | 7,500 | 40.00 |
| 1979 Dandelions | 7,500 | 45.00 |
| **Westminster Collectibles** | | |
| **Holidays** | | |
| 1976 All Hallows Eve | 5,000 | 38.50 |
| 1977 Christmas | 5,000 | 38.50 |
| **Westmoreland** | | |
| **Christmas** | | |
| 1972 Holy Birth | 2,500 | 35.00 |
| 1973 Manger Scene | 3,500 | 35.00 |
| 1974 Gethsemane | 1,500 | 35.00 |
| 1975 Christ Is Risen | 1,500 | 45.00 |
| **Edward Weston Editions (Viletta)** | | |
| **Unicorn Fantasies** | | |
| 1979 Follower of Dreams | 5,000 | 55.00 |
| 1980 Twice Upon a Time | 5,000 | 55.00 |
| 1981 Familiar Spirit | 5,000 | 60.00 |
| 1982 Noble Gathering | 5,000 | 65.00 |
| **Weddings Around World** | | |
| 1979 Hawaiian Wedding | 5,000 | 75.00 |
| 1980 Dutch Wedding | 5,000 | 75.00 |
| **Wheaton** | | |
| **Presidential** | | |
| 1971 Adams | 9,648 | 5.00 |
| 1971 Eisenhower | 8,856 | 5.00 |
| 1971 Hoover | 10,152 | 5.00 |
| 1971 Kennedy | 11,160 | 5.00 |
| 1971 Lincoln | 9,648 | 5.00 |
| 1971 Madison | 9,504 | 5.00 |
| 1971 Monroe | 9,792 | 5.00 |
| 1971 F. D. Roosevelt | 9,432 | 5.00 |
| 1971 Taft | 9,648 | 5.00 |
| 1971 Van Buren | 9,576 | 5.00 |
| 1971 Washington | 10,800 | 5.00 |
| 1971 Wilson | 8,712 | 5.00 |
| **Whitehall China** | | |
| **Raphael Soyer** | | |
| 1979 Model on Bed | 10,000 | 39.95 |
| **Wildlife Internationale** | | |
| **Water Fowl** | | |
| 1983 Wood Ducks | 5,000 | 65.00 |
| **Windemere Collection** | | |
| **Classical Images** | | |
| 1984 Piano Moods | 7,500 | 60.00 |
| 1985 Young Flutist | 7,500 | 60.00 |
| **Yankee Collection** | | |
| **Birds of Prey** | | |
| 1986 The Bald Eagle | 1,000 | 250.00 |
| **Zanobia** | | |
| **African Violet Miniatures** | | |
| 1985 Half Pint | 5,000 | 29.50 |
| 1986 Luvkins | 5,000 | 29.50 |
| **Violet Portraits** | | |
| 1986 Canadian Sunset | 5,000 | 34.50 |
| 1987 Kiss't | 5,000 | 34.50 |

# INDEX OF PLATE TITLES

# INDEX OF PLATE TITLES

# INDEX OF PLATE TITLES

# INDEX OF PLATE TITLES

# INDEX OF PLATE TITLES

# INDEX OF PLATE TITLES

# INDEX OF PLATE TITLES

# INDEX OF PLATE TITLES

# INDEX OF PLATE TITLES

## Y

## Z

# GLOSSARY OF COMMONLY USED TERMS

## A

**Aftermarket.** See *Market*.

**Alabaster.** A dense, fine-grained form of gypsum (calcium sulfate) stone, usually white to pink and slightly translucent. Alabaster stone can be carved in fine detail for ornamental objects and hardened by intense heat. Italian alabaster is also called Florentine marble. Ivory alabaster is composed of alabaster but is non-translucent and acquires a patina with age like that of old ivory.

**Allotment.** A number of plates, all alike and usually at issue, allocated by a maker to a distributor or dealer. See *Lot*.

**Alloy.** Two or more metals combined while molten. Alloying is done to achieve hardness, toughness, or luster. See *Pewter*.

**Annual.** A plate issued once each year as part of a series. The term is most often used when a plate does not commemorate a specific holiday.

**Annular kiln.** A round oven made from brick used to fire ceramic plates.

**Art Deco, Art Décoratif.** A style of decoration popular in Europe and America from 1920 to 1945. The Art Deco movement sought to glorify progress and the future by using as motifs such shapes as the cylinder, circle, rectangle, and cone.

**Art Nouveau.** A style of decoration in Europe and America from 1890 to 1920. The Art Nouveau movement used twining floral patterns as its primary decorative motifs.

**Asked Price, Ask.** The offering price posted for a plate by a seller on the Exchange.

**At Issue.** A plate being offered for sale at the time of its manufacture and at the original price set by the maker.

## B

**Back Issue.** See *Issue*.

**Backstamp.** The information on the back of a plate, usually including the maker's signature, name, or trademark (logo-type). It may also record serial number, title, artist's signature, edition limit, explanation of the plate, sponsor, production techniques, awards, or release initials. It may be hand-applied, stamped, incised (cut or pressed), or applied as a decalcomania.

**Banding.** A method for hand-application of precious metals, such as gold, silver, or platinum, to the edge or other parts of a glazed plate. The decorator uses a camel's hair brush to apply a liquid metal suspended in special oils. The plate is then fired to adhere the metal to the glaze.

**Baroque.** An elaborate style of decoration developed in Europe in the seventeenth and eighteenth centuries and noted for exaggerated gesture and line. Example: Dresden **(22-D68-0.0)**.

**Bas-relief.** See *Relief Sculpture*.

**Bavaria (Bayern).** A province in the southwest corner of Germany long known as a center for porcelain factories. The region contains large deposits of kaolin, the key porcelain component.

**Bearish.** Marked by declining prices, either actual or expected. A bear market is one of declining prices.

**Bedroom Dealer.** A trade term for a small dealer who usually operates from his home, buys discounted plates, and resells them for a small profit.

**Bid Price, Bid.** The amount a prospective buyer offers to pay for a plate on the Exchange.

**Bisque, Biscuit.** A plate that has been fired but not glazed, leaving it with a matte texture. So called because of the biscuit-like appearance. Example: Lladró **(72-L41-0.0)**.

**Blue Chip.** An established series by a well-known maker in which nearly every issue shows a steady sequence of price rises above issue price, usually over an extended period of time.

**Body. 1.** The formula or combination of substances that make up potter's clay, generally referring to stoneware and earthenware. **2.** The basic plate form to which ornamentation is applied.

# GLOSSARY OF COMMONLY USED TERMS

**Bone Ash.** Calcium phosphate, a component of bone china, added to give whiteness and translucency. It is obtained by calcinating (reducing to powder by heat) animal bones, usually those of oxen.

**Bone China (Bone Porcelain).** A type of china developed by Josiah Spode in England in the 1790s. By replacing part of the kaolin in the china formula with bone ash, greater translucency and whiteness is obtained at lower firing temperatures. The finest bone china contains up to 50% bone ash. It is the most commonly made china in England. Example: Royal Doulton **(26-R62-0.0).**

**Bradex.** Common term for the *Bradford Exchange Current Quotations*, a periodic listing of the current market prices of collector's plates now listed on the Exchange. See *Listed Plate, Exchange.*

**Broker.** A representative of the Bradford Exchange Trading Floor who enters bids and asks of all traders and confirms all transactions.

**Bullish.** Marked by rising prices, either actual or expected, and optimistic atmosphere. A bull market is one of rising prices.

**Buy Order.** An offer by an individual or dealer to purchase one or more plates on the secondary market. See *Bid Price, Exchange.*

## C

**Cameo Effect.** Ornamentations in relief on a background of contrasting color or to resemble a cameo. Examples: Wedgwood Jasper ware **(26-W90-0.0)** and Incolay Studios **(84-I31-0.0).**

**Carnelian.** A hard translucent quartz that has a reddish color.

**Celsius, Centigrade.** The thermometric scale in which 0° represents the freezing point of water and 100° the boiling point. Celsius temperature is denoted by "C" after the number.

**Ceramic.** A general term applying to all of the various plates made from clay and hardened by firing.

**Certificate.** An attestation of authenticity which may accompany each plate in an edition. A certificate authenticates a plate as being part of an issue and usually confirms the plate's individual number within the edition.

**China, Chinaware.** A hard, vitreous ceramic whose main components are kaolin and china stone fired at high temperature. Originally the term was used for those ceramics which only came from China. Later it was applied to all "hard" and "soft" porcelain. China is often used as a generic term which includes porcelain, but is properly distinguished from it by a high bisque firing temperature and a lower glaze firing temperature. The main firing (bisque) of china is approximately 7% lower than the main firing (glaze) of porcelain. In china production, the glaze is applied after the main firing and fixed with a second lower-temperature firing. A typical china formula is 40% kaolin, 10% ball clay, and varying proportions of china stone, feldspar, and flint. See *Porcelain.*

**China Clay.** See *Kaolin.*

**China Stone, Petuntse.** A feldspathic material in china formulas. China stone acts as a flux which helps dissolve and fuse the other components into a vitreous mass.

**Christmas Plates, Christmas Series.** Annual plates issued to commemorate Christmas, usually as part of a series. Plate names for Christmas include Noël (French), Weihnachten (German), Jul (Danish), Navidad (Spanish and Portuguese), and Natale (Italian). The oldest Christmas series is that of Bing & Grøndahl, produced continuously since 1895 **(14-B36-1.0).**

**Clay.** Any of various plastic, viscous earths used to make plates. It is formed by the decomposition, due to weathering, of igneous rocks such as granite, feldspar, and pegmatite.

**Close.** Last traded price on the Exchange.

**Closed-End Series.** A series of plates with a predetermined number of issues. Example: D'Arceau-Limoges *Douze Sites Parisiens de Louis Dali (Twelve Parisian Places)* **(18-D15-6.0).**

**Cobalt Blue.** Cobalt oxide in the form of a dark black powder which, when fired, turns a deep blue. It was the first known and is still the most commonly used ceramic underglaze color because of its ability to withstand high firing temperatures. It can produce a variety of shades. Examples: Kaiser cobalt blue **(22-K4-0.0),** Bing & Grøndahl Copenhagen blue **(14-B36-0.0),** Royal

Copenhagen Danish Blue **(14-R59-0.0),** and Rörstrand Scandia blue **(76-R54-0.0).**

**Collector's Plate.** A decorative plate produced in a limited edition for the purpose of being collected. Although the earliest plates were not produced with this objective, they have since acquired the name by virtue of being collected and are now produced for this purpose.

**Commemorative Plate.** A plate produced in remembrance of an event. Example: Wedgwood *Bicentennial of American Independence.* **(26-W90-3.0).**

**Coterie Plate.** A collector's plate with a limited following which is traded too infrequently to be listed on the Exchange.

**Crystal.** See *Lead Crystal.*

**Cut Glass.** Glass decorated by the cutting of grooves and facets, usually done with a copper engraver's wheel.

## D

**Damascene.** An electroplating effect, created and patented by Reed & Barton **(84-R18-0.0),** of etching and then depositing layers of gold, copper, and silver on bronze. Originally the term referred to the art, developed in Damascus, of ornamenting iron or steel with inlaid precious metals.

**Dealer.** A marketer of plates who buys primarily from makers or distributors and sells primarily to the public.

**Dealer-Broker.** A dealer who acts as an agent of the Bradford Exchange to transact secondary market purchases and sales for his customers via the Instaquote Trading System. See *Broker, Instaquote Trading System, Market.*

**Decalcomania.** The printed reproduction of original artwork which is produced by individual color separations, either in offset lithography, silk-screen printing, or a combination of both.

**Delftware.** Earthenware covered with an opaque white glaze made of stannic oxide, and oxide of tin. Originally developed in Delft, Holland, in the sixteenth century, Delftware has the appearance of being covered with a thick white paint. Similar ware is the majolica of Italy and faience of France and Germany. See *Faience, Majolica, Tin Glaze.*

# GLOSSARY OF COMMONLY USED TERMS

**Dilute Colors.** Solutions of metallic salts which are absorbed by the bisque body of a plate when it is glazed and fired, producing soft, impressionistic tones. Perfected in Copenhagen in about 1883. Examples: Royal Copenhagen **(14-R59-0.0)**, Bing & Grøndahl **(14-B36-0.0)**, and Grande Copenhagen **(14-G65-0.0)**.

**Distributor.** A marketer of plates who buys from manufacturers and sells to dealers. Some distributors also act as makers and as dealers.

**Dresden, Meissen.** Neighboring cities now in East Germany where the first hard-paste porcelain outside of China was produced by Johann Friedrich Böttger in 1708.

**Dresden China.** Term used in England beginning in the eighteenth century to describe true hard-paste porcelain. See *Dresden, Porcelain.*

# E

**Earthenware.** A term for any ceramics which are not vitrified. Typical components of earthenware are 43% ball clay, 24% kaolin, 23% flint, and 10% pegmatite. Fired earthenware is normally covered with either a transparent or opaque glaze. High-fired earthenware is fired at a higher temperature to produce a harder ware. Example: Royal Doulton *Beswick Christmas* series **(26-R62-1.0)**.

**Edition.** The total number of plates, all with the same decoration, produced by a maker. Editions of collector's plates are normally limited to a fixed number and are not repeated. To do so would constitute a violation of the edition limit.

**Electroplating.** A process by which metal plates are coated with another metal by electrical charges.

**Embossed Design.** Raised ornamentation produced by the plate mold or by stamping a design into the body of the plate. Example: Belleek **(26-B18-0.0)**.

**Enamel.** A glaze material colored with suspended mineral oxides for decorating plates.

**Engraved Design.** Decoration produced by cutting into the surface of metal, glass, or china plates with either a tool or acid, as in etching. See *Intaglio.*

**Etched Design.** Decoration produced by cutting into the surface of a plate with acid. The plate is first covered with an acid-resistant paint or wax, and the design is carved through this coating. When the plate is immersed in acid, the acid "bites" into the plate surface in the shape of the design. Example: Franklin Mint silver plates **(84-F64-0.0)**. See *Intaglio.*

**Exchange.** A place where plates are traded, most commonly the Bradford Exchange, the world's largest trading center in limited-edition collector's plates. Incorporated in 1962, it was formerly known as Bradford Galleries Exchange. See *Trading Floor.*

# F

**Faience.** Tin-enameled earthenware from France, Germany, or Spain developed in the seventeenth century and named for the Italian town of Faenza, a center for majolica, another name for this ware. See *Delftware.*

**Feldspar.** A mineral composed of aluminum silicates with either potassium, sodium, calcium, or barium. Feldspar decomposes to form kaolin, the key ingredient of china and porcelain. The addition of undecomposed feldspar to china formulas gives the ware greater hardness.

**Fine China.** A designation of quality which is made after firing; those plates which do not merit the designation are simply called "china."

**Fire.** The heating process which hardens ceramic plates in a kiln. Ceramic clay begins to undergo chemical change at 500° C and vitrifies at around 1300° C.

**First Edition.** The first, and presumably the only, edition of a collector's plate. The term (or its abbreviation, "FE") is sometimes used for the edition which is the first issue in a series of collector's plates. However, since no edition is normally ever reopened and therefore no "second edition" is possible, all issues of collector's plates are properly termed first editions.

**First Issue.** Chronologically, the first plate in a series, i.e., the plates issued in the first year of an annual series.

**Flint Glass.** See *Lead Crystal.*

**Flux.** Finely ground material added to porcelain formulas which lowers the vitrification temperature and helps fuse the components. See *Feldspar.*

**Foot Rim.** A slightly projected ring on the convex side of a plate. The foot rim raises the plate in the kiln during firing.

# G

**Glaze.** Glassy, hard surface coating on plates made of silicates (glass-forming compounds) and mineral oxides. Glaze is put on ceramic ware to make it wear-resistant, waterproof, decorative, and to seal the pores. Glaze material suspended in water is applied after the first firing and is heated to the glaze's vitrification point when it fuses to the plate body. Glaze is applied by dipping, spraying, or painting. Decorating is added under, over, or with the glaze layer. See *Underglaze Decoration, Overglaze Decoration.*

# I

**Incised Design.** Ornamentation cut into the body of the plate. Example: Veneto Flair **(38-V22-0.0)**.

**Incolay Stone.** The material from which the cameo-like plates produced by Incolay Studios are made. Incolay stone may contain, among other minerals, semi-precious carnelian and crystal or topaz quartz. Example: Incolay Studios **(84-I31-0.0)**.

**Inlaid.** Decoration on a plate created by etching, incising, or engraving a design on the surface and filling with another material.

**Instaquote Trading System.**™ The computerized auction market for collector's plates that is an exclusive service of The Bradford Exchange Trading Floor. Both individual collectors and dealers may trade on the system.

**Intaglio.** Decoration created by cutting beneath the surface of the plate. Example: Morgantown Crystal **(84-M58-0.0)**. See *Engraved Design, Etched Design.*

# GLOSSARY OF COMMONLY USED TERMS

**Iridescence.** A rainbow effect on a plate's surface caused by the diffraction of light. True iridescent color effects are readily distinguished from a plate's inherent color because the pattern will change as the plate is moved. Example: Belleek (26-B18-0.0).

**Issue. 1.** The release for sale of an edition of plates by a maker. **2.** A plate in an edition. **3.** An edition within a series. A new issue is the release of the most recent plate in a continuing series. A back issue is a plate other than the most recently-issued plate in a series. Back issue usually denotes a plate that has sold out at issue price and is available only on the secondary market. See *Market.*

**Issue Price.** Original or first price of the plate established by the maker at the time the plate is released for sale.

## J

**Jasper Ware.** Hard, fine-grained, unglazed stoneware made by adding barium sulfate to clay, developed by Josiah Wedgwood in the 1770s. The term "jasper" does not indicate the presence of jasper stone but most likely denotes the variety of colors in which Jasper ware can be produced. Though white in its original form, Jasper ware can be stained in blue, green, lilac, yellow, maroon, pink, taupe, or black to serve as a background for embossments of white Jasper relief for a cameo effect. When stained throughout, the body of it is called solid Jasper ware. Example: Wedgwood (26-W90-0.0).

**Jigger.** A machine with a revolving mold on which plates are formed. Semi-malleable clay is thrown on the revolving mold forming the top of the plate. The bottom of the plate is formed by a metal blade which is fastened to a pivotal arm.

## K

**Kaolin.** The only clay which yields a white material when fired and the indispensable element of porcelain and china plates. Also called true clay or china clay, it is formed by the complete decomposition by weathering of feldspar. Kaolin is a refractory clay which can be fired at high temperatures without deforming. It produces a vitreous, translucent

ceramic when fired with fluxes (fusible rocks) such as feldspar. The components of kaolin clay are 50% silica, 33% alumina, 2% oxides, 1% magnesia, 2% alkali, and 12% water.

**KPM.** The trademark on plates from Königliche Porzellan-Manufaktur, Berlin, Germany. Plates made by this manufacturer date from as early as 1763.

## L

**Lead Crystal.** Extremely transparent fine quality glass, also called flint glass and lead glass, which contains a high proportion of lead oxide to give extra weight, better refractiveness and a clear ringing tone when tapped. Full lead crystal is the term used to identify glass with a 24% or greater lead content. Example: Lalique (18-L3-0.0).

**Lead Glass.** See *Lead Crystal.*

**Limited-Edition Plates.** Plates produced in a fixed quantity, either predetermined by number or determined by a specific period of issue or by a period of production. All true collector's plates are limited-editions.

**Limoges.** A town in south central France famous for its porcelain production since the discovery of kaolin deposits nearby in 1768. Limoges porcelain manufacturers have joined together to enforce quality standards. Examples: D'Arceau-Limoges (18-D15-0.0), Haviland (18-H6-0.0), Haviland & Parlon (18-H8-0.0), and Limoges-Turgot (18-L52-0.0).

**Listed Plate.** A plate listed and regularly quoted on the *Bradford Exchange Current Quotations.* Such a plate is often referred to as being "Bradex-listed." See *Bradex, Exchange, Over-The-Counter Plate.*

**Lot.** A number of plates, all in the same edition and represented by a sell order on the Exchange, usually on the secondary market and not at issue. See *Allotment.*

**Luster.** Decoration applied to a plate surface by application of metallic oxides such as gold, silver, platinum, or copper over the glaze. When gently fired, this leaves a thin metallic film.

## M

**Majolica, Maiolica.** Earthenware finished with opaque white enamel, similar to faience and Delftware, but first made in the Spanish island of Majorca. See *Delftware.*

**Maker.** The name by which a plate is known or under which it is issued, e.g., manufacturer, distributor, or sponsor. In most cases the "maker" is the actual manufacturer, e.g., Bing & Grøndahl (14-B36-0.0). However, it can also be a commissioner or distributor, e.g., Schmid (22-S12-0.0), using a trade name, while the physical production is in fact done by a sub-contractor.

**Market.** The structure within which plates are bought and sold. The primary market consists of new issues which are sold by the makers or their sales representatives to dealers and distributors. Dealers and distributors in turn normally sell the new issues to the public at issue price. Secondary market or aftermarket refers to the buying and selling of plates previously sold, and usually sold out, on the primary market. In many cases secondary market prices are higher than those of the primary market.

**Market Bradex.** A kind of "Dow Jones" index of the overall collector's plate market expressed as a percentage, based on the current price/issue price ratio of twelve key indicator series.

**Market Price.** The price at which a plate is currently traded, regardless of its issue price. See *Issue Price.*

**Market Price Order.** An open bid posted on the Exchange to purchase an issue at the price the market demands. Only over-the-counter plates are currently traded in this way on the Exchange. See *Over-The-Counter Plate.*

**Meissen.** See *Dresden.*

**Mint Condition.** A plate in new or like-new condition (free of manufacturer defects and damage) accompanied by any original certificates and packing materials included at issue.

**Modeling.** The process of making the original pattern from which the master mold is made for a sculptured plate.

**Mold.** A general term for the form which gives a plate its shape. Clay, metal or glass is pressed into a mold to form a blank (without ornamentation). Intaglio decoration or raised ornamentation may also be formed in the mold. China or porcelain slip-casting is done in plaster-of-paris molds. Slip (diluted clay formula) is poured into the mold, and the excess water is absorbed into the plaster-of-paris. When the plate is jiggered, the mold forms the back and a tool forms the front using a moist clay mixture. See *Slip.*

# N

**New Issue.** See *Issue.*

# O

**Open-End Series.** A continuing series of annual plates with no established termination. Example: Royal Copenhagen *Christmas* series **(14-R59-1.0).**

**Open Stock.** Plates available in or produced in unlimited numbers or for an unlimited time period (and therefore not considered collector's plates).

**Overglaze Decoration.** A decoration consisting of precious metals such as gold, platinum, or silver and/or lithographic patterns in up to twenty-five colors, applied by hand to a porcelain piece after it has been glazed and fired a second time (glost fired). Hand-applied lithographic decoration—the most widely used form of overglaze decoration—can also be used underglaze. See *Glaze, Underglaze Decoration.*

**Over-The-Counter Plate.** A collector's plate not traded in sufficient volume to be *listed* on the Exchange. The majority of such plates, however, are *traded* on the Exchange and can be obtained, when available, at the prevailing market prices. See *Listed Plate.*

# P

**Parian China.** A highly vitrified, translucent china characterized by an iridescent luster and rich, creamy tint much like that of parian marble, for which it is named. The process for making parian ware was invented by the Copeland and Garrett firm in England in the mid-nineteenth century. Example: Belleek **(26-B18-0.0).**

**Paste.** The combination of substances that make up potter's clay, generally that for porcelain or china.

**Pewter.** An alloy of tin with copper and antimony as hardeners. The greater the amount of copper and antimony, the harder the ware. Fine pewter is composed of 80% tin and 20% antimony and brass or copper. See *Alloy.*

**Plate, Exchange.** See *Swap'n'Sell.*

**Point, Bradex Point.** One percentage point of the Market Bradex.

**Porcelain.** The hardest vitreous ceramic fired at the highest temperatures. Although the term porcelain is often interchanged with china, true porcelain, as the term is used in the field, is distinguished from china by its very high glaze firing and low bisque firing temperature compared with the high bisque firing and lower glaze firing of china. The main firing (glaze) of porcelain is approximately 7% higher than the main firing (bisque) of china. The glaze fuses with the porcelain plate body and produces an extremely hard surface. Hard-paste or true porcelain is made from a formula whose primary components are kaolin and china stone (petuntse). When fired, the china stone vitrifies, producing a hard, glassy ceramic. True porcelain is translucent when thin, white unless colored, impervious to scratching, and transmits a ringing tone when struck. A typical porcelain formula is 50% kaolin, 25% quartz and 25% feldspar. Soft-paste porcelain was developed in Renaissance Europe in an attempt to imitate the true porcelain of China. Soft-paste porcelain was a mixture of white sand, gypsum, soda, alum, salt, and niter, fired until it vitrified. It had a soft texture, great sensitivity to sudden temperature changes, was warmer to the touch than true porcelain, and could be scratched with a file. The terms "hard" and "soft" porcelain refer to the "hard" firing temperature (around 1450°C) required for true porcelain and the "soft" firing temperature (around 1150°C) used for soft-paste porcelain. See *China.*

**Pottery.** 1. A general term used for all ceramic ware, but in fact properly applied only to earthenware and non-vitrified ceramics. 2. The place where ceramic objects are made and fired.

**Primary Market.** See *Market.*

# Q

**Queen's Ware.** An earthenware of ivory or cream color developed by Josiah Wedgwood. The name "Queen's Ware" was adopted by other potters for similar stoneware; also often referred to as "white ware."

**Quote.** The Exchange's best estimate of market price at the close of the current bi-monthly trading period.

# R

**Relief Sculpture.** Sculpture in which the design or figure is not freestanding but is raised from a background. There are three degrees of relief sculpture: Alto-relievo or high relief, where the design is almost detached from the background; Basso-relievo or bas-relief, where the design is raised somewhat; and Relievostiacciato, where the design is scarcely more than scratched. Relief designs on plates may be formed in the plate mold or formed separately and applied to the plate body. Examples: Davenport Pottery *Toby Plate Collection* **(26-D8-1.0)** and Edwin M. Knowles *Biblical Mothers Collection* **(84-K41-6.0).**

# S

**Saggers.** Boxes of fire-clay into which objects to be glost fired are put for protection against direct contact with the flames.

**Second, Second Sorting.** A plate judged to be a grade below first quality, usually indicated by a scratch or gouge through the glaze over the backstamp on the back.

**Secondary Market.** See *Market.*

**Sell Order.** An offer at an asked price given by an individual or dealer to sell one or more plates on the secondary market. See *Asked Price, Exchange.*

# GLOSSARY OF COMMONLY USED TERMS

**Slip.** Ceramic paste or body diluted with water to a smooth, creamy consistency used for slip-casting. See *Mold*.

**Sponsor.** Authoritative body (prestigious organization, museum, or person) which attests to the authenticity of the artwork depicted on a plate.

**Steatite, Soapstone.** A natural rock whose primary component is talc. Steatite is used in porcelain formulas as a flux.

**Sterling Silver.** An alloy which, by United States law, must have the minimum fineness of 92.5% by weight of pure silver and a maximum of 7.5% by weight of a base metal, usually copper. Example: Franklin Mint *Christmas* **(84-F64-1.0)**.

**Stoneware.** A hard ceramic fired to vitrification but not to translucency. Typical components of stoneware are 30% ball clay, 32% kaolin, 15% flint, and 23% cornish stone. Example: Wedgwood's Jasper Ware **(26-W90-0.0)**.

**Supermarket Plate.** Common term for a plate edition of dubious limitations, cheaply produced and not considered a true collector's plate.

**Swap 'n' Sell Event.** An open buy and sell auction for the trading of plates from one collector to another. Swap 'n' Sell events have been organized at major plate conventions, traveling shopping mall shows, and between collector's clubs. A registration fee is normally charged for those plates offered by sellers.

# T

**Terra Cotta.** A general term for any kind of fired clay. Strictly speaking, terra cotta is an earthenware produced from a clay which fires to a dull ochre or red color. The ware, left unglazed is coarse and porous. Example: Veneto Flair **(38-V22-0.0)**.

**Tin Glaze.** A glaze, colored white by oxide of tin, which produces a heavy opaque surface when fired. See *Delftware*.

**Toriart.** The process by which wood shavings and resin are combined to form a wood material which is then molded and carved into three-dimensional forms. Example: Anri **(38-A54-0.0)**.

**Trader.** An individual or a dealer who buys, sells, or bids on plates through the Exchange. See *Trading Floor, Exchange*.

**Trading Floor.** The physical area of The Bradford Exchange where the trading of plates takes place. All secondary market trading on the Exchange originates here, and it is the daily market activity on the Trading Floor that determines the prices quoted on the Exchange. See *Broker, Bradex, Quote*.

**Transfer-Printing.** Method by which an engraved design may be transferred from an engraver's plate or lithographer's block to the surface of a plate. Originally, thin papers were inked with a mixture of metallic oxide in an oily medium, or sometimes used with a greasy substance onto which metallic oxide could be dusted. Transfer-printing may be overglaze or underglaze.

**Translucency.** The quality of transmitting light without transparence. In a plate, translucency depends on the quality of the china or porcelain, thickness of the plate, and firing temperature. Underfired porcelain is not translucent.

**Triptych.** A set of three panels hinged side by side, bearing paintings or carvings, usually on a religious theme and originally used as a portable altarpiece. Example: Anna-Perenna **(22-A3-3.0)**.

**True Clay.** See *Kaolin*.

# U

**Underglaze Decoration.** Decoration applied after a plate has been fired once (bisque fired) but before it is glazed and fired a second time. Underglaze painting is most commonly done in cobalt blue pigment (although other colors can be used) because this is the most stable color and can withstand high firing temperatures. True underglaze technique indicates that such painting was done by hand. See *Glaze, Overglaze Decoration*.

# V

**Vitrification.** A fusion of potters clay at temperatures between 1250°C and 1450°C to form a glassy, nonporous substance. With continued heating, the substance will become translucent.